PLANT PHYSIOLOGY

HENRIK LUNDEGÅRDH

Translated by
F. M. IRVINE, M.Sc., Ph.D.

Translation edited by
Professor W. O. JAMES, F.R.S.

NEW YORK
AMERICAN ELSEVIER PUBLISHING COMPANY, INC.

© H. Lundegårdh

AMERICAN ELSEVIER PUBLISHING COMPANY, INC.
52 Vanderbilt Avenue
New York, New York 10017

Library of Congress Catalog Card Number: 66-24001

Translated from the revised
German edition *Pflanzenphysiologie*, Jena 1960
of the original Swedish
Lärobok i växtfysiologi med växtanatomi, Stockholm 1950

First published in English 1966
By Oliver & Boyd Ltd., Edinburgh and London

Printed in Great Britain

EXTRACT FROM PREFACE TO
THE FIRST (SWEDISH) EDITION

This book is a review of the present position of the science of plant physiology and is suitable for use as a textbook for more advanced students and as an introduction to the subject for research workers. The book arose from lectures given in the Plant-Physiological Institute in Uppsala-Ultana. As in my earlier work *Klima und Boden in ihrer Wirkung auf das Pflanzenleben* (5th edition 1957), I have attempted to examine critically facts and hypotheses on the basis of the relevant literature, using also the experience from my own research work over many years in various spheres of physiology. The literature references make no claim to completeness, but there are excellent hand-books of plant physiology as well as *Fortschritte, Reviews, Abstracts* etc., in which the literature is covered almost completely.

Uppsala and Penningby, January 1950

H. LUNDEGÅRDH

PREFACE TO THE GERMAN EDITION

In the preparation of a German edition of this work it proved necessary to extend the text and partly rewrite it and in the course of this the anatomical review was somewhat shortened to save space. The literature, greatly expanded in the intervening ten years, was evaluated as far as possible within the given space, and in the chapters on the uptake of nutrients and enzymes I was able also to use my own experimental work. The manuscript was completed in August 1958; for technical reasons, work which was published later could not be taken into account.

Almost all the diagrams for this edition were redrawn or photographed.

Penningby (Sweden), 15th January 1960

H. LUNDEGÅRDH

TRANSLATOR'S FOREWORD TO THE ENGLISH EDITION

Chapter 3 of the German edition, on 'The anatomical basis of physiology', has been omitted, apart from Table 19 and half a dozen short paragraphs which were transferred to the remaining chapters. This eliminates the main part of the 'plant anatomy' that was mentioned in the title of the original Swedish edition. For the information included in this Chapter 3 (54 pages, 66 figures) the original German should be consulted. By this omission the English translation has been shortened but it still covers all that is usually understood by 'plant physiology'.

Other changes from the author's German text have been kept to only about a dozen minor rearrangements, apart from the chemical formulae, which have in some cases been rearranged to show inter-relations more clearly, and seven others have been added. The index has been enlarged, and divided into three parts.

The whole translation has been most carefully edited by Professor W. O. James, F.R.S., Professor of Botany at the Imperial College of Science and Technology, University of London.

Special thanks are due to Mrs. J. Hooker for undertaking the arduous task of audio-typing the translation.

F. M. IRVINE

Wraysbury, Buckinghamshire
August 1966

CONTENTS

Chapter 1
THE CELL AND THE PROTOPLASM

A. The General Organisation of the Cell

The basis for the construction and functions of an organism is the individual cell. The science of plant physiology is thus essentially cell physiology. The bearer of the life functions is the *protoplasm*. The expression *protoplast* is also commonly used (after HANSTEIN 1880) to indicate the complete protoplasmic mass with its organs and structures which belong to the cell.

In plants the protoplast is generally surrounded by a *cell wall*, which gives the cell the necessary mechanical rigidity and makes possible the alterations in cell forms which are so important for the differentiation of tissues. The cell wall is the 'skeleton' of the plant cell. In exceptional cases plant cells can however appear to be naked, as, for example, in the swarming spores of algae and the spermatozoids of cryptogams; but on closer investigation it is found that even naked protoplasts or those that have been released, e.g. after plasmolysis of tissue cells, are surrounded by a tough extensible surface layer. This *protoplasmic membrane* attains normally only sub-microscopic thickness (values of $5m\mu$ have been quoted), but in other cases can be microscopic in thickness ($0.2\,\mu$ or more).

The protoplasmic membrane, which forms the boundary layer between the external medium and the protoplast, also regulates the exchange of dissolved substances. This membrane is sometimes called *plasmolemma* and also *ectoplasm*. It is a characteristic of the external protoplasmic membrane that it is easily dissolved by the activity of the internal plasma and can be re-formed. It is thus not an autonomous organ, as are cell nuclei and plastids. In contact with foreign protoplasts, however, this ability to re-dissolve the surface layer usually disappears. If two kinds of slime fungus (*Myxomycetes*), whose vegetative bodies form a mobile protoplasmic mass (*plasmodium*), happen to collide, they do not fuse together. This however would occur with two extensions (*pseudopodia*) of one and the same plasmodium.

The individuality of the protoplasm is thus preserved by the surface layer, which can also possibly aid in regulating the water uptake or the swelling of the internal plasma. Few details are known about the chemical composition of the surface layer. By indirect methods (measurement of the permeability for dissolved substances) the conclusion has been reached that the surface layer contains both fatty substances (lipoids) and proteins.

The main mass of the protoplasm is a colourless, normally somewhat cloudy liquid with a viscosity higher than that of water (according to HEILBRONN (1914) 24 times, and according to PEKAREK (1930) 6 times higher). It has however been found that the viscosity changes markedly e.g. under the influence of light (STÅLFELT 1946) or with differences in temperature (PRUDHOMME VAN REINE 1935). The biochemical causes of these alterations in viscosity are still unknown but they probably depend in the first instance on other manifestations of the *irritability of the protoplasm*, which can express itself also by contractibility and flow of the protoplasm.

In young cells the protoplasm ordinarily fills the whole cell. During the extension of the cell water-filled *vacuoles* appear which gradually fuse to a central sap cavity; this in fully grown cells occupies by far the largest part of the cell space, so that the protoplasm covers the cell wall only as a thin layer (Fig. 2). The protoplasm of such cells is usually in a state of flow and fine fibrous branchings can be seen to traverse the cell vacuole. In certain algal cells the protoplasm and its organs form characteristic shapes. The boundary layer between the protoplasm and the vacuole (complementary to the external surface layer) is named the *vacuole membrane* or *tonoplast*.

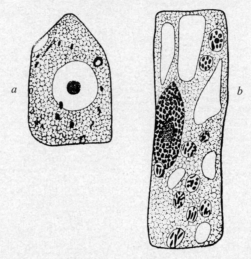

Fig. 1. Cells from living root tips of *Vicia faba* (× c. 3500): (*a*) from the primary meristem; proplastids and mitochondria; (*b*) at the end of the extension zone; clearly-marked vacuoles and fully formed plastids with grains of starch (from LUNDEGÅRDH 1922).

The term *protoplasm* was introduced by PURKINJE (1840) and MOHL (1844). BROWN (1833) had already discovered the *cell nucleus*, although its importance as an indispensable organ for the life of the protoplast was recognised only later. The cell nucleus, surrounded by the remainder of the protoplasm (= *cytoplasm*), is a spherical or spindle-shaped bubble enclosed by the nuclear membrane and ordinarily contains one or more central bodies or *nucleoli* (Fig. 3). In more recent times the nuclear membrane has been investigated under the electron microscope (BAIRATI and LEHMANN 1952), which showed a certain porosity. The nucleolus consists, according to CASPERSSON and SCHULTZ (1940), of ribonucleic acid, probably in combination with proteins, and is believed to be important for the synthesis of the proteins in the cell.

The importance of the cell nucleus for the life of the cell can be demonstrated by micro-dissection, e.g. by section of an amoeba into two parts, one containing a nucleus and the other without a nucleus (HOFER 1889). It is then found that the part without a nucleus can respire, feed and show plasma flow, but no longer grows. Segments of a protoplast lacking a nucleus enclosed in a plant cell behave similarly. They have lost the ability to form cell walls (KLEBS 1886, TOWNSEND 1897; see Fig. 4). HARVEY (1938, 1939), however, prepared nucleus-free fragments of sea-urchins' eggs, which divided as many as 500 times. In this case some residual effect of the cell nucleus was still apparent.

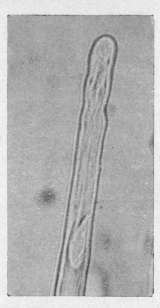

Fig. 2. Living root hair of wheat with spindle-shaped nucleus. According to BĚLAŘ, SHINKE (1937) the even granulation of the quiescent nucleus is the optical section of the chromonemata wound round each other.

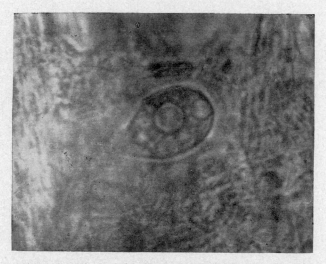

Fig. 3. Cytoplasm and nucleus from the lower part of a live stinging hair of the stinging nettle. Both nucleoli and nuclear membrane are visible.

B

The cell nucleus contains a series of enzyme systems, but not those which effect cell respiration and energy production (LANG 1952). There is an abundant crop of hypotheses about the biochemical functions of the cell nucleus in the life of the cell (e.g. MAZIA 1952), but the picture is still indistinct.

Some observations are of interest, e.g. the results of MARSHAK (1944), according to which the cell nucleus in amoebae regulates the buffering of the protoplasm against changes in pH. The cell nucleus, however, is certainly concerned also in the regulation of a number of other processes. The characteristic wanderings of the cell nucleus in those cells which form root hairs (Fig. 5) indicate e.g. the regulation of the formation of the wall and shape of the cell.

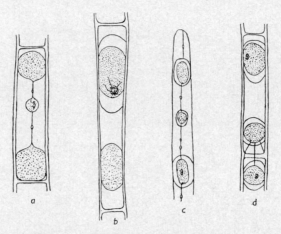

Fig. 4. The influence of the nucleus on the formation of the cell wall.
(a) Plasmolysed hair cell of *Cucurbita*.
(b) Hair of *Gaillardia*; the part containing the nucleus has surrounded itself with a membrane.
(c) Root hair of *Marchantia*; the influence of the nucleus is transmitted through the protoplasmic threads.
(d) A hair of *Cucurbita*; a possible transfer of the influence of the nucleus through plasmodesmata (after TOWNSEND 1897).

The cell nucleus is the site of the carrier of heredity, the *gene*; there must however be a constant transfer between the nucleus and cytoplasm, by which the hereditary tendencies are documented as visible properties. A physiological-morphological expression of the collaboration of the nucleus and the cytoplasm is the ratio nucleus/ plasma (R. HERTWIG, revised by TROMBETTA 1942), i.e. the fact that the size of the protoplast or of the cell is to a certain extent determined by the volume of the nucleus.

When the cell has reached a certain size the nucleus normally begins to divide. The *nuclear division* is usually followed by a *cellular division*, but this can sometimes be lacking, and then there arises a giant cell with several nuclei in a continuous cytoplasm. The nuclei tend to be distributed according to their size, so that the larger nuclei are surrounded by a larger volume of cytoplasm, whilst the smaller remain closer together. One thus gets the impression of a certain *sphere of effectiveness of the nucleus*, but one should not be misled into the all-too-simple conclusion that the nucleus influences only the immediately adjacent parts of the cytoplasm. Especially in plant cells the uninterrupted flow of protoplasm (see below) can transmit an influence of the nucleus to the more distant parts of the cell (compare Fig. 5).

Multinucleate cells occur in higher plants e.g. in the initials of conducting or vascular bundles in root tips, in latex cells or in the embryo-sacs before the formation of the endosperm; but otherwise the uninucleate state predominates. The multinucleate state is the rule in Siphonaceae, many fungi, Myxomycetes and other thallophytes. In the lowest cell forms, the bacteria and blue algae, the differentiation between nucleus and cytoplasm is less clear. In *Bacillus mycoides* an individualised nuclear body (*nucleoid*) can be easily distinguished, but no chromosomes on division (PIEKARSKI 1940).

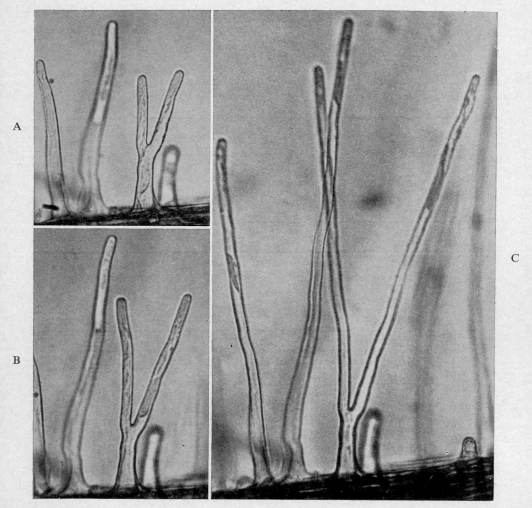

Fig. 5. Micro-photographs of a living branched root hair of wheat.
A. The nucleus is still below the fork.
B. The nucleus has gone into one of the arms.
C. Both branches continue to grow at the same speed, although the nucleus is near the tip of one arm and the other arm is thus without a nucleus (after I. EKDAHL).

Together with the nucleus most plant cells also contain *plastids* (Fig. 1, p. 2). These are independent organs which like the nucleus propagate themselves by division. Physiologically they are considerably more specialised than the nucleus. One distinguishes between *leucoplasts* and *chromatophores*; the former are colourless and serve for the formation of starch; of the latter the chloroplasts (chlorophyll bodies) take care of the photosynthesis in the green parts of plants and algae. Certain cells of algae have richly formed chromatophores. Modern literature has striven to simplify the nomenclature of the plastids. It now differentiates *leucoplasts*, *chromoplasts* (only with carotenoids) and *chloroplasts* (with carotene+chlorophyll).

B. The Properties of Cytoplasm

1 MICROSCOPIC STRUCTURE

The cell nucleus to a large extent directs the functions of the cell, and correspondingly the cytoplasm can be considered as the executive organ. It would not be quite accurate to state that the cytoplasm usually has a specially formed characteristic microscopic structure; only on special occasions, such as cell division, do thread-like structures appear in it. A trend towards a *filament or fibril structure* can however generally be observed. The tendency towards a fibrillar arrangement of the structural elements of the protoplasm is shown by the *double refraction* frequently observed in the polarisation microscope. Earlier workers (FLEMMING, HEIDENHAIN) rather over-stressed a pervading fibrillar structure. It cannot be affirmed either that the cytoplasm has a pervading 'foam structure' (BÜTSCHLI, RHUMBLER).

The term 'kinoplasm' was introduced by STRASBURGER to indicate the fibrillar differentiation that occurs in connection with nuclear division (*karyokinesis* or *mitosis*) and also occasionally at other times. As we shall see later, the hypothesis of a definite, or continuing, visible differentiation in the cytoplasm is scarcely supported by known microscopic and chemical findings; surface layers and *mitochondria* (see below) form exceptions.

A characteristic of the cytoplasm is its *ability to change its internal and external form and structure, without this being reflected in a persistent microscopically-visible structure.* For this reason it is logical that A. MEYER includes under the term 'alloplastic formations' structures which appear transitorily in order to carry out definite temporary tasks in the life of the protoplasm.

The ability to form internal structures appears less obvious in plant cells than in animal cells, which in this respect are richly endowed. The cilia of swarm-spores and of spermatozoids may however be noted here. Filamentous objects arranged radially during the formation of the nuclear spindle, during sporulation of many fungi, etc., have been called kinoplasm by many workers, as they clearly participate in the formation of the walls. One can imagine that, in this activity, special types of molecule which tend to a fibrillar arrangement are activated.

In the extraordinary multiplicity of chemical processes it is naturally not easy to show whether 'liquid crystals' (first discovered by LEHMANN in 1906) may occasionally be formed. These are interesting intermediates between the liquid and the solid states. The condition has been termed 'mesomorphic' (VANHOEK 1947). The stages are described as:

solid form←smectic state←nematic state←liquid form.

In the smectic state the molecules are held together in weakly bonded layers which are displaced over each other in a staircase formation. In the nematic state the fibrillar structure predominates i.e. the molecules lie parallel to each other. The preconditions for the formation of liquid crystals are strong dipole moments and a tendency to form easily polarisable groups. Since such preconditions are given by the characteristics of many organic molecules (e.g. filament- or rod-form of a molecule which has both hydrophobe [$=CH_2$ or $\equiv CH$] and hydrophile [—OH or —COOH] end groups), the spontaneous formation of layered membranes or of freely suspended structural bodies is favoured, which can serve as the physico-chemical basis also for the fine structure of more durable plasmatic organelles.

It is becoming ever clearer (especially by the development of electron microscopy) that the ingeniously collaborating enzyme systems of living matter are held together in strictly regulated sub-microscopic structural associations conforming with the general laws of surface chemistry and physics.

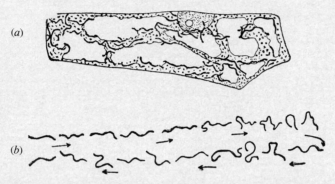

Fig. 6. (a) Mitochondria in a cell of the petals of *Tulipa*.
(b) Movement and change in form of a mitochondrion (after
GUILLERMOND).

The opinion has been expressed (SISSON, FARR, 1941) that in growing cotton-fibres cellulose formation takes place in colourless plasmatic particles which are then evacuated into the growing cell surfaces. This may serve as an example of a specific transport activity by 'mitochondria' or similar objects, about which little is yet known. It has recently been stated that the mitochondria accumulate salt ions and liberate them into the vacuoles (ROBERTSON *et al*. 1955).

2 MITOCHONDRIA AND MICROSOMES

ALTMANN and BENDA (1894-7) discovered in animal cells discrete inclusions which were named *mitochondria* (or *chondriosomes*) (see NEWCOMER 1940, BONONE 1951). Later similar bullet-shaped or fibrous, mobile bodies were observed also in plant cells (GUILLERMOND 1919; Fig. 6).

In microscopic work the mitochondria are mostly considered as being characterised by vital staining with Janus Green B. The diameter of the mitochondria in most cell types lies between 0·5 and 2 μ; they are thus easily visible under the microscope. On *homogenisation* (grinding of the tissues in a mortar or comminution by rapidly rotating knives) the mitochondria appear to keep best in 0·2-0·5 M sugar solutions. One must however always allow for the possibility (PFEFFERKORN and PERNER 1953) that the mitochondria are partly irreversibly denatured during the isolation from the protoplasm, and that artefacts thus arise whose biochemical properties do not agree with those of the intact structures.

Disintegration and dissolution of the structure of the mitochondria appear to proceed in step with the inhibition of the oxidative phosphorylation, when the rod-shaped mitochondria break up into spherical pieces. Diluted media favour an abnormal swelling and loss of enzymes (HUNTER and FORD 1955), and it has also been observed that the mitochondria collapse in the absence of oxygen. Aerobic respiration is also a condition for a certain osmotic activity, which is possibly connected with the transport and accumulation of salts in plant cells.

The growing interest in mitochondria is based on the discovery that these formations are carriers of the respiration enzymes and the phosphorylation processes. As the mitochondria, or, more accurately expressed, the isolatable particle fractions of the protoplasm, thus represent the seat of the central energy transfer of the cell, it is not surprising that in general a positive relationship has been found between oxygen respiration, high-energy phosphate formation and the state of the mitochondria of a tissue. There is an interesting observation that the formation of mitochondria is stimulated by certain ions, e.g. Ca^{++} (FLORELL 1956); other important cations are Mn^{++} and Mg^{++}.

For the isolation of mitochondria the procedure is generally to homogenise the tissue in sugar solution and then to free it from fragments of cell walls by centrifuging, e.g. for quite a short time at $1,000-2,000 \times g$ and then for 15-45 minutes at about $4,000-10,000 \times g$. The deposit then contains many mitochondria, but also partly *microsomes*. These latter, which are defined as sub-microscopic particles with a diameter between 50 and 150 $m\mu$, are sedimented in greater amounts with an acceleration of at least $20,000 \times g$.

It is not known with certainty whether the mitochondria are actual organs of the protoplasm, which propagate by division, or whether they can arise anew. The boundary between mitochondria and microsomes is also not sharply defined. Certain workers think that similar relationships exist between mitochondria and plastids. With the electron microscope it has been shown that the mitochondria are surrounded by a membrane, which PALADE (1952) estimates as 7-8 $m\mu$ thick. Researches on the internal structure of animal mitochondria has shown (e.g. SJÖSTRAND 1953), that they are not small structureless sacs in which the enzymes are imprisoned; they appear rather to have an extraordinarily complicated structure in which the enzyme proteins are arranged.

Chemically the mitochondria are built up from fat and protein, and ribonucleic acid has also been found. The microsomes differ but little in their chemical composition from the mitochondria. Certain workers, as mentioned, are of the opinion that the microsomes are fragments of the mitochondria, an opinion which is also supported by spectrophotometric studies on the enzyme content (LUNDEGÅRDH 1957).

Isolated mitochondria show the addition effect (TISSIÈRES 1954), and one thus cannot exclude the possibility that during the preparation substances of the non-mitochondrial mass of the cytoplasm accumulate on the surface of the liberated particles. It is however interesting that a number of enzymes, such as peroxidase, ascorbic oxidase, hexokinase, invertase etc., are not contained in the mitochondria. It is believed that many of these enzymes are anchored in the external protoplasmic surface layer (GODDARD and STAFFORD 1954).

3 Proteins

The chemical analysis of protoplasm encounters many technical difficulties (see GORTNER 1938, BROYER 1939, LOOFBOUROW 1940, STERN 1943 and others). The protoplasm of every embryonic cell has in itself the power to produce the extraordinarily diverse chemical compounds which are necessary for the construction of various cell types and organs. It must consequently be assumed that many of the chemical equilibria from which these compounds arise are patterned in the embryonic protoplasm as it were in sketch form, although in this genotypical state the quantity of the possible reaction products is immeasurably small. A summary analysis of embryonic protoplasm, however, shows only the types of material occurring in larger amounts.

The plasmodium of the myxomycete *Reticularia lycoperdon* contains, according to KIESEL (1925) the following materials, calculated as percentage of dry weight:

Proteins, including plastin	29·1
Nucleic acids	3·7
Lipoproteins	1·2
Lecithin	4·7
Soluble N-compounds	12·0
Cholesterol	0·6
Fats	17·9
Carbohydrates, reducing	2·7
Carbohydrates, non-reducing	20·6
Polysaccharides	1·8
Unknown substances and salts	5·7
Total	100·0

Of these groups of substances the proteins, lipoproteins and nucleic acids give the protoplasm its characteristic properties, and these high-molecular substances form, as already mentioned, the basis of the protoplasmic structure. The amounts of protoplasm in meristematic tissues, and often also in developed organs (for grass leaves see PETRIE and WILLIAMS 1938), are mainly proportional to the protein content. Meristematic cells, as also certain storage organs, contain much protein and phosphatid as well as abundant inorganic P, K and Mg, but on the other hand only small quantities of Mn and Ca. This last element, as well as Si, is more concentrated in fully developed cells (GOLA 1946), and in these soluble N-compounds also occur to a greater extent.

(a) The Construction of Proteins

The protein molecule is usually built up of optically active α-amino acids. The amino acids are amphoteric, i.e. they react both as acids and as bases. This is due to the fact that both the amino group —NH_2 and the carboxyl group —COOH dissociate. The former gives rise to OH-ions by attraction of H-ions from water, and the latter give off H-ions. The degree of dissociation is determined by the hydrogen-ion concentration. According to whether the hydrogen-ion concentration rises or falls, the amino acid thus reacts as a base or as an acid. A medium pH values the amino acid occurs as a zwitter ion, since the positive and negative charges are equal. The pH value at which the two opposing degrees of dissociation are in balance is called the *isoelectric point* (IEP). At certain ratios of the two dissociation constants pK 1 and pK 2, due to the sigmoid form of the dissociation curve, this point can spread out to an isoelectric zone, covering 1-4 pH units, with an almost constant degree of dissociation. Examples are glycine (Fig. 7) and tyrosine.

Fig. 7. The dissociation curve of glycine (aminoacetic acid) (0·1 M) at 18° C. The isoelectric zone stretches between pH 4 and 8 (after SÖRENSEN, from HITCHCOCK 1938).

In the isoelectric zone amphoteric substances ordinarily have their minimum solubility. For glycine, for example, this zone lies between pH 4 and 8 (Fig. 7); in this zone the amino acid appears as a zwitter ion. With a difference in pK 2-pK 1 smaller than 2-3 there appears, however, a sharp isoelectric point and the amino acid accordingly appears, except in a small range of pH, either as an anion or as a cation.

The dissociation of the amino acids is usually weak, e.g. for α-alanine pK 1 (acid) = 9·87 and pK 2 (basic) = 11·65. On the other hand, if the basic group in the molecule is screened off the amino acid is more acidic than the corresponding aliphatic acid, which shows pH values of about 4·7. The dissociation, however, never reaches high values in ordinary aqueous solution. Moderate acidic dissociation is shown by the dibasic aspartic and glutamic acids, and moderate basic dissociation by arginine, lysine and, to a lower degree, histidine.

All the amino acids (the L-series) forming the protein molecule appear to have the same steric structure, with the general formula:

$$\underset{^+H_3N}{\overset{H}{\diagdown}}\ \overset{R}{\underset{COO^-}{\diagup}}C$$

in which the radical R can be, for example: H in glycine, CH_3 in alanine, $CH_2 \cdot CH(CH_3)_2$ in leucine, a phenol-substituted methyl group in tyrosine, a similar imidazole group in histidine, and $CH_2 \cdot SH$ in cystëine. These side-chains determine the individual chemical properties of the protein molecule. The chain formation of the amino acids takes place through *peptide linkage*, in which the carboxyl of one amino acid is combined with the α-amino group of another. Thus by repeated peptide formation there arise long rows of molecules which with the increasing length of the chains form dipeptides, polypeptides, peptones and proteins. The peptide linkage corresponds to an increase in energy of about 3 kilogram-calories (kg-cal.), as is explained in greater detail in Chapter 8.

Since the carboxyl groups of the individual amino acids remaining after repeated peptide linkage show different dissociation constants, there is in a protein usually a complicated dissociation- (or titration-) curve which can also show several branches.

The titration-curve for gelatine is distinguished by a fairly narrow isoelectric zone (Fig. 8). Ordinarily, however, the curve can be calculated on the basis of the assumption that only a few (3-7) dissociation constants will predominate, which is to be ascribed partly to the fact that the protein molecule contains only relatively few types of multivalent amino acids; and furthermore, similar groups have similar constants.

The *positive charge of the protein molecule* is chiefly due to the imidazole group of histidine, the ϵ-amino group of lysine, and the guanine group $\left(-C\!\!\begin{array}{c}\diagup NH_2\\\diagdown NH\end{array}\right)$ of arginine, whilst the α-amino groups are screened off by the peptide linkage. The histones are basic but are exceeded by the protamins, which consist chiefly of arginine residues (salmine has the molecular weight of 5,600 with 34 arginine groups out of the 36 that are possible) and behave as bases.

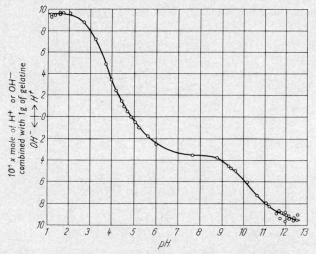

Fig. 8. The dissociation curve of gelatine at 30° C. The isoelectric zone is fairly small (after HITCHCOCK 1938).

The *negative charge of the protein molecule* is due exclusively to the carboxyl groups. Since one carboxyl group is always screened off by the peptide linkage, the second carboxyl of the dicarboxylic acids causes the negative charge. Of these dicarboxylic acids three are known, viz. aspartic, glutamic and β-hydroxyglutamic acids. The dissociation constants of the free carboxyl groups, as already mentioned, exceed those of the fatty acids. The dissociation is increased by the peptide linkage and by the neighbouring side-chains (on protoplasmic proteins and their formation see MADDEN and WHIPPLE 1940).

A part of a fully stretched polypeptide chain is illustrated in Fig. 9. Information about the opposing situation of the atoms and about the valency angles is given by X-ray diagrams, but its interpretation is always a complicated task and must be made with the necessary care. Conclusions about the shape of the molecule (whether it is filamentous or spherical) can be drawn from observations of the optical double refraction in flowing liquids. A double refraction is found in the polarisation microscope when the particles are small in one direction in comparison with the wavelength of the light. Molecules of filament-form or rod-form tend to have a parallel orientation. when the solution is forced through a narrow tube (MEHL 1938, EDSALL 1942).

The type of linkage of the individual building units results in the protein molecule mostly assuming the filamentous form. The filaments are, however, in zigzag form (Fig. 9) and are easily twisted together like skeins. One accordingly distinguishes between *globular* (corpuscular) and *fibrillar proteins*. Only a few of the globular proteins form ideal spheres, even though the ratio of the axes is usually not particularly high (ABRAMSON, MOYER and GORIN, 1942; for protein crystalloids see COHN 1941). By denaturation, i.e. by treatment with heat, formation of surface films, or chemical influences, the convolutions are again unravelled to fibres. The molecule of the tobacco mosaic virus is regarded as a half-way stage between globular and fibrillar structure.

The denaturation of globular proteins is usually irreversible. Many proteins are destroyed merely by being concentrated in a surface film, since the molecule is broken up by the surface-tension forces. This is however not always the case. Insulin, for example, is also effective as a surface film. It is believed that in these cases the specific reaction of the substance, e.g. the hormone effect, is effected through side-chains, which are not screened in the interior of a globular molecule but point outwards. From optical-polarisation observations NEEDHAM and his school (DAINTY 1944) distinguish the following *groups of proteins*:

1. Proteins which occur in solution and in surface films as rod- or filament-shaped molecules (to this group belong tobacco mosaic virus and the nucleoproteins);
2. Proteins which do not show double refraction solution but more as a surface film (these are globular molecules, which can be unfolded to filaments);
3. Proteins which in no circumstances show double refraction (insulin and methaemoglobin).

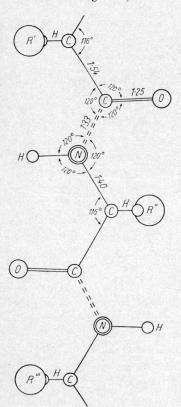

The fact that the solubility of the proteins diminishes on denaturation is due to the dissolving out of hydrophobe groups. In a compact globular molecule these groups are directed inwards and are thus screened, whilst the hydrophile groups are directed outwards. The breaking up of a globular molecule appears also to be connected with the occurrence of —SH groups instead of the —S—S bridges. Substances like urea and guanidine break up the molecular backbone and thus cause denaturation in the same way as a rise in temperature and in certain cases also cold. One of the secrets of living protoplasm is the wide extension of 'reversible denaturation': in the phenomena of life there occur not only the unwinding of globular molecules to flat filamentous systems, but also the contrary process, i.e. the folding together of the molecular filaments.

An intermediate stage between reversible and irreversible denaturation is the *thixotrophic state*

Fig. 9. Diagram of a stretched polypeptide chain, using the distances between atoms and the valency angles calculated from crystals of diketopiperazine and glycine. The double broken lines indicate resonance linkages (1·33) between the carbon of the keto group and the nitrogen atom (after CAREY, from COHN and EDSALL 1943).

(FREUNDLICH 1942), which arises when the molecular filaments have the tendency to hold together and to form cords or, in general, in systems held together by adhesion. In a true solution the molecules move easily past each other in all directions and the liquid obeys the principles of NEWTON and POISEUILLE on flow in tubes. On account of the aforementioned intermolecular forces of attraction the thixotrophic solutions however do not do this: they behave non-Newtonically. It is characteristic of a thixotrophic gel that it can change over into a sol on shaking.

Of the amino acids, eighteen can be considered as commonly occurring while 29 are less known or rare (VICKERY 1941; formulae of the important amino acids are given in Chapter 5 E). The analytical methods for the identification of the various acids were for many years rather unsatisfactory (see STEIN et al. 1946), but paper chromatography and paper electrophoresis have produced good results in this sphere, and with the help of these methods one can quickly identify the amino acids present in a protein. The amino acids are first liberated by treating the proteins with proteolytic enzymes, which break the peptide linkages, but it should be noted that every enzyme is specialised on certain groups or on groups in a particular position in the molecular chain. The breaking up of a protein molecule thus ordinarily occurs in stages with the co-operation of a series of enzymes.

The attempt has also been made to utilise the ultra-violet absorption spectrum for the quantitative analysis of proteins (BUSWELL 1942). Because of their aliphatic structure most proteins, however, give only fairly similar spectra, with very weak bands at 280 mμ and end absorption below 250 mμ. Only the three amino acids with aromatic groups, viz. phenylalanine, tyrosine and tryptophan, show utilisable absorption bands (SMITH and COY 1946).

The separation of the various proteins can be carried out by electrophoresis in specially constructed apparatus. With the aid of electrophoresis the various types of virus can also be separated (WYCKOFF 1946). By a variety of methods, e.g. by observing the diffraction of light in those layers which are formed because of the different speeds of migration of protein varieties, one can determine whether the unknown sample is an electrically homogeneous protein or a mixture of several. Even when only one characteristic, i.e. the electrophoretic speed of migration, is singled out, such a separation can be utilised to give clinical diagnosis, e.g. on blood plasma.

Adsorption analysis has also been proposed. In this the solution under test is allowed to flow slowly through a column of adsorbent material, on which the dissolved components separate as bands at various levels. The subsequent successive elution of the adsorption bands is registered continuously by interferometric or conductometric methods (TISELIUS 1942, JUTISZ and LEDERER 1947).

For the identification of the amino acids microbiological methods can also be used. These are based on the usually sharp specialisation of micro-organisms with respect to their sources of nitrogen (KUIKEN 1943, CARDON and BARKER 1947). In the semi-quantitative paper chromatography already mentioned use is made of the variations in the partition coefficients between two solvent phases, e.g. butanol or phenol and water. The various components of a mixture of amino acids are in this way deposited at various heights of a damp strip of filter paper through which the organic solution flows. In association with the isotope technique in which certain atoms in the amino acid chain are 'labelled', and in combination with the radio-photometric methods of measurement, chromotography has been able to yield interesting evidence on the course of synthetic processes.

It is ordinarily assumed that in the fibrillar proteins every amino acid is repeated at a certain distance, so that a periodic grouping is formed. The *cyclol hypothesis* (WRINCH, LANGMUIR) on the other hand puts forward the view that the amino acid radicals are bound together not by simple peptide linkages but by two- or three-sided peptide linkages, so that the molecules occur originally in flat planes and later in a hexagonal cyclol cage.

The cyclol hypothesis has been used to explain the molecular construction of the globular proteins which crystallise in regular forms, e.g. lactoglobulin and pepsin. It is, however, conceivable that more convoluted protein molecules arise by the folding together of the threadlike molecules at certain periodically repeated amino acid esters. A possibly reversible conversion of globular into fibrillar proteins has already been mentioned. In this connection the monomolecular films which are formed at the surface of a protein solution and which cause a re-formation of globular proteins into a fibrillar form have been studied.

It is not very probable that very large protein molecules arise from only one molecular thread knitted together. Electron microscopic observations of haemocyanin and edestin seem to indicate that the molecule forms a disc of 20-29 mμ diameter (STANLEY and ANDERSON 1942). On the other hand hypotheses have been proposed about flat or 'book-like' molecules (DERVICHIAN 1943), also screw chains (PAULING *et al.* 1951). SZENT-GYÖRGYI (BANGA and SZENT-GYÖRGYI 1940) is of the opinion that globular and fibrillar proteins can change into each other as required. According to him, a mobile plasma consists of globular proteins which on the formation of stiffer structures pass over into rod- or thread-molecules.

The molecular weight of proteins has been determined by measurements of the osmotic pressure, the speed of diffusion or the speed of sedimentation in the ultra-centrifuge. The values obtained vary between very low ones, e.g. cytochrome c (13,000-15,000) or lactoalbumin (17,000), and very high ones, e.g. haemocyanin (6,000,000). Horse antibody globulin has probably a still higher molecular weight. These large molecules are alleged to have a length of 90-120 mμ.

Very high molecular weights are shown by the complicated proteins which are named *viruses* (see section B6 below). LEPESCHKIN (1939) assumed the occurrence of giant molecules in protoplasm with a molecular weight of 17-25 million. They were stated to scatter infra-red radiation (the Plotnikow effect) and to split up on ageing. These ideas show relationship with the more modern concepts of 'multi-enzymes' or 'electron transport particles' which have been discussed in connection with the results of extensive centrifugal fractionation of tissue homogenates (cf. p. 8). Here, however, it is scarcely a case of single macromolecules, but of aggregates of various kinds of macromolecules, which finally reach particle size ('ultramicrosomes'). The boundaries are fluid. One is in the transitional zone between macromolecules and protoplasmic structure which we have discussed above. Most macromolecules are, moreover, composed of two or more parts of molecules linked through their bridges, and in enzymes the protein represents the greater part.

Among molecular weights of individual proteins may also be mentioned those of egg albumin and pepsin (31,000-40,000), potato protein (40,000-50,000; LEVITT 1945), haemoglobin (63,000-68,000), edestin and catalase (250,000-300,000). It has been assumed that the molecular weights of proteins in certain size ranges are represented by multiples of 17,600 (Svedberg-unit) (criticised by NORRIS 1946). Quite apart from this hypothesis, there is no doubt that most large molecules show a group construction, an assumption which is supported by observations on splitting which can easily occur e.g. as a result of changes in pH or by irradiation with ultraviolet light (ERIKSON, QUENSEL, SVEDBERG 1939). The decrease in the viscosity of protoplasm after irradiation with X-rays which has been observed by some workers may possibly be based on a corresponding cleavage of larger molecules (ALSUP 1942, WANNER 1945, SPARROW and ROSENFELD; the literature on the effect of light and viscosity of protoplasm is in STÅLFELT 1946). The cleavage or the disintegration into a number of fragments can sometimes take the character of a reversible dissociation (SÖRENSEN). Such reversible cleavages have often been observed in enzymes, which can be subdivided into co-enzyme and apoenzyme (protein) (see Chap. 4). According to BANGA (1947) there are also, however, very resistant proteins, the so-called protines.

(b) *Protein Molecules as the Structural Elements of Protoplasm*

The method of construction of the protein molecule explains many of the physical and chemical properties of protoplasm. We have found that a considerable part of the energy transformation in the cell is undertaken by isolatable particles, mitochondria and microsomes, whose sub-microscopic construction can be related essentially to a strictly regulated arrangement of large molecules in membranes or surface layers. Very little is known about the hyaline ground mass of the protoplasm. The *hyaloplasm*, i.e. the microscopically 'empty' ground substance of the protoplasm, is filled with small shining, mobile particles. These results were doubted by some later research workers (BOTAZZI, A. MEYER), but it is already evident that there must be microsomes of various sizes going well into the sub-microscopic region (for the older literature references see LUNDEGÅRDH 1922). It would not be wrong to think that hyaloplasm contains molecules and small molecular groups of proteins and other high-molecular substances, e.g. nucleic acids, which as required build up organised particles or bodies (microsomes and mitochondria). The characteristic molecular construction of the proteins must however already confer on hyaloplasm a non-Newtonian fundamental character, which is expressed e.g. by the isolated protoplasts showing double refraction in the polarisation microscope when they are stretched in one direction (PFEIFFER 1942).

One must obviously assume that in hyaloplasm the fibrillar protein molecules have a tendency to combine to threads which are perceptible in the microscope. Forces of attraction exist partly between dissociated side-chains and partly between certain groups of atoms (SEIFRIZ 1935, FREY-WYSSLING 1938, K. H. MEYER 1942; cf. below). In addition, firmer unions between side-chains of two molecular threads, e.g. —S—S—, form bridges. Such sulphur bridges are found between the cystëine chains in wool (HARRIS, MIZELL *et al.* 1942). Sulphur bridges are believed to explain the improved elastic properties of rubber obtained by vulcanisation.

The attraction between dissociated hydrophile side-chains makes possible a shift of the molecular threads. Alterations in the viscosity can be called forth by reversible hydrogenation of —S—S— to —SH + HS—, which is associated among other things with the redox potential. Great importance is attached to bivalent cations as, for example, Ca^{++}, as they can combine side-chains of two neighbouring thread-like molecules as a 'cement' (cf. Fig. 10) and thus make the consistency firmer. In addition, bivalent metal ions may perform a similar bridge function in neighbouring globular molecules. Of biological importance also are undoubtedly the '*hydrogen bridges*' (PAULING 1940), which arise when a hydrogen atom which is chemically combined with e.g. O, N, Cl, etc., attracts an unshared electron pair of another negative atom. The hydrogen bridge can be represented as follows:

$$R—X—H \ldots Y=R$$

where . . . represents the hydrogen bridge and X and Y represent negative atoms (O, N, Cl, etc.). The atomic distances $X \ldots Y$ of the hydrogen bridges determined by infra-red measurements are in this case larger than the atomic distances in a chemical compound, and the attraction is thus diminished to 1/10-1/100 of that between neighbouring atoms of a chemical compound. The attractive force in a hydrogen bridge can thus be overcome even by mechanical influences, e.g. hydration or streaming. This looser linking can consequently explain the variable or 'sliding' attraction between chain molecules in streaming protoplasm.

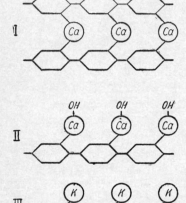

Fig. 10. Diagrammatic representation of the linkage between metallic cations and polyvalent molecular chains.
I. The bivalent calcium can unite two neighbouring chains with each other.
II. In the one-sided linkage of calcium the surface reaction is changed in the basic direction.
III. The monovalent potassium cannot act as 'molecular cement'.

Stable structures can arise by firm combination with the help of bivalent metal cations, sulphur bridges or complex linkages with carbohydrates or phosphatides. As would be expected, the tendency of such complex bonds to break down increases with the dilution of the protein solution. In casein the Ca-ions form the cementing substance. A further illustration of the cementing effect of micro quantities of metal ions (Zn, Cd, Ni, Co) is given by the crystallisation e.g. of insulin which is favoured by them. The associations of thread molecules which form the muscle fibres of animal cells are dissolved by formamide, urea or certain concentrated salt solutions, which explains why the solid organic structure is destroyed by these substances.

Dissociation relationships must of course play a large part in the degree of attraction between thread molecules. The dissociation influences the hydration (swelling and shrinking) and the solubility. The degree of hydration is also influenced by the exchangeable linkage of metal ions in the negative valency positions. Quickly exchangeable cationic linkages also change the distribution of the electrical potential along the surface of a thread molecule and thus influence also such phenomena as the stretching and knitting together of a molecular thread. It is tempting to see in this an explanation for muscular contraction, although obviously chemical energy, e.g. high-energy phosphate, is also transformed. Many speculations are connected with the spiral structure of organic macromolecules probably widely distributed (WATSON and CRICK 1935) that has been considered as the original cause of torsion structures e.g. in protoplasm (SEIFRIZ 1945) and in the secondary cell walls.

Protein solutions, and hence also protoplasm, belong to the class of *colloids*. If dissolved particles exceed a certain size the solution assumes the colloidal character. It does not matter whether the particles are molecular aggregates or giant molecules. NÄGELI (1879) introduced the concept of a *micelle*, defined as an ultramicroscopic crystalline particle. According to modern interpretations, which have extended the concept to non-crystalline molecular aggregates, the micelle is an isodiametric particle which has a regular internal structure (PICKEN 1940). Such particles are commonly built up of molecular chains, which are arranged more or less regularly. We thus understand that a certain developmental series, molecule→micelle→microsome, arises which probably reflects the structural chemical relations between the construction elements of the hyalo-

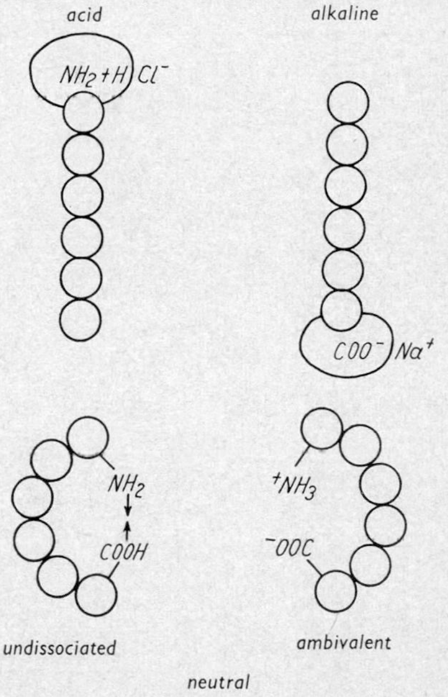

Fig. 11. Diagrammatic representation of the behaviour of amphoteric molecules in the isoelectric state (externally neutral) and with acid or alkaline reaction of the medium. In the isoelectric state the molecules can be undissociated or ambivalent (zwitterions) (after K. H. MEYER).

plasm and the visible particles. As the particle size continues to increase the colloidal solution passes over into an emulsion of particles, which has lost many of the properties of the former.

Colloids whose particles do not attract water molecules are called *hydrophobe* or *lyophobe*. The biologically more important colloids are, however, *hydrophile* (*lyophile*), i.e. the particles attract the surrounding water molecules. This *hydration* depends on the bipolar nature of the water molecule.

The large protein molecules of course have groups of both hydrophile and hydrophobe (*lipophile*) character. They thus do not attain such a simple polar orientation as, for example, the simple fatty acid molecules, whose hydrophile heads go into the oil/water boundary layer, whilst the hydrophobe tails turn towards the oil/air boundary. For the complicated orientation of the protein molecule in phase boundaries the side-chains play an important role. As an example of hydrophobe side-chains the methyl (CH_3) group in leucine may be mentioned, whilst one carboxyl group (COOH) from asparagine and one —NH_2 group of lysine are hydrophile. The differing location of hydrophobe and hydrophile groups often determines a characteristically fixed position of the protein molecule, e.g. in the surface layers.

The degree of hydration can be measured by the resultant *swelling pressure* on moistening a dry colloid. During the swelling the thread molecules are held together by the more hydrophobic co-ordination points, whilst the hydrophilic points are forced apart by the water molecules. Thus there arises a network that surrounds innumerable hollow spaces containing hydration water; the water can also collect in layers. This is the *gel state*. When the swelling has gone so far that the thread- or disc-shaped molecules separate from each other, the swollen gel gradually passes over into a viscous *sol*. Alternatively the swelling, as in gelatine, stops short at a limiting value determined by weak or, as with a rise of temperature, by completely sundered molecular linkages. Some colloids, however, hold together as gels even in the fully hydrated state, as they have firmer intermolecular bridges which are destroyed only by chemical attack.

The hypothetical concepts of the steric state of the protein molecule in mobile protoplasm have not yet ripened. The hypothesis put forward by WRINCH, that the larger crystal-like molecules are held together by short threads similar to the links of a chain, cannot easily be reconciled with the consistency of protoplasm which is at times flowing and at times gel-like, and with its tendency to elasticity and fibrous structures. On the other hand it appears quite clear that large globular molecules, e.g. the 'multi-enzymes', do occur in protoplasm. The foregoing facts certainly support the assumption that wire-shaped molecules predominate in hyaloplasm, in which the fibres are either interlaced irregularly or bound at certain points like a net. SEIFRIZ and FREY-WYSSLING speak of 'points of adhesion', i.e. a more or less temporary adhesion at a point (cf. above). FREY-WYSSLING appears to assume that these adhesion bonds have a more accidental character.

It seems probable, however, that more chemical, i.e. specific, linkages are decisive between the side-chains, since otherwise the important and regular alterations in the viscosity of protoplasm would be harder to explain. There would also be no explanation for the fact that e.g. a Myxomycete plasmodium, which can, without application of force, pass unchanged through a parchment paper with a pore diameter of only 5×10^{-5} mm, is killed when it is forcibly pressed through a silk web of 5×10^{-2} mm pore diameter. The mechanical pressure probably destroys the molecular bridges and consequently alters the chemistry of the protoplasm.

Evidence for the protoplasmic structure being held together by considerable forces is given by its restricted swelling. The water content of the normal protoplasm must be fairly limited or perhaps even low, and most of the water is consequently 'bound' or 'polarised' (cf. BLANCHARD 1940). The probable domination of the filamentous molecules in hyaloplasm was discussed above, but it may also be said that network formation is a condition for the linear stretching of fibres. From statistical considerations it may be deduced that freely rotating fibrillar protein molecules should only seldom remain stretched out, whereas folded fibres should predominate; in this, however, the folding is not unrestricted but is possible only within the allowable valency angles. The mixture of hydrophile and hydrophobe groups and compounds can also have an effect.

The degree of hydrophilia of the protoplasm varies furthermore in various organs. According to GAGETTI (1947) the protoplasm of the leaf-mesophyll is more hydrophilic than that of the epidermal cells. Since the protoplasm of mature plant cells is under the fairly high osmotic pressure of the sap cavity, a dehydrating factor comes into effect.

Special concepts about the state of hydration of protoplasm were developed by the Dutch workers KRUYT and BUNGENBERG DE JONG (1936). They defined as *coacervate* a transitional stage between gel and sol, in which the colloidal particles are assembled in larger units which are held apart by hydration forces.

The rapid and reversible transition between the sol and the gel states which is characteristic of living protoplasm can be induced by mechanical stimulation and also by certain anaesthetics, e.g. ether, carbon dioxide, certain salts, etc. This thixotropic solidification is then followed by a partial hindrance to the metabolism, which is dependent on a certain mobility of the structural elements. In this connection it may be mentioned that according to more recent views the resistance of plants to cold is dependent not so much on high osmotic pressure as on the resistance of the proto-plasm to coagulation by cold. One thus finds a certain parallelism between the resistance to cold and the ability of the cell to tolerate rapid changes in the water content, in other words the resistance to dryness.

Colloidal particles are characterised by a potential difference against the medium. Without this charge, which is usually negative, the particles would easily form clumps and gradually settle. The causes of the charge can be various. In biologically important colloids, i.e. primarily the proteins, it can certainly be connected with the electrolytic dissociation. The large molecules behave in this respect like polyvalent ions. The amphoteric nature of proteins makes the colloidal condition very sensitive to alterations in the hydrogen-ion concentration and to metal ions. In the neighbourhood of the isoelectric point, when the acid and basic dissociations are equal, the proteins are most easily precipitated.

The solubility of proteins is influenced by salts or in general by the ionic strength of the medium, especially since salt ions change the electric charge of the particles. Discharge of the particles, i.e. precipitation (salting out), can easily be started with neutral salts. Higher ionic strengths can bring reversal of the charge on the colloidal particles and thus re-entry into solution. Surface-chemical factors also influence the solubility and the dissociation of the proteins, as they can alter the state of tension in the molecule, i.e. the mutual positions of the atom chains.

(c) *Hydration*

Neutral salts influence not only the solubility of proteins but also, and to a greater extent, their hydration. Inorganic anions, and especially cations, in an aqueous solution are surrounded by a swarm of water molecules, of which those which lie nearest are so strongly attracted that they decrease the speed of migration of the anions and cations in diffusion and in electrophoresis as well as the adsorbability. In homologous series the hydration is in inverse proportion to the cross-section of the ions. In the alkali series it is thus highest at Li^+ and lowest at Cs^+. The hydration increases with the charge and is larger with Ca^{++} than it is with K^+, which have about the same molecular weight. The hydration is best calculated from the speed of diffusion; electrophoresis gives unreliable values. The results obtained by various workers are however not in good agreement. According to ULICH (1933) the biologically important ions show the following hydration values (number of water molecules per ion):

Li^+	Na^+	K^+	Rb^+		Mg^{++}	Ca^{++}	Ba^{++}
6	4	2·5	2		9-13	8-10	6-8

Fe^{++}	Cu^{++}	Zn^{++}	Pb^{++}		Cl^-	Br^-	I^-	NO_3^-
11-13			5·7		3	2	0·5	2

Among the organic substances which have been investigated may be mentioned urea, whose molecule is but little hydrated and which therefore moves quickly in a

c

diffusion field. Glycerol also is weakly hydrated, but the sugar molecule on the other hand is strongly hydrated.

The speed of migration in diffusion is influenced by the simultaneous presence of dissolved substances, both electrolytes and non-electrolytes, due to their own hydration (ÖHOLM 1944). Thus the relative values can be greatly altered, and the speed of migration can even exceed that in pure water. For example, LiCl diffuses more quickly than KCl in 2 M sugar solution, and in nitrate and sulphate solutions more quickly than in water. In addition there are the alterations in the viscosity which are caused by the added substances.

The hydration of inorganic ions influences the properties of protoplasm in various ways. If an ion is attached to a large organic molecule by exchange with an H- or OH-ion which has been dissociated off, the water molecules' own attraction has an influence on the hydration of the organic molecule. In this way the composition of

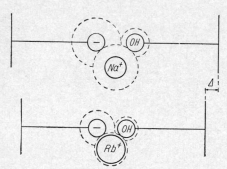

Fig. 12. Diagrammatic representation of the influence of hydration on the adsorption of inorganic ions on the side-chains of polypeptides (after FREY-WYSSLING 1938).

the structure can be influenced (Fig. 12). The hydration of an ion also affects its linkage or adsorption. This generally decreases in homologous series with increasing hydration; for example, the strongly hydrated sodium ion is less strongly adsorbed than the weakly hydrated potassium or rubidium ions.

4 FATS AND PHOSPHATIDES

Among the substances in addition to protein which are part of the structure of protoplasm, an important place is taken by the phosphatides (phospholipids; the term 'lipids' has partly displaced the older term 'lipoids'; BULL 1940), which are related to the fats. The phosphatide molecule is a glycerol/fatty acid ester, in which one fatty acid radical has been replaced by phosphoric acid, to which is attached an ammonium base. In the best-known phosphatide, *lecithin*, the base is choline; the two fatty acid radicals are formed by palmitic, stearic, oleic or perhaps linoleic acid. The structural formula is:

$$H_2C \cdot O \cdot CO \cdot R_1$$
$$HC \cdot O \cdot CO \cdot R_2$$
$$H_2C \cdot O \diagdown$$
$$O \diagup P \diagup O^- \diagdown O-CH_2 \cdot CH_2 \cdot N^+ (CH_3)_3$$

The phosphatides have not been investigated in detail chemically, but several have been prepared synthetically, although in nature a more abundant selection is found. Due to their amphoteric properties and their tendency to form complexes with proteins (the so-called *lipoproteins*) or with carbohydrates, they are very reactive and must play an important part in metabolism.

In the phosphatides one encounters the important organic esterification with phosphoric acid, by which the dissociation constants (about $pK = 2$) can be further increased. The water-solubility of the phosphatides increases by complex formation with proteins, and they tend in this condition to enter the living cell. Similar complex formations with proteins are known for carotene of carrot and for lycopene of tomatoes, in which these pigments, themselves insoluble in water, occur either in water-soluble form or at least as hydrophilic colloids in the living cells. The same probably also applies to the chlorophyll in the chloroplasts. It is believed that in such complex formations a contact exists between the hydrophobe groups of the proteins and the undissociated tail of the fatty acid radical.

As already mentioned, the fatty acid molecule has an extended hydrocarbon chain with a hydrophobe —CH_3 group at the end. The screening of this group by complex formation thus weakens the lipid character, by which the hydrophilia of the dissociatable phosphoric acid, carboxyl and ammonium-base groups is favoured. In order that an organic compound can dissolve in water it must have at least *one* hydrophilic group. These relations are undoubtedly of great importance in the living cell, since the tendency towards chemical reaction is in general dependent on the degree of hydrophilia. The pure fats are predominantly chemical storage materials and reserve nutrients. They may also possibly play a certain role as intermicellar substances in young cell walls.

A much-discussed problem is the presence or absence of pure fats and phosphatides in the surface layers and plastids (MENKE and JACOB 1942). The balance between hydrophilic and hydrophobic groups in the molecule determines the effect of a dissolved substance on the surface tension of water. Predominantly hydrophobic substances lower the surface tension, as, in accordance with Gibbs's theorem, they collect at the surface of the solution. As regards the phosphatides it is assumed from their fat-like character that they accumulate in the interphase between the aqueous medium and the protoplasm, and thus apparently form a main constituent of the external surface layer. The thinness of the membrane makes a direct chemical analysis difficult, but observations on the electro-chemical properties of the plasma membrane tell against a dominance of the highly dissociated phosphatides. From further observations the presence of phosphatides inside the protoplasm or possibly also in the cell nucleus can be concluded; and mitochondria also apparently contain phosphatides. In addition, oil droplets have been found as inclusions in protoplasm or in plastids. It is doubtful whether one can assume in the living cell obedience to rules which are valid in ideal, simple conditions, since in the cell the subdivision of materials is to a large extent dependent on the localisation of metabolic activity. In fact one would not be wrong in assuming that the lipids play an important role as regulators of the speed of reaction in the structure-bound systems, as they are a means for arranging the active groups in regular structural unions. This seems to apply e.g. to the mitochondria, plastids and surface layers.

5 NUCLEIC ACIDS

In addition to proteins the main constituents of the cell nucleus are nucleic acids (polynucleotides), which are partly united with proteins to form nucleoproteins. In the *nucleotides* or mononucleotides, inosic, adenylic, guanylic, cytidylic and uridylic acids can be determined. The components of the three first-named nucleotides are: a purine base (hypoxanthine, adenine or guanine; for the formulae see pp. 236-237), D-ribose and a phosphoric acid group attached to the sugar residue, which accounts for the strongly acid character of the nucleotides. After the abscission of the phosphoric acid a *nucleoside* remains. The combination of nucleotides with each other leads to the formation of nucleic acids, and this can happen in various ways. The form of the connection can only be ascertained indirectly, from the products of the hydrolysis. Yeast-nucleic acid decomposes under the influence of the enzyme ribonuclease (LORING and CARPENTER 1943) into guanylic, uridylic, cytidylic and adenylic acids. The molecules are apparently not very large (M about 10^4-10^5). On the other hand thymus nucleic acid, which was obtained first from the thymus gland of animals is high-molecular (M about 10^6-10^7).

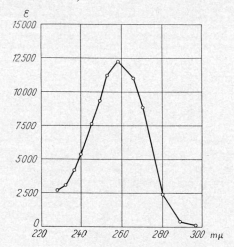

Fig. 13. The absorption spectrum of adenylic acid.

A distinction is made between ribosenucleic acids (RNA) and desoxyribosenucleic acids (DNA). (For the formula of D-ribose and of D-2-desoxyribose see below, p. 95.) To RNA belongs yeast nucleic acid, and to DNA thymus nucleic acid, which contains adenine, guanine and cytosine and also thymine and 5-methylcytosine. DNA has been discovered in wheat germ, various bacteria and animal sperm, and other sources. RNA occurs in yeast and also e.g. in tobacco mosaic virus.

By the breakdown of the nucleic acid molecule the molecular weight of e.g. the thymus nucleic acid can be reduced from about 500,000 (TENNENT and VILBRANDT 1943) to 7,000-3,000. As all preparations, however, have the same average cross-section of the molecule ($1·5$ mμ), it must be concluded that the small molecules are fragments of long threads. According to later investigations DNA has a spirally twisted molecule (WATSON and CRICK 1953). The individual nucleotides are held together by phosphoric acid linkages.

Desoxyribosenucleic acid is believed to occur quite generally in cell nuclei. It is determined mostly by the Feulgen reaction (a purple coloration with basic fuchsine), which however may not be fully specific (DANIELLI 1946). The nucleic acids uniformly give a strong absorption band in the ultra-violet at about 260 mμ (Fig. 13). Based on this is a method for the microscopic identification of the distribution of the nucleic acids in cells, in which quartz lenses and mercury lamps are used. This method is not without its drawbacks, but has been widely used. By careful measurements in the absorption spectrum it has been possible to distinguish also the various purine-bases; and the deamination of adenosine has also been followed by this method (MITCHELL and McELROY 1946).

The nucleic acids are to a large extent combined with proteins, especially histones, to nucleoproteins. These are composed of a kind of salt formed between the strongly acidic nucleotides and the strongly basic arginine groups. The nucleic acids are weakly acidic and are soluble in strong salt solutions. In physiological salt solutions near the IEP, however, they are insoluble; which explains their occurrence as solid masses in the chromosomes. Thymus nucleoproteins (DNA) occur in the cell nucleus and ribose-nucleoproteins (RNA) are widespread in cytoplasm. They form a chief component of the virus molecule. It has been assumed that the linking together of nucleic acid and protein threads is facilitated by the fact that the atomic distances in the two correspond (ASTBURY and BELL 1938).

6 VIRUSES. THE SELF-REPRODUCTION OF LARGE MOLECULES

Ribosenucleic acids (RNA) form a universal component of the pathogenic viruses. In them the molecular weight is very high, e.g. $11·6 \times 10^6$ for the bean mosaic virus (MILLER and PRICE 1946) and 48×10^6 for the tobacco mosaic virus. The virus particles are probably to be conceived as nucleoproteins (STANLEY 1941). The tobacco mosaic virus contains a notable proportion of aromatic amino acids, e.g. 3·8% of tyrosine, 4·5% of tryptophan and 6% of phenylalanine. The protein content amounts to about 94% and the content of nucleic acids to about 6% (with 0·56% phosphorus; STANLEY 1946, in GREEN 1946). As in the large protein molecules, the molecule of tobacco mosaic virus appears to be built up from smaller units which have the dimensions $6·8 \times 8·8 \times 8·8$ mμ. These units combine together to form regular aggregates. The whole molecule is roughly spherical, with a cross-section of 25·5 mμ and with the properties of a regular crystal aggregate (PRICE, WILLIAMS, WYCKOFF 1946). According to other data the individual virus particle is about 28 mμ long and 1·5 mμ in cross-section (Figs. 14 and 15). Still smaller particles are inactive. The elementary particles arrange themselves on a hexagonal grid, and the activity seems to be connected with the regular sub-microscopic structure. MILLER and PRICE (1946) quote for 'southern bean mosaic virus' a molecular cross-section of 31·2 mμ (in the dehydrated state 24·0 mμ). When dry, the molecule is spherical but after hydration with 75% water it takes on a lengthened form with an axis ratio 5 : 1. LABAW and WYCKOFF (1957) find in the 'southern bean mosaic virus' crystals which are tightly packed together in a cubical grid. The tetra-molecular cube has a length of side $= 34·5$ mμ, and in the dry state 24·5 mμ.

A virus can be carried over from one host plant to another. If the virus molecule penetrates into the protoplasm of the host cell, it is able to increase itself. The virus thus requires for its growth an exchange of materials with the protoplasm of the host. It can partly crystallise even in the host cell, and after extraction of infected leaves crystallising preparations have been obtained (BAWDEN and PIRIE 1945, STANLEY 1946; Fig. 16). The purified virus preparations are then examined in the electron microscope and also chemically. The nucleic acid can be split off from the virus molecule by salicylate (BEST 1945).

Individual kinds of virus have a very variable molecular size from about 1 up to about 30 mμ in cross-section. The smallest, e.g. lucerne mosaic virus, are smaller than the haemocyanin molecule. Virus vaccinicum on the other hand is larger than the micro-organisms of the pleuropneumonia group. The virus is thus at once smaller than large protein molecules and larger than some micro-organisms. The large virus molecules contain among other things enzymes and hormones that are known also in cells, but the small ones do not. There are thus numerous transitions from simple molecules to molecular aggregates of complicated construction, which approach living cells or which can at least be compared to the smallest microsomes, which form an intermediate stage between large molecules and microscopically visible microsomes and which show a detectable expenditure of energy (cf. STERN 1943).

There is a distinction between large virus particles and simply constructed micro-organisms in that the former require the protoplasm of a host in order to multiply. The pathogenic bacteria, however, can multiply also on artificial substrates. There exist certain similarities between the effect of a virus on the protoplasm of the host and the effects of hormones or vitamins; the former, however, change the cell proteins in a way which is dangerous to life.

The study of viruses has already attained a special interest, since these large molecules show in a striking way the phenomenon of *self-reproduction* which is also a characteristic of cell nuclei and plastids. Increase of the cytoplasm naturally means a multiplication of the number of protein molecules. Even if one compares the cytoplasm to a factory that has raw materials and machines available for the production of a series of materials, it is nevertheless a distinguishing mark of the living production that the 'machines' in the factory are self-made. Self-reproduction is thus a fundamental principle of living matter.

Clear ideas about the biochemical mechanism of self-reproduction have not yet been attained. Modern research, however, hints at *resonance phenomena* (*mesomerism*; see KALCKAR in GREEN 1946, *et al.*). Mesomerism or resonance is the name for the oscillation of an electron between two tautomeric states of a molecule, in which one state is the mirror image of the other. By oscillating movements of an electron plus a hydrogen atom e.g. the keto- and enol-forms change into each other:

$$H—C—CH_2— \qquad H—C=CH— \tag{1}$$

$$\underset{\text{Keto form}}{\overset{\|}{O}} \qquad \underset{\text{Enol form}}{\overset{|}{OH}}$$

In this case the process proceeds so slowly that the components can be isolated. In mesomerism the oscillation proceeds so quickly that isolation is impossible.

A variant of self-reproduction is encountered in the relationship between toxins and antitoxins. The antibodies are not originally present in the living cell, but are formed by contact of the toxin with the protoplasm. It has been suggested that when the antibody is a protein certain points on the surface of the toxin molecule attract protein

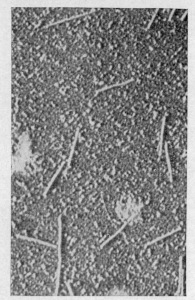 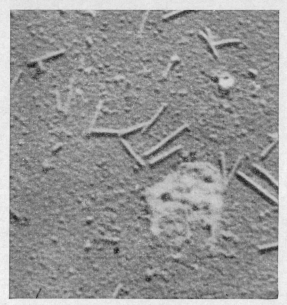

Fig. 14. Electron microscopic enlargement ($\times$ 30,000) of sap pressed from the leaves of Turkish tobacco infected with tobacco mosaic virus (after SIGURGEIRSSON and STANLEY 1947).

Fig. 15. Electron microscopic enlargement ($\times$ 34,800) of the cell contents of the leaf hairs of Turkish tobacco infected with virus (after G. OSTER and W. M. STANLEY 1946).

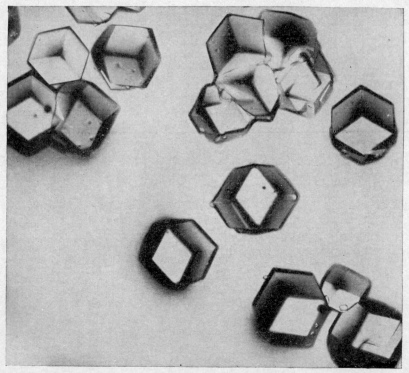

Fig. 16. Crystals of 'tomato bushy stunt virus' ($\times$ 224) (after W. M. STANLEY 1940).

fragments with mirror-image configuration. These fragments are collected gradually to antibody molecules, which thus can attach themselves closely to a toxin molecule in such a way that this is impeded in its harmful chemical activity.

A certain basis for such speculative ideas is supplied by experience on the specificity of enzymes. Thus it has been found that the proteolytic enzymes normally attack only one of two stereoisomers. This is probably due to the fact that, owing to the configuration of their reactive positions, they come into contact only with those substrate molecules which form a negative matrix of their reactive positions. Cases are also known however in which enzymes, e.g. trypsin, can produce their effect through a protective film of orientated molecules 10-25 mμ thick (ROTHEN 1946, 1947). For such cases the above-mentioned hypothesis obviously is not valid.

These general ideas about the importance of form (configuration, stereochemistry) of the large molecules for their chemical activity are undoubtedly stimulating. The occurrence of nucleic acid in the viruses and in chromosomes (see below) as well as in growing protoplasm probably hints at a special function of these compounds in the self-reproduction of nucleoprotein molecules. Attention has been directed to the strong electric potential difference which can arise in acid dissociation of nucleic acid, as well as to the sometimes high energy-content of phosphoric acid compounds. Energy-rich phosphoric acid linkages play a decisive part in numerous metabolic processes e.g. in muscle contraction, in the polymerisation of glucose molecules, and in the formation of protein. The best known are the adenosine phosphates which are always present in nucleic acids. We will return to this question in Chapter 4.

C. The Cell Nucleus

The discussion here is confined to those parts of cytology which touch on physiological and biochemical problems. Detailed accounts of cytomorphology are given by SHARP (1934, 1943), TISCHLER (1934, 1952), DARLINGTON (1937), WHITE (1947), HAAS (1955) et al.

The living nucleus of a mature cell, the 'resting nucleus', is a transparent body in which one or more drop-like nucleoli can be observed. The nucleoli contain ribonucleic acid (RNA) and possibly also phosphatides. They may have morphological-physiological exchanges with the chromosomes. If cell nuclei are fractionated from homogenates, one always finds 5%-15% of lipids, which probably occur as liponucleoprotein, although some appear to be phosphatides. Protein is always present. In newly developed cells, e.g. in the epidermis of root tips, the main mass of the living nucleus appears to be granulated (Fig. 1, p. 2). After fixation with the usual cytological fixation media (osmic acid, acetic acid, chromic acid, mercuric chloride, etc.) an irregular network appears, which is dyed more or less strongly by basic dyestuffs and which absorbs ultra-violet light (about 260 mμ). It contains desoxynucleic acid (DNA) and appears to have some connection with the chromosomes (GATES 1942). The strongly staining structures are called *chromatin* (LUNDEGÅRDH 1910) and the hyaline ground substance *nuclear sap*.

In the *interphase*, i.e. the state between two successive divisions, it has been observed both optically (SHINKE 1937) and more especially electron-microscopically that there are chromosome filaments which form a tight network and consist of ultrafibrils 8-10 mμ thick, which probably show spiral windings (DENNES 1951). According to

HOFFMAN-BERLING and KAUSCHE (1951), more complex unions arise by the twisting together of two double etc. spirals (cf. also ONCLEY 1959).

In the approach to *vegetative (somatic) nuclear division (mitosis)*, the chromatin-components of higher plants are contracted and multiplied. They are differentiated into chromosomes, easily distinguishable even while alive, which occur in a length, form and number characteristic for each species. The first stage of nuclear division is called the *prophase*. Almost from the very beginning the chromosomes show a longitudinal split into two *chromatids*. Soon afterwards the nuclear membrane is dissolved.

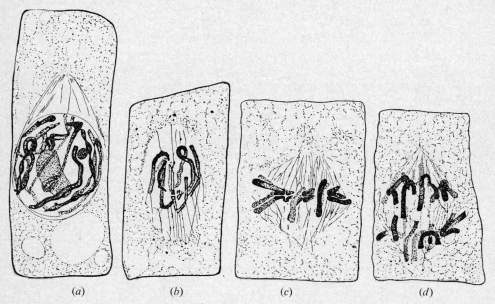

    (a)   (b)   (c)   (d)

Fig. 17. Division of the nucleus in the root tip of *Vicia faba*, (a) prophase shortly before the dissolution of the nuclear membrane; (b) transition from prophase to metaphase; (c) metaphase; (d) anaphase (from (LUNDEGÅRDH 1922).

At the same time there arise in the cytoplasm the bipolar *nuclear spindles*, whose radiating fibrillar structure is probably connected with the movement of the chromosomes. Division now starts: this is the *metaphase*. The nuclear spindle is optically double-refracting and shrinks on plasmolysis (i.e. on removal of water) in its width, but not in its length; thus it must have a fibrous structure (BĚLAŘ, STROHMEYER). The chromosomes arrange themselves in the equatorial zone, after which the two chromatids of each chromosome move apart from each other (*anaphase*), probably with the help of energy derived from adenosine triphosphate (LETTRÉ and ALBRECHT 1951) Colchicine acts against this and disturbs the processes of movement. In fixed preparations it is seen that the spindle fibres are joined to the chromosomes and that they show, at the place of attachment, a small point or elevation which is named the *centromere*. After the separation of the halves of the chromosomes from each other they collect into two heaps, which are gradually surrounded by a new nuclear membrane (*telophase*). The outline of the chromosomes becomes indefinite at this stage, until finally the resting nucleus has regained its granular appearance.

Mitosis is usually combined with a *cytokinesis* in which small drop-like particles collect together in the equatorial plane of the spindle (see phragmoplast in Fig. 18) and gradually fuse to a plate. This *cell plate* spreads centrifugally and finally fuses with the cell wall, and at this point the cell division is completed. In somatic mitosis every daughter cell thus gets a complete set of chromosomes. The polarisation of the central protoplasm during division usually extends even further so that larger or smaller parts of the protoplast are included. The formation of hyaline 'polar plates' (centrosomes) is observable during the prophase and, in many cells, especially in lower organisms, ray-shaped collections of cytosomes or plastids. In addition there are changes in the position of the nucleus and of the spindle within the cell, by which the position of the new cell wall can be determined.

In *meiotic nuclear division*, which introduces the formation of the sex cells, the chromosomes pair off two by two, a stage which precedes an extended prophase (*synapsis*). The synapsis is characterised by paired chromosomes at first long and filamentous, but later short and arc-shaped (*diakinesis*; the pairs are sometimes called bivalents). In the subsequent nuclear division therefore one-half of the chromosomes of the somatic cells go to one side and the other half to the other side, so that the sex cells obtain the simple (*haploid*) chromosome number. The haploid nuclei divide once more, so that the four sex cells are formed. After fertilisation, when two haploid nuclei fuse, the doubled, *diploid* chromosome number is formed again.

Normally one finds throughout the whole individual the diploid chromosome number, but *polyploid* nuclei can arise in individual cells, as a result of cell division not having occurred and of the fusion of the daughter nuclei. Polyploid nuclei can also be evoked artificially by certain poisons, e.g. colchicine, which influence the viscosity of the protoplasm (WADA 1940) and the functions of the nuclear spindle (LEVAN and ÖSTERGREN 1943). When such alterations occur in connection with the formation of the sex cells, heritable polyploidy (tetraploid etc. plants) can arise, which is commonly revealed in certain racial characteristics. Ploidy up to 1,024 has been observed (GEITLER 1941). In such cases the daughter chromosomes are usually grouped together. It is noteworthy, however, that a corresponding reduction in the chromosome number by fusion within the groups does not occur. This behaviour is an expression of the individuality of the chromosomes, a fact which plays a large part in the science of heredity and which earlier led to the assumption that every chromosome somehow remained constant during the resting stage of the cell nucleus as well, although one cannot then distinguish the individual chromosomes by optical methods.

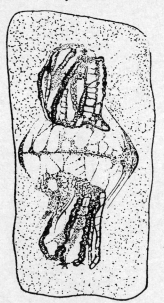

When polyploid cells arise the relationship between nucleus and cytoplasm is shifted, and this favours the formation of giant cells and, in certain cases, of large dimensions of the organs also. The physiological properties are also changed. Polyploid plants may show a lower dry weight with higher water content and reduced respiration (STÅLFELT 1943). The sugar content and the intensity of photosynthesis can also be reduced (SULLIVAN and MYERS 1939, LARSEN 1943, NOGGLE 1946).

Fig. 18. Telophase from the root of *Vicia faba*. This shows a clear phragmoplast and the commencement of wall formation (after LUNDEGÅRDH 1922).

The chromosomes can show very variable sizes in different plants, but there are also differences within one and the same plant. The mutual size relationships and also the tendency of certain chromosomes to form parts half or entirely split off (*satellites* or *trabants*) are however usually maintained. The small chromosomes in fungi, e.g. *Saprolegnia*, are spherical with a diameter less than 0·5 μ, whilst the largest chromosome in *Trillium* has a length of 30 μ. The chromosomes in maize are 8-10 μ, in *Melandrium* 2-6 μ, and in *Datura* 1·5-4 μ long.

The *chromosome number* varies greatly in plants. No connection can be discovered between chromosome number and phylogenetic development. Among plants with very low chromosome numbers may be mentioned *Crepis capillaris* and *Crocus*, which have only three chromosomes in the haploid state, whilst other higher plants can show numbers up to several hundred. In a comparison among about 2,500 species the numbers were grouped preferentially in the following order of frequency (going from the more to the less frequent): 12, 8, 7, 9, 16, 6, 10, 14 (FERNANDEZ 1931, DARLINGTON and AMMAL 1946).

As in the interphase (see above), so also in the metaphase the chromosomes are far from being optically homogeneous. One can usually distinguish under the microscope basophile spiralled structures (*chromonemata*) running in the longitudinal direction. It seems however to be still uncertain whether every chromosome has only one chromonema or whether it has several. The chromonemata may be self-reproducing before the visible splitting of the chromosomes. Optical analysis is of course made difficult by their small dimensions (limit of visibility about 0·25 μ). Electron microscopic analysis shows a further subdivision of the chromonemata into fibre bundles. According to RUCH (1945) the meiotic chromosomes have ordinarily a simple spiral composed of two parallel fibres, on which small particles (*chromomeres*) are strung. Still finer structure could not be distinguished microscopically. According to the general opinion there are thus in chromonemata transverse basophile bands or discs (chromomeres) which are held together by a non-basophile substance, probably protein. Under the electron microscope these elements appear, as stated, to be most probably composed from fibres spirally wound and arranged in bundles. Chemical investigations on the giant chromosomes in the salivary glands of certain insect larvae have tended to show that the main mass of the chromosomes is formed from protein with nucleic acid groups inserted in places, the phosphoric acid groups forming the necessary bridges (MAZIA 1941, RIS and MIRSKY 1951, ONCLEY et al. 1959).

Data on the optical-polarisation properties of the chromosomes are rather contradictory. According to one result they are not clearly anisotropic, which would tell against a fibre structure. Other research workers (SCHMIDT 1930, PICKEN 1940) on the other hand found optical double refraction in the chromosomes, and this would indicate that the nucleic acid molecules are arranged parallel to the polypeptide chains and that the straight chromosomes according to MANTON (1945) can be arranged as bundles of parallel protein chains. As mentioned above, ASTBURY and BELL (1938) assume that the nucleotides are joined directly to the fully stretched protein fibres.

The differentiation of the chromosomes in prophase can be explained as a dehydration of the tight chromatin network. In this the long irregularly orientated chain molecules are gathered together into parallel bundles. In telophase, dehydration and relaxation occur in opposing sequence so that the chain molecules slide apart in places but in others cling together as in a strongly hydrated gel. Since the chromosome elements in the resting nucleus are irregularly orientated, no uniform result could be expected from optical polarisation studies. In certain circumstances, however, a double refraction is seen when the resting nucleus is stretched. The assumption, disputed by many cytologists, that the chromosomes possess a certain morphological individuality even in the resting nucleus, thus appears to be not altogether wrong. BOVERI had already observed in the eggs of *Ascaris* that chromosomes in the prophase occur at about the same positions as in the preceding telophase. In certain cases small visible residues of the chromosomes persist in the resting stage (*prochromosomes* according to J. B. OVERTON, chromocentres according to GRÉGOIRE). In the formation of the head of spermatozoa a dehydration and parallel orientation of chromatin fibres are also involved.

By the collaboration of cytologists and geneticists the earlier-developed theory of chromosomes as carriers of heredity has been further strengthened. JOHANNSEN introduced the concept of the *gene* to indicate the undiscovered material foundation for the transmission of properties from one generation to the next. Plant-physiologically one can of course conceive of the gene in various ways. On the whole the hypotheses of the genes as individual particles already sketched by DARWIN, DE VRIES and others have been retained in more modern form. These hypotheses have acquired considerably greater probability from the work of protein chemistry. The giant molecules in regular aggregate chains can hypothetically be equipped with all the properties which are ascribed to the gene.

The gene is a centre from which the chemical activity of the cytoplasm is guided. Thus one can imagine the gene either as a group of enzymes which regulate special changes, or as a self-reproducing object from which the multiplication of special materials proceeds. Reference has been made to the great similarities in principle between genes and viruses; the opinion that viruses also are very complex submicroscopic particles was taken into account.

According to SPIEGELMANN and KAMEN (1946), in the self-reproduction of the gene so-called *plasmagenes* are formed, which can continue to live and act independently at least for a certain time. They may hypothetically be effective in protein formation due to energy-rich phosphoric acid compounds. The active phosphoric acid groups must have a specific location in the molecule in order to dominate syntheses, whilst e.g. adenosine triphosphate (ATP; see Chap. 4) represents only a non-specific energy reservoir. SPIEGELMANN and KAMEN also conceived the possibility that retrograde inductions, caused by plasmagenes, could have a modifying effect on genes, from which it would be possible to speak of 'acquired characteristics'. Here one encounters the old controversy between Lamarckism and Darwinism-Mendelism; it must however be said that, even though a change of milieu of the genes is not theoretically excluded, definite evidence has so far not been produced.

Interesting conclusions on the activity of the genes have been reached by the studies on pigment formation in the flour moth (BUTENANDT 1953) and on the mutants of the bread mould (*Neurospora*) or of other fungi (FRIES 1945, BEADLE 1947). These studies seem to have led mostly to the opinion that the individual genes control quite specific points of a chain of syntheses. When a gene is missing, as happens in the majority of the observed mutations, a reaction chain is thus blocked at a key point.

Furthermore BUTENANDT has expressed the hypothesis that both protein molecules and polysaccharides are not synthesised step by step from their raw materials under the influence of enzymes, but are composed and specifically arranged structurally by a single catalyst from simple raw materials. Genes could play the part of such 'total catalysts'. In the strict sense there is no fundamental difference between this concept and the hypotheses about antibody formation mentioned above. One can only say that it is all the same theoretically whether one conceives of the gene as an aggregate of enzymes which induce all partial processes, e.g. of protein synthesis according to a sequence, or as a single giant molecule which includes in itself the whole of these abilities. In the synthesis of such a product intermediate stages are traversed. The speed of the partial processes is however variable. With a suitable speed the formation of a giant molecule can appear as the work of a *deus ex machina*.

Since even the largest giant molecules lie below the limit of ultramicroscopic visibility there is no possibility of identifying the gene with microscopically distinguishable granules. Genetic analysis usually results in a very large number of hereditary units independent of each other. The existence of the chromosomes, however, requires the assumption that a particular arrangement of genes occurs, i.e. their arrangement in a spatial structure. This assembly would thus hold together a considerable number of genes in micelles or something similar. The virus crystal aggregates discovered in recent years could serve as a model of such an arrangement. As already mentioned several times, it has been assumed that the nucleic acids play the role of a cohesive skeleton. The great increase of nucleic acid (DNA) in nuclear division seems to make this carrier role still more credible.

Various methods have been tried to calculate the absolute size of the gene (e.g. PONTECORVO 1952) and have led to a value of about 10 mμ, which indeed is very similar to the size of a giant molecule such as a nucleoprotein. The calculations, however, give widely varying values. It is believed that the X-chromosome in *Drosophila* contains 1,800 genes and that altogether 3,000 genes are present. FREY-WYSSLING assumes that the gene forms a circular disc with a diameter of 120 mμ and a thickness of 4 mμ. If these calculations were correct one should be able to observe the gene directly under the electron microscope. DEA (1946) calculates that a *B. coli* contains only 250 genes with a diameter of 12 mμ and a molecular weight of 750,000. Each gene would thus contain five molecules, and the total amount of gene would be 0·1%-1·0% of the protein content of the cell.

Certain conclusions about the activity of the chromosomes as bearers of heredity are obtained through the mutations caused by *X-ray irradiation*. These mutations are believed to arise through the splitting of the chromatin by ionisation at two or more points, and the re-uniting of the fragments in a new arrangement, so that the arrangement of genes in the chromosomes is altered. According to TIMOFÉEFF-RESSOWSKY (1940), for successful irradiation, ionisation must be caused within a gene region of, at the most, 0·4 mμ.

A rearrangement of the genes can also take place by particles being exchanged between two parent chromosomes (bivalents). This 'crossing over', which is believed to occur in synapsis, has been studied in insects. In experiments with ultra-violet radiation the greatest effect was obtained when using the wave-lengths which are strongly absorbed by nucleic acids (260 mμ) and proteins (280 mμ). Similar experiments were carried out with viruses, which however were often destroyed. Certain alterations in the genes, which can later be passed on by heredity (cf. above), can also be caused by chemical stimulants.

A chemical analysis of isolated cell nuclei (the method of MIRSKY and POLLISTER 1943) shows in addition to nucleic acid (DNA) the occurrence also of various proteins (basic histones, STEDMAN's chromosomin; cf. GULLAND *et al.* 1945, DAVIDSON 1953) and inorganic substances, e.g. much calcium (up to 1·4%) in connection with the phosphorus. This fact has been explained by assuming that the nucleic acids exist as neutral calcium salt (WILLIAMSON and GULICK 1944). In addition a number of enzymes has been found, viz. hydrolases such as arginase, esterase, phosphatase, etc. (DOUNCE 1943; the data on cytochrome oxidase are, however, doubtful). There are also lecithin and other lipids. The sulphur which is found can be combined elsewhere than in the proteins. All these analyses, which refer only to animal cell nuclei (liver, thymus) are rather uncertain and should not be generalised.

The structure of spermatozoa shows that their chromosome substance can exist for a considerable time regardless of their minimal quantities of cytoplasm, and this suggests a molecular construction resembling a virus. Otherwise there is of course in somatic cells an active exchange between cell nucleus and cytoplasm, even if earlier ideas (HABERLANDT *et al.*) of a direct relationship between the positions of the nucleus and of local growth differences are not valid.

Measurements on the speed of exchange and the uptake of radioactive isotopes confirm the relatively stable structure of the chromosomes. Unlike cytoplasmic nucleic acid, the chromosome substance takes up radioactive phosphorus only during multiplication. The chromosome material once synthesised thus appears to be very stable.

In lower plants the differentiation of nucleus and cytoplasm appears less clearly (for bacteria see KNAYSI 1944, PORTER 1946). It is believed that in yeast cells ribosenucleic acid (RNA) has been found in the cytoplasm and desoxyribosenucleic acid (DNA) in the small particles, which are interpreted as primitive nuclei. Similar observations are available for bacteria (TULASNE and VENDRELY 1947). In Actinomycetes the whole protoplasm shows the Feulgen reaction (PLOTHO 1940). In certain bacteria this reaction also occurs in the protoplasmic surface layer, which otherwise consists of lipids and proteins in firm combination (KNAYSI 1946). The main chemical groups of the protoplasm of higher organisms are thus already present in the initial stages of phylogenetic development (cf. the analyses on p. 9), although they are not divided among different organs.

It is fortunate that, although the genes are carried by apparently crudely formed chromosomes even in the highest organisms, yet in spite of this the mechanism of division so seldom goes wrong. From the figures given above for the possible size of the genes it follows that they would have plenty of space in the chromosomes to occur as large molecular aggregates. Even a short molecular chain of a protein has in itself the possibility of great steric variation, even when the same amino acid members are repeated rhythmically at fixed distances. Variations could occur, for example, in the side-chains.

How strongly the chemical properties of a molecule can be influenced even by a fairly unimportant re-arrangement or alteration of a side-chain can be studied, e.g. in the sex hormones and related substances such as gallic acids and cardiac poisons. As far as reliability of the reproductive mechanism is concerned, it should be remembered that the most frequently occurring 'manufacturing errors' are probably eliminated during the formation of the sex cells and are thus put out of action without burdening the function of the undamaged genes.

Actual mutations presume rearrangement of the whole molecular construction of a gene. In the sphere of molecular dimensions there must thus be incessant competition between identical and modified gene molecules, ending with the dominance of one or the other. The mechanism for the transfer of heritable characteristics is, of course, not infallible, but obviously it possesses a high degree of effectiveness and resistance to change.

D. Plastids

Plastids are independent organs enclosed in the cytoplasm, which are propagated by division. They occur already in the cells of the primary meristem as grains or droplets (Fig. 1, p. 2), which then develop either into colourless leucoplasts (starch-formers) or into coloured plastids (chromoplasts and chloroplasts). Chromoplasts form only yellow pigments and no longer fulfil the function of 'trophoplasts' which belongs to most leucoplasts and chloroplasts. As an example of the independence of the plastids it may be mentioned that they grow even in cells without nuclei and form starch (e.g. in the algae *Spirogyra* and *Zygnema*) and that in the formation of zygotes in *Spirogyra* a reduction in the characteristic number for the vegetative cells occurs (Tröndle 1907). Individual chloroplasts are not present in blue-green algae. In their relation with cytoplasm plastids have a certain analogy with the cell nucleus, in that, according to Winkler (1916), larger cells have also larger chloroplasts.

Characteristic inclusions of many algae chloroplasts are the *pyrenoids*, which are alleged to consist of reserve proteins and also to show certain connections with the formation of starch and oil (Bose 1943).

Fig. 19. The layered construction of the chloroplast with laminae and grana (diagrammatic, after Menke 1940).

The chloroplasts consist of a colourless *stroma* and a number of *grana* which are mostly ellipsoidal discs of $0.3\text{-}2\ \mu$ in axis length (Heitz 1936, Metzner 1937, Algera *et al.* 1947, Granick 1950). The grana, which contain the largest part or the whole of the chlorophyll, are normally arranged in layers (*laminae*). Strugger (1951) finds the grana arranged like stacks of coins (further data in Oncley *et al.* 1959).

It is maintained that photosynthesis itself occurs in the grana (Aronoff 1946), whilst the starch formed is located in the stroma (Jungers and Dontrelique 1943). The leucoplasts can thus be considered as grana-free chloroplasts. Studies under the electron microscope have cleared up certain structural details which are probably connected with the observed double refraction. An electron-microscopic structure has also been observed in the stroma (Algera *et al.* 1947).

By fractional centrifugation one can isolate almost pure chloroplasts from homogenised leaves. The chloroplasts contain much nitrogen: in oats, according to Galston (1943), 30%-40% of the total N-content of the leaves. The chlorophyll is combined with protein—according to Smith (1940) 16 chlorophyll: 100 protein, or according to Comar (1942) the ratio is 9 : 100. This complex-formation accounts for the absorption spectrum of the pigment extracted with alcohol or acetone (WILLSTÄTTER and STOLL 1913) not quite resembling the native chlorophyll. 'Colloidal' chlorophyll gives a more nearly natural spectrum (MEYER 1939). Similar differences in the spectra of living material and of extracts have been found with the pigments of algae (MOTHES *et al.* 1939).

Chloroplasts of spinach leaves contain 45%-50% of protein, 34%-36% of lipids (ether-soluble products), 5%-8% of chlorophyll and 7% of ash, which has much potash and magnesium as well as iron and copper. The chloroplasts form 11%-31% of the dry weight of the leaves (NEISH 1939). Calculations of the volumetric ratio between cytoplasm and chloroplasts ordinarily give the values 2 : 1, from which it follows that the functional chloroplasts form an important part of the living cell content. According to a calculation of HABERLANDT a leaf may contain 30-90 million chloroplasts. Analyses show that the main mass of the lipids is contained in the chloro-plasts, predominantly in the grana. According to data of several research workers, the chloroplasts are surrounded by a semi-permeable membrane.

The chloroplasts being the organs of photosynthesis have their own metabolism, which is in fact maintained for a considerable time when they are isolated. Ascorbic acid synthesis also occurs in the chloroplasts (BUKATSCH 1940). A number of enzymes have been found in the chloroplasts, e.g. carbonic anhydrase (which catalyses the reaction $CO_2 + H_2O \rightleftharpoons H_2CO_3$), a number of haem enzymes, catalase, cytochrome f and possibly b (HILL and WHITTINGHAM 1955) and chlorophyllase (which splits the phytol group from chlorophyll). This enzyme, like catalase, may also be present in non-green tissues. Chlorophyllase, according to NOACK (1943), is effective in the yellowing of leaves in autumn.

The important pigments of the chloroplasts are *chlorophylls* and *carotenoids* (ZSCHEILE 1941, SEYBOLD and WEISSWEILER 1943, RABINOWITCH 1945, KARRER 1948). The latter are also widespread in chromoplasts.

The chlorophyll molecule resembles a tadpole in shape and is composed of a weakly hydrophilic metallo-porphyrin head (four pyrrole groups surrounding a Mg atom) and a tail which consists of the hydrophobic aliphatic primary alcohol phytol ($C_{20}H_{39}OH$, tetramethylhexadecenol).

No certain evidence has however been found for the view that a definite chlorophyll-protein unit, similar to the haem proteins, may exist. According to a hypothesis by HUBER (1936) the head of the chlorophyll molecule adheres to a protein layer, whilst the tail is attached to a lipid layer. A granum would have a number of such protein-, chlorophyll- and lipid-layers arranged like a sandwich. Similar views are expressed by FREY-WYSSLING (1938), whilst RABINOWITCH (1945) takes up a non-committal position. HANSSON (1939) has made interesting observations on the properties of chlorophyll, and surface films have also been made experimentally in imitation of complex-formations by chlorophyll. A positive correlation between chlorophyll and protein was given by SIDERIS (1947) for the leaves of pineapple (cf. also GASSNER and GOEZE 1935).

Chlorophyll occurs in two modifications:

$$a \text{ is } C_{55}H_{72}O_5N_4Mg \quad \text{Mol. Wt. } 893$$
$$b \text{ is } C_{55}H_{70}O_6N_4Mg \quad \text{Mol. Wt. } 907$$

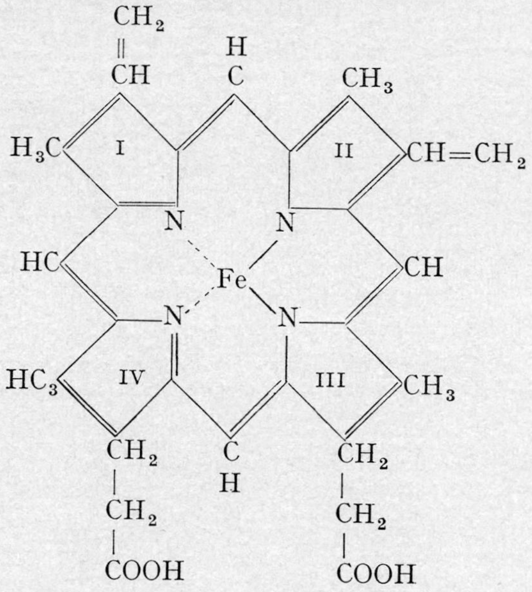

Iron-protoporphyrin IX
(protohaem IX)

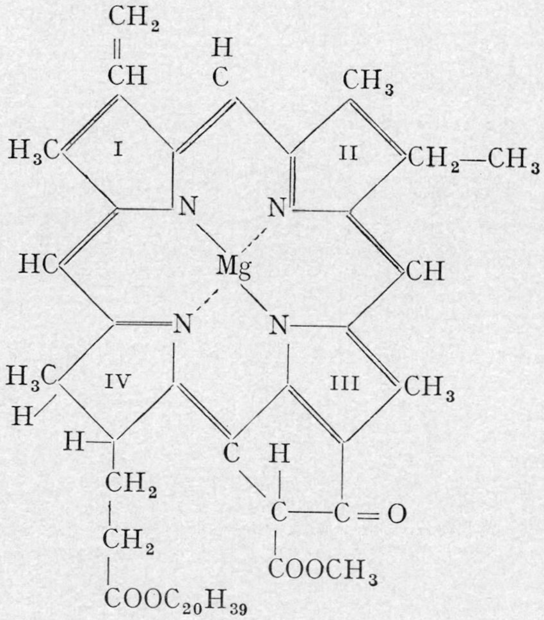

Chlorophyll a

D

The colours and the absorption spectra of the two chlorophylls are somewhat different (Fig. 20). Chlorophyll a is bluish-green and chlorophyll b is yellowish-green.

The ratio a : b is not constant but changes with the light relationships of the location (SEYBOLD 1940, 1941). In a number of sun plants it averaged 4·4, in plants in 'blue shadow' about 3·9, and in 'green shadow' about 2·6. Submerged plants show a very low ratio of 2·2. The maximal ratio, a : b=9·3, was found by SEYBOLD and EGLE (1940) in single alpine plants, which on average showed the ratio 5·5.

In etiolated leaves the chlorophyll occurs in the form of *protochlorophyll*, which is distinguished by the lack of 2H in the pyrrole rings. On illumination it passes over into chlorophyll. When etiolated oat plants are illuminated chlorophyll a is first formed and chlorophyll b only after three hours (GOODWIN and OWENS 1947). These differences in the ratio a : b and the very variable amounts of chlorophyll per unit of leaf area influence the intensity of assimilation. A number of lower plants, e.g. diatoms (WASSINK and KERSTEN 1946), blue-green algae, brown algae and red algae, contain only chlorophyll a. This seems to be also the case in certain green algae (*Vaucheria* and species from the Heterokontae).

Red and green bacteria contain green pigments which resemble chlorophyll, viz. *bacteriochlorophyll* (with 2 additional H atoms in the fourth and second pyrrole rings) and *bacterioviridin* which resembles chlorophyll a.

In general chlorophyll formation depends on illumination, but the seed plants of coniferous woods form chlorophyll in the dark. Red light has a favourable effect on chlorophyll formation, whilst blue light favours more the formation of carotene

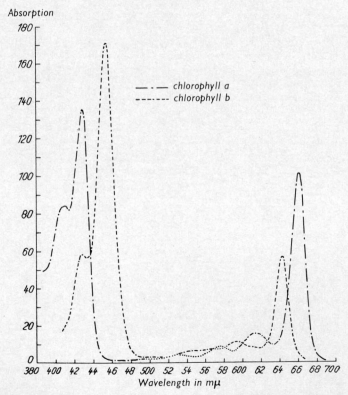

Fig. 20. Absorption spectra of chlorophyll a and b in ether solution (after ZSCHEILE 1941).

(RUDOLPH 1933, HARDER *et al.* 1938, SIMONIS 1938, SEYBOLD and EGLE 1938). A number of nutrients cooperate indirectly in the formation of chlorophyll, e.g. iron. RODHE (1948) noted a parallelism between the supply of iron and the amount of chlorophyll in *Scenedesmus*.

There is close relationship between haem and chlorophyll, and the formation of both is dependent on the synthesis of the pyrrole rings. According to researches of SHEMIN and RUSSEL (1953) *et al.* the pyrrole rings are formed from the amino acid glycine and a 4 C-compound ('activated' succinic acid). A direct precursor of porphyrin (i.e. the metal-free tetrapyrrole nucleus) is porphobilinogen:

'Activated' succinic acid

$$
\begin{array}{ccccc}
\text{COOH} & \text{COOH} & & \text{COOH} & \\
| & | & & | & \\
\text{CH}_2 & \text{CH}_2 & \text{COOH} & \text{CH}_2 & \text{COOH} \\
| & | & | & | & | \\
\left\{\begin{array}{c} \text{CH}_2 \\ | \\ \text{CO}^- \\ | \\ \text{CH}_2\text{NH}_2 \\ | \\ \text{COOH} \end{array}\right\} & \rightarrow & \begin{array}{c} \text{CH}_2 \\ | \\ \text{CO} \\ | \\ \text{CH}_2 \\ \diagdown \\ \text{NH}_2 \end{array} & + & \begin{array}{c} \text{CH}_2 \\ | \\ \text{CH}_2 \\ | \\ \text{COCH}_2\text{NH}_2 \end{array} & \rightarrow & \begin{array}{cc} \text{CH}_2 & \text{CH}_2 \\ | & | \\ \text{C}\!-\!\!-\!\!-\!\text{C} \\ \| & \| \\ \text{CH} & \text{CCH}_2\text{NH}_2 \\ \diagdown & \diagup \\ & \text{NH} \end{array}
\end{array}
$$

Glycine   δ-Aminolevulinic acid   Porphobilinogen

Porphyrins are quickly formed from cell extracts in the presence of δ-aminolevulinic acid. GRANICK (1953), who discovered the presence of porphyrin derivatives in mutants of *Chlorella*, expressed the opinion that the formation of chlorophyll and haem compounds followed the same path until either magnesium (in chlorophyll) or iron (in haems) entered into the tetrapyrrole ring (protoporphyrin).

According to recent work by J. H. SMITH, protochlorophyll is formed on partial oxidation of the magnesium derivative of protoporphyrin, and then goes over to chlorophyll a after a light-induced reduction. This reduction depends on a photochemical process in the molecule of the protochlorophyll and consequently takes place even at very low temperatures. These reactions take place very quickly.

Carotenoids are also a regular component of the chloroplasts. These yellow, red or orange pigments consist of a straight hydrocarbon chain, which at one or both ends is provided with a hexamethylene ring. Most carotenoids have 40 carbon atoms with 11 or more double bonds, many of which are conjugated; which accounts for the characteristic colour absorption (cf. formula of β-carotene, see p. 38). The nomenclature of the carotenoids is still rather unsettled (LUCK *et al.* 1946), but it seems usual at present to name the oxygen-free carotenoids (the hydrocarbons $C_{40}H_{56}$) *carotene* and the oxygen-containing ones *xanthophyll*. Among the latter luteol, $C_{40}H_{56}(OH)_2$, is the most usual. In autumn it passes over into the isomer zeaxanthol.

Carotene occurs in many isomeric forms; only two of them have been clearly shown in green leaves, namely α- and β-carotene (absorption spectra in Fig. 21), of which the latter is the more common (MACKINNEY 1935). STRAIN (1938) distinguishes eight different xanthophylls. Four carotenoids occur in the purple bacterium *Rhodospirillum rubrum* (MANTEN 1948; on algae see also KYLIN 1939). Vitamin A arises in

β-Carotene

animal bodies (probably in the liver) by hydrolysis of the middle double bond (see the formula alongside) in β-carotene.

A construction of the hydrocarbon chain reminiscent of that in carotene is encountered in the mother-substance of rubber, viz. isoprene. The similarity between carotene and phytol has also been remarked.

Among the carotenoids of the algae (brown algae and Diatomeae) *fucoxanthin*, $C_{40}H_{60}O_6$ (HEILBRONN and PIPERS 1935) may be mentioned, and further a number of pigments in purple bacteria, *rhodovibrin*, *rhodopurpurin*, etc.

The carotenoids are lipophilic and hydrophobic and combine with phosphatides and proteins. Like most unsaturated compounds the carotenoids are very reactive and easily oxidised by oxygen. It has been suggested, however, that the union with lipids affords some protection against oxidation. In the living cell the carotenes are actually very stable. The idea has also been expressed that the carotenoids protect chlorophyll against photo-oxidation (ARONOFF and MACKINNEY 1943). As a curiosity it may be mentioned that the yellowing of mineral oil during storage is due partly to the formation of carotenoids in the bacterium *Mycobacterium lacticicola* (HAAS and BUSHNELL 1944).

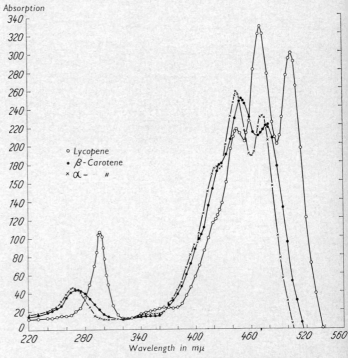

Fig. 21. Absorption spectra of α- and β-carotene and lycopene in a mixture of 20% diethyl ether and 80% ethanol (after MILLER 1937).

In blue-green algae other pigments occur which by reason of their relationship to the bile pigments are collected under the name *phycobilins* (LEMBERG and LEGGE 1949). They can be described as tetrapyrrole derivatives with a bilan structure, i.e. with an open chain, in contrast to the closed porphyrin group of chlorophyll. A formula is given as $C_{19}H_{16}N_4$. In the living cell the pigment is combined with protein, probably with acid globulins, considerably more strongly than the union between chlorophyll and protein and is consequently similar to a prosthetic group. Of the two phyco-bilins from the red alga *Porphyra tenera* which have been investigated in detail, *phycoerythrin* has the molecular weight 291,000 and *phycocyanin* 273,000. Every mole-cule of the pigmented protein is believed to have 8-16 prosthetic groups (as in the

$$CH_3 \quad C_2H_5 \quad CH_3 \quad C_2H_4COOH \quad HOOC \cdot C_2H_4 \quad CH_3 \quad C_2H_5 \quad CH_3$$

Mesobiliviolin (LEMBERG)

formula above), and the ratio between prosthetic groups and protein is similar to that in haemoglobin, 4/68,000 or cytochrome c 1/14,000 (1 prosthetic group per protein 'molecule', M.W. 14,000). The molecule, like those of most proteins, is however easily split by changes in pH (ERIKSSON and QUENSEL 1938).

E. Protoplasmic Membranes
Permeability and Ion Exchange. Vacuoles

1 THE GENERAL PROPERTIES OF SURFACE LAYERS

The external and internal surface layers of mature vacuolated cells possess properties which are of importance for the exchange of material by the protoplasm between the external medium and the internal sap. The study of the surface layers is accordingly carried on mostly by indirect means and is chiefly concerned with permeability. The vacuole, which usually occupies far the largest part of the cell volume, can on the other hand be analysed chemically. Cell sap and protoplasm can be recovered from leaves by hydraulic pressure (CHIBNALL 1923); but it is important that a high enough pressure be used, as with too low a pressure the sap is expressed only from damaged protoplasm (PHILLIS and MASON 1941).

By the active functioning of the protoplasm the vacuole receives such high con-centrations of inorganic and organic salts and of sugar, etc., that the osmotic pressure necessary for turgor is built up and maintained. Some substances are secreted in the cell sap which have a definite biological purpose, e.g. anthocyans, flavones, etc.; certain others are regarded as metabolic waste products which cannot be stored elsewhere.

That the surface layer of the vacuole, the *tonoplast*, may be composed of skeletal materials is seen e.g. from its development of form in the capillitium of Myxomycete sporangia. Glochidia, i.e. characteristic hair formations on the massulae of the microsporangia of *Azolla*, also show development of form proceeding from the vacuolar membrane (Fig. 22). This is a fairly rare case (for plants) of direct develop-ment of form within the protoplasm. The structure-forming tonoplasts are ordinarily fairly thick and thus cannot be directly compared with the thin tonoplasts of ordinary plant cells.

As regards the shape-forming ability of the *external* plasma membrane, it should be remembered that this thin layer must be involved in building up the fine structures of the cell wall, e.g. in the vessels and tracheids, with their ingenious pores and spiral thickenings. The external surface layer also has an effect on the construction of the fine canals (plasmodesmata) which unite neighbouring protoplasts with each other.

The *cilia* can be understood either as organised prominences of the protoplasmic membrane or as pseudopodia. Here one manifestly encounters a fibrillar orientation of the sub-microscopic surface structure. The cilia of bacteria, according to KOFFLER *et al.* (1957), consist of protein fibres ('flagellin'), which are spirally wound. The movements may be connected with rhythmical contractions of the stretched chain-molecules.

Many types of cilia are anchored to special cytosomes, so-called *blepharoplasts*, or even to cell nuclei (LUNDEGÅRDH 1922, p. 333 ff.) and even under the ordinary microscope show fine structure, e.g. spirals, granulation and inner and outer layers. Thus specialised protoplasmic organs are involved. Most cilia move like snakes, and the rhythmical contractions can be observed stroboscopically under the ultramicroscope as sudden flashes of light. The transmission of light stimulation perceived elsewhere in the cell body, e.g. in *Euglena*, presupposes of course a certain intraplasmatic transmission of stimulus.

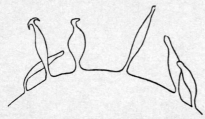

Fig. 22. Vacuole membrane of the massulae of the microsporangium of *Azolla*; glochidia in various stages of development (after HANNIG 1911).

The movements of the larger or smaller extensions of the protoplasm, the *pseudopodia*, of amoebae and plasmodia are often related to local changes in the surface tension or molecular contraction, but this has not led further than to certain general assertions. The observations (e.g. of OSTERHOUT) on the 'action currents' arising in electrically stimulated algae point to a fibre-like molecular structure of the surface layer.

SEIFRIZ and other research workers on protoplasm believe that *contractility* is a general property of protoplasm although it only exceptionally appears as clearly as it does in the cilia. It is usually found that with an electric shock thin filamentous extensions of a plasmodium are suddenly shortened.

A power of rhythmical contraction resembling that of the cilia is shown by the wall of the *contractile vacuoles*, which are encountered in many of the Protista. The rhythmical contractility of the ground mass of the protoplasm appears to support the supposition, discussed earlier (p. 16), of chain molecules gathered together in a bundle or reticulum, whose degree of stretching is determined by the charge on the side-chains which are dissociated and surrounded by swarms of ions. A surge of electric current must of course momentarily change these charges and thus cause a contraction or dilatation of the molecular fibrils. The transmission of an electrical stimulus in a particular direction can, of course, also be considered as a lightning conduction of ions along a series of such molecular chains.

Unlike cell sap, the thin surface layers mostly elude direct chemical analysis. Only in certain bacteria does the surface layer attain microscopic thickness, e.g. $0.2-0.4$ μ in *Bacillus cereus* and *B. megatherium* (KNAYSI 1946). There is evidence which may show that it consists of lipids and proteins in a strong union and also contains nucleic acids. The question whether the surface layer of the cells of higher plants contains protein is still disputed.   Among the indirect evidence the fact may be mentioned that the surface layer shows properties resembling those of artificial oil-protein films (DAVSON and DANIELLI 1943). In certain animal cells, e.g. erythrocytes, weak basic properties similar to those of amino groups are found. On the other hand evidence that the external surface layer may consist *chiefly* of proteins is not available.

2 PERMEABILITY THEORIES

(a) *The Lipoid Theory*

Modern ideas about the external protoplasmic membrane were considerably influenced by the researches of OVERTON (1932) on *cell permeability*. Investigating the relative speeds of entry into the cell of various organic compounds, he found that only those which are soluble in fats ('lipoids' or lipids) penetrate easily. On the other hand substances, e.g. sugars and inorganic salts, which are only with difficulty or not at all soluble in fats, are taken up only very slowly or not at all. These investigations have been repeated by a number of later workers, e.g. COLLANDER and BÄRLUND (1933; cf. Fig. 23), and in the main confirmed. It was found that substances with lipophile

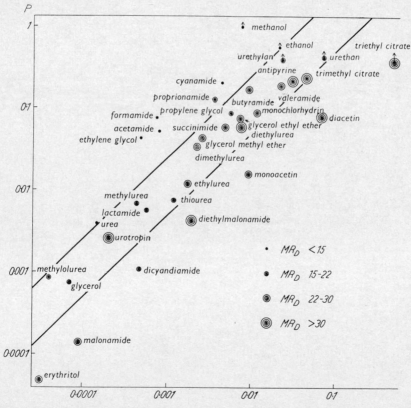

Fig. 23. Investigations on permeability with *Chara ceratophylla*. The ordinate P shows the permeability constants found. The abscissa shows the partition coefficients for olive oil/water. The molecular volume (MR_D = the molecular refraction) of the organic compounds investigated is shown by the four special signs. Small molecules were taken up more readily (after COLLANDER and BÄRLUND 1933).

or hydrophobe properties, especially those which contained many CH_3, CH_2 and CH groups, belong to OVERTON's lipoids. Even when variations in permeability occur in different plants and cell types the fat-soluble materials are still in general the more favoured.

From his observations OVERTON drew the conclusion that the surface layer contains fat-like compounds, or could even be considered as a 'lipoid layer'. The precise determination of the fat-like components is not yet available. Phosphatide or phosphatide acids have mostly been considered; but neutral fats, fatty acids and lipoproteins also would give similar results. It was soon recognised that the surface layer could not consist of a closed oil film, since water passes through easily and water-soluble compounds, e.g. salts and sugars, also permeate, even if at slower speed. OVERTON's theory was accordingly recast and it is now assumed that the surface layer of higher plant cells is composed of several different substances and behaves in general like a mosaic of lipophile and hydrophile materials, of which the former often predominate.

Various arguments have been put forward in support of the lipoid theory, but they relate predominantly to animal cells (DAVSON and DANIELLI 1943). The lipid content of red blood corpuscles reaches a level at which it would correspond approximately with a double layer of molecules, whose hydrophile groups point outwards and inwards, whilst the hydrophobe ends meet in the middle. The surface layer has a high electrical resistance, which indicates a restricted penetration by water. The inner cytoplasm shows a higher conductivity. It has been

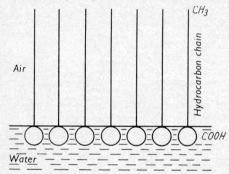

Fig. 24. Diagram of the arrangement of fatty acid molecules in a monomolecular layer on water.

found that the enzyme lipase splits fatty acids from the surface of red blood corpuscles (BALLANTINE and PARPAT 1940), and that the permeability is then altered. Unlike plant cells, erythrocytes are impermeable to cations but let anions through unhindered (DEAN 1942). According to STILES (1936) there is a close parallelism between the toxicity of alcohols and their relative surface activity; which also supports the lipoid theory.

(b) *Monomolecular Layers*

Still further progress in the investigation of the surface layers was prepared by the work on surface films (LANGMUIR, ADAM, 1941).

An oil droplet which falls on a water surface quickly spreads out into a very thin film. If the area of the film is measured and the weight of the drop as well as the molecular weight of the oil are known, it is possible to calculate that the oil film must consist of a *monomolecular* layer of fatty acid molecules, which are arranged vertically to the surface of the water with the head downwards (Fig. 24). The oil film can be transferred to a solid surface by sinking a glass or metal disc through the film. When the disc is withdrawn the oil film remains firmly adherent to it.

The individual molecules of a monomolecular layer are not firmly anchored as in a crystal, but can slide round each other, and turn head over heels, even though their statistical position of rest corresponds to a single layer with a definite orientation. Such a film shows great inner cohesion, since the hydrocarbon tails cling to each other and form an uninterrupted oil phase, whereas the hydrophile heads show the opposite tendency.

The cohesion of the oil film causes a high resistance to mechanical pressure; which explains, among other things, its lubricating properties. It can thus be said that mono-molecular film is an intermediate stage between a crystal and a liquid. Molecules of complicated structure usually adopt an angle to the water surface which varies according to the number and the position of the hydrophile groups in the molecule. In the phosphatides, for example, there are two fairly closely situated hydrophile groups, the phosphoric acid and the ammonium base. Both are attracted to the water surface, whilst the remainder of the molecule, including the two fatty acid radicals and the hydrocarbon skeleton of the glycerol, forms the hydrophobe phase.

As indicated above, still more complicated molecules, e.g. proteins, are necessarily distorted when they adapt themselves to a surface layer, and this may also have chemical reactions. Globular proteins with an almost isodiametric molecule 2·5-3 mμ across in free solution are so flattened out in the surface film that a layer only 0·8-1·0 mμ thick is formed. Many protein molecules are thus split or denatured; which is interpreted as meaning that the carbon chains are pulled apart, so that the hydrophobe groups together form a hydrocarbon layer, whilst the hydrophile groups become orientated towards the water. A protein film would thus be built up like a network of carbon chains lying parallel to the surface.

As the proteins usually produce surface tensions still lower than those of most fats, the possibility arises, according to Gibbs's theorem, that the surface layer might con-sist of a lipoid film overlaid with a protein film. Such a layering should not be taken too literally; one must imagine that the hydrophile groups both from protein and from fat stand in contact with the water phase, so that a kind of mosaic is formed, which can offer space to still further partly hydrophile groups.

Although the theory of monomolecular layers is so important, it should not be transferred uncritically to biological relationships. Of course, the general principles still apply, but in the surface layer of protoplasm certainly *bi-* or even *multi-molecular layers* are always involved and these have a correspondingly complicated structure and are probably provided with their own chemical mechanism. Such an assumption is supported by a number of data on the enzymes active in cell surfaces (see Chap. 4). It may further be imagined that the formation of cell walls proceeds from the surface layer. One has no choice but to assume that the surface layer of protoplasm in higher plants has a fairly complicated structure, as is also indicated by its numerous special permeability properties.

The chemical processes in the surface between protoplasm and medium should also not be overlooked. According to HEILBRONN (1929) the calcium content of the medium is of special importance; which may be due to the formation of organic calcium salts. Ca-ions, as is known, have an astringent effect on protoplasm, in contrast to the relaxing effect of K-ions (cf. SAKAMURA and KANAMORI 1935). This question has already been raised in the discussion of hydration. There should also be mentioned here the insoluble or slightly soluble organic calcium compounds, e.g. those with phytin (cf. MATTSON 1946). Ca-nucleotides as well as Mg-nucleotides are also soluble only with difficulty, and the latter may serve as a kind of protoplasmic skeleton in bacterial cells. WEBER (1932) showed that Ca is necessary for the formation of a normal surface layer. Traces of this ion are always present in the protoplasmic surface, and if these traces are removed with potassium oxalate, the formation of a normal surface layer fails to occur. Similar observations are available on Amoeba (POLLAK 1928).

The fact that the surface layer probably has no independent life, such as plastids and the nucleus have, but is quickly re-formed after wounding of the protoplasm, teaches us that the organic components necessary for its construction are available everywhere in the cytoplasm. The surface layer therefore probably consists of a surface film of protoplasm; from which of course it in no way follows that the materials forming the surface layer occur in the same ratios as in the ground mass of the protoplasm.

A function for the nucleotides (RNA) as special structural materials in a complicated surface layer would not be surprising, as they form persistent components of the cytoplasm. The effect of Ca-ions on surface layer formation mentioned above represents a counterpart to the effect of calcium salts on lecithin and stearic acid (HARKINS and ANDERSON 1937). Here also Ca causes shrinking, and Na causes swelling.

The formation observed in *Allium*-cells of a 'haptogen membrane' (KÜSTER 1910; Fig. 25) might well depend on such a precipitation with Ca^{++}. In this it would of course not be necessary that the Ca-ions should come from outside, as they are always present in protoplasm and

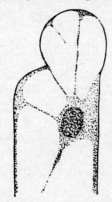

Fig. 25. Part of a plasmolysed protoplast of *Allium cepa*. The thickened protoplasmic membrane ('haptogen membrane') is bursting under the pressure of the protoplasm swelling on deplasmolysis (after KÜSTER 1910).

demonstrably go to the surface, e.g. as exchange partners for H-ions (LUNDEGÅRDH 1932).

On account of its consistency the surface layer forms a 'still zone' in contrast to the streaming protoplasm and it also affords some mechanical protection for naked protoplasts. A definite individuality of the surface layer, comparable e.g. with that of the mitochondria, is supported by earlier observations of surface layers, which still 'survived' after the inner plasma had been killed with strong (e.g. electrical) irritants (KLEMM 1895).

(c) *The Molecular Sieve Theory*

Long before OVERTON had laid the foundation of the lipoid theory, TRAUBE (1867) had propounded an 'ultra-filter theory' which was later successfully advocated by RUHLAND (1912) and his collaborators. According to this theory of permeability the protoplasmic surfaces behave as a 'molecular sieve', i.e. like a finely porous solid or semi-solid membrane with a reticular ultramicroscopic structure. Investigations on the sulphur bacterium *Beggiatoa* (SCHÖNFELDER 1930) showed that there are cells into which dissolved compounds diffuse with a speed which is in inverse ratio to the molecular volume. According to HOFE (1933), cells of *Psalliota* behave in the same way, even though the pore size here is different. Also in higher plants it has been found that fat-soluble materials can be subject to a special retarding effect if the molecules are large. These facts led to the propounding of the 'lipoid filter theory' (COLLANDER *et al.*; cf. Fig. 23) as a compromise between the ideas of OVERTON and of TRAUBE.

It now appears quite natural that the plasma membrane, whatever its chemical composition may be, refuses entry to the larger molecules. All investigations on permeability have been carried out in such a way that the rate measured has been that at which substances dissolved in water have diffused into the cell. Whether the molecules are 'dissolved' in a semi-fluid membrane or penetrate between the molecules of a monomolecular layer, the velocity will depend on mass and volume, i.e. on the molecular weight and the molecular volume, including any water of hydration and the effects of dipole moments.

A membrane composed of various chemical groups, some lipophile and some hydrophile, that is a *mosaic* in the sense used by NATHANSOHN (1904), offers of course the possibility of wide variation in permeability. Where the lipoid content is predominant, e.g. in *Fucus* eggs (RESÜHR 1935), the entry of fat-soluble materials is favoured. One must of course also take into account factors such as surface tension, partition coefficients, etc., and the supply of energy which is necessary to release the molecule from the inner surface of the membrane. According to DAWSON and DANIELLI (1943, p. 127) an addition of 0·5–2·5 kg-cal. is necessary per mole of hydrophobe CH_2 group.

In other cases, when the plasma membrane has a greater number of hydrophile groups, dissolved molecules diffuse through the membrane without notable disturbances or loss of energy, and in this case the molecular size is decisive. In addition to the previously mentioned organisms *Beggiatoa* and *Psalliota*, yeast cells also behave as 'pore permeable' (ÖRSKOV 1946). Hydrophile organic compounds generally carry some hydrophobe groups, e.g. the hydrophobe side-chains of proteins, whose effects can make themselves felt.

The numerous data which show that molecules with very large dimensions cannot penetrate into living cells must be judged with care, as it is always relative speeds that are concerned. Thus the concluson has been drawn that particles larger than 0·55-0·75 mμ do not penetrate into animal cells; while for muscle cells and frog's bladder, dimensions of 0·73 ± 0·09 mμ have been given. Similar data are available for plant cells. The fact that large virus molecules, for example, undoubtedly penetrate into the cells can only be interpreted as meaning that the surface has pores of widely varying sizes, but that the large pores are very infrequent.

It may also be supposed that there are no truly porous membranes, but only layers of orientated molecules, between which large molecules can penetrate with loss of energy. In a purely physical-chemical sense, permeability is thus a very tangled problem, and the fairly simple methods which most workers on permeability have used are no longer suitable for achieving an effective solution of the main question, namely the chemical constitution of the membrane.

Numerous investigations have shown that the permeability of a cell may easily be affected if the cell is damaged by mechanical, chemical or photo influences. Colourless protoplasm, according to LEPESCHKIN (1930), is changed by light of wavelengths between 320 and 420 mμ. Changes in permeability have also been observed in connection with tropisms (see Chap. 10). The permeability of onion leaves changes with the seasons (KRASSINSKY 1930).

The permeability for a range of organic compounds, e.g. ethylene glycol, glycerol and urea, changes with the temperature. As the Q_{10}-values lie remarkably high, e.g. 2·5 to 5·5, with a maximum 9·2 (WARTIOVAARA 1942), it cannot be only physical changes, e.g. of the speed of diffusion (for which $Q_{10} = $ a little over 1), that are concerned, but probably more deeply based alterations dependent on metabolism. It is scarcely permissible to transfer the results on general colloid reactions, e.g. on swelling, which were carried out with simple membrane models, directly to living cells (cf. LUNDEGÅRDH 1932, 1940).

3 THE IONIC PROPERTIES OF THE PROTOPLASMIC SURFACE

The most difficult problem of research on permeability is the uptake of salts by cells and organs. It is well known that every cell contains inorganic ions, e.g. Ca^{++}, K^+, NO_3^- and $H_2PO_4^-$, which get in somehow, in spite of their insolubility in fats. The protoplasmic surface of certain cells, such as the epidermal cells of young roots, is traversed continuously by large amounts of salts. This fact can scarcely be reconciled with the assumption of a closed oil film. On the other hand a mosaic-like structure, in which e.g. proteins occur in spots, would allow a passage of salts. The difficulties are increased because the uptake of salts by the roots obeys no simple rules of diffusion. Salt uptake does not increase to the same extent as the concentration of the medium; indeed there is a vigorous uptake at quite low external concentrations. In roots the salts are partly accumulated in high concentrations in the inside of the root tissue. The salt uptake of roots is thus dependent not only on a simple diffusion, but on active processes. The same is true of various storage tissues.

In the uptake of electrolytes one encounters new properties of protoplasm, which play a very subordinate part in the simple uptake by diffusion of non-electrolytes. A primary stage of electrolyte uptake is an ion exchange between the medium and the protoplast. The protoplasm shares the capability for ion exchange with most colloids, e.g. the soil colloids. One speaks quite generally of 'ion exchangers'. As an example of ion exchange in a living tissue may be mentioned the fact that a root which contains much Ca^{++} gives up Ca-ions to a dilute solution of KCl, in exchange for K^+ which is taken up. From a solution of $Mg(NO_3)_2$ the Mg^{++} is taken up in exchange for K^+, Ca^{++}, etc. (LUNDEGÅRDH et al. 1932). This ion exchange occurs independently of energy-providing metabolism, e.g. even in an atmosphere of nitrogen. Exchange of anions is less conspicuous than the active exchange of cations; this may be connected with the fact that protoplasm as a whole behaves as an amphoteric colloid dissociating mainly as an acid. On this account the surface layer normally takes on an electro-negative charge relative to the medium. As well as its chemical properties which are so important for diffusion uptake of non-electrolytes, the surface layer thus also has ionic properties, which play an important role in salt uptake and ion exchange.

4 ION EXCHANGE. MEMBRANE POTENTIALS

Ion exchange is generally a form of electrovalent chemical reaction between large hydrophile ions of a stable phase and the smaller ions of a mobile electrolyte. Ion exchange obeys the law of mass action as was shown for example for proteins (KLOTZ 1946). A characteristic of ion exchange, compared with ion fixation in a crystal lattice, is the fact that the activity of the reacting components, i.e. of the colloids and of the salt ions, is determined to a high degree by their hydration. Strong hydration means that the swarm of attached water molecules (p. 19) prevents a close approach of the ions to the oppositely charged valencies, and this facilitates ion exchange. With weak hydration ion linkage is stronger, and exchange takes place less easily.

The presence of negative, i.e. acid or 'acidoid' groups at the surface of a root causes a relatively high electro-negative charge against the surrounding medium. The charge arises by the dissociation of hydrogen ions from the acidoid groups. If a root tip is dipped into a dilute salt solution and an unpolarisable connection made between the medium and the upper part of the root, an electric current is maintained by the electromotive force (PD) at the boundary layer between root and solution (Fig. 26). The potential difference (PD) is high in dilute salt solutions and falls with increasing concentration, a relationship that may be connected with the ion exchange between the H-ions combined with the acid groups (R_a^-) and the cations of the salt M^+X^- (M = metal cation, X = anion of an acid of low molecular weight), according to the equation

$$H^+R_a^- + M^+X^- \rightleftharpoons M^+R_a^- + H^+X^- \tag{2}$$

If the reaction goes to the right, the negative potential, expressed by the ratio $\dfrac{H^+ \text{ internal}}{H^+ \text{ external}}$, decreases. 'Internal' here means the H-ion concentration at the surface of the root, and 'external' means the H-ion concentration in the medium. The root surface takes on a negative potential relative to the medium, since according to Nernst's theorem the higher H-ion concentration of the surface causes a tendency to send H-ions into solution and consequently to lower the positive potential.

Various circumstances indicate that the root surface also contains basic groups (R_bOH), which dissociate off OH-ions. These ions are in a state of ion exchange with salt anions and HCO_3-ions in the medium. As the normal potential of the roots is negative, the conclusion seems to be that the basic groups are in the minority.

It has been found by special investigations that the charge of the roots is borne by the protoplasmic surface of the epidermal cells (LUNDEGÅRDH 1938, 1940, 1941). *The protoplasmic surface thus behaves like an amphoteric colloid with predominantly acid dissociation.*

The chemical nature of the acid groups of the protoplasmic surface is at present a matter of opinion. If we start with the assumption that the negative boundary charge $(-PD)$ of the protoplasmic surface is determined by the dissociation of acid groups, we can construct a titration curve from PD measurements in a medium of increasing mineral acid concentration, a curve which shows that wheat roots are discharged (that is show a $PD = 0$) at an external pH value of about 3 (0·001 M acid). This means that at this pH the apparent concentration of acid groups in the surface layer is 0·001 M. On dilution of the medium to 0·0001 M of mineral acid the PD rises to about 58 millivolts, which shows that the number of the acid groups of the protoplasmic surface has not increased, but that the acid dissociation has become a maximum. If now at pH = 3 an almost maximum dissociation occurs, the dissociation constant cannot be lower than pK = 1-2, which corresponds to a relatively strong acid. Inorganic orthophosphoric acid has pK = c. 2, but we know that in organic combination phosphoric acid shows still higher dissociation constants. In this connection one can consider e.g. phosphatidic acids or nucleic acids, both of which may be present in the surface layer. Nucleic acids are normally secreted from the root surface (LUNDEGÅRDH and STENLID 1944, STENLID 1947). In bacteria also nucleic acids are present in the surface. Considering the composite nature of the surface it is not surprising that less acid groups also occur, and this involves certain deviations from the ideal state of the protoplasmic surface as a 'hydrogen-ion electrode'. On this account it is more difficult to determine the apparent total concentration of the acid groups. The data vary between about 0·01 and 0·1 M (see Figs. 27 and 28).

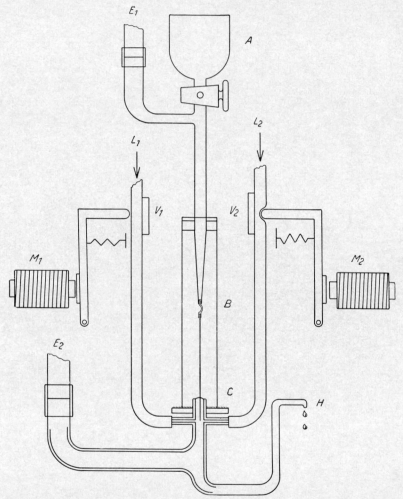

Fig. 26. Apparatus for measuring the electrical surface potential of thin roots. The two electrode vessels A and C are connected by Ag-AgCl electrodes (E_1 and E_2) with an appropriate measuring device, e.g. an oscilloscope. The upper vessel A is drawn out below (at B) into an S-shaped point, into which the upper end of the excised root is introduced. The lower part of the root is introduced into the narrow opening (C) of the lower electrode vessel. A contains a 0·2 M solution of KCl in order to eliminate the Donnan-potential of the upper cut surface of the root. C is filled with the solution under test, e.g. 100·0 M KCl, and a potential arises at the surface of contact with the root epidermis. By the valves (V_1, V_2) which are controlled by electromagnets (M_1, M_2) a quick change of solution (L_1, L_2) through C is provided for. Overflow is at H. (After LUNDEGÅRDH 1938; for the measuring technique using the oscilloscope: cf. also 1941.)

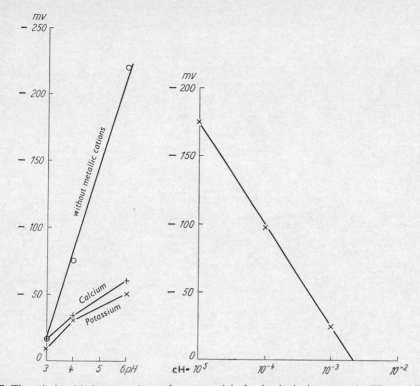

Fig. 27. The relationship between the surface potential of a desalted wheat root ($-PD$, as millivolts) and the ionic activity of the surrounding medium. In the absence of metallic cations, that is in various concentrations of a mineral acid, the root behaves approximately like a hydrogen electrode, as the dominant H^+R^- -groups (cf. Fig. 29) dissociate off only H-ions, which now alone determine the *PD*. In presence of a 0·005 N solution of KCl or CaCl₂ metallic cations are partly exchanged, as is evidenced by a sinking Donnan-potential.

Fig. 28. The surface potential of desalted tomato roots in solutions of varying amounts of HCl. The potential here also follows approximately the curve of a hydrogen electrode. Because of the high inherent acidity of the tomato roots they are discharged only at a pH-value below 3. [cH = hydrogen ion concentration i.e. the inverse of pH.]

As in other membranes, the protoplasmic surface layer must be subject to the principles of the Donnan *membrane equilibrium*. The condition for a Donnan equilibrium to be formed is the presence of large non-diffusible ions on one side of a membrane, which cannot leave this side, and of small mobile ions, which can pass through the membrane in either direction. The mobile ions are equilibrated with the immobile ions; from which it follows that the side which has the large ions has a different combination of small ions from the other side which has small ions only (cf. Fig. 29).

The Donnan principle states that the products of mobile ions on both sides of the membrane are equal. If we think of a neutral salt MX, which splits up in aqueous solution into the ions M^+ and X^-, they distribute themselves as follows:

$$M_o^+ \cdot X_o^- = M_i^+ \cdot X_i^-$$

$$\text{or } \frac{M_i^+}{M_o^+} = \frac{X_o^-}{X_i^-} \tag{3}$$

The subscript o here indicates ions in the external medium, and i means ions on the side where the large ions are found. If we take a salt with polyvalent ions ($n=$ valency) the equation assumes the following form:

$$\frac{(M_i^+)^{1/n}}{(M_o^+)^{1/n}} = \frac{(X_o^-)^{1/n}}{(X_i^-)^{1/n}} \tag{4}$$

If several salts are present, their ions are divided in the same way: and the water ions H^+ and OH^- are no exception. This is a great advantage in the measurement of the Donnan equilibrium, since the H-ions can be easily determined even in very low concentrations.

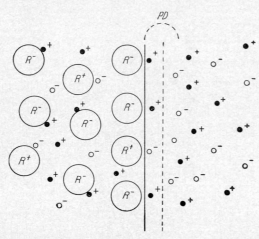

Fig. 29. Diagram of bilateral ion-exchange between protoplasm and the surrounding medium, and the resultant Donnan potential (*PD*).

The equations for the Donnan equilibrium are of course 'ideal' in the sense that, for exact calculations, the ionic activity and the influence of surface tension and hydration must be taken into account. Any application of the Donnan principle to biological phenomena must therefore be made with a due dose of approximation. It is however obvious that this principle should find application in all cases where large relatively immobile or firmly anchored organic ions occur together with easily mobile inorganic ions.

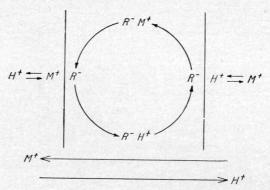

Fig. 30. Diagram of the exchange of cations between the medium and the cell sap. R^- are the cation bearers of the protoplasm. The direction of the exchange is determined by the relation of the external and internal concentrations of H^+ and M^- (=metal cations) and tends towards a condition of equilibrium with the same concentration externally and internally. With the cooperation of active processes, e.g. of an internal H-ion production, the equilibrium is shifted in the direction of the arrows.

It can be imagined that in the protoplasmic surface layer large organic ions lie as islands surrounded by non-ionised molecules. It is to be assumed that the non-ionised regions of the surface layer permit the passage of inorganic ions only with difficulty, as these have a large total diameter on account of hydration. The Donnan equilibrium must therefore be applied to a mosaic of large ions which are surrounded by salt ions. The salt ions can thus be conveyed along the larger oppositely charged ions to the rear of the surface layer and so produce the inner phase of the equilibrium.

Equilibria also arise around free-moving molecular aggregates (micelles) or proto-plasmic inclusions such as mitochondria, or round large protein ions (ADAIR and ADAIR 1940, ABRAMSON, MOYER and GORIN 1942). If the particle itself has a negative charge, there arises round it a layer of positively charged liquid. This accumulation of ions is the inner side of the double layer defined by GOUY (1910), while the free surrounding ions form the outer side. In electrophoresis the outer side tends to move in a direction contrary to the inner side, whereby the movement is retarded or can even be reversed. The mobile ions of the outer zone thus maintain their kinetic energy. Hence the result of electrophoresis is dependent on the ionic strength (or concentra-tion). With large ions however the charges are scattered in such a way that this complex effect becomes weaker than with smaller ions. The ρ-potential often mentioned in the literature is the resultant potential of the surface which can be considered as the sum of those potentials which depend on all neighbouring ions plus the specific charge of the particle.

Where the protoplasmic surface and similar partly dissociated colloids which are ion-exchangers are concerned, the observed potential difference is conceived most simply as a Donnan potential. Of course, the possibility should not be excluded that in the living cell other potentials may also arise, e.g. those that are determined by the partition coefficients of ions between two phases. Similar potentials could be produced e.g. between a predominantly hydrophile cytoplasm and predominantly lipophile mitochondria.

If cations and anions penetrate through a surface with different speeds *diffusion dotentials* arise. How far ions are taken up merely by simple diffusion into cells has not yet been adequately investigated. The so-called non-metabolic uptake of ions to be discussed later is largely a question of adsorption and ion exchange. Diffusion processes however always form an integral part of the total exchange of material, but their share in the formation of potentials still requires investigation. In any case diffusion potentials do not influence the course of the diffusion (WILLIAMSON 1939).

The measurable potential difference between the cell surface and the surrounding medium arises from the difference in activity between the 'adsorbed' and 'free' M- and X-ions according to the equations:

$$-PD = \frac{RT}{nF} \ln \frac{(M_i^+)}{(M_o^+)}$$

$$-PD = \frac{RT}{nF} \ln \frac{(X_o^-)}{(X_o^-)}$$

(5)

in which PD = the potential difference between the cell and the solution, R = the gas constant, T = the absolute temperature, F = Faraday's electrochemical equivalent (96,501 coulombs), and n = the ionic valency.

Since M_o^+ is easily determined one can, if $-PD$ is also measured, calculate the ion

E

density (M_i^+) e.g. at the surface of a root tip. If the medium consists of a dilute mineral acid and M_o^+ is thus the hydrogen-ion concentration, one gets, as was shown above, a picture of the hydrion concentration of the root surface. For wheat this $= 10^{-3}$, or $pH = 3$. The values of course are only approximations, since all calculations are valid only for a thermodynamically ideal distribution of ions.

Roots of oats and barley show about the same acidity, roots of rye a rather lower and roots of tomatoes and flax a considerably higher (up to $pH = 2$). Here there are probably certain differences between species and even varieties, which are certainly of ecological importance, since the root acidity is an index of the ability of the roots to obtain nutrients from the soil. The dissolving power of roots is very considerable because of their high inherent acidity and (contrary to most statements) does not depend only on the liberation of carbon dioxide.

It is an important point that the actual acidity of the root surface depends on its saturation with bases. If salts are present, metal ions are quickly exchanged and the H-ion concentration of the surface falls (Figs. 27 and 28 on p. 49). In a normal nutrient solution, in which about 0·001 M K, Ca, etc. are usually present, the H-ion concentration of the surface of wheat roots sinks to about 10^{-5} (i.e. $pH = 5$). The potential difference thus falls to about -58 millivolts, against -150 to -250 millivolts in a weak aqueous solution of carbon dioxide with the same pH. Tomato roots show in a 0·00001 N solution of HCl ($pH = 5$) *PD* values of about -150 millivolts, and thus have a very high surface acidity (Fig. 28). If the concentration of the nutrient solution rises to 0·01-0·1 M, so many metallic cations are exchanged at the root surface that the potential difference sinks to nil and may even acquire a positive value.

Discharge of the root surface is harmful. Acidification of the medium in the absence of metallic cations is particularly dangerous because the protoplasm is then flooded by acid anions and dies. The isoelectric point of protoplasm lies usually towards the acid side, e.g. $pH = 5·3$ in the epidermis cells of *Allium cepa* (BRAUNER 1943) and pH 2-4 in bacteria (YAHAMA and ABE). Cytoplasmic granules in root hairs migrate anodically, according to SEN (1934), and are therefore negatively charged.

A normally negative surface potential affords a valuable protection against anions. It can be calculated that at a $-PD = 58$ millivolts the anion concentration in the surface amounts to only one-tenth of that of cations (cf. equation (5) on p. 51). Because of its predominantly anionic character, protoplasm is well buffered against cations. A transitory discharge of the root surface by high salt concentrations is therefore much less dangerous than a discharge in pure acid solutions. In the former case the large quantities of metallic cations neutralise the acid anions, and the internal pH value does not fall dangerously. These cell-physiological relationships clarify the ecological finding that plants are particularly sensitive towards low pH values in the soil when it is deficient in salts. Abundant addition of nutrient salts increases considerably the ability to withstand low pH values.

Measurements and calculations on the state of the surface of roots (LUNDEGÅRDH 1938-45) refer to the protoplasmic sufaces of the epidermis cells. The *cellulose* of the cell walls is very weakly dissociated, and its coarse-grained micellar network allows unrestricted passage to both ions and large organic molecules such as nucleic acids and phosphatides. On the other hand *pectin*, abundantly present in young cell walls, has more clearly marked acid properties, which however have been found not to compete with those of the protoplasm.

The presence of a surface potential in root hairs can be determined directly by electrophoresis (LUNDEGÅRDH 1941). The determinations were carried out in the following way. A root tip richly supplied with root hairs was placed in a small electrophoretic chamber in such a way that the root hairs were vertical to the direction of the current. The chamber was placed on the stage of a microscope. The platinum electrodes were supplied with a low-periodic (10-20 per second) alternating current at 2 volts. In a dilute salt solution the root hairs vibrate strongly, and with a measuring eyepiece one can determine the amplitude of the vibrations. If the salt concentration is increased, the amplitude diminishes. The concentration at which the surface of the root hairs is discharged (i.e. when the amplitude of vibration becomes nil) agrees with that at which the measurement of potential shows PD=nil.

On measuring the PD along the whole root tip it is found that it decreases towards the older zones. The surface charge thus varies with the ontogenetic development of the cells. The high charge in the zone in which the root hairs are situated (in wheat 2-4 mm from the tip), indicates the presence of a relatively high number of acidoid groups and a vigorous exchange of ions caused thereby. As the cell ages, these groups apparently decrease and probably disappear altogether, and a decreasing tendency to ion exchange with the surroundings may be connected with this. These questions need further investigation.

It has been possible to demonstrate electrophoretically the presence of negative surface charges with bacteria (MCCALLA 1940, 1941). Gram-negative bacteria, as would be expected, adsorb cations (RANDLES and BIRKELAND 1944, DYAR and ORDAL 1946). The effect of certain disinfectants and antibiotics is also connected at times with adsorption at valency positions on the bacterial surface; the normal exchange of nutrients necessary for the bacteria is competitively depressed. Similar effects may occur with streptomycin and the basic dyestuff acridine (MASSART et al. 1947), which combine with nucleoproteins.

The theory given here of the ionic properties of the protoplasmic surface layer of cells characterised by a 'salt exchange', is in line with concepts developed by OSTERHOUT, K. H. MEYER (1935), TEORELL (1935) and others. OSTERHOUT conceives the salt uptake as a chemical reaction between the salt and certain materials in the plasma membrane. He and other workers also have found that the membrane shows a high electrical resistance, a fact that suggests a relatively restricted supply of ions in the membrane. OSTERHOUT, however, goes too far when he describes the membranes as 'non-aqueous' and refers all permeability only to partition coefficients. Both the relatively rapid water uptake by the protoplast, e.g. after plasmolysis, and the actual penetration of electrolytes indicate the contrary.

The protoplasmic membrane is penetrable both by water and by dissolved ions, but the membrane's own ionisation is not specially high. A negatively charged membrane favours the unaided passage of cations, but anions also can be shown to pass through, even if unaided, more slowly. Acid dyestuffs belong to this strongly retarded group, whereas basic dyestuffs, e.g. Neutral Red and Neutral Violet, diffuse through quickly (GUILLERMOND and GAUTHERET 1946). As will be shown later, aerobic metabolism largely overcomes this relative screening of the anions due to their charge. That chemical linkages of ions in the protoplasm can also have an effect is seen from the fact that the basic Neutral Red, for example, is absorbed up to 20,000 times more quickly than the much smaller urea molecule (COLLANDER et al. 1943).

MEYER and TEORELL assume that the protoplasmic surface behaves like an amphoteric dissociated protein film. In this it is assumed that a charge varying with the salt concentration mediates a salt uptake which proceeds only by diffusion. Experience shows, however, that salts are also taken up through a membrane with constant charge and that the uptake depends relatively little on the salt concentration. A simple diffusion of salt ions through the membrane of course always occurs; otherwise water would not be able to pass through; but the ionic properties of the membrane are nevertheless very remarkable.

Instructive experiments on the importance of the membrane charge for the spontaneous diffusion of ions have been carried out with fine-pored collodion membranes, which can easily be charged by addition of ionising materials. The salt uptake of the living cell, however, is so closely connected with the energy exchange that the detailed treatment of this question must follow in the section on cell respiration.

In the study of the permeability relationships of the cell it has usually been found that the external and internal surface layers show different permeabilities. WEEVERS (1931) believes he found that the external surface layer allows sugar to pass easily, but that the tonoplast on the other hand is almost impermeable to it. According to WEEVERS, translocation of the sugar formed in photosynthesis is favoured, and only a little of it remains in the vacuoles. The opposite may occur with respect to ion uptake, i.e. there may be a relatively large resistance to uptake at the external surface and a strong accumulation in the vacuoles.

The term *intrability* has been suggested to describe the intermediate position of the cytoplasm caused by these conditions (Fig. 31). Since the accumulation of materials,

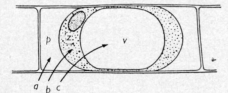

Fig. 31. 'Cap plasmolysis' according to HÖFLER. Plasmolysing solution (*p*) passes unhindered through the cellulose wall (*a*). Permeability of the external protoplasmic membrane (='intrability') is indicated by (*b*) and that of tonoplasts by (*c*). Z is the cytoplasm.

particularly in the vacuole, is often dependent on respiration, these phenomena cannot be completely understood unless the energy aspect of the problem is taken into account.

5 VACUOLES

What has been said above about the external surface layer of the protoplasm applies in the main also to the tonoplasts. The name 'tonoplast' was suggested by DE VRIES (1885). As the external surface is quickly regenerated after wounding, a membrane is formed round each drop of solution in the protoplasm. One cannot speak of an individual organ any more than in the case of the external surface layers. Only the contractile vacuoles of the Protista seem to form an exception (see LUNDEGÅRDH 1922, p. 315). Earlier observations (KLEBS 1882, DE VRIES 1885, DEGEN 1905) and also later ones (OSTERHOUT 1945) show that when a cell is damaged the tonoplast can survive the external surface layer. This does not however necessarily indicate that the membranes are of fundamentally different kinds. Differences can be caused by the fact that vacuoles normally have much higher salt contents than the medium, which naturally reacts on the composition of the membrane. According to HOLM-JENSEN (1944) cation transport occurs in the Characean *Tolypellopsis* much more slowly through the external than through the internal surface layer.

As far as occurrence of vacuoles is concerned, large or connected vacuoles usually occur only in expanding or mature cells. There are however also young, strongly vacuolated cells, e.g. in the cambium and in many algae (BAILEY 1930, ZIRKLE 1937).

On account of surface tension the vacuoles have of course a tendency to contract. This 'centripetal pressure' recognised by PFEFFER (1897) may, according to him, amount to 1·5-3·0 atmospheres for a diameter of 0·5 μ, and diminishes with increasing diameter. This pressure, the importance of which was doubted by other workers, can be offset by a moderate osmotic pressure of the materials located in the vacuole. In this way the volume of the vacuole increases with the growth of a cell.

There are also oil vacuoles or oil bodies (A. MEYER 1920), but normally the content of the vacuole is an aqueous solution, which at times has partly crystallised out, e.g. solutions of sugars, inulin, potassium salts, etc. (MOLISCH 1913). Reversible precipitations also can occur in the protoplasm.

Special interest is aroused by the 'aggregation' first observed by DARWIN in *Drosera* tentacles. Here the protoplasmic volume increases at the expense of the vacuole which undergoes characteristic movements (Fig. 33) ending with the division of the vacuole into several elongated vacuoles. The phenomenon is evoked by stimulation of the small heads of the tentacles, e.g. with pepsin (cf. Chap. 10, section F2, p. 469 and also p. 248).

Ordinary vacuoles always contain inorganic salts, particularly potassium nitrate and phosphate, but also sulphates, chlorides or iodides (in the Florideae), often organic acids (oxalic, malic, citric, tartaric, etc.), sugars (sucrose, glucose, fructose, lactose, etc.) or hexahydric alcohols (mannitol, sorbitol, dulcitol), pectic mucilages (especially in xerophytes and halophytes), alkaloids, glycosides, tannins, amides (asparagine and glutamine), sometimes proteins, etc. (Fig. 32). The vacuoles thus represent storage chambers for substances which are produced during metabolism and accumulated, or perhaps for waste products which cannot be secreted elsewhere (cf. Fig. 34).

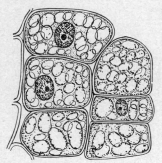

Fig. 32. Cells from the root of *Vicia faba*, three days after germination. The cells show large vacuoles, which contain proteins etc. (after LUNDE-GÅRDH 1922).

Fig. 33. Epidermis cells in the tentacles of *Drosera rotundifolia*. (*a*) unstimulated cells, (*b*) commencement and (*c*) maximum of the aggregation after chemical stimulation. The cell sap is shown dark. Plastids and nucleus can be observed in the protoplasm (after ÅKERMAN 1917).

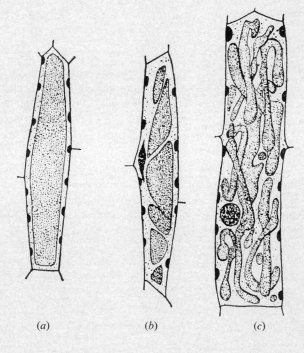

(a)   (b)   (c)

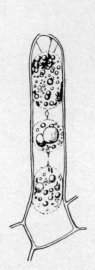

Fig. 34. Root hair of *Trianea* after plasmolysis with 3% potassium nitrate solution. The tannins of the vacuolar sap have separated out as drops (after PFEFFER 1890).

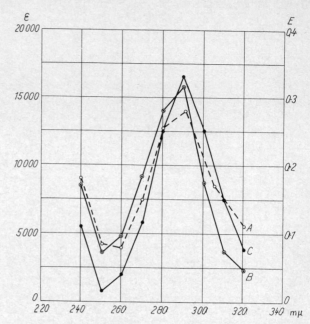

Fig. 35. Absorption spectrum of flavanones in the ultraviolet.

Of the pigments dissolved in vacuoles flavones and anthocyanins may be mentioned. The *flavones* are derivatives of benzopyrone; flavanone is dihydroflavone, and flavonol is 3-hydroxyflavone.

Flavone (2-phenyl-1,4-benzopyrone

Flavanone

This diverse group of yellow pigments occurs especially in floral leaves, but in many cases also in other organs, e.g. in roots (LUNDEGÅRDH and STENLID 1944), in the wood of conifers (strobopinin; ERDTMAN *et al.* 1944; Fig. 35), etc. Well-known flavones are chrysin in poplar buds and luteolin in *Reseda*. Among flavonols may be mentioned quercetin in the bark of *Quercus tinctoria* and kaempferol in the blue flowers of *Delphinium*. It occurs here as a glycoside (quercitrin), a phenomenon usual with the flavones, through which a higher solubility in water is attained. The same applies to carotene, e.g. in the yellow petals of *Verbascum*. Another flavanone derivative is hesperidin.

The red and blue *anthocyanins* can be considered as reduction products of the flavones. The chemistry of the anthocyanins has been worked out especially by WILLSTÄTTER and ROBINSON (see BLANK 1947). The anthocyanins are pyran derivatives and occur always as glycosides. Three basic types are recognised: pelargonidin, cyanidin and delphinidin (absorption spectra in Fig. 69, p. 121) which by ester formation produce further types. The anthocyanins easily form amphoteric ions, and, for example, they give salts with mineral acids (see formula):

Pelargonidin chloride

The colour is connected with the dissociation and depends on the linkage of the amphoteric ion with a base or an acid. The cyanin of *Centaurea cyanus* is e.g. blue at pH 3. The red colour of *Centaurea jacea* on the other hand is produced by pelargonidin. The red colour ordinarily occurs on combination with an acid, whereas the metal salts are blue and in the isoelectric state a purple-red colour is formed. As the reaction of the cell sap is dependent also on external conditions, which shift the chemical equilibria, the flower colour can be altered, for example, by the effect of temperature or by the presence of certain metal ions, such as aluminium. Aluminium determines the flower colour of *Hydrangea* (ALLEN 1943). The red autumn tints, e.g. of maple and aspen, depend on the occurrence of anthocyanin (SEYBOLD 1943). The red pelargoniums depend of course on pelargonidin, whereas cyanidin also determines the colour of red roses. Many of these colours were prepared synthetically by ROBINSON (see GILMAN 1944, p. 1319). The glycosides contain glucose, rhamnose or pentoses, sometimes also organic acids.

The anthocyanins, because of their relationship with the hydration product catechin, are also akin to the bile pigments. Bile pigments as well as flavonols occur in the stomatal guard cells (METZNER 1930).

As regards the physiological conditions for the formation of the anthocyanins it is known only that they have a certain connection with photosynthesis (KUSAKA 1931, 1933).

In studies on the effect of nutrient uptake, THIMANN and EDMONDSON (1949) have shown that, in *Spirodela* and buckwheat, sugar accumulation favours anthocyanin formation; copper-containing enzymes may also collaborate. Copper-fixing reagents restrict anthocyan formation, even if sugar is available (EDMONDSON and THIMANN 1950). MEVIUS (1935) found that anthocyanin is formed only in the light, obviously on account of the sugar formation. Its disappearance in a CO_2-free atmosphere occurs more quickly if NO_3 is supplied. KUILMAN (1930) believes that the light changes a prochromogen into a chromogen, which in its turn forms anthocyanin in a dark reaction. The pigment formation is favoured by low temperatures. The best combination is warm light periods with cold dark periods. ROBINSON (1935) also assumes a colourless precursor, which is oxidised to anthocyanin. He believes that flavones and anthocyanins, in spite of their striking relationship, are built up from a common starting-point independently of each other. Chromatographic separation of the anthocyanins in genetic clones of maize seems to indicate that there is a series of anthocyanin variants (ZARUDNAYA 1950).

6 METHODS OF DETERMINING PERMEABILITY

Investigations of permeability generally use indirect methods, as the penetration can be observed directly under the microscope only by the use of dyestuffs (PFEFFER 1886, RUHLAND 1908). Only with very large cells, such as those of the algae *Valonia* and *Nitella*, has it been possible to suck out the contents of the vacuole and analyse them chemically (OSTERHOUT and later workers). Qualitative investigation is possible if the entering material causes precipitation, e.g. precipitation of tannins by pyrazolone or caffeine (VON WISSELING 1910; Fig. 34). Colour changes in anthocyanin-bearing cells can be taken as signs of the penetration of acids or bases.

Among indirect methods may be mentioned those which are based on plasmolysis and alterations of tissue tension.

Many tissues are composed of cells with elastic walls. Here the method of *tissue tension* is applicable. With unrestricted access of water the cells are maintained in a stretched condition by the internal osmotic pressure (*turgor*). In this condition the osmotic pressure of the vacuole and the elastic extension of the wall are in equilibrium. Any change in the osmotic relationships causes a measurable change in the extension of the cell wall. For individual cells this can be measured microscopically, but the measurement is easier if whole pieces of tissue can be used. For instance, one can use root tips 10-15 mm long which show an extension of 10%-20% (LUNDEGÅRDH 1911). When the piece of tissue is brought into a solution whose effect is to be investigated, it initially shrinks a little until osmotic equilibrium is established. If the dissolved material does not penetrate, no further alteration is observed, but if the tissue is permeable the tissue tension increases with the amount of the compound taken up. In this way permeability coefficients can be calculated. The method can be applied conveniently to all tissues or cells with sufficient elasticity in the walls, and also to the guard cells of stomata (REUTER 1843). In quantitative measurements one must of course remember that changes of size are occurring in three dimensions.

The *plasmolysis method*, which was introduced by DE VRIES (1885), requires the application of solutions of such a concentration that their osmotic value somewhat exceeds that of the cells. In this way plasmolysis starts, i.e. the cell wall is first completely relaxed, and the protoplast begins to separate from it (Fig. 31). If the external surface layer is impermeable for the osmotically effective substance, the plasmolysis persists. If on the other hand the material is allowed through, the plasmolysis is reversed, and the speed of this *deplasmolysis* can be taken as a semi-quantitative expression of the permeability coefficient. The accuracy of course increases if numerous cells are observed at the same time. Epidermal cells of *Tradescantia* leaves, onions or tulip petals are suitable. With the higher degrees of permeability one must begin with a fairly strong plasmolysing solution in order to get plasmolysis at all. To obtain a relative osmotic value of the material under investigation it is usual to take a substance which penetrates only slowly, e.g. cane sugar.

The plasmolysis methods suffer from many theoretical defects, of which a few may be mentioned here. Owing to the plasmolysing solution and the diminution in volume, the cells are brought into an abnormal state. Not only the permeability itself but also the original cell sap pressure and the swelling pressures of the protoplasm suffer uncontrollable alterations (ILJIN 1928, WEIXL-HOFMANN 1930). RYSSELBERGHE (1902) and HÖFLER (1918) have attempted to improve the accuracy of the method by a '*plasmometric*' *procedure* in which they carried out measurements of the dimensions of the cells and of the protoplasts before and after the plasmolysis. In this way it was possible to draw certain conclusions about intrability (see above).

A general defect of plasmolysis methods is the fact that the normal metabolism of the cells is disturbed and that the dynamic component caused by it, e.g. the active salt uptake, is neglected. The plasmolysis methods can thus distinguish only the grosser differences in permeability. The numerous attempts that have been made to investigate characteristics of the plasmamembrane by determinations of permeability, e.g. for urea and glycerol, have yielded hardly any valuable information about the surface layer. Fundamental physical phenomena, such as the dependence of diffusion on the composition of the medium at the time (ÖHOLM 1944), are all too easily forgotten, as well as the undoubtedly large influence of the hydration relationships which are changed in the high concentrations needed for plasmolysis (BOGEN 1938). It is found, for example, that the permeability of *Rhoeo discolor* is influenced by salts (BOGEN 1940). The data in the literature on the influence of light, withering, etc., on permeability are also open to doubt.

Almost all permeability investigations refer to the passive uptake of non-electrolytes. This may be called *diffusion permeability* or *passive permeability*. It is not really known to what extent pure diffusion processes alone are responsible for the uptake of dissolved non-electrolytes. Diffusion is of course concerned in everything, and at microscopic and sub-microscopic dimensions it can usually operate quickly enough. Chemical factors are, however, so often concerned even with non-ionised substances that it is difficult to calculate the 'passive' molecular movement separately. For the movement of salts through the protoplasm and into the vacuole, aerobic respiration and the active transport which it causes are decisive. As ARISZ (1943) has shown, a similar coupling of energy can also be observed with certain non-electrolytes, e.g. for the uptake of asparagine in leaves of *Vallisneria*. Sugar (glucose) also is actively taken up by roots. i.e. against the concentration gradient (LUNDEGÅRDH and BURSTRÖM 1944). These questions are dealt with in Chapter 6.

7 PERMEABILITY FOR WATER

Even although most cells take up or give up water without great difficulty, some degree of resistance can often assert itself. The water permeability can be calculated from the speed of plasmolysis and deplasmolysis. The non-physiological water permeability is affected by temperature (BRAUNER 1943) even although the Q_{10} value is considerably lower than for chemical processes. IRMAK (1943) gives $Q_{10} = 1.3$ for the passage of water through cellophane. The values for dead layers of plants, e.g. seed scales or potato periderm, may be only slightly higher, i.e. between 1 and 1.4. Among other influences those of ions may also be mentioned (LUNDEGÅRDH 1911, DE HAAN 1935, KAHHO 1937).

A comparison of individual plants shows variations from 1 to 50 (HUBER and HÖFLER 1930) and very distinct values are shown by different tissues. According to HOF-MEISTER (1939) the hydathode cells of *Saxifraga lingulata* are three or four times more pervious to water than the mesophyll cells. The root hairs are distinguished for their very high permeability to water.

BREWIG (1937) has expressed the opinion that the water permeability of the root cells is influenced by the shoot. This may well be an effect of hormones, similar to that which the shoots exert on the growth of roots. It is obvious that permeability to water is influenced by the state of hydration and viscosity. For these reasons the influence of temperature on the chemical processes in protoplasm can have important supplementary effects on the transfer of water. Thus according to ROUSCHAL (1935) a fall in temperature may slow down water conduction by roots and thus also limit transpiration. This cold shock must depend on the protoplasm and is thus more effective than mere effects of pores; it also has a certain induction time.

During plasmolysis dehydration of the cytoplasm often causes precipitation, fibril formation and probably also coacervation (see p. 18); which suggests partial reversible coagulation. These phenomena can probably explain in part the diminution in water permeability usually observed after plasmolysis (LUNDEGÅRDH 1911). The water permeability of the protoplasm must influence to a certain extent the resistance which the root tissues offer to the suction pressure of the transpiration stream (ROUSCHAL 1935) or to the transport of water during 'bleeding' (LUNDEGÅRDH 1945). It is remarkable how little interest this question has aroused. It must however be admitted that it is not easy to investigate experimentally, since water finds its way everywhere and follows new paths according to the requirements of the shoot's transpiration (cf. Chap. 8).

F. The Water balance of the Cell

1 THE OSMOTIC STATE

The presence of osmotically active substance in the cells is a pre-condition for water uptake. According to VAN 'T HOFF's kinetic theory, which is based *inter alia* on the experiments of the plant physiologist PFEFFER (1887), the osmotic pressure arises from the tendency of the dissolved particles to move away from one another. The principle is thus the same as for gas pressure; in a closed vessel the pressure corresponds to the tendency of a gas to expand. In a solution the kinetic energy of the molecules expresses itself as an effort to increase the volume, i.e. the distance between the molecules, by water uptake. This tendency to increase the water volume is revealed as a hydrostatic wall pressure, when a cell permeable to water and filled with solution is placed in pure water. The osmotic pressure can be measured by a manometer connected to the cell. In the living cell the osmotic pressure shows itself as a wall tension, i.e. as *turgor pressure*.

The cellulose wall allows water and dissolved substances to pass almost unhindered (SKENE 1943), but the protoplasm or its surface layers are semipermeable, i.e. the water passes through easily, but many dissolved substances cannot pass at all, or can pass only with difficulty, and so the conditions for osmotic pressure to develop arise. The water uptake continues until the equilibrium between the osmotic pressure (O) and the elastic counter-pressure of the wall (Tg) is reached, i.e. $O = Tg$.

The osmotic state has of course a special interest in relation to cells with an elastic wall. If the cell wall, e.g. because of water loss following transpiration, is fully relaxed, the actual osmotic pressure is nil. The cell, however, always retains its potential osmotic pressure, often called its *osmotic value* (O_v), which is determined by the molecular activity of the osmotically effective materials dissolved in its interior. On addition of water, water is sucked in on account of the potential pressure, until finally the wall tension reaches the equilibrium value.

The difference between the actual wall pressure Tg and the potential pressure is called the *suction pressure* (Sp). The equilibrium between potential osmotic pressure, wall tension (Tg) and suction pressure is thus expressed by the equation

$$Tg + Sp = O_v \qquad (6)$$

As a relaxed elastic cell increases its volume on taking up water again, the cell contents are of course diluted, i.e. the osmotic value sinks, in a proportion determined by the elastic extension. If one calls the volume of the fully relaxed cell V_0 and the elastic extension V_t then $V_0 + V_t$ is the volume of the completely turgid cell. If the osmotic value of V_0 is indicated by O_v, then this sinks in the turgid cell to $\dfrac{O_v}{1 + \dfrac{V_t}{V_0}}$. Equilibrium is reached when $\dfrac{O_v}{1 + \dfrac{V_0}{V_t}} = Tg$.

$$\qquad (7)$$

Every change in O_v, whether due to active absorption, exudation or metabolic processes (e.g. respiration of sugar), must also change V_t. As any change in V_t causes uptake or loss of water, the water balance of the cells is to a high degree dependent on the current osmotic state.

The physical relations between concentration, water volume and pressure are best studied in artificial osmotic cells. The osmotic pressures in parenchymatous tissues usually amount to several atmospheres. In spite of its thinness the cellulose wall is very tough. According to MÜNCH (1930), a wall only 1 μ thick will stand a pressure of 40 atm, if the cross-section of the cell is 10 μ. With a larger volume the wall must be thicker for the same pressure, e.g. with a cross-section of 1 mm it would need to be 0·1 mm.

The guard cells of leaf stomata usually have a very high turgor pressure, apparently 45-90 atm, much higher than the pressure in the surrounding epidermal cells; which accounts for their independent turgor movements.

The potential osmotic value of a cell is expressed as a molar concentration (or, more correctly, activity). The pressure of a cell at the threshold of plasmolysis is equal to the osmotic pressure of the plasmolysing solution, e.g. a sugar solution. The potential osmotic pressure of 0·1 M glucose amounts to about 2·4 atm. Because of its dissociation a 0·1 M KNO_3 solution has a pressure of about 4·3 atm, as had been found by DE VRIES even before ARRHENIUS. To this must be added also the van der Waals-forces which must be taken into account in the calculation of activity. They are appreciable when the concentration is more than about 0·2 M. For exact calculations of the osmotic pressures of plant cells, which normally show higher concentrations than 0·2 M, the necessary corrections must be applied.

Hydration of the protoplasm may also be a complication. The measured osmotic value refers to the whole protoplasts, on the assumption that the plasmolysing solute stops at the surface layer. For cells with very thin layers of protoplasm lining the walls the pressure comes near to that of the vacuole. This is the case in most mature parenchyma cells. In cells with more protoplasm the relations are more complicated. For example, the external surface layer may be at least somewhat permeable for the plasmolysing solute, while the tonoplast, on the other hand, is impermeable. This may lead to delayed plasmolysis and to high values. Unfortunately very little is known about the intrinsic osmotic pressure of protoplasm. Since the protoplasmic lining is pressed between the vacuole and the wall, it must of course sustain the full pressure. It opposes to it its own osmotic pressure plus its imbibitional swelling pressure.

A final equilibrium between osmotic value and turgor extension is reached only in mature cells. In cells that are still growing a continuous production of organic substance takes place and variations of the wall elasticity also occur—all circumstances which make the calculation of the osmotic state more difficult. Periodic variations of the osmotic factors may at times also occur in mature organs and they are then usually combined with nastic processes (see Chap. 10).

The turgor of elastic cells has a considerable biological function in stiffening parenchymatous tissues which of themselves are soft. The contrast between a wilted and a turgid leaf is obvious. The extent of the pressure of course partly determines the degree of rigidity. Even plants which are protected against wind or drought tend to show pressures of at least about 2·4 atm (equivalent to 0·1 M cane sugar). Roots of cereals, etc., show pressures of 6-8 atm, which make possible remarkable mechanical effects, as PFEFFER originally showed. Bursting due to tree roots with secondary thickening may result from the osmotic pressure in the cambium layer.

To these mechanical tasks of osmosis may be added a probably still more important function, the regulation of water transport. Any difference in concentration within a connected osmotic system may result in water passing to the more concentrated parts from the less concentrated. In a water shortage, therefore, those cells suffer first which have the lowest pressure. With abundant water supply, however, all cells maintain their turgidity. This is because the suction pressure, as was shown above, depends both on the osmotic value and on the turgor pressure (Tg) at the moment (cf. RENNER 1913):

$$Sp = O_v - Tg \qquad (8)$$

i.e. the suction pressure (Sp) increases when the turgor pressure falls from its maximum value, and it reaches its highest value when the cell wall is completely relaxed and Tg is nil. In this condition, which ecologically means complete wilting, water is absorbed with the full force of the osmotic value (O_v).

This simple law is of fundamental importance for understanding water movements in tissues. It is very important to know that the suction force alone supplies the motive force for such movements. Let us take an example. If the wall of a cell which has a potential osmotic pressure of 4 atm is half relaxed, a suction force of 2 atm arises. This cell now absorbs water from a cell which, for example, has twice the potential pressure (8 atm) but a turgor pressure of 7 atm and therefore a suction force of only 1 atm. For water to be absorbed from the root system to the leaves it is thus not at all necessary that the leaf cells have a higher osmotic value than the root cells. It is important only that the leaf cells have a higher suction force.

The idea that higher osmotic values are needed in leaves than in roots, started by the earlier results of URSPRUNG and BLUM (1921, 1928), URSPRUNG (1935) and others, is not correct. It is possible, e.g., for the root epidermis to have a higher pressure than the cortex. The determinations of pressure in leaves inserted at various heights have also shown no positive correlation between height and pressure (WALTER 1930). The importance of high osmotic values lies in the fact that in severe water shortage they can develop a maximum suction force. Since the leaves are more exposed to dangerous dry periods than the roots are, higher osmotic values represent a kind of protection against catastrophe. But roots also suffer severe damage from drought and the consequent increases in concentration of the soil solution. Wilting of the roots is of course more dangerous than a transient wilting of the leaves.

Osmotically effective substances are chiefly inorganic salts, salts of organic acids, e.g. malic, and sugars. According to KNODEL (1938), these three groups account for 90% of the osmotic pressures. The inorganic salts are absorbed into the cell through a special respiration mechanism (ionic respiration, see Chap. 6), and can reach high concentrations. Wheat roots, for example, normally contain about 0·1 M KNO_3, with a total pressure of about 6 atm. In the algae *Valonia* and *Halocystis* the NO_3-ions reach concentrations 500-2,000 times higher than in the medium (JAQUES 1938). As further examples the following values for *Nitella* may be cited (HOAGLAND 1930):

Table 1

Millimoles per litre	Na	K	Mg	Ca	Cl	SO$_4$	H$_2$PO$_4$	Total
Cell sap	86	59	22	19	107	21	3·5	317·5
Medium	1·2	0·05	1·3	1·3	1·0	0·67	0·0008	7·22

The total salt content corresponds here to a pressure of 7—8 atm.

Large quantities of potassium nitrate and other inorganic salts enter the root cells of wheat, where they are temporarily stored and gradually released into the rising sap stream. Young wheat plants contain, according to BURSTRÖM (1945), 0·04-0·14 equivalents per litre of malic acid, whilst the leaves may contain up to 0·25. The glucose values can rise to 0·1 mole per litre. These estimates refer to the total sap. One does not know of course how much comes from the cell sap and how much from the protoplasm, but quantitatively the sap predominates. The vacuolar sap and the protoplasmic sap can be separated to a certain extent by fractionated pressing.

The osmotic values vary according to the state of nutrition of the plant. The osmotic pressure may diminish with a shortage of potassium and conversely rise with a shortage of water (KNODEL 1939). Whilst it is obviously of the greatest importance that the balance between the cations and the acid anions should be maintained in order that the pH value should not change, the osmotic value can safely vary over short periods of time. There are apparently, however, cases in which alterations of pressure cause shifts in the metabolism. Thus EYSTER (1946) mentions that diastase activity is increased by pressure. One may also assume that certain self-regulating processes come into action to avoid excessive cell sap pressures, arising e.g. through active accumulation of nitrates (LUNDEGÅRDH 1950).

Variations in the osmotic values of the cells are usually seasonal, but day-length variations can also sometimes arise (JIMBO 1931). It has been found that in *Ilex*, *Hedera* and *Pinus* the winter values are 46%-50% higher than the summer values (STEINER 1933). In *Gardenia* a winter pressure as much as 300% higher has been observed. This winter increase of osmotic pressure is usually regarded as a protection against frost, since higher osmotic pressures lower the freezing point (LEVITT and SCARTH 1936). As the increased pressure often depends on an accumulation of sugar, light and photosynthesis are also involved (TUMANOW 1931). In *Gardenia* mannitol may be the variable osmotic medium (ASAI 1937). The sugar content in over-wintering cereal plants can even increase to 67% of the dry weight and 23% of the fresh weight (ANDERSON 1944).

There are however doubts about the simple explanation of the resistance to cold as being due to reduction in the freezing point (PREISING 1930). It has usually been assumed that it is the ice crystals which are indeed observable microscopically (STUCKEY and CURTIS 1938) in the cell sap which destroy the protoplasm. Against this it can be said that certain plants, e.g. cacti (SEIBLE 1939) and seaweeds from southern regions (BIEBEL 1939), die of cold even at temperatures above zero, and so without the formation of ice. Other facts also, e.g. the connection with nutrition (SCHAFFNIT and WILHELM 1933), seem to indicate that the physiology of frost resistance is more complex. Special attention has been devoted here to the hydration and chemistry of the protoplasm, which also affect heat and drought resistance in similar ways.

2 METHODS OF DETERMINING THE OSMOTIC VALUE

Determinations of the osmotic value of cell sap are carried out with the greatest certainty by microscopic measurements. *Determinations of the freezing point* of expressed sap can lead to wrong conclusions because salts belonging to the protoplasm come with it (PHILLIS and MASON). In fleshy parts of plants, e.g. in succulents, the freezing point can be determined by inserting a thermo-electric needle (CARRICK 1930, CURTIS and SCOFIELD 1933). The osmotic value has been determined by cryoscopic methods (VOLK 1937) for other xerophytes also, e.g. *Aster linosyris, Potentilla arenaria* and *Carex humilis*. A microcryoscopic process has been proposed by CAPPELLETTI (1939). False results can arise through overcooling (ILJIN 1933).

Determinations of the osmotic value by indirect methods, using *measurements of the vapour pressure*, can be carried out in the following way (VAN HONERT 1935, HERTEL 1939). The tissue is weighed and then enclosed in a desiccator over a dish of dilute sulphuric acid. Repeated weighing shows whether the tissue has lost or gained water. By variations in the concentration of the sulphuric acid one finally reaches a point at which the tissue maintains an unaltered water content. As the vapour pressure of the sulphuric acid solution is known, one can determine the vapour pressure of the tissue ('hydrature' according to WALTER) and thus, according to known physical laws, calculate the osmotic value. An increase in weight over pure water is an indication of the presence of a suction pressure.

The *plasmolytic methods* have already been discussed above. In addition to the difficulties of measurement already mentioned, e.g. the correct noting of the actual beginning of plasmolysis, the time factor must also be taken into account (ERNEST 1935). The choice of the plasmolytic substance must be made with care, since at times the permeability to sugar, for example, may be high, as in the alga *Chaetomorpha* (HOFFMAN 1932). A further trouble occurs with seaweeds, particularly Rhodophyceae, due to the strong imbibition pressure of the cell wall (KYLIN 1938, DE ZEEUW 1938).

An abnormal swelling of the protoplasm of higher plants, the so-called *cap plasmolysis* (cf. Fig. 31, p. 54), occurs mostly during plasmolysis with alkali salts. The alkali cations drive the calcium ions out of the protoplasm, so that hydration and swelling increase. Balanced solutions containing a mixture of potassium and calcium salts should therefore be used.

Determinations of suction pressure cause still greater difficulties. With tissues thin slices have to be used, in which the water balance is easily altered. It must also be noted that parenchymatous tissues are usually under negative tension, since they are compressed by the epidermis or cortical layer (PRINGSHEIM 1931). It is clear that determinations of suction pressure can be carried out only on cells with extensible walls (cf. WALTER 1931). The technique is as follows. The dimensions of the cells are first measured in paraffin oil soon after cutting. The cells are then transferred into a series of solutions with increasing osmotic values. The solution which causes no change from the original cell dimensions gives the osmotic equivalent of the suction pressure. Objections have been raised to the method, first introduced by URSPRUNG and BLUM (1921), and it cannot be considered particularly reliable. PRINGSHEIM (1931) on the other hand believes that determinations of suction pressure by the method of URSPRUNG and BLUM can be carried out on sufficiently extensible parenchymatous tissues.

All the negative tissue tensions of inner layers of tissue are of course caused by the fact that their cell walls grow more quickly than those of epidermis or cortex layers. This phenomenon occurs very frequently and leads to the surface of the organ being stretched more strongly than the inner part, a fact which is important for the mechanical stiffness of the organ. The internal layers thus have a potential suction pressure, but this causes no water uptake, as long as the outer layer is fully turgid. Any reduction in the surface turgidity however at once sets the internal suction pressure in action.

3 THE DEGREE OF SWELLING OF THE PROTOPLASM

As the protoplasm is enclosed between cell sap and cell wall, its degree of swelling is naturally influenced by alterations in the osmotic value and in the turgor. Some dehydration of the protoplasm of plant cells is unavoidable, even when it contains in itself osmotically active substances.

At osmotic equilibrium the pressure on the protoplasm is equal to the turgor pressure. The counter-pressure of the protoplasm is produced by the hydration of the proteins, and by the salts, sugars, etc. transitorily present in the protoplasm, and by the respiratory carbon dioxide. The protoplasmic pressure is thus also dependent on the metabolic processes. If the volume of the protoplasm is large in comparison with the volume of the vacuoles, rapid changes in metabolism can also bring about rapid changes in turgor, which may involve movements.

Normally, transitory variations in pressure do not seem to influence the functions of the cell to any notable extent. It may e.g. be mentioned that in leaf cells of *Elodea* swollen protoplasm still shows vigorous streaming (WEBER 1930). Swelling and shrinking can be repeated several times without influencing the streaming. On the other hand HÖFLER (1940) has found that protoplasm in a state of cap plasmolysis due to alkali salts, when it absorbs up to 5-10 times its volume of water, suffers from a kind of paralysis or narcosis, from which it can be awakened only by treatment with calcium salts.

In special circumstances protoplasm can be dehydrated to air dryness, without its life being endangered. This applies to seeds and to certain plants which are adapted to periodic drying out. Alpine forms of *Erica* e.g. endure 30% water loss (PISEK and CARTIELLIERI 1933), and the ericoid *Passerina* 47% (THODAY 1921). The Mediterranean fern *Ceterach officinarum* even tolerates drying out over concentrated sulphuric acid in a desiccator (ROUSCHAL 1938). Liverworts also tolerate strong desiccation (HÖFLER 1942).

Xerophytes, which are resistant to drying and whose protoplasm tolerates dehydration, mostly tend to show high sap pressures. This is probably partly due to the fact that onremoval of water their starch is transformed into sugar (LUNDEGÅRDH 1914, GIESSLER 1928). That the protoplasm has a high imbibition pressure is seen from the fact that it is sometimes very hygroscopic. The green alga *Pleurococcus vulgaris* at 62% air humidity can live solely on water taken up hygroscopically (cf. LUNDEGÅRDH 1957). Mosses also absorb moisture from the air and, as is well known, so do many seeds. It has been found in experiments with cereal roots that they also can take up water vapour, and the cells increase their osmotic pressure accordingly (MÄGDEFRAU 1931). WENT (1950) has reported a method of breeding plants in a kind of 'vapour chamber'.

In connection with the shrinking and dehydration of protoplasm mechanical distortions easily set in, which in certain circumstances endanger life, viz. in cells with thin protoplasmic linings and much cell sap. Conversely, dangerous disturbances have been observed when dehydrated protoplasm regains water too rapidly (ILJIN 1931, 1934); but with slow moistening a protoplast which has dried out, as in xerophytes, can be recalled to life. In general plasmolysis is less dangerous than deplasmolysis, since in the latter the change of water content takes place more violently. Dry embryos of *Iris* survive if they are allowed to swell slowly (WERCKMEISTER 1934).

As shown above, low resistance to frost appears to be due not only to low cell sap pressures but also to sensitivity towards changes in hydration of the protoplasm (MAXIMOV 1929, SCARTH 1944). One can in general distinguish between water which is 'unfree', i.e. connected with hydration, and that which is 'free', i.e. outside the hydration shells of the molecules or colloidal particles. It is assumed that 'combined water' offers a protection against large fluctuations in water content and temperature (LEBEDINCEV 1930, JONES and GORTNER 1932, DÖRING 1934, ILJIN 1934, KESSLER and RUHLAND 1938, SCARTH *et al.* 1940). The viscosity of protoplasm rises with its proportion of water of hydration.

Australian workers (WOOD 1932, PETRIE 1937, PETRIE and WOOD 1938) have found a relation between water content and pentosan-protein metabolism. The metabolism appears to be shifted by water deficiency towards a higher production of these substances; it appears, in agreement with what has been said already, to increase heat resistance by increased production of pentosan, pentosan-proteins and pentosan-aromatic products. It is also well known that the succulents, which are rich in mucilages, tolerate high temperatures. How thermophile algae behave in this connection (VOUK 1929) is not known.

In the swelling of seeds the protoplasts, the ergastic inclusions and the cell walls act together and pressures up to 100 atm or more can be developed (PRINGSHEIM 1930). The swelling occurs in general exothermally. Older cell walls usually stand the strain caused by swelling and osmosis, but there are also cases of sudden bursting of the cell walls, such as are sometimes observed in growing root hairs. This bursting occurs when the root hairs are put into a dilute acid (pH 3-4) (LUNDEGÅRDH 1946, EKDAHL 1953) and may be due to a sudden swelling of the protoplasm when the acid removes the Ca-ions (cf. 'cap plasmolysis', p. 54). The still soft rounded end of the root hairs which grow at the tip does not withstand the sudden wave of pressure thus caused. Whether the 'pulsation' of the leaf cells observed by some workers (STÅLFELT, GREGORY, 1937) is due to periodic changes in swelling of the protoplasm is not known. On the other hand, osmotic pressure changes do seem to be responsible for the changes of form of stomatal guard cells.

G. Protoplasmic streaming

Movements of material in protoplasm caused by diffusion and convection of course always occur and Brownian movement has been utilised as a means of determining viscosity. Visible streaming in a definite direction is seldom observed in the cells of primary meristems, which have few vacuoles. Regular protoplasmic streaming seems to occur chiefly in naked protoplasmic masses and in cells with large vacuoles. The amoeboid movements in the plasmodium of Myxomycetes and Amoeba, that is the formation of pseudopodia, are of course connected with internal streaming, and the 'euglenoid' movements of certain flagellates also belong here. In the Myxomycetes the external movements are coupled with rhythmical to-and-fro streaming ('shuttle movements', according to SEIFRIZ). Protoplasmic streaming also seems to have some connection with the sliding movements observed in desmids, diatoms, certain bacteria and blue-green algae, but the excretion of slime through pores may also come into the question. Sliding movement is sometimes observed at the boundary between vacuole membrane and cell sap. This less definite to-and-fro movement has usually been considered a preliminary stage to actual protoplasmic streaming.

In protoplasmic streaming itself one distinguishes between rotation and circulation.

Protoplasmic rotation can be studied in the large cells of the alga *Nitella*. The rotating protoplasm close to the wall usually carries chromatophores along with it, while in *Chara* cells the nucleus is also brought into the circulation. Rotation streaming is also characteristic of the cambial cells of many higher plants, and of leaf cells of *Elodea, Sagittaria, Vallisneria*, etc. Rotation streaming is a uniform movement of the whole protoplasm round the central vacuole. The cell sap may also rotate with it.

Circulation movement is shown by cells whose sap cavity is traversed by cytoplasmic strands. This streaming can be studied without difficulty in root hairs or leaf hairs of cucumbers, nettles, etc. (Fig. 36). Classical objects are the green alga *Spirogyra* and the giant cells of *Caulerpa*, traversed by protoplasmic bridges.

A peculiar form of protoplasmic movement can be observed in the hyphae of fungi. As in naked pseudopodia, the whole protoplasm streams to and fro and an external mantle surrounds an inner one in which the movements take place in reverse. The pulsation seems to be connected with the rhythmical tip growth of the hyphae.

A number of observations of the *speed of the protoplasmic streaming* have been made over the last century. The streaming in the hyaloplasm cannot, of course, be observed directly; one must follow the movement of small particles or 'microsomes'. But it can be seen that the hyaloplasm itself streams, because the smaller particles move more quickly than the larger. The latter are usually slowed down by unevennesses in the wall.

Attempts have been made to record the movement cinematographically. OLSON and DU BUY (1940) obtained usable pictures, and attempted to measure the speed of the particles by graduated exposures, in which each particle showed as a shorter or longer streak. SWEENEY and THIMANN compared under the microscope the speed of streaming particles with the speed of a band driven by a motor. The highest speeds were measured in the protoplasm of Myxomycetes, e.g. 1·25 mm per second. In the root hairs of wheat the author has measured speeds of 0·2-0·6 mm per minute at room temperature.

Concerning the *mechanism of protoplasmic streaming* nothing is known with

F

certainty, but various hypotheses have been suggested. One hypothesis sees the cause of the streaming in the presence of electrical potential differences and the electrophoretic movements resulting from them. This hypothesis sounds rather improbable. The surface potential (*PD*, see p. 47) of protoplasm can vary by cation exchange within wide limits, e.g. between -150 and ± 0 millivolts, without the streaming changing, as observed in wheat root hairs. In addition it is known that the streaming takes place more slowly near the surface layer than near the tonoplasts; which can scarcely be reconciled with a streaming actuated by surface potentials.

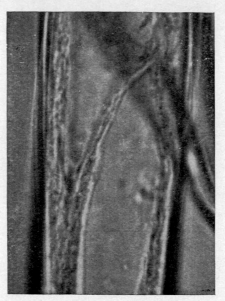

Fig. 36. Strands of cytoplasm in a hair of *Urtica*, clearly showing a tendency to the formation of fibrils.

A notable fact is the multifarious influence of oxygen respiration. In certain cases the streaming stops when oxygen supply is deficient, in others, e.g. in root hairs of wheat, it still continues after days in pure nitrogen. In the slime fungi also it maintains its progress undisturbed in absence of oxygen, even when the creeping movement ceases (SEIFRIZ and URBACH 1944). HCN may cause a check when the cytochrome oxidase regulating the respiration is inactivated by cyanide. In other cases, however, the streaming surprisingly continues in spite of the cyanide. BOTTELIER (1934) observed in the coleoptiles of *Avena* an effect of illumination; the streaming was restricted most strongly at wavelengths of about 430 mμ. According to SWEENEY and THIMANN (1942), who worked with the same object, the streaming is hastened by β-indoleacetic acid (heteroauxin) in presence of malic acid, and it reacts to monoiodoacetic acid as growth does.

It is difficult to bring all the observations on protoplasmic streaming into unison. As a beginning one can only say that the streaming may be regarded as an expression of the general metabolic activity. It is inhibited e.g. by narcotics and carbon dioxide. With temperature changes the speed follows the VAN 'T HOFF rule, but transitory shock effects are observed as a consequence of rapid lowering of temperature (ROMIJN 1931). One cannot believe that the surface tension between protoplasm and vacuolar sap can be responsible for the streaming, since streaming occurs also in cells without vacuoles. The hypotheses proposed by KUHNE (1864) and VERWORN (1915) about the 'contractility of living substance' are even less successful as an explanation of protoplasmic streaming. These hypotheses were later attacked by SEIFRIZ and FREY-WYSSLING (1938).

It is difficult to understand how the ideas of a coherent sub-microscopic fibrous network of micelles or giant molecules can be combined with a streaming protoplasm. All 'contacts' must be of the 'sliding' nature discussed above. The double refraction observed in protoplasm (p. 15) shows that fibrous molecules are passively carried along by the streaming.

DU BUY (1940) believes that particles like mitochondria and microsomes have a polar construction, with respiratory enzyme systems at one end, and that the activity of the enzymes in consequence of a rocket-like return flow would cause a forward movement of the particles. The step between such ideas and the hypotheses mentioned above about rhythmical contractions of fibrous molecules—whose streaming according to FREY-WYSSLING (1938, p. 141) would be supported by the phosphatides present as 'lubricants'—is not very great.

The importance of protoplasmic streaming for the physiology of cells and tissues is also difficult to fathom. The obvious idea that the streaming protoplasm may be a means of transport was first expressed by DE VRIES (1885). He referred to the slowness of diffusion as calculated by GRAHAM, according to whom 1 mg of NaCl traversed a stretch of only 1 m in 319 days. He was of the opinion that cells must have other ways of moving substances necessary for metabolism. Attempts have been made later to answer experimentally the question of protoplasmic movement as a 'stirrer' of the cell (BIERBERG 1909), but without getting any decisive results. One must, however, remember that in the primary meristematic cells filled with protoplasm no mass movement is observed at the growing points.

In view of the small dimensions, diffusion should not be underestimated and transport along surface layers, e.g. of sugar along the interphase between two liquids (VAN DEN HONERT 1932) also occurs. A similar rapid movement of materials can also take place in the direction of elongated giant molecules or micelles. Ions, in any case, can utilise such rapid pathways (cf. p. 16). These sub-microscopic ion paths are themselves mobile, so that surface transport could also cause streaming in the ground substance of the protoplasm by recoil. There thus exist abundant materials for speculation about paths of transport in protoplasm, but they need to be tested experimentally.

Among the hypotheses on the significance of protoplasmic streaming may finally be mentioned that of CASTLE (1936) and others, which assumes that the direction of the streaming determines the location of the thickening in vessels and lignified cells. It has also been suggested that the spiral arrangement of the thickening and of the fibrils in lignified cell walls is determined by spiral streaming of the protoplasm (SEIFRIZ 1943). Against this hypothesis is the fact that the external surface layer, which forms the wall, does not partake in the streaming. It is better to look for the pattern of the wall structures in the molecular make-up of the wall itself.

H. Plasmodesmata

Plasmodesmata are extremely fine protoplasmic fibrils which penetrate the cell walls and so unite the living content of neighbouring cells. They were discovered and described in the period about 1880, but are recognisable in living objects only in exceptional cases e.g. in Volvox colonies and in the endosperm of *Strychnos* and *Aesculus*. To detect plasmodesmata one must usually apply methods such as swelling in sulphuric acid and staining with methyl violet or iodine. It is now usual to assume that plasmodesmata unite almost all mature living cells, both in higher plants and in mosses, liverworts and ferns. They occur also in meristematic tissues, though not in the youngest cells.

Various opinions have been expressed about the formation of the plasmodesmata. RUSSOW (1883) was of the opinion that plasmodesmata are the remnants of the spindle fibres from telophase. This hypothesis was however not confirmed. We have come, on the contrary, to the opinion that the young cell walls are secondarily pierced, point by point, with the two neighbouring protoplasts showing equal activity, until finally their two projections fuse together. As the wall thickens the canals are correspondingly lengthened. Ordinarily the thin pit membrane, normally formed in strongly thickened walls, is traversed by plasmodesmata.

Because the plasmodesmata are so thin (about 0.2μ or near the lower limit of microscopic visibility) one cannot easily ascertain whether they consist of protoplasm or only of its surface layer. It has, however, been observed that protoplasm or even cell nuclei can pass through these fine canals. The number of plasmodesmata varies in different tissues. Up to about 500 have been counted in bark cells of *Viscum* (Fig. 37) and 10-50 in the pit membranes of conifers.

MÜNCH (1930) coined the expression *symplast* to describe the protoplasmic unit of a tissue united by plasmodesmata. The degree of association can, however, vary greatly according to the type of tissue. Plasmodesmata can also link together cells which belong to different types of tissue. Connections occur even between stock and scion. Certain tissues, however, are more shut off from each other, e.g. sieve tubes and cambiform or bark parenchyma.

There is no doubt that the plasmodesmata fulfil important functions, e.g. in the distribution of materials or in the transmission of stimuli. That even large molecules are thus passed from cell to cell is seen from the spread of virus infections (LIVINGSTONE 1933). The diameter of a plasmodesma (about 200 mμ) is sufficient for the mass transport of even the largest molecules (cf. for viruses p. 23 above). It has been found that the mobilisation of hemicellulose in certain endosperms starts from the plasmodesmata; they must, therefore, promote enzymic reactions.

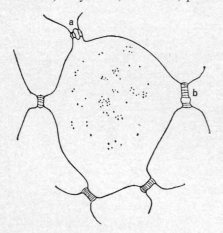

The occurrence of plasmodesmata acquires a special interest in connection with the so-called 'sliding growth' in certain meristems first studied by KRABBE (1886). If the cells slid over one another, the plasmodesmata would certainly be torn, and the presence of plasmodesmata has been taken as contrary to the assumption (PRIESTLEY 1929, 1931). It would not perhaps be altogether wrong to imagine that plasmodesmata are sometimes formed after sliding has finished.

Fig. 37. Plasmodesmata in bark parenchyma of *Viscum album* ($\times c.$ 1000) (after KUHLA 1900).

The arguments against a sliding growth have, however, increased and MEEUSE (1941) also assumes that sliding growth along the middle lamellae of neighbouring cells does not happen. He thinks that all cases of apparent sliding are due to non-uniform common growth (see Chap. 2).

I. Ergastic Cell Inclusions

Under this title A. MEYER (1920) groups together all visible inclusions of the cells which can arise and vanish without the general functions being altered. The ergastic inclusions consist of fairly simple chemical compounds and represent either reserve nutrients or waste products. Typical ergastic products are starch grains, oil droplets, aleurone grains and protein crystalloids, which are all reserve nutrients, and crystals of calcium oxalate or other inorganic or organic precipitates, which ordinarily are considered as waste products. Small vacuoles rich in contents are also often included, e.g. tannin sacs, fucosan droplets of the Phaeophyceae (Brown Algae), etc. Anatomically distinguishable cells or cell groups may have specialised in the formation of ergastic products.

Fig. 38. Starch grains. On the right, simple grain from *Pellionia deveauana*, surrounded with chloroplast stroma. On the left, composite starch grains from the rhizome of *Canna indica* (after A. MEYER and STRASBURGER).

The solid inclusions which are the most important physiologically are usually found in the plastids. The *starch grains* are important transitory storage carbohydrates. In chloroplasts starch is either formed or dissolved according to the intensity of photosynthesis. The deposit of starch may exceed 1,000 times the volume of the surrounding living stroma. Starch grains are found which are readily visible to the naked eye, e.g. in *Lathraea* where the diameter may be up to 0·275 mm. Starch grains are sometimes composed of hundreds of parts. Their structure is crystalloid and usually shows a layering traversed with radial stripes. The form and structure of starch grains are usually specific, which facilitates the analysis of drugs and foodstuffs. The coloration with iodine-potassium iodide may also be specific. The typical blue coloration is very common but certain species give a reddish colour. Floridean starch also shows abnormal colouring. The *paramylon* of the Flagellates is related to the starch of higher plants, but is formed on the surface of the chromatophores.

Fat droplets at times assume a crystalloid structure, as e.g. in the seeds of *Elaeis* and *Bertholletia*. Whether fats are separated out in special plastids ('elaioplasts') is considered doubtful. Ordinarily they are secreted in the cytoplasm or in vacuoles; but they also occur in, or on the surface of, chloroplasts in such plants as orchids, cactuses, etc.

Protein crystalloids are found as needle- or disc-like formations in or outside chloroplasts, in the cytoplasm or in vacuoles of Orchidaceae, Boraginaceae, etc. Many seaweeds, e.g. Florideae, show well-developed protein crystalloids. The external parenchyma layer of potato skins contains fine hexahedral crystalloids of protein. Otherwise these can assume very variable forms (Figs. 40, 41).

Proteins in solid form occur frequently as *aleurone grains*. The aleurone of cereal seeds forms small granules; in fatty seeds, however, e.g. in *Ricinus* and the Umbelliferae, they are up to 60 μ in size and show a complex structure. Here they are formed in protein-rich vacuoles, which lose their water, and consist ordinarily of globulins. Like starch, they are used up on germination.

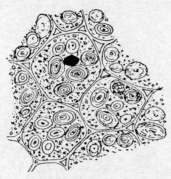

Fig. 39. Ergastic inclusions in the cells of pea cotyledons ($\times c$. 240) (after STRASBURGER).

Lime and *silica* can be considered mostly as waste products. *Calcium oxalate* is found in the majority of plants, both higher and lower. The crystal form is strictly tetragonal or monoclinic; at times larger simple crystals (Fig. 43), mostly crystal druses, are formed, but also spherical crystalloids, which, like starch, can show a concentric construction.

Though oxalic acid is an intermediate product in metabolism only in special cases, when once formed it is fixed as the insoluble calcium salt by the calcium ions which are always present in the cell sap. It has, however, been observed that the crystals of calcium oxalate are redissolved if a shortage of calcium occurs.

Magnesium oxalate, calcium phosphate and calcium carbonate can also be found either inside or outside the protoplasts or even in the cell wall. Concretions of silicic acid occur in the cells of certain cryptogams and monocotyledons (grasses, palms).

Rubber (HIRST and JONES 1942) is found in the form of small spheres in the latex of a number of different plants (Moraceae, Euphorbiaceae. Asclepiadaceae, etc.) Rubber is chemically a hydrocarbon made up of molecular chains of polyisoprene. The unit, isoprene, is C_5H_8, with two double bonds (2-methyl-l,3-butadiene). The molecular weight of the polyisoprene in natural rubber is estimated at 20,000-30,000. Rubber is not regarded as a reserve nutrient (TRAUB 1946).

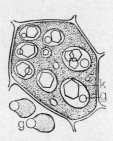

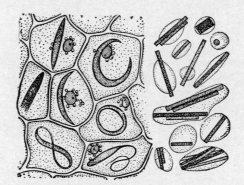

Fig. 40. Aleurone grains with protein crystalloids (*k*) and globoids (*g*) from the endosperm of *Ricinus* (after STRASBURGER).

Fig. 41. Protein bodies (ergastic inclusions). On the left, from the epidermal cells of *Epiphyllum*. On the right, crystalloid vacuoles from the latex of *Musa chinensis* (after MOLISCH).

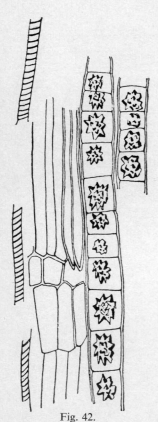

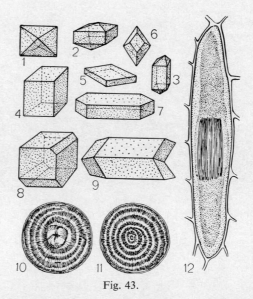

Fig. 43.

Fig. 42.

Fig. 42. Longitudinal section of a winter bud of *Euonymus europae*. Crystal-bearing cells (calcium oxalate) (after LUNDEGÅRDH 1922).

Fig. 43. Crystals of calcium oxalate. (1) tetragonal pyramid, (2) and (3) combination of pyramid and prism, (4) monoclinic rhomboids, (5) rhombic plate, (6)-(8) various combinations, (9) twin, (10) and (11) spherical crystalloids, (12) raphide bundle (after ZIMMERMANN, MÖBIUS and STRASBURGER).

Chapter 2
DEVELOPMENT AND SHAPING OF THE CELL

A. The Growing Cell

1 GENERAL

The multiplication of uninucleate cells, which represent the main structural elements of the tissues of higher plants, is closely connected with nuclear division (mitosis, see Chap. 1, C, p. 27). A *cell plate* is formed betweent he daughter nuclei, by secretions at the spindle equator. It appears first as a collection of drops or granules, which fuse together and, after centrifugal extension of the plate, finally coalesce with the wall of the mother cell.

The young cell plate is said to show a pectin reaction. It is converted into the middle lamella of the future cell wall, which holds the mature daughter cells together like an intercellular cement (see Fig. 44). As soon as the division is completed the deposition of cellulose on to the middle lamella begins from both sides. Only then is a true cell wall formed. The middle lamella remains during the continued growth of the cell and makes the daughter cells cohere. In the opinion of several workers the finished middle lamella consists of pectins and partly of calcium pectate (BONNER 1936).

Pectic acid consists of esters of galacturonic acid, which by α-glucosidal linkages form chains of up to 1,000 units (BONNER 1946) with a molecular weight of 100,000 or more. Some of the carboxyl groups are esterified with methanol. The remaining

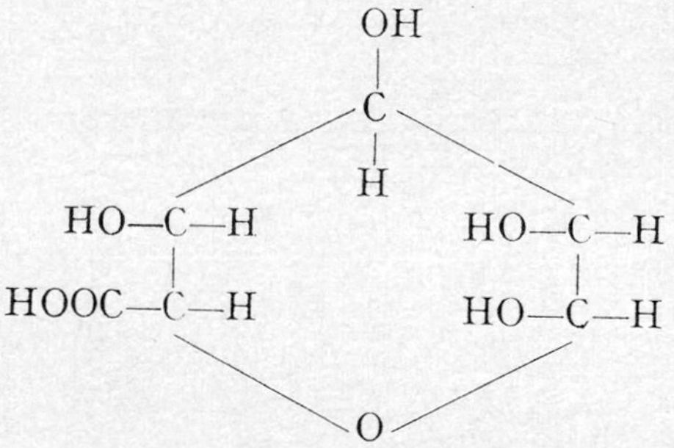

$$
\begin{array}{c}
OH \\
| \\
C \\
| \\
H \\
HO-C-H \qquad\qquad HO-C-H \\
| \qquad\qquad\qquad\quad | \\
HOOC-C-H \qquad\quad HO-C-H \\
O
\end{array}
$$

D·Galacturonic acid

free COOH groups are strongly dissociated (pK is between 2·7 and 4), from which it follows that pectic acid behaves as a strongly acid colloid (HORN 1940, DEUEL 1943).

Pectic acid and pectin have a fibrillar structure and form long micelles. On stretching they arrange themselves in parallel strands in which the galacturonic acid chains lie parallel with the long axis of the micelles (WUHRMANN and PILNIK 1945). The molecular structure of pectin thus reminds one of that of cellulose. Compared with those of cellulose the molecular filaments of pectin are irregularly interlaced, somewhat as in crude rubber. Such a tangled fibrillar structure is ascribed not only to calcium pectate but also e.g. to sodium pectate (PALMER and LOTZKAR 1945). It is still undecided whether the pectin in the middle lamellae contains branched molecular chains, similar to those of the amylopectin of starch (HASSID 1943) or rubber (HIRST and JONES 1942).

The linking of the pectin filaments, which seem to have a more irregular structure than the cellulose filaments, is chiefly the work of calcium ions, which combine with the carboxyl groups of adjacent molecules and so join the pectin filaments together. If the calcium is removed the pectin is hydrolysed and the cells fall apart. Calcium pectate consequently reduces the plasticity of the middle lamella (CORMACK 1943). Solution of the lamella can also be effected by the enzyme protopectinase. Autumnal leaf fall is an example of the loosening of cell cohesion in the so-called abscission or separation layer.

Protopectinase is excreted by certain parasitic fungi, which are thereby able to penetrate between the cells of the host tissue. The nomenclature of the pectin-dissolving enzymes is not yet finally settled. BONNER (1950) proposes the following classification:

1. Protopectinase, which attacks protopectin and gives soluble pectin.
2. Pectinase or polygalacturonase, which attacks pectic acid or pectin and gives galacturonic acid.
3. Pectase, which attacks pectin and forms pectinic acids.

Pectin esterase or pectin methyl esterase splits off methanol. This enzyme occurs in two modifications, one in higher plants and one in fungi (McCOLLOCH and KERTESZ 1947). In many tissues the middle lamella between particular cell groups is dissolved so that large intercellular spaces arise, e.g. in pith, root cortex, leaf mesophyll and fruits. In such cases pectin residues can be found in the cells adjacent to the cavities. Recent experiments have shown that oxalic acid, supplied to the nutrient medium of tissue cultures, removes calcium from the tissue. As a result the lateral walls fall apart and loose cell aggregates or even free cells are formed (NORTHCRAFT 1951).

Besides its task already mentioned of acting as 'cement' between the cells, pectin probably forms a filler between the cellulose micelles of the primary cell wall. It would thus play an important role in extension growth. At this stage while the cell wall is still unlignified pectin seems to have the function of a plastic binder.

The cellulose in the primary wall may also be amorphous, i.e. form bundles of tangled fibrils without cross linkages (TREITEL 1946). KERR (1951) investigated the

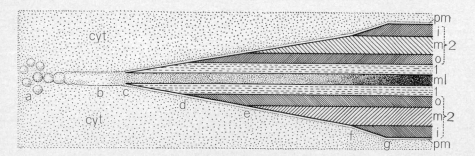

Fig. 44. Diagram of the development of the wall between two daughter cells. (*a*) the cell plate; (*b*) its conversion to the middle lamella ('intercellular substance' *ml*); (*c*) beginning of the primary wall (*l*); (*d*) (*e*) (*f*) deposition of the outer (*o*), middle (*m*) and inner (*i*) parts of the secondary wall (2); (*g*) completion of the wall thickening; (*pm*) protoplasmic membrane; (*cyt*) cytoplasm (after SHARP 1943).

structural changes in the various stages of growth and came to the conclusion that the properties of the primary wall could be explained only by assuming that protopectin forms a continuous phase and the micro-fibrils of cellulose a discontinuous phase. He imagined that alterations in the elastic stretching of the wall were caused by alterations in the hydration of the pectin gel and that the cellulose fibrils formed a stiffening material rather than a stiff network. Electron microscope studies of the cell walls of the *Avena* coleoptile showed a network of microfibrils of various thicknesses, of which the thinnest had a cross-section of 15-20 mμ (ELVERS 1943). The cellulose microfibrils can be broken down by ultrasonic vibration (FREY-WYSSLING and MÜHLETHALER 1946). The finest crystallites were 5-10 mμ thick. They assemble together as microfibrils, which in turn are bound together to microscopically-distinguishable threads (cf. RÅNBY 1952).

According to an earlier hypothesis, which still has its supporters, the cell wall is infiltrated by the living protoplasm. Decisive evidence for this is however still lacking, even though the existence of a plastic intermicellar substance must be acknowledged. The fibrillar structure of the primary wall has been revealed by X-ray diagrams and by the polarisation microscope (FREY-WYSSLING 1938, PRESTON 1939, 1948, HEYN 1940). One speaks of 'tubular structure' i.e. the wall is constructed on similar principles to a pipeline, which has to withstand a high internal pressure. Such a pipeline must be strengthened with bands, since the radial pressure is higher than the longitudinal tension. The cellulose fibrils of expanding cells are, in fact, arranged like the hoops of a barrel. Ideas about the origin of this efficient structure are however divergent. It has not been shown with certainty that they represent an anatomical adaptation to heightened turgor pressure, as Dutch research workers (DIEHL *et al.* 1939) have maintained. Here we touch on the problems of cell growth.

2 THE MECHANISM OF GROWTH

The primary phase in the development of the cell after division is, as already stated, increase in volume. In the tips of roots and shoots volume increase takes place predominantly in the longitudinal direction of the organ. Cell divisions occur principally at the growing point, after which the almost cubical cells elongate. In this extension phase the walls are enlarged many times in the longitudinal direction, but hardly change their thickness. New material is inserted during the extension of the wall. This growth mechanism is called *intussusception*. Only after the extension phase is finished does the wall begin to increase its thickness by deposition of new material. This is called *apposition*.

According to a fairly widespread opinion the stretching of the young cell wall caused by the osmotic pressure of the cell contents is an important precondition for extension growth (HEYN 1940). In this connection the somewhat vague expression 'plastic stretching' has been introduced, by which is understood a stretching beyond the elastic limit. It is believed that the separation of the micelles which this causes makes room for new cellulose fibrils. It is also assumed that the stretching is controlled by the plant growth hormone *auxin* (see Chap. 9) as well as by salts and other factors which favour the swelling of hydrophile colloids.

Other workers are of the opinion that turgor tension is not in itself a necessary precondition for extension growth (BURSTRÖM 1942). BURSTRÖM, who investigated wheat roots, distinguishes between first and second phases of growth. The first phase, which is characterised by the stretching of the primary wall, can be hastened e.g. by temperature increase and the increase in elasticity thus caused. Auxin (β-indole acetic acid, IAA) also hastens the first phase. The second phase, in which the active cell extension caused by accumulation of new cellulose micelles occurs, is on the contrary retarded by rising temperature. Excessive auxin concentrations also have a retarding effect and so give rise to shorter cells. Conversely, sugar favours the second phase of growth (Fig. 45). In this case, an increase of the osmotic pressure is caused by over-production of materials, but BURSTRÖM thinks that the accompanying stretching of the wall does not in itself influence the extension growth.

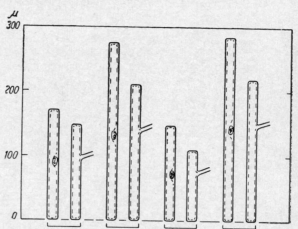

Fig. 45. Epidermal cells from wheat roots (diagrammatic). Cells with root hairs (trichoblasts) are shorter than those without (atrichoblasts). The nucleus lies in the middle of the latter, and in the root hair of the former. Growth is favoured by glucose (second and fourth pair) more than by nitrate (third pair) (after BURSTRÖM 1941).

PRESTON and CLARK (1944) have found that, in spite of the increase in the amount of wall substance, the cell walls of oat coleoptiles become thinner during elongation, and take this as evidence of an increased distension of the wall. It is clear that extension of the wall consists partly of a 'softening' of the wall, and partly of the construction of new wall elements—and that these processes work together in different ways in different cases. The 'softening' of the wall, that is to say the process by which room is made for the deposition of new components, may be a mechanical stretching, or it may be the result of an enzymatic process.

As KYLIN (1946) has found, the cell walls of the algae *Ulva* and *Enteromorpha* contain pectins (ulvin and ulvacin) as well as cellulose; of these ulvin is soluble in water and ulvacin is an insoluble Ca-Mg-salt of ulvic acid (an alkylsulphuric acid which contains a methyl-pentose).

The secondary importance of turgor pressure is apparent also through observations on root hairs. Root hairs are outgrowths of epidermal cells. The growth of the hairs can be very exactly measured by a cinematographic technique (LUNDEGÅRDH 1946, EKDAHL 1953, CASTLE 1940). Characteristic of the root hairs is their pronounced tip growth. The parabolic tip of the cylindrical hair is pushed forward by accretion of new wall elements. The accretion is strongest at the tip and decreases as one moves towards the sides (Fig. 46). This process is apparently independent of changes of osmotic pressure in the medium (Fig. 47), and can thus scarcely be connected with osmotic stretching. It is known that the cell walls of roots also grow as it were from within, since the growth proceeds even when elongation is prevented by embedding the root in plaster of Paris. The walls then eventually become folded like a bellows, as was shown by PFEFFER. The new components must therefore be incorporated into the walls in such a way that they push asunder the micelles already present. In this, molecular forces similar to those of crystal formation are active and hydration also may play a part. It may be considered that one of the functions of auxin is to regulate hydration and so make room for the deposition of new cellulose microfibrils. The hypothesis assumed by some workers that auxin screens off the point of attachment between pectin and cellulose fibrils is a somewhat vaguer expression for the same thing. It should not be said on this account that auxin is an essential precondition for extension growth.

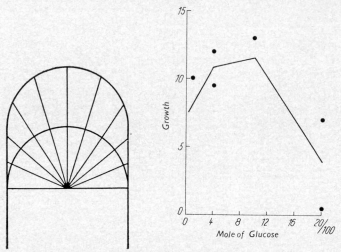

Fig. 46. Diagram of the tip growth of a root hair. The production of wall material occurs most intensively at the tip and gradually diminishes sidewards. It can be supposed that the cellulose strands spread out radially from the tip and grow continuously in length by addition of new molecules at the ends. In extension growth on the other hand new strands are apparently deposited between those already present.

Fig. 47. Growth of some root hairs in glucose solutions of increasing concentrations. The growth increases up to about 0·10 M glucose, corresponding to an osmotic pressure of about 2·4 atm. Starting at 0·20 M (4·8 atm.) the growth decreases again.

The accretion of new wall molecules or micelles cannot be compared directly with crystallisation, since the material always preserves a certain plasticity caused by the loose construction, the strong hydration and some irregularity in the arrangement of the fibrils (TREITEL 1946). Cell walls of hydrated cellulose, with relatively irregular micelles, have an elasticity rather similar to that of rubber, whereas a non-hydrated cellulose with fibrils arranged in parallel shows an elasticity similar to that of metals (TREITEL 1947). This is reminiscent of the various properties of root-hair tips and the expanding side walls of epidermal cells.

X-rays reveal a crystalline structure of cellulose only in dried walls of young cells and in older walls. The cellulose microfibrils are also orientated to some extent in the living walls of young cells, and the strongest growth ordinarily takes place at right angles to the average direction of the microfibrils, simply because the resistance to addition of new microfibrils is then at its minimum. This is the essence of the 'tubular structure' mentioned above (p. 76). PRESTON (1947) has also shown that the transverse arrangement of the microfibrils in the longitudinal walls of growing cells, e.g. in the tracheids of conifers, is not dependent on any tensions. The spiral arrangement, which occurs in the hyphae of fungi, should certainly not be referred to a general organic tendency to spiral formation. It is however much more pronounced in the secondary wall layers.

The carbohydrates necessary for the growth of the cell wall must of course be supplied from inside the cell. The raw material is mostly glucose, which builds the long unbranched molecular chains by α-glucoside formation. It is assumed that such a polymerisation takes place by means of phosphorylation, that is with the co-operation of energy-rich phosphate compounds, e.g. adenosine triphosphate (ATP). The route from glucose to pentoses and pectin is not altogether clear, but an enzymatic conversion of ribose, e.g. into adenosine, or of ribose-5-phosphate into glucose-6-phosphate (Robison ester), has been described (WALDVOGEL and SCHLENK 1947).

It appears doubtful whether the complete cellulose synthesis is carried out at the final location, that is in the surface layer of the protoplasm. Feeding roots with glucose evokes no direct increase in growth of root hairs; the reaction follows only after several minutes, when the glucose has penetrated into the cells (LUNDEGÅRDH 1946). Some workers (BARROWS 1939, FARR 1940, 1941, SISSON 1941) think they have found ellipsoidal cellulose crystalloids of about 1 μ diameter in the protoplasm of various plants. They also believe that these particles build up the new wall like bricks. Similar 'dermatosomes' hypotheses turn up several times in the older literature, but must be considered with a certain scepticism in the light of the facts mentioned above. Only in dried, denaturised young walls or in secondarily thickened walls does the cellulose take on the form of micelles or 'crystallites', composed of bundles of cellulose fibrils or filamentous molecules. According to MEYER and MARK (1929-30) there are little rods 6 mμ long and 5 mμ in diameter. It is assumed that these micelles are held together by filamentous molecules, somewhat like pearls on a string. The ends of the strings of pearls may be partly rotated round each other, as in a spun yarn; which explains the well-known high tensile strength (SPONSLER; see SEIFRIZ 1942).

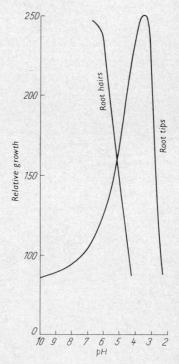

There is nothing against assuming a slow solidification or crystallisation of the ageing wall. The form in which the cellulose is supplied by the surface layer of the protoplasm need not be decisive for the course of wall formation. All the enzymes necessary for reversible secretion and redissolving of the building material are already available in the cell surface. The hypothesis previously mentioned, according to which the configuration of wall construction is determined by the specific arrangement and molecular structure of the wall layer, as by a template, should receive more consideration; it must however be conceded that actual experience leaves us in the lurch. The only case in which formation

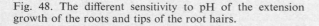

Fig. 48. The different sensitivity to pH of the extension growth of the roots and tips of the root hairs.

of cellulose could be observed outside cells is in *Acetobacter xylineum* (HESTRIN *et al.* 1947). A mother substance, possibly glucosan, is probably formed within the cells and is then polymerised in the medium.

Calcium ions, which are necessary for the chain linking of the pectin molecules of the middle lamella, may fulfil a similar task in extension growth, where pectins knit the cellulose microfibrils together. Calcium ions are always present in protoplasm, and they are among the nutrients important for life. The continuance of the growth of roots and root hairs for a time in distilled water is probably due to supply of calcium from inside. If, on the other hand, the distilled water is replaced by very dilute mineral acid (pH = 4) the growth of the root hairs stops at once, unless a small amount of calcium is supplied simultaneously (Fig. 48). The strongly increasing hydration of the pectin and of the surface layer of the protoplasm after exchange of H-ions usually leads to a bursting (plasmoptysis) of the root-hair tips. The total root growth on the other hand is less sensitive to lower pH values; which must be due to the fact that the inner parts of the tissue are protected by the outer layer.

Extension growth is dependent on the supply of structural materials (carbohydrates), auxins and calcium ions but also on the new production of osmotic substances, since experience shows that the cell volume is increased without a corresponding decrease in the osmotic pressure. This new production of osmotic material takes place independently of its possible collaboration in membrane growth (cf. above and BECK and ANDRUS 1943). It has been found that the protoplasm also increases in volume during the cell extension (FREY-WYSSLING 1945), although only in the same ratio as the cell sap. Extension growth therefore also needs a supply of nitrogenous nutrients.

B. The Size of the Cells

The relationship between nucleus and protoplasm (p. 4) is often considered as a regulator of nuclear and cell division; and it is usually supposed that the number and size of the chromosomes also have a certain influence. If the chromatin is increased only by division of the chromosomes and this process introduces mitosis and cell division, the cells of an active embryonic tissue must attain a certain 'division size'. If the mitosis is inhibited shortly before telophase, e.g. by chloral hydrate, colchicine or other mitotic poisons, the chromosome number is doubled and the cell size increased (Fig. 49). The relationship of nucleus to protoplasm is however also subject to other influences, and the size at division varies according to the environment of the cells.

These phenomena can be observed also in lower organisms. The vegetative cells of *Oedogonium* reach a much larger size before they proceed to division than those which form the male sex organs. Small cell sizes have also been induced experimentally in algae such as *Spirogyra* by treatment with cane sugar or Congo Red (KLEBS 1888). Different cell sizes in a meristem are caused through the nuclear spindle being arranged asymmetrically, the so-called unequal division (Fig. 49).

The relation between nucleus and protoplasm seems to depend more on the amount of chromatin than on the amount of surface. This follows from the investigations of GERASSIMOFF on *Spirogyra* (1902-4). GERASSIMOFF induced tetraploidy by treatment with chloral and found that cells with a single tetraploid nucleus were about the same size as cells with two diploid nuclei which had not yet fused and which therefore had a considerably greater nuclear surface but equal chromosome numbers. GERASSIMOFF further found that the volume of the cell increased more than the volume of the nucleus, but that the ratio between chromosome number and nuclear surface did not alter. In tetraploid cells the chromosome number increased in the ratio 1·94 : 1, but the cell volume on the other hand in the ratio 2·88 : 1.

Investigations on tetraploid higher plants (EKDAHL 1945, 1949) have shown that the cell size increases differently in different directions, so that an invariable ratio 4*n*: 2*n* does not occur. In tetraploid *Hordeum* the guard cells of the stomata, for example, were about 30% longer but only about 20% wider than in the diploid mother

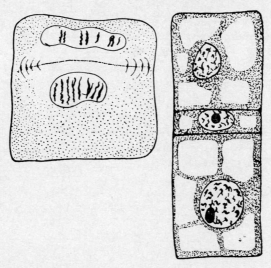

Fig. 49. Unequal cell division in the root tip of *Allium cepa* (after LUNDEGÅRDH 1922).

form. In the leaf epidermis the cells grew about 54% in length but only about 27% in width. The volume ratio between cytoplasm and cell sap also varied. In leaf cells the thickness of the protoplasmic lining did not increase to the same extent as the diameter of the cell. The water content of the cells thus increased. In root cells on the other hand the ratio between protoplasm and cell volume was maintained, so that in this case the water content remained unaltered.

Polyploidy with the accompanying increase in cell size is found normally in certain tissues of higher plants (Fig. 50). Thus WINKLER (1910) found up to 16-ploidy in the medulla, starch parenchyma and collenchyma of *Solanum lycopersicum*. Interference with all division and consequent polyploidy can thus be caused by internal factors, and is usually connected with the differentiation of tissues, for which large cells are sometimes desirable.

In the formation of the embryo-sac, latex vessels and certain sclerenchyma cells several nuclei may occur in one cell. The final result is however the same. In the formation of the endosperm, wall formation between the nuclei is gradually introduced, and the sac is divided up into a tissue of smaller cells. In certain algae, e.g. *Sphacelaria* (GEYLER 1866) and *Halopteris* (GOEBEL 1928), the growing point is restricted to a single giant cell which gradually splits off smaller cells (Fig. 51). One can consider these cases as a transition between those algae which consist wholly of giant cells, e.g. *Caulerpa*, and the higher plants, in which small cells give place to multinucleate giant cells only for the fulfilment of special functions.

By variation of the cell size in individual cases Nature has efficiently solved con-
structional problems. In land plants mechanical rigidity is of the first importance,
and is generally provided by a special form and structure of small cells. The construc-
tional principle depending on intracellular supports (Fig. 52), which is characteristic
of the giant cells of *Caulerpa*, would in this case be impractical.

In view of the great variation in the size of species it is of interest to note that the
size of cells varies relatively little (cf. EAMES and MACDANIELS 1947). Whereas the size
of organisms varies from 1 to 100,000,000, cell sizes vary only within a range of 1 to
about 70. Few mature uninucleate cells are larger than 0·2 mm or smaller than 0·015
mm, although cells visible to the naked eye occur at times with a length of 1 mm, e.g.
in the pith of *Sambucus* and *Impatiens*. Cambium cells usually attain considerable
lengths, as in the tulip tree, where they may be 600 μ long with a cross-section of
8-25 μ. Very long cambium cells are found in conifers, in pines up to 4 mm. These
cells have a vacuole and show protoplasmic streaming. Extraordinarily long cortex
cells—in *Urtica* up to 77 mm, and in *Boehmeria* apparently up to 220 mm—are however
usually multinucleate. Very large tissue elements, e.g. vessels, arise by cell fusion,
that is to say by penetration of completed walls. Finally, as an example of long cell
parts visible to the naked eye, one may mention the root hairs which are outgrowths
of epidermal cells several millimetres long.

How far the relatively narrow variation in the size of most tissue cells is actually
connected with the relation between nucleus and protoplasm appears doubtful, when
one knows that the mature cell consists mostly of cell sap. The streaming of the protoplasm makes exchange of materials possible between the nucleus and all corners of
very elongated cells such as those carrying root hairs. It is difficult to survey to what

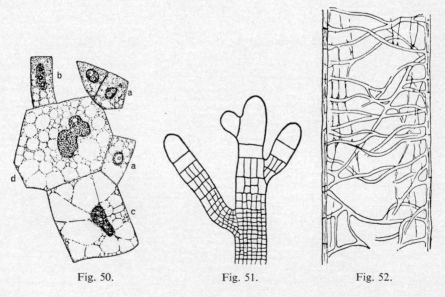

Fig. 50.   Fig. 51.   Fig. 52.

Fig. 50. Cells from the endosperm of *Secale cereale*. (*a*) normal triploid nuclei; (*b*) ditriploid; (*c*) tetra-
triploid; (*d*) octotriploid nuclei (after NĔMEC 1910).

Fig. 51. Branching thallus of *Sphacelaria scoparia* (after HABERLANDT 1918).

Fig. 52. Cellulose strands in *Caulerpa* (after OLTMANNS 1904).

degree correlations, i.e. influences from surrounding cells, affect cell size. Usually, however, it is found that cells which have been torn away from their natural milieu, e.g. those in callus formations on wood surfaces (Fig. 53) or the cells sloughed off by the root cap, grow considerably beyond their 'normal' size.

Among other factors limiting cell growth may be mentioned the less favourable surface/volume ratio caused by increasing size, which restricts exchange of materials with the surroundings. It is probable that the rapid metabolism of bacteria is directly connected with their small cell volume. A *Staphylococcus*, with a diameter of 0.8μ, has a volume of only $1/17,000,000,000$ mm³. Several million such cells could thus find a place in a tissue cell; but the smallness of their diameter enormously increases their effective surface.

On the basis of the knowledge that extension growth depends on auxins and anti-auxins, it is not surprising that cell size is connected with position in a tissue, or that a cell mechanically removed from its natural milieu resumes a growth that had stopped. It has, for example, been known for a long time that the tracheids of pine wood become smaller towards the middle of the trunk. The pith cells change their size as one passes from the tip to the bottom, and the same applies, according to SIERP (1914), to the epidermal cells, the width of the vessels, etc., in a number of herbaceous plants.

C. The Form and Structure of the Cell

1. GENERAL

The form of the cell is obviously determined by the distribution of surface growth. Only freely-living cells can develop their form unhindered. United in a tissue, they are always restricted to a certain extent.

The unicellular organisms show that an isolated plant cell can assume almost any conceivable form. Only spherical bacteria and blue-green or green algae are distinguished by uniform (isotropic) growth. The extraordinary variety of forms which e.g. the Peridinieae show, is usually supported by a finely constructed wall, but protoplasts, surrounded by a thin membrane, can also attain a considerable development of form (*Ceratium hirundinella*, Fig. 54). The giant cells of the algae *Botrydium*, *Bryopsis* (Fig. 55), *Caulerpa*, *Vaucheria*, etc., can show a differentiation equal to that of many of their multicellular relatives. They form stem, root and leaves in one single giant cell, in which separate conductive tissue is no longer required, as the transport function is performed by the streaming protoplasm. They have, however, a counterpart to the mechanical supporting tissues of multicellular plants, as in the cellulose supports across the cell cavity of *Caulerpa* (Fig. 52). A certain similarity to this rich diversity of forms in unicellular organisms is offered in the higher plants by the formation of hairs, etc., which project from the epidermis.

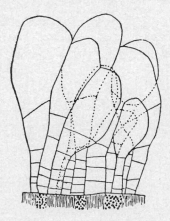

Fig. 53. A callus from the wood parenchyma of a seedling of *Populus nigra* (after SIMON).

G

A more or less independent development of form in cells which are enclosed in a tissue presupposes either a considerable mutual displacement of the walls, i.e. 'sliding growth', or differential growth of various parts of the walls. Ideas about sliding growth are very fluid (cf. p. 70, and LUNDEGÅRDH 1914, PRIESTLEY 1929, SINNOTT 1939, MEEUSE 1941). In parenchymas, tissue tensions can result from the failure of sliding. Ordinarily no regular sliding should occur, but a mutual adaptation of the speed of growth of neighbouring cells (Fig. 56). The organ thus grows as a

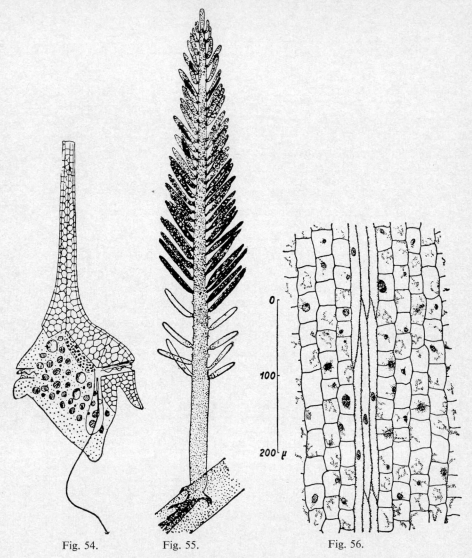

Fig. 54.   Fig. 55.   Fig. 56.

Fig. 54. *Ceratium hirundinella*. An evenly developed individual. The cell form has already been assumed from the naked part of the protoplast (after LAUTERBORN).

FIG. 55. *Bryopsis cupressoides* (after OLTMANNS 1904).

FIG. 56. The development of a fibre baulk (support) in the ground tissue of *Sanseviera*. The extension growth of the future sclerenchyma fibre is not 'sliding' but made possible by differential growth of the neighbouring parenchyma cells (after MEEUSE 1938).

whole and the growth of the individual cell is regulated by an overall plan. 'Rebel' growth of individual cells or cell groups destroys the unity of the organ, as one can observe after doses of auxin above the optimal, or in swellings (Fig. 57), galls and tumours. In special cases, e.g. in branched latex vessels, the cell behaves like a parasite, forcing its way between the host cells. Other specialised cells (idioblasts) contain crystals and oil droplets.

A more systematic differential growth is shown by the cells of many supporting tissues, e.g. sclerenchyma, wood and bark. The cells are usually pointed, with the ends wedged between each other. The increase of the contact surfaces thus obtained provides greater tensile strength. In other cases of differential growth the middle lamella is torn in places so that the cells partly separate from each other and an air-filled tissue with many intercellular spaces is formed (Fig. 60, p. 88).

2. Uniform and Non-uniform Growth

The non-uniform (anisotropic, heterotropic) cell growth forms the first and probably the most important phase of tissue differentiation. As the anisotropic growth is to a great extent determined genetically, one must assume that it is directed by the cell nucleus. Even if the nucleus usually lies in the neighbourhood of those points in the wall which grow specially strongly or show local thickenings (HABERLANDT 1924), it is nevertheless clear that the gene impulse is transmitted by the cytoplasm, and the increased wall formation is thus not dependent on a direct contact between nucleus and wall. In loose parenchymas, e.g. leaf mesophyll or medulla, the wall grows simultaneously at several separate points, and the cell assumes a star shape (Fig. 58).

As a typical example of anisotropic growth the formation of root hairs may be mentioned. It has been studied in detail by SINNOTT and BLOCH (1939) and BURSTRÖM (1941). The root hairs are formed as outgrowths of the still-growing walls of the epidermis cells, not on all cells, but on about every other one. This dimorphism of the epidermal cells is recognisable at an early stage. The cells forming root hairs (the *trichoblasts*) grow somewhat more slowly than the others (the *atrichoblasts*) right from the beginning. About half-way through their expansion the hair initial looks like a small outward bend of the outer wall immediately below the nucleus (as seen from the root tip), which at this stage takes up a position near the middle of the cell. The

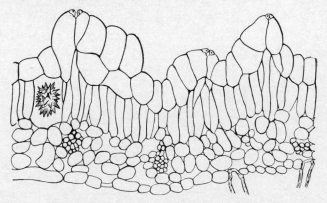

Fig. 57. Swellings on the leaves of *Hibiscus vitifolius* (after DALE).

distal part of the cell temporarily stops growing, from which it follows that cells with hairs are finally shorter than those without (Fig. 45, p. 77). Since, according to SINNOTT, there is no sliding growth, the root tip shows zones of stronger and weaker cell extension. The root hairs grow exclusively at the tip (Fig. 47). The occurrence of points or areas of local growth gives a considerable degree of individual character to the surface layer.

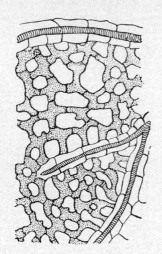

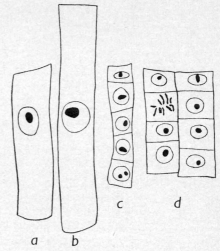

Fig. 58. Stellate parenchyma cells in petals of *Verbascum nigrum*. (× *c*. 400) (after LUNDEGÅRDH 1922).

Fig. 59. Cells from a longitudinal section of the root tip of *Allium cepa*. (*a*) and (*b*) two cells from the plerome, (*c*) from the inside, and (*d*) from the outside of the periblem layer (after LUNDEGÅRDH 1922).

3. GROWTH IN THICKNESS

After the end of extension growth the cell can either remain in the state already reached, so that a thin-walled parenchyma is formed, or can begin secondary growth in thickness of the walls. This consists of apposition of new material and a simultaneous change in the composition of the primary wall through deposition of new substances. The secretion of cellulose fibrils appears to proceed in the secondary wall in a different way from that in the primary. In elongated cells a transverse structure predominates in the primary wall (cf. above) which may turn into close coils, whilst the secondary wall is distinguished by a longitudinal spiral structure, ordinarily with a direct transition from primary to secondary wall (PRESTON 1947). This could be due to a rearrangement of the molecular configuration of the surface layer or even to an abnormal hydration of the cellulose (cf. p. 76). The wall structure of collenchyma cells was studied by PRESTON and DUCKWORTH (1946).

The epidermis of leaves and vegetative shoots tends to be covered with a secondarily separated *cuticle*. This contains wax that consists partly of esters of higher fatty acids, e.g. cerotic acid (hexacosanoic acid, $CH_3(CH_2)_{24}COOH$), partly of the alcohols cerotin (hexadecanol) and friedelin (LÜSCHER 1936) and partly of the high-polymer membrane materials, cutin and suberin, which contain suberic acid ($HOOC(CH_2)_6COOH$).

According to MARTENS (1934), the cuticle is excreted in liquid form through the cellulose wall and hardens after contact with the air. According to PRIESTLEY (1934,

1943; cf. also THODAY 1933) transpiration may co-operate in this as a means of transport. The physiological importance of the cuticle lies in mechanical protection and the restriction of transpiration (see Chap. 8).

Storage and deposition of suberin occur also in the *cork cells* formed from the cork cambium (phellogen), in cortical cells and in special layers such as those in the radial walls of the endodermis. It is obvious that cork formation alters the permeability for water fundamentally. According to SCOTT (1948) partial suberification may be a common phenomenon in a variety of tissues. Chitin, which may also be mentioned here, occurs in the cell walls of fungi, and is a complex nitrogen-containing polysaccharide, which on hydrolysis yields glucosamine and acetic acid.

The most usual and the most thorough conversion of the cell wall occurs in *lignification*, by which is meant the impregnation and covering of cellulose with the woody material lignin (about the occurrence of lignin see JUNKER 1941). Pectins have also been found in wood (ANDERSSON 1946).

Lignin is an amorphous substance about whose chemical nature information has been obtained only comparatively recently. According to PERRENOUD (1943, 1944), lignin consists of a network of molecular chains which are held together by covalencies. The side-chains are principally derivatives of phenols, which contain hydroxyl-, carbonyl- and methoxy-groups and which are combined with the cellulose. These are the linkages which impede abscission of the lignin from the cellulose, since the covalent bonds must first be broken. In lignin from spruce wood, according to PERRENOUD, the ratio $C/O = 3$ and the molecular weight is about 2,300. According to GRALÉN (1946), the lignin nucleus has the empirical formula $(C_9H_9O_3.OCH_3)_n$ with a molecular weight of about 7,000. The molecule is long, with an axis ratio of 5 : 1. There are probably chemically different variants of lignin.

Lignification begins in the middle lamella and gradually penetrates the remaining layers, which thus gain increased mechanical rigidity, without the water permeability being notably diminished.

In thick cellulose walls, as mentioned above, the classification of the layers is as follows: (1) the primary cell wall, which is closed as far as the plasmodesmata; (2) the secondary wall, which is usually provided with pits (see below) e.g. in wood fibres, where the thickened walls are otherwise closed. In certain cases the thickenings are arranged as rings or spirals, as e.g. in the vessels. The various layers often show inclined or spiral striations scarcely visible microscopically. As mentioned above, these striations usually run in different directions in the primary and secondary layers.

Among more specialised alterations in the cell walls may be mentioned the deposition of hemicellulose in fruits, the secretion of mucilage in flax seeds, of silicic acid in *Equisetum*, grasses, etc. Cystoliths are formed in the epidermis of *Ficus* and *Cannabis* as local thickenings of the wall. Calcium carbonate as well as oxides of iron and manganese may separate out in the cell walls, and also a number of organic compounds, e.g. flavones (ERDTMAN 1944) and other pigments in the wood of conifers, alders, etc. The secondary walls appear to serve chiefly as a dumping ground for waste products of neighbouring living cells, as in the medullary rays of wood. Many of these substances can, however, have some biological importance, e.g. as materials preserving the central part of the woody stem. The strongly lignified walls and the lumen of cells in the heart wood of stems are clogged with various secretions such as oil, rubber, resin, tannins, aromatic pigments such as flavones and flavanones, etc. Inorganic compounds, e.g. calcium carbonate or silicic acid, are also deposited (ANDERSON and PIGMAN 1947).

4. PITS

Pits, which are mostly found in the secondary wall layers, are places in the wall that have not been thickened. A pit is thus a canal between two cells, that is closed at the centre by the primary cell wall. The true nature of pits was first explained by VON MOHL (1828, 1851).

Pits have forms, distributions and frequencies typical of the species (Fig. 60). Plasmodesmata occur in the pore membrane, which means that the wall has a certain importance for translocation in the tissue. Translocation is necessary as long as the wall-thickening process continues.

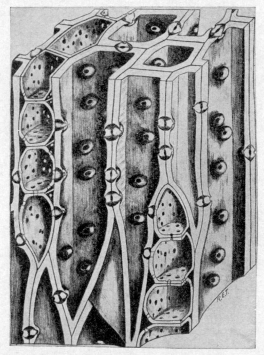

Fig. 60. Wood from *Picea canadensis*. Medullary rays with simple pits and tracheids with bordered pits (after JEFFREY).

In addition to this important function as a transport route during the final phase of the morphological specialisation of the cell, the pits fulfil a *post-mortem* function which should not be underestimated, viz. the regulation of the lateral movement of water and possibly also of gases through the wood. In this connection the elaborately formed bordered pits are of special interest (Fig. 61). They have a pit cavity and a

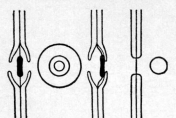

Fig. 61. Transverse sections and front views of a simple pit (right) and of a bordered pit (after JEFFREY).

closing membrane, which is usually provided at the centre with a thickening, the *torus*. Bordered pits are best developed in Gymnosperms, e.g. conifers, but also occur in Angiosperms (see Chap. 8). The opening of the pit cavity is at times reduced to a narrow slit (Fig. 60).

5. REVIEW OF CELL TYPES

The most important types of cell are the following:
A. *Forms without specialised wall structure*
    1. Relatively uniform (isotropic) growth: e.g. parenchyma cells of storage organs, such as tubers, cotyledons (Fig. 39), endosperm, fleshy fruits, etc., and water-storing cells of succulents. These cells form fleshy tissues, and their function consists chiefly in serving as containers for water and ergastic products.
    2. Non-uniform (anisotropic) growth:
        (*a*) The parenchyma in the fleshy parts of roots and stems of herbaceous plants with their axially elongated cells. They have vertical cross-walls and tend to form longitudinal intercellular spaces. The palisade cells of the leaves and parenchyma round the central vessels are also long and cylindrical.
        (*b*) Tube-shaped, sometimes branched cells: root hairs, pollen tubes, latex vessels (multinuclear and branched; Fig. 62).
        (*c*) Spongy parenchyma of the leaves, aerenchyma (internal air spaces), stellate parenchyma in the pith (Fig. 58), petals, etc.
B. *Skeletal forms* (*tissue elements with characteristic wall structure*)
    3. Epidermis at times with wavy walls, endodermis, cork cells.
    4. Stone cells, thickened endosperm cells.
    5. Collenchyma (Fig. 63).
    6. Sclerenchyma fibres.
    7. Vessels and tracheids.
    8. Other spirally thickened cells, e.g. in the velamen of aerial roots.
    9. Parenchyma with infolded walls in pine needles, fan-shaped epidermal cells, rhizoids with conical wall thickenings, etc.
C. *Special cells*
    10. Stomata.
    11. Pollen grains.
    12. Hairs: star- and scale-like hairs, stinging hairs, multicellular glandular hairs, etc.
    13. Idioblasts: containers of crystals, oil, etc.
The tissues built up of more or less specialised mature cells fulfil all the essential functions of the organism and one can usually perceive a clear connection between the anatomical structure and the physiological function. HABERLANDT (1924) especially, in his *Physiologische Pflanzenanatomie* has carried the physiological classification of tissues very far, and sometimes to artificial lengths, as in the subdivision of leaf tissues into surface, ventilation and conducting systems, etc. Recent research has been more inclined to emphasise the unity of the organs and to consider anatomical differentiation as an expression of a physiological division of labour. Certain functions may be

carried out by different organs in similar ways, e.g. surface protection or the transport of water and dissolved substances. The genetic constitution mostly offers only a limited range of possibilities for the structural solution of such problems. Anatomical differentiation, therefore, often follows similar or even identical paths. On this account the suggestion of a complete physiological-anatomical correspondence should be avoided.

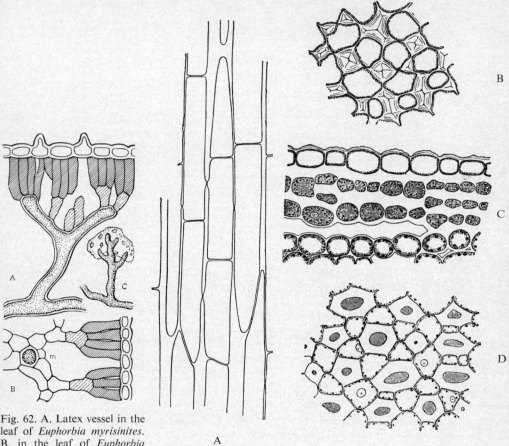

Fig. 62. A. Latex vessel in the leaf of *Euphorbia myrisinites*. B. in the leaf of *Euphorbia biglandulosa* (*m* latex vessel). C. in the leaves of *Hypochoeris radicata*. The palisade cells are shown shaded (after HABERLANDT).

Fig. 63. A. Longitudinal section; B. cross-section through the collenchyma in the leaf stalk of *Salvia sclarea*; C. cross-section through the collenchyma of *Astrantia major*; D. of *Petasites niveus* (after HABERLANDT).

Chapter 3

PHOTOSYNTHESIS AND FORMATION OF CARBOHYDRATES

A. Carbon dioxide and Light as General Factors in Nutrition

The central chemical process in plant life is the reduction of carbon dioxide and water to carbohydrate, with the aid of light energy, according to the summary equation:

$$6CO_2 + 6H_2O + 708 \text{ kg-cal.} \rightarrow C_6H_{12}O_6 + 6O_2 \qquad (9)$$

The investigation of photosynthesis was started by the Englishman PRIESTLEY (1772) who showed that the air in a covered vessel was 'improved' if plants were included with it. When a lighted candle was introduced it was not extinguished. Animals similarly enclosed spoiled the air. Actually the Swede SCHEELE discovered oxygen before PRIESTLEY, although his observations were not published until 1777. Soon after that the Dutchman INGEN-HOUSZ (1779) found that an 'improvement' of the air occurred only when the plants were illuminated. The co-operation of carbon dioxide was made clear by SENEBIER (1782) and that of water by DE SAUSSURE (1804). These two were Swiss from Geneva. With this one of the greatest scientists discoveries was completed, although certain supplementary observations were supplied by the Frenchman BOUSSINGAULT and the German ROBERT MEYER.

The further investigation of the discovery belongs to quite modern work. In this the simple summary equation is split up (as in almost all biochemical processes which have been studied in greater detail) into a series of simultaneous or successive physical and chemical events. Organic chemists have elucidated the constitution of chlorophyll and other pigments effective in chloroplasts or photosynthetic micro-organisms. Plant physiologists and experimental ecologists have investigated the dependence of photosynthesis on the external conditions, light, carbon dioxide and temperature.

The clarification of the mechanism of photosynthesis has thus become in recent decades the object of intensive biochemical research, which however is far from being concluded, although important advances can be reported. It is known with certainty that both photochemical and 'dark reactions' co-operate in photosynthesis and that the former can be replaced in certain heterotrophic micro-organisms by exothermal chemical reactions (WOOD and WERKMAN: see WOOD 1946). Because of its high content of oxygen, carbon dioxide can in many cases serve as an oxidising agent, and its reduction is a process possible in all protoplasm (EVANS 1942). In particular, there exist many connections between the reaction chains which form carbon dioxide during respiration and those in which this process, on addition of energy, takes the reverse direction (cf. Chap. 4).

Instead of the older term 'carbon dioxide assimilation' the term 'photosynthesis' has now been adopted, which appears logical since CO_2 is also assimilated chemically, and the reduction effected by light is the most important part of this process. There are however also other photosynthetic processes, e.g. those which are connected with phototropic and photonastic movements. These have so far been but little investigated biochemically, and are undoubtedly concerned with more specific photo-processes which have no direct nutritional importance.

The photochemical assimilation of carbon dioxide is the prime mover of the carbon dioxide cycle on the earth. Carbon is the keystone of the organic world, and the dry substance of plants contains more than 50% of carbon. Because of its insolubility and non-volatility carbon cannot take part in a cycle as an element or an ion. On the other hand its highest stage of oxidation, carbon dioxide, because of its volatility, solubility in water and quick diffusion, is extremely suitable to enter into widely branching cycles. In these cycles plants and animals, air, water and soil are all included (see LUNDEGÅRDH 1924, 1957). The carbon dioxide combined in minerals can also be involved.

Determinations of the carbon dioxide content of air were made by the pioneers of photosynthetic research, DE SAUSSURE and BOUSSINGAULT, and were continued later by a number of workers. An average value of about 0·03% by volume ($=0·56$ mg per litre at 18° C) was established. Analyses of the CO_2 content of waters are less com-

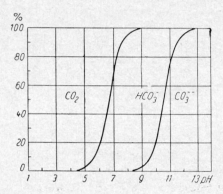

Fig. 64. The dissociation curves of carbonic acid (first and second dissociation).

prehensive, but it seems to be about the same as in air, though the formation of bicarbonate with alkalies has the effect of increasing it. The relationship between the concentration of free carbonic acid ($CO_2 + H_2CO_3$) and bicarbonate ions (HCO_3^-) is given by the following equation

$$\log [CO_2] = pK_1 - pH + \log [HCO_3^-] \qquad (10)$$

in which pK_1 is equal to the negative logarithm of the first dissociation constant of carbonic acid (about 6·6). From this equation one can calculate the total quantity of carbonic acid which is available for photosynthesis by water plants in the presence of a known excess of bases.

It is of great physiological and ecological interest to calculate approximately the total quantity of carbon dioxide available for photosynthesis, as well as the annual CO_2-turnover (cf. RABINOWITCH 1945). The conclusion is reached that land plants, with an average turnover of 1,300 kg per hectare per year, convert about $1·9 \times 10^{10}$ tons of carbon dioxide into carbohydrates. Much more important, however, is the capacity of the plants in the oceans. It has been calculated that the water plants fix 3,750 kg of carbon per hectare per year, which amounts for the total area of the oceans to $15·5 \times 10^{10}$ tons. The total carbohydrate production would thus amount to $15-20 \times 10^{10}$ tons per year. But in this gigantic production, which is about 20 times the total industrial consumption of fossil carbon (cf. SCHRÖDER 1919, LUNDEGÅRDH 1957 Chap. 2), only about 3% of the carbon dioxide content of the atmosphere and about 0·3% of that of the oceans is used.

As dead plants and animals after decay bring into circulation again the carbon dioxide required by the still-living plants, there is a balance, a 'steady state', between photosynthesis and decay. Alterations in the balance are brought about on the one side by the fossils withdrawn from the cycle and on the other by the activity of mankind (burning of coal and oil). The solid surface of the earth contains about $2\text{-}8 \times 10^{16}$ tons of carbon as limestone which may largely be considered as fossil and thus as coming from the atmosphere of earlier epochs.

In comparison with carbon, the amounts of water available for photosynthesis are superabundant and variations in this factor can therefore scarcely influence carbohydrate production. As living parenchyma normally contains at least 90% water, this factor has its greatest importance as a general precondition of life.

With respect to light both variations in intensity and spectral composition play important ecological roles. Pigment content, spectral sensitivity, etc., of the photosynthetic tissues have their effects and cause significant variations in the efficiency quotients of light utilisation. It is calculated for example that on the average only 1%-2% of the sun's energy reaching the earth's surface is converted into chemical energy (as carbohydrate), although with monochromatic illumination maximal quotients of 20% or more have been measured (KOK). This is of course due to the fact that by far the largest part of the spectrum, including the whole of the infra-red and the greatest part of the ultra-violet, are photosynthetically inactive. According to a calculation by RABINOWITCH (1945), the earth's surface receives each year about

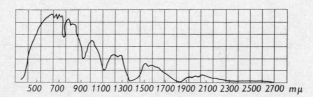

500   700   900 1100 1300 1500 1700 1900 2100 2300 2500 2700 $m\mu$

Fig. 65. The distribution of the energy in the sun's spectrum at the earth's surface (i.e. the terrestrial normal spectrum). Wavelengths in $m\mu$ (after DORNO).

6×10^{23} cal. and of this about 3×10^{21} cal. are fixed as carbohydrate. Even the transpiration of plants utilises, according to SCHRÖDER (1919), at least five times as much of the sun's energy as photosynthesis does.

Regarded as energy, light behaves like a stream of particles, photons, each of which bears a quantum of energy. The energy equivalent of a photon is directly proportional to the frequency of the light i.e. to the number of waves per unit length, and thus is inversely proportional to the wavelength. This is expressed in the equation

$$E = h \cdot c \cdot v$$

where E = radiation energy

$\quad h$ = Planck's constant i.e. the elementary effective quantum ($= 6\cdot624 \times 10^{-27}$ ergs/second)

$\quad c$ = speed of light ($= 3 \times 10^{10}$ cm/sec)

and $\quad v$ = the frequency of the radiation.

An ultra-violet photon of wavelength 100 $m\mu$ thus has four times as much energy content as one of wavelength 400 $m\mu$ and eight times as much as an infra-red photon of wavelength 800 $m\mu$. We will return later (pp. 113–114) to the spectral quantum effects and the theoretical quantum yield of photosynthesis.

B. Carbohydrates and Fats

According to the summary equation of photosynthesis the volumes of carbon dioxide used up and of oxygen formed are equal. The photosynthetic quotient O_2/CO_2 is thus equal to unity, and this was found experimentally by BOUSSINGAULT (as early as 1864) and later by a number of other workers, among them WILLSTÄTTER and STOLL (1918). In the metabolism of succulents there are complications which change the photo-synthetic quotient (see below).

Starch was considered by SACHS (1875) to be the first detectable assimilation product; but later the formation of sugars became prominent. A knowledge of the various forms of sugar and their transformations is indispensable for the study of metabolism.

Starch is a condensation product of the hexose D-glucose (dextrose). The forms of sugar usually arising in connection with photosynthesis are D-glucose, D-fructose and their condensation product sucrose (cane sugar). Chemical analyses of a leaf before and after a period of exposure to light frequently show an increase especially of the sucrose content. This fact earlier misled many researchers into assuming that the disaccharide sucrose was the first product of assimilation. It should however be remembered that almost all cells contain enzymes which can quickly convert one kind of sugar into another. In barley, for example, mechanisms have been found for the interconversion of sucrose and the monosaccharides glucose, fructose, mannose and galactose as well as the disaccharides maltose and lactose (McCREADY and HASSID, 1941).

Cane sugar has only half the osmotic effect of the hexoses and is therefore more suitable as a sugar for storage. Conversely, the smaller molecular weight of the hexoses favours diffusion. In the opinion of many workers, e.g. MASON and MASKELL, sucrose is, however, the preferred sugar for transport, especially since it is apparently concentrated in the cytoplasm. The hexoses, on the other hand, appear as the first assimilation products.

The idea that a hexose monophosphate might be the first reduction product, which was then quickly converted into sucrose, was expressed by SMITH (1944). The sucrose is easily hydrolysed again to hexose. This interpretation finds support in the research work of recent years which has shown that the first assimilation products are compounds simpler than hexoses and that they are first converted to these hexoses by phosphorylation processes, as set forth in greater detail below.

1. MONOSACCHARIDES

The hexoses, pentoses and heptoses (named after the number of carbon atoms in each) form part of the group of *monosaccharides*, which also includes a diose, trioses and tetroses.

(a) *Hexoses*

Of the monosaccharides with six carbon atoms, $C_6H_{12}O_6$, the most common are *glucose* and *fructose*. The former is an aldose, characterised by the group $\overset{\displaystyle H}{\underset{\diagdown}{}}C=O$,

and the latter is a ketose with the group $C=O$. The living cell appears generally to be able to convert glucose and fructose reversibly into each other; but the two hexoses are not equivalent in their physiological effects. The conversion takes place at the phosphorylation stage, where glucose monophosphate is changed into fructose monophosphate by the enzyme isomerase. Glucose is the dominant hexose in plants.

Among hexoses should also be mentioned *mannose, galactose* and *sorbose*. Galactose is, together with glucose, a component of lactose (milk sug. r).

(b) *Pentoses*

Monosaccharides with five carbon atoms, pentoses ($C_5H_{10}O_5$), play no great part as free sugars in the life of plants, but, according to recent researches, the pentose *ribose* is highly important for the first stages of carbon dioxide fixation. According to the investigations of CALVIN (1954), carbon dioxide is introduced into the photosynthetic reaction chain by fixation as ribose-1, 5-diphosphate.

D-Ribose (β-D-ribofuranose)   D-2-Desoxyribose (β-D-2-desoxyribofuranose)

Enzymatic conversions of pentose phosphate into hexose phosphate have been observed by HORECKER and SMYRNIOTIS (1951) *et al.* A further fundamental role in metabolism is played by pentoses in their combination with purine bases and phosphoric acid to form nucleic acid or other active nitrogenous groups. The active pentose here is ribose, and apparently *xylose* (wood sugar) and *arabinose* (from gum arabic) are much less important. The two latter occur as components of pectin-like polysaccharides. According to McCREADY and HASSID (1941) there is no conversion mechanism between sucrose, arabinose and xylose in barley roots. Hexitols, which are alcohols with six carbon atoms, e.g. *mannitol* and *sorbitol*, also cannot be used for synthesising sucrose. Conversions between pentoses and hexoses are discussed below.

(c) *Heptoses*

Sedoheptulose ($C_7H_{14}O_7$) which occurs e.g. in abundance in *Sedum* species (NORDAL 1942) may be mentioned as a ketose with seven carbon atoms. This type of sugar may also, according to recent investigations, have a key position in the biochemistry of carbon dioxide fixation. It is conceivable that the formation of sedoheptulose occurs by condensation of a C_4-fragment with a triose (HORECKER and SMYRNIOTIS 1953).

2 DISACCHARIDES

Of the disaccharides with twelve carbon atoms ($C_{12}H_{22}O_{11}$) only two occur widely, viz. *sucrose* and *maltose*, of which the former is the more usual. The enzyme invertase catalyses the inversion of sucrose into glucose and fructose with the uptake of a molecule of water. Maltose is a condensation product of two molecules of glucose and is itself condensed to the polysaccharide starch, which consequently on hydrolysis is decomposed first into maltose and then into glucose. In spite of this only a little free maltose is encountered in plants. This sugar thus has nothing like the same importance as cane sugar.

Like maltose, the disaccharide *trehalose* is built up of two molecules of glucose. In maltose they are combined through one reducing group but in trehalose through both. Trehalose occurs in Trehala manna (*Echinops persicus*), also in *Selaginella*, ergot, yeast, algae and bacteria (MYRBÄCK 1948). It is hydrolysed by the enzyme trehalase. Trehalose is one of those sugars that accumulate predominantly in the protoplasm. In the yeast cell the trehalose may occur only in a surface layer. As the trehalase on the other hand occurs only in the inner regions of the cell, the trehalose is protected against hydrolysis and rapid fermentation.

A fourth disaccharide, *cellobiose*, arises on the hydrolysis of cellulose by the action of the enzyme cellulase. Further hydrolysis gives rise, as in the hydrolysis of maltose, to two molecules of glucose. The difference lies in the steric configuration of the glucose (see below).

3 TRISACCHARIDES

The best-known of the trisaccharides ($C_{18}H_{32}O_{16}$) is *raffinose*, which is composed of glucose, fructose and galactose.

4 TETRASACCHARIDES

The only tetrasaccharide ($C_{24}H_{42}O_{21}$) that need be mentioned is *stachyose*, found in *Stachys tubifera* and some other plants. It is composed of one molecule each of glucose and fructose, and two of galactose.

5 PENTASACCHARIDES

A pentasaccharide occurs in abundance as a reserve carbohydrate in the roots of *Verbascum* (MURAKAMI 1940). It consists of three molecules of D-galactose, one molecule of D-glucose and one molecule of D-fructose.

The di-, tri-, tetra- and penta-saccharides are known collectively as *oligosaccharides*.

6 POLYSACCHARIDES

Of the polysaccharides ($C_6H_{10}O_5$)n which are formed by polymerisation of hexoses, starch and cellulose are incomparably the most important. *Cellulose* is indeed the general building material of the plant body, whilst *starch* is the commonest storage carbohydrate. Polysaccharides ($C_5H_8O_4$)n also occur which are based on pentoses, especially arabinose and xylose; these polysaccharides like cellulose consist of long chains of mono-saccharides. Examples are the *arabans* which occur in cell walls or as mucilages in Cacti and other succulents, also in gum arabic, cherry gum, etc.; and the *xylans*, which in some wood and seed coats can form up to 15% of the organic substance.

(a) *Cellulose*

The molecules and micelles of cellulose have been discussed in the treatment of the primary cell wall. The molecules are chains of several hundred glucose units, which are bonded through oxygen bridges and can be conceived as extended cellobiose molecules.

Cellulose is outstandingly resistant to chemical solvents; it is, however, attacked among other things by ammoniacal copper oxide (Schweizer's reagent). On hydrolysis in dilute mineral acids it yields glucose, whereas cold caustic soda solution alters the molecular structure and forms a product which strongly absorbs dyes ('mercerisation'). Decomposition into cellobiose occurs after treatment with acetic acid and sulphuric acid. In nature this splitting is effected by enzymes.

Cellulose contains free hydroxyl groups, which can be esterified and methylated. Methylated cellulose is used in industry as a plastic. Acetylated cellulose (cellulose acetate) is worked up into acetate rayon and cellulose acetate film. Cellulose nitrate gives an explosive and, with a lower nitrogen content, the raw material for collodion and celluloid. No other natural product is technically so versatile in applications as cellulose.

Cellulose derives its importance as a wall-building material through the tendency of the unbranched fibrillar molecules to form interlaced crystalloid micelles which attain high mechanical strength.

(b) *Starch*

The starch molecule, also composed of glucose units, has chemical properties different from those of cellulose. This fact is due to the different steric configuration, in that starch consists of α-glucose and cellulose of β-glucose (see the formulae above). The starch molecule is usually represented as spiral; it is also shorter than the cellulose molecule and contains about 200 glucose units. According to FREUDENBERG (1940), MYRBÄCK and AHLBORG (1940), HASSID (1943) *et al.*, each turn of the spiral is made up of 8 glucose units.

Starch occurs in two modifications:

1. Amylose with unbranched molecular chains, which forms 10%-20% of maize starch; and
2. Amylopectin with strongly-branched chains, which forms 80%-90% of maize starch.

The relative quantities of the two components are, however, very variable in different kinds of starch. Starch breaks up on hydrolysis first into maltose and finally quantitatively into glucose. In the first stages of the hydrolysis *dextrins* arise. Amylopectin always contains 0·02%-0·16% of phosphoric acid, which facilitates the breaking down by a group of enzymes which are called amylases (diastase). Amylases are widely distributed in plants, especially in germinating cereal grains (MYRBÄCK and NEU-MÜLLER 1950). Enzymes are of course also active in synthesis.

Cytochemically starch is identified by the Sachs leaf test. The formation of starch during photosynthesis is demonstrated by the Sachs method as follows: one half of a starch-forming leaf previously kept in the dark is illuminated and, after several hours' exposure, is boiled, and extracted with alcohol until all the chlorophyll is removed, and then treated with a solution of iodine in potassium iodide. Comparison with the half which was not illuminated but otherwise treated in the same way then shows the blue coloration of the starch formed.

The iodine reaction is extraordinarily sensitive. It is explained by an atom of iodine finding a place in the molecular spiral of the starch. Only amylose is coloured blue by iodine; amylopectin assumes a violet colour. The latter is almost insoluble in cold water, but on heating forms a paste. Amylose dissolves in water without forming a paste. The spherical crystalloids of starch, as mentioned on p. 71, have shapes typical of the species.

(c) *Inulin*

In certain plants e.g. *Dahlia*-tubers, artichokes and Jerusalem artichokes there is a special polysaccharide, inulin, which on hydrolysis by the enzyme inulase splits into fructose. Many other plants also contain polyfructosans as reserve material. Inulin dissolves fairly easily in water, but is precipitated by alcohol.

(d) *Glycogen*

Among the lower plants certain groups of Algae, such as the Chlorophyceae and Rhodophyceae, form starches whereas Cyanophyceae and fungi contain glycogen.

Glycogen takes the place of starch in animals and is very closely related to it chemically. It is, however, assumed that glycogen forms shorter and more branched molecular chains. According to CORI the formation and breakdown of glycogen occur via glucose-1-phosphate. Glycogen has also been observed in higher plants e.g. in maize grains.

(e) *Laminarin*

The Phaeophyceae form neither starch nor glycogen but a dextrin-like polysaccharide, laminarin. It may be hydrolysed to glucose and is utilised by the seaweed for storage.

Most of the carbohydrates listed here do not arise directly in photosynthesis, but by secondary enzymatic processes which also take place in cells which show no photosynthetic activity. This applies in the first place to the polysaccharides, but also to the simple types of sugar, pentoses and hexoses. Conversions between hexoses and pentoses take place in all growing cells during pectin formation. Pectin may also separate out in older cells such as those of fleshy fruits. Enzymatic conversions of glucose into pentoses are known (see above); one route goes through hexuronic acid (ascorbic acid, $C_6H_4O_2 (OH)_4$). The living cell interconverts aldoses and ketoses and their tautomeric structural types without difficulty. It is, however, notable that optically active hexoses of the D-series (structurally related to D-malic acid) are selected. This is explained by the fact that an asymmetric enzyme is active in the photosynthesis.

The commonest carbohydrates are collected together in the following diagram.

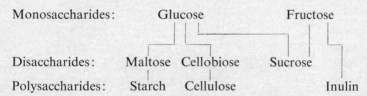

The D-hexitols ($CH_2OH(CHOH)_4CH_2OH$), e.g. mannitol and sorbitol, which occur in pears, etc., are found occasionally and also the cyclohexane derivative inositol, $C_6H_6(OH)_6$, which is isomeric with the hexoses, and is widespread as its phosphoric acid ester *phytic acid* $C_6H_6(H_2PO_4)_6$.

The central position of carbohydrates in the metabolism of the living cell is shown for all plants, both higher and lower, in the two-fold task of transport and storage. As transport sugars, particularly over long distances, the easily soluble mono- and di-saccharides are suitable. Sucrose serves specially as a storage product in monocotyledons, in beetroot, etc., but it takes part also in the general sugar balance almost everywhere. As storage products the polysaccharides are of course suitable for osmotic reasons. All these forms of carbohydrate have about the same energy content.

7 FATS

The fats (lipids) are also very suitable for storage. They are esters of monobasic fatty acids with the tribasic polyol, glycerol. As an example the formula of palmitin may be taken:

H

$$C_{15}H_{31}COO\text{------}CH_2$$
$$|$$
$$C_{15}H_{31}COO\text{------}CH$$
$$|$$
$$C_{15}H_{31}COO\text{------}CH_2$$

Glycerol tripalmitate

(palmitin; tripalmitin)

The fats are richer in energy than the carbohydrates, into which they are easily converted reversibly in the living protoplasm (PRIESTLEY 1924). In germinating fat-containing seeds only the water-content needs to be altered to cause a conversion into glucose and starch or the reverse (LUNDEGÅRDH 1914). This applies especially to fatty-acid formation.

Glycerol is formed as a by-product of the breakdown of carbohydrates in anaerobic respiration (Chap. 4). Although the reversible conversion of starch into fat proceeds *in vivo* remarkably easily, it has not yet been possible to examine the mechanism adequately. A hypothetical system was proposed by BÜRKLE (1929). There is, however, no doubt that the fatty acids take their origin from simple acids with short carbon chains and that acetic acid takes part in the respiration cycle (see Chap. 4). BARKER (1947) followed the synthesis of higher fatty acids from alcohol and acetic acid through *Clostridium kluyveri*. According to him it may proceed in the following way:

$$\overset{+C_2H_5OH}{CH_3COOH\text{------}\!\!\to CH_3(CH_2)_2COOH}\overset{+C_2H_5OH}{\text{------}\!\!\to CH_3(CH_2)_4COOH} \quad (11)$$

Energy-rich phosphates, acetyl phosphate and adenosine triphosphate (ATP) probably take part, and about this there is more in Chapter 4. Oxidative decarboxylation of pyruvic acid, which occupies a central position in respiratory metabolism, yields acetyl-coenzyme A ('active acetate'), from which there arise, via acetoacetic acid, fatty acids with long carbon chains. The reversibility of oxidative decarboxylation is, however, still doubtful, whereas reversal of the reactions from glycerol to glucose affords no difficulties.

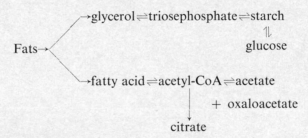

Fat occurs directly in the chloroplasts only in certain Algae, particularly Diatomaceae, *Vaucheria* and others. It was earlier thought that it was the first photosynthetic product analogous to starch. It has, however, been known for some time that the pyrenoids participating in photosynthesis in algal chloroplasts contain protein, which can scarcely be regarded as a direct photosynthetic product. It is quite clear that these chromatophores are provided also with the reaction-systems necessary for the formation of proteins. Evidence that the fat droplets in diatoms are formed only by further conversion of the first photosynthetic products is given by the fact that the assimilatory quotient, O_2/CO_2 has the value 1·05, whereas a direct reduction of carbon dioxide to fat would theoretically give the value 1·42 (from $55CO_2 + 52H_2O \to C_{55}H_{104}O_6 + 78O_2$)

C. The Mechanism of Photosynthesis

1 INTRODUCTION

It has been known for some time that photosynthesis includes two groups of processes, one photochemical (the 'light reaction'), and a purely chemical reaction (the 'dark reaction'); the latter was named the Blackman reaction after its discoverer F. F. BLACKMAN (1905). Today, however, we know that both the dark and light processes include a large number of individual steps.

That purely chemical reactions occur in photosynthesis as well as photoreactions can be concluded from their dependence on temperature. Photochemical reactions give Q_{10}-values which are very little more than 1, whereas chemical reactions give values of 2 or somehwat more. The Q_{10}-values of photosynthesis actually measured are of the latter magnitude (cf. below). EMERSON and ARNOLD (1932) separated the light and dark processes by intermittent illumination. Green algae were illuminated with short flashes of light, e.g. 50 per second. It was found that these interrupted doses of light did not reduce the speed of photosynthesis in comparison with continuous illumination, so long as the sum of the flashes amounted to more than a quarter of the duration of the continuous illumination; with a lower total of light there was a decrease of photosynthesis. This experiment was interpreted as meaning that the light reactions occur more quickly than the dark reactions and that the former therefore had a limiting effect only when the dark intervals were prolonged. By simultaneous variation of the temperature it could also be shown that the light reaction—unlike the dark reactions—is practically independent of temperature.

The dark reactions include both the absorption and the reduction of carbon dioxide, and the light reaction establishes the material preconditions for the reduction, which appears to be essentially photoreduction (photolysis) of water, even though according to recent investigations the photosynthesis of energy-rich phosphates is also involved. The light reaction has a duration of 10^{-5} seconds, a temperature coefficient $Q_{10} \approx 1$, and is independent of narcotics and of the CO_2-concentration. The dark reactions have a duration of $0{\cdot}04$ seconds, $Q_{10} = 2\text{-}3$, and they are strongly inhibited by cyanide, but on the other hand are little influenced by narcotics or the CO_2-concentration.

What has been said here about the effect of the CO_2-concentration does not prove that CO_2 is concerned as a photosynthetic component. It is in fact found also in respiration, that higher CO_2-concentrations inhibit certain steps in the electron transfer, similarly to narcotics (about the double effect of CO_2 on photosynthesis of *Chlorella* see STEEMANN-NIELSEN 1955).

The step from the highest oxidation stage of carbon to the high energy level of carbohydrates corresponds to a transfer from a hydrogen donator to a hydrogen acceptor. The assumption that water represents the donator was of course natural, since the photosynthetic production of oxygen as well as the consumption of water was early recognised. As VAN NIEL (1937, 1941) showed, photosynthesis by purple bacteria can be represented by the following equation:

$$2H_2S + CO_2 \rightarrow (CH_2O) + 2S + H_2O \tag{12}$$

It was concluded by analogy that in photosynthesis by green plants H_2O has taken over the role of H_2S and consequently occurs as hydrogen donator. Research in recent years has given here also a more differentiated picture.

From the summary equation of photosynthesis (p. 91) it is seen that at least half of the oxygen produced would come from the water. Investigations with the heavy oxygen isotope ^{18}O (RUBEN *et al.* 1941) now show that practically 100% of the oxygen comes from the water. One could of course imagine that as a result of exchange processes e.g. $CO_2 + H_2O \rightleftharpoons H_2CO_3$, the isotope was gradually worked into the carbon dioxide. A better explanation, however, is that twice as much water as is shown in the summary equation takes part on the left side of the equation and that on the right side a quantity of water appears which originates from half of the amount of oxygen in the carbon dioxide, in agreement with the equation:

$$6CO_2 + 12H_2O^x \rightarrow C_6H_{12}O_6 + 6O_2^x + 6H_2O \qquad (13)$$

where x indicates the oxygen isotope. The correctness of this equation follows in the first place from consideration of the biochemical fate of the carbon dioxide (cf. GAFFRON 1942). As e.g. BROWN and FRANKEL (1953) emphasised, the results with isotopes obtained in different laboratories are often too little consistent with each other to serve as support for the theory of the reduction of water.

2 THE PIGMENTS AND THE TRANSFER OF LIGHT ENERGY

(a) *The Assimilation Pigments*

At quite an early stage the uptake of light energy was considered to be the function of the chlorophyll, but the opinion was also expressed that it had some biochemical (enzymatic) activity. Recent work on light perception appears to support most the assumption of a mere transformation of visible light into a wavelength better suited for the photochemical process, in which the last receiver, chlorophyll a, is combined direct with a photochemical 'reaction centre'.

One of the most striking properties of the living cell is the close chemical connection between the pigments which are concerned with photosynthesis and respiration, on the one side *chlorophyll* and on the other side the *haem* enzymes. The close chemical relationship of the two was established by the fundamental work of WILLSTÄTTER and HANS FISCHER. Both pigments are cyclic tetrapyrroles: four pyrrole groups, combined through methine (CH-) bridges. The essential difference lies in the metal atom anchored to the pyrrole groups, which in chlorophyll is magnesium. but in haem enzymes is iron. Other differences are the presence of a cyclopentanone ring in chlorophyll and of a propionic acid radical at the corresponding position in haem. One of the four pyrrole groups of chlorophyll is reduced (see the graphic formulae on p. 35).

The structural similarities between chlorophyll and haem stimulated researches on the biosynthesis of the pigments (GRANICK 1953). The biochemical formation of the porphyrin nucleus (i.e. the metal-free pyrrole ring) is a relatively simple process, which probably occurs in all cells. Protoporphyrin arises by the condensation of eight glycine molecules with eight molecules of a 4-carbon derivative from α-hydroxy-glutaric acid, probably aminolevulinic acid (NEUBERGER and SCOTT 1953). These investigations were helped by the use of isotopes (SHEMIN and RITTENBERG 1951). Other workers found intermediate stages of this process in mutants of *Chlorella vulgaris* which showed deficiency of one or more enzymes. Whereas normal *Chlorella* cells are dark green and contain chlorophyll and carotene, a mutant was reddish-brown and contained protoporphyrin IX, i.e. the same complex as the haem of red blood corpuscles, cytochrome b and peroxidase (GRANICK 1953). The first porphyrin is probably uroporphyrin, from which protoporphyrin then arises.

From protoporphyrin there are two routes, one to magnesium and the other to iron. The route to iron leads through some of the respiration enzymes, whereas intermediate stages of chlorophyll formation proceed *via* protochlorophyll and then after reduction of a pyrrole ring lead to chlorophyll a.

A notable conclusion from these investigations is the identity of the reaction chains which lead to chlorophyll and haem. From the phylogenetic point of view certain facts support the opinion that those porphyrins which occur now as intermediate compounds have had at one time photosynthetic functions. Phycoerythrin, phycocyanin and chlorophyll c are related to precursors of chlorophyll a and thus are possibly phylogenetic relicts. They appear now to have taken over the functions of light transformers for chlorophyll a.

In the discussions about energy transfer the phenomenon of fluorescence has played an important part. The fluorescence spectrum of a mixture of the two types of chlorophyll (cf. p. 34) in organic solvents shows a strong band in the red and a weaker near the infra-red. This fluorescence belongs almost exclusively to the chlorophyll a. The fluorescent light can amount to 10% of the primary light.

KAUTSKY, MCALISTER and MYERS, FRANCK, FRENCH, WASSINCK *et al.* have studied the fluorescence phenomenon in connection with the intensity of assimilation. In living objects the fluorescence may be influenced by other substances e.g. cell wall substances (VIRGIN 1956). Whereas in total photosynthesis 20%-30% of the light energy is transformed into chemical energy, the fluorescence in the living cell amounts to only 0.1%-1%; KAUTSKY as well as MCALISTER and MYERS (1940) found an inverse ratio between the intensity of the fluorescence and that of photosynthesis. This can be interpreted as a phenomenon of competition, which however was doubted by FRANCK (1949). The fluorescence light probably represents a loss of energy from the system, i.e. a fraction of the light energy which is not used photochemically.

Light is transferred from chlorophyll b to chlorophyll a, which has the longer fluorescence wavelength. The transfer is by means of an inductive resonance and can take place when the distance between molecules is less than 6 mμ, and may amount to almost 100%. If other pigments take part, as in certain algae and bacteria (see below), a multi-stage energy transfer occurs from shorter to longer fluorescence wavelengths. In bacteria, bacteriochlorophyll plays the role of chlorophyll a. Since the fluorescence light always has a longer wavelength than the primary light, there is a gradual transformation into red light quanta, which are then converted into chemical energy.

The carotene which almost always occurs with chlorophyll has also been assumed to co-operate in photosynthesis in some way, either as a light transformer or as a protective material. The available data, however, do not justify any final conclusions (cf. TEALE and WEBER 1957). As the yellow pigments contribute relatively little to the total light absorption of green parts, the energy transformation which is undoubtedly observed (WASSINK and KERSTEN 1946) may play no great part quantitatively. A possible function as an intermediate carrier of hydrogen or oxygen should of course not be excluded (OLÉRISSY 1946). In this connection it should be mentioned that according to LAMPRECHT (1944) cereal mutants, which contain no carotene but do contain chlorophyll, cannot exist autotrophically.

Phycobilins (phycocyanin and phycoerythrin) undoubtedly take part in photosynthesis as light transformers. DUYSENS (1951) found a 100% energy transfer from fucoxanthin to chlorophyll a (see below, under purple bacteria).

Various views have been expressed about the condition of the chlorophyll in living objects (RODRIGO 1955). The fact that the red absorption band of chlorophyll lies more towards the higher wavelengths in living cells than in solutions of the pure pigments in organic solvents is generally interpreted as indicating that the chlorophyll in living materials is molecularly combined with protein. Investigations on the physical effect of illumination at various angles of incidence have shown that the molecules of chlorophyll and carotene are to a certain extent orientated (GOEDHER 1955). It is assumed that *in vivo* the flat chlorophyll molecules lie preferentially in the plane of the lamellae. The carotene molecules also present (p. 38) are similarly arranged.

As explained in Chapter 1D, p. 33, the chlorophyll in chloroplasts is localised in disc-like grana, which have a cross-section of about 300 mμ (GRANICK and PORTER 1947, GRANICK 1953, THOMAS 1955). A granum consists of 10-20 thin lamellae, each of which is about 7·5-10 mμ thick. The surface of the grana consists of spherical macromolecules of protein with a cross-section of about 3·5 mμ. They may possibly be spirally wound.

In most chloroplasts the grana are embedded in a protein-rich intermediate substance, the stroma; in others the stroma is absent, and the chloroplast is similar to a large granum, e.g. in *Euglena* and other green algae. In still simpler photosynthetic organisms the grana lie free in the cytoplasm.

If one assumes (RABINOWITCH 1945) that the chlorophyll concentration of the grana amounts to 0·06-0·2 M and compares this concentration with the maximum intensity of photosynthesis, one comes to the conclusion that about 100-200 chlorophyll molecules are grouped round a 'reaction centre', i.e. round an enzyme aggregate, which converts the radiation energy into chemical energy (EMERSON and ARNOLD 1932, EHRMANTRAUT and RABINOWITCH 1952, DUYSENS 1952, THOMAS *et al.* 1953).

EMERSON and ARNOLD (1932), using flashes of light of 10^{-5} second's duration, obtained maximum photosynthetic yields with dark periods of several hundredths of a second. TAMIYA and CHIBA (1949), who worked with longer flashes (10^{-2} to 10^{-3} second), obtained maximal yields with 0·1 second dark periods. The length of the necessary dark periods is thus many times greater than length of the light periods. This implies a short period available for light reception in the chlorophyll. It is assumed that a group of 100-200 molecules (EMERSON and ARNOLD believe even about 2,000) is combined with an enzyme body as a 'reaction centre'. The light flash taken up by a molecule is transferred to a neighbouring one and this intermittent resonance transfer through all the chlorophyll molecules of a reaction group acts as a delay and indirect prolongation of the primary photoreception. It can thus be imagined that the light quantum taken up by a chlorophyll molecule is transferred to the neighbouring ones before it reaches the reaction centre. In this way a time extension of light reception would occur, making possible the acceptance of short flashes of light. The findings of TAMIYA and CHIBA (1949), which differ somewhat from the results of EMERSON and ARNOLD, were obtained with flashes of longer duration, and seem to show that the photochemical transfer includes two successive reactions.

Chlorophyll a is the pigment that is present in all photosynthetically active higher plants and algae. As it has been shown that the photosynthetic light transformation ends with chlorophyll a, it can be assumed that, in combination with a 'reaction centre', it carries out the transformation of light into chemical energy.

The mechanism of photochemical energy transformations was studied with fluorescein (LEWIS and KASHA). Unlike the light transformation in fluorescence, the chemical transformation shows connections with the phenomenon of phosphorescence, which has a longer duration than fluorescence. In it the molecules of the pigment are found in the triplet state and chemically have the character of a bi-radical with paramagnetic properties.

It is not yet known whether chlorophyll reacts in the same way, but the fact that a bi-radical operates both as an oxidising agent and as a reducing agent, and thus can react with an electron donor and an electron acceptor, would accord very well with the general idea (cf. VAN NIEL 1953) that in the photochemical series of reactions the water is decomposed into a reduced component XH and an oxidised component YOH, of which the former reduces the carbon dioxide. X and Y here correspond to the donor and acceptor of electrons respectively. This interpretation was defended by GAFFRON (1944) in experiments with *Scenedesmus*. The possibility was also taken into account that chlorophyll a behaves as a hydrogen carrier, which thus forms first HX and then YOH.

Several workers (VAN NIEL 1937, 1943, FRANCK and HERZFELD 1941, GAFFRON 1942) formerly assumed that the transfer of hydrogen from water to a hydrogen acceptor was the principal or sole photochemical process. The chlorophyll would in this way exchange the hydrogen atom in position 10 (see p. 35). Later it was considered necessary to assume for the photolysis of water a redox reaction in which the chlorophyll oxidised in the formation of HX would form the photoperoxide $Y(OH)_2$.

As the photochemical process of photosynthesis operates with high energy yield (see below) one must assume that there is a strong tendency to reverse the process in the dark. Such a reverse reaction has actually been observed (STREHLER and ARNOLD). It is, however, supposed that the insertion of the chlorophyll apparatus into a complicated organic structure would have a retarding effect on the reverse reaction in the dark. It is also believed that the primary products of the photolysis, viz. $\frac{1}{2}XH_2$ (= 'active hydrogen') and $\frac{1}{2}Y(OH)_2$ (= 'photoperoxide'), are protected against re-uniting by the structural anchoring of the chlorophyll apparatus to the biological systems belonging to the dark reaction complex. The two-stage course of the photolysis (p. 104) operates also in the same direction.

The photochemical primary reaction, which contributes to the photolysis of water, takes place in comminuted chloroplasts, in isolated grana and even in isolated lamellae. By supersonic treatment the chloroplasts have been still further broken down and it has been found that below a critical size of about $10^5 Å^3$ the ability to photolyse water is lost. From this the conclusion can be drawn that in still smaller fragments the chlorophyll molecules are separated from the photoenzyme. This dimension for the intact particle is not far from the magnitude of the macromolecules on the surface of the grana already mentioned. The requirements of the other partial processes of photosynthesis are probably located in the stroma or, in stroma-free chromatophores, between the lamellae. Because of this they can easily pass on homogenisation into the medium, a fact that delayed the discovery of overall photosynthesis in isolated chloroplasts.

(b) *The Hill Reaction*

The photochemical process in isolated chloroplasts and chloroplast-fragments can be studied in the reduction of ferric oxalate, discovered by HILL (1939):

$$4Fe^{+++} + 2HOH \xrightarrow{\text{Light}} 4Fe^{++} + 4H^+ + O_2 \tag{14}$$

The reaction has also been studied by the suppression of the phosphorescence of certain dyestuffs (FRANCK 1945). WARBURG and LÜTTGENS (1944, 1946), modified the Hill process in the following way:

$$2O : C_6H_4 : O + 2HOH \xrightarrow{\text{Light}} 2HO \cdot C_6H_4 \cdot OH + O_2 \qquad (15)$$

$$(p\text{-benzoquinone}) \qquad\qquad (hydroquinone)$$

The general formulation of the Hill reaction is thus the following:

$$\text{Light} + A + H_2O \longrightarrow H_2A + \tfrac{1}{2}O_2 \qquad (16)$$

in which A is an acceptor of electrons or hydrogen (electron + proton) other than CO_2.

This reaction takes place also in chlorophyll solutions (ARONOFF 1946). The photo-chemical formation of H-ions according to equation (14) can also be used in the method of measurement (CLENDENNING and GORHAM 1950, FRENCH and MILNER 1951). CLENDENNING and EHRMANTRAUT (1950) studied the Hill reaction in intact *Chlorella* cells. WARBURG and LÜTTGENS believed that Cl^- co-operated as a coenzyme or acti-vator in the Hill reaction. This may be a case of the same general activating function of inorganic ions on the oxidation-reduction processes combined with electron transport, which has also been encountered in active salt transport (cf. also GORHAM and CLENDENNING 1951, and Chap. 6).

(c) *The Release of Oxygen*

According to an older interpretation, in the photolysis of water hydrogen peroxide might first be formed and then split by the catalase present in green leaves (see Chap. 4) into water and oxygen.

Catalase is a haem enzyme with active iron. The sensitivity of photosynthesis towards cyanide was first interpreted as an inhibition of catalase (WARBURG 1924). Later, however, this view was criticised (RABINOWITCH 1945, GAFFRON 1946), and it was suggested that the inhibition by cyanide was not a photoprocess. This criticism is supported by the investigations of ARNON and collaborators (1955, 1956), which showed that the photoperoxide was most probably utilised for the production of energy-rich phosphates e.g. in the reaction adenosine diphosphate (ADP) + $PO_4 \rightarrow$ adenosine triphosphate (ATP).

It follows from the study of the enzymatic processes connected with aerobic respiration, that ATP is an energy-storage product of the terminal oxidation of glucose, in which water arises as a by-product from oxygen and the hydrogen taken from the glucose. According to ARNON the production of ATP would thus represent a stepwise recombination of the 'active hydrogen' [H] and photoperoxide [O] formed in the photolysis, in which the energy developed in the resynthesis of water (about 115 kg-cal. per mole) would suffice for the synthesis of several molecules of ATP (requiring about 12 kg-cal. per mole of phosphate). The energy stored in ATP would then take part in the reduction of CO_2, as will be shown in greater detail below. The following equations illustrate ARNON's idea:

$$\text{Light} + H_2O \rightarrow 2[H] + [O]$$
$$2[H] + [O] + ADP + PO_4 \rightarrow ATP + H_2O \qquad (17)$$

According to this interpretation the reaction represented in the summary equations (9) and (13) (pages 91 and 102) would be split into two parts:

$$1.\ 12H_2O \xrightarrow{\text{Light}} 24[H] + 6O_2$$

$$2.\ 12H_2O \xrightarrow{\text{Light}} \text{energy-rich phosphate} \tag{18}$$

ARNON later developed his ideas still further. One can assume that in this difficult field of research final ideas have not yet ripened.

According to this theory of photophosphorylation, the active hydrogen [H] would be transferred to coenzymes (cf. VISHNIAC and OCHOA 1952), which together with energy-rich phosphates would carry out the reduction of CO_2 to hexose. The equivalence of the partial reactions 1 and 2 is explained by both phases of the complete CO_2 reduction using the same number of electrons and protons.

An illustration of the complicated course of photosynthesis as a whole is afforded by the irregularities observed in the carbon dioxide balance with oxygen production when conditions are changed, viz. in the initial stages (BROWN and WHITTINGHAM 1955, SPRUIT and KOK 1956, CLENDENNING and HAXO 1956). This obviously depends on the fact that the partial processes themselves take place at different speeds and that synchronisation into a 'steady state'

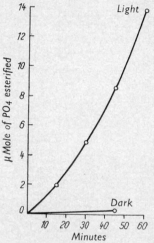

Fig. 66. Photosynthetic phosphorylation in isolated spinach chloroplasts under anaerobic conditions. The synthesis of inorganic phosphoric acid into high-energy phosphate does not occur in the dark (after ARNON 1956).

occurs only after several minutes have elapsed. This fact is important from the point of view of method, since it applies when the energy relations of photosynthesis (quantum yield) are being investigated.

(d) *The Path of the Carbon Dioxide*

The uptake and incorporation of CO_2 into organic reaction chains is part of the complex of dark reactions.

The CO_2 of the air is easily dissolved in water and partly hydrated to H_2CO_3. Because of the low dissociation constants of carbonic acid (pK $= c.$ 6·6), at the normal pH of plant cells only the univalent HCO_3^- ions are present in appreciable amount. The solubility of CO_2 in the chloroplasts is possibly increased by the phytol groups of the chlorophyll. According to STEEMANN NIELSON (1947), CO_2 diffuses through the tissues nine times faster than HCO_3^-. According to KROGH, the CO_2 and O_2 move at about the same speed in animal tissue and in water, O_2 however somewhat faster than CO_2; the corresponding diffusion coefficients are 1·80 for O_2 and 1·35 for CO_2.

The attainment of the equilibrium state $CO_2 + H_2O \rightleftharpoons H_2CO_3$ is rather sluggish.

BURR (1936) calculated that carbon dioxide becomes photosynthetically available about twenty times faster than the hydration occurs, so that in strong light the above equilibrium can act as a limiting factor.

It is known that respiration is accelerated in animal tissue by the presence of the enzyme *carbonic anhydrase*. The earlier views on the presence of this enzyme in green plants were rather contradictory (according to BURR 1936 and MOMMAERTS 1940 it was absent, but according to NEISH it was present; the literature is reviewed by ROUGHTON and CLARK 1951). BRADFIELD (1947) showed the presence of carbonic anhydrase in the leaves of various plants; but in the roots it was absent. WAYGOOD and CLENDENNING (1950) found positive results in the leaves of 22 species. The white parts of a variegated *Tradescantia* show only 50% of the activity of the green areas; and albino barley leaves have 50%-75% less anhydrase than normal leaves. Mature leaves show higher content than the germinating plants. WAYGOOD and CLENDENNING calculated that because of their content of carbonic anhydrase leaves are able to hydrate CO_2 at the same rate as the reverse process occurs in human blood. The enzyme is a protein with about 0.15% of Zn (SCOTT and MENDIVE 1941) and, like photosynthesis, is inhibited by cyanide.

Carbon dioxide is adsorbed by leaf powder. Leaves of *Vicia faba* e.g. absorbed 50 times more than would be due to solution equilibrium (SCHAFER 1938), owing to the formation of bicarbonates in the presence of phosphate buffer (SMITH 1940). The cations Ca^{++} and Mg^{++} are especially effective. The formation of bicarbonate of course increases the actual CO_2 concentration, which is valuable in view of the low content in the air (0.03% by volume). On the other hand the bicarbonate buffer is inadequate to build up a CO_2 reserve. It has been calculated that the quantities held would suffice for only a few minutes of photosynthesis.

The investigations of RUBEN *et al.* indicate that the CO_2 is introduced into the reaction chain as a carboxyl, COOH, group by the agency of an organic carrier. Some addition of energy would be necessary here, since the carboxyl equilibrium $R \cdot H + CO_2 \rightleftharpoons R \cdot COOH$ lies far over towards the decarboxylation. Earlier hypotheses about cytoplasm as the location of the carboxylation (FRANCK 1945) have not been confirmed, as it has been found that isolated chloroplasts can be brought to as high an intensity of photosynthesis as intact cells. On the other hand the cytoplasm naturally regulates to a certain extent the gaseous exchange between the surroundings and the chloroplasts, about which, however, very little is known definitely.

The investigations of CALVIN, BENSON, BASSHAM (1953) *et al.* showed that the photosynthetic carboxylation was different in many respects from the purely chemical synthesis from carbon dioxide. The investigations were carried out using the isotope ^{14}C, whilst RUBEN and collaborators worked with the less suitable ^{11}C. As the whole photosynthetic series of reactions from CO_2 to hexose occurs in a very short time, to isolate intermediate stages the object under investigation must be exposed to light for only a few seconds and then killed instantly with alcohol or some similar liquid. Usually work was done with *Chlorella* or *Scenedesmus* and the intermediate products isolated by paper chromatography.

CALVIN and collaborators (CALVIN *et al.* 1951, ARONOFF 1951, BASSHAM *et al.* 1953) found that *phosphoglyceric acid* is the predominant intermediate product in the assimilation of CO_2. The first carbon atom into which ^{14}C enters is in the carboxyl group. As phosphoglyceric acid is an intermediate product in fermentation (glycolysis) and respiration of glucose (see Chap. 4) the idea arose that it is reduced to hexose in photosynthesis by a kind of inversion of glycolysis. The light energy bridges the gap between phosphoglyceric acid and phosphoglyceraldehyde.

The next problem is the identification of the primary CO_2-acceptors. CALVIN proposed a cycle in which a C_5 sugar (ribulose), trioses (C_3), sedoheptulose (C_7) and glyceric acid occur mostly in the phosphorylated state. At each turn of the cycle a molecule of hexose is split. Ribulose diphosphate, that is a C_5 compound, plays the part of a CO_2 acceptor, which then decomposes into two molecules of 3-phosphoglyceric acid. The reduction of phosphoglyceric acid, which represents the central

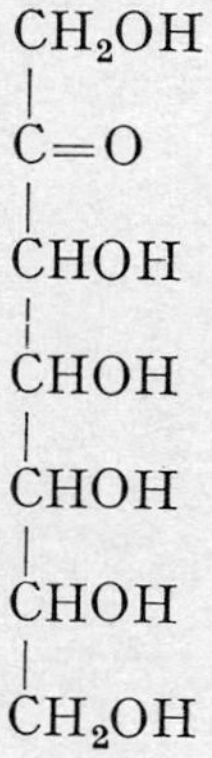

Sedoheptulose

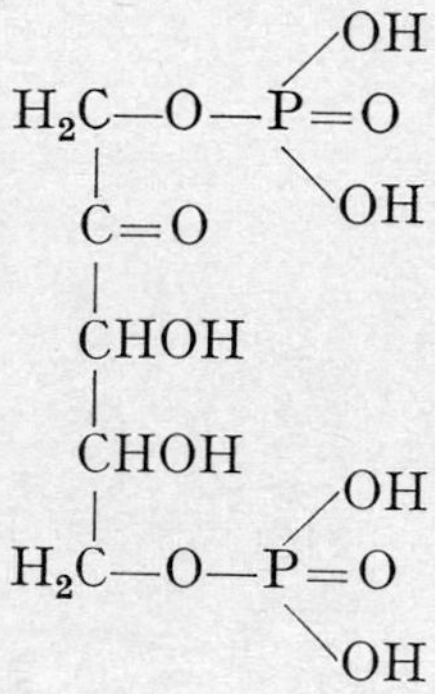

Ribulose 1,5-diphosphate

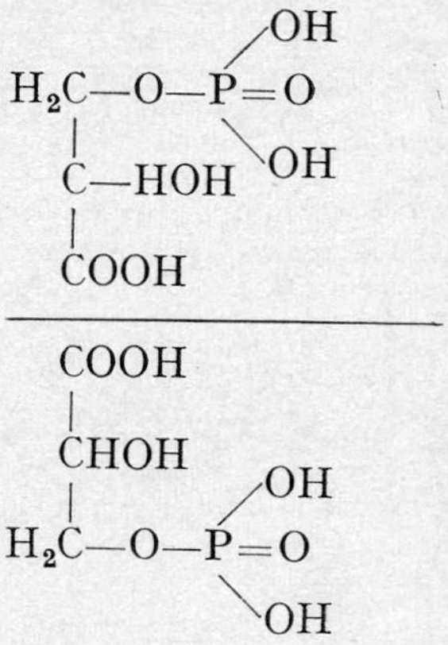

3-Phosphoglyceric acid (two molecules)

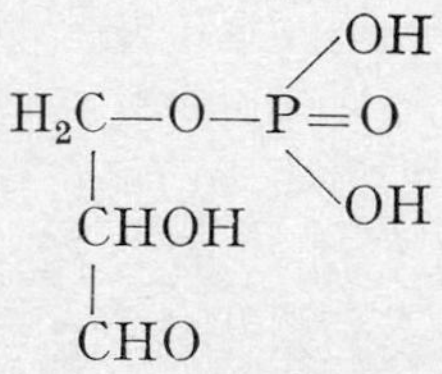

3-Phosphoglyceraldehyde

Some of the compounds taking part in photosynthesis.

biochemical process of photosynthesis, occurs with the help of reduced coenzyme (I or II or both) and adenosine triphosphate (ATP), which arise from the reduction of oxidised coenzyme in the presence of ADP by the photolytic component HX (see above). The reduction via phosphoglyceraldehyde finally yields glucose diphosphate.

The phosphate groups are separated from the glucose, according to CALVIN's scheme, and re-enter the cycle by regeneration of ribulose diphosphate, that is of the primary CO_2-acceptor. In the cycle of intermediate products, at each turn of the cycle five of the diphosphoglucose molecules are re-converted to ribulose diphosphate. i.e. to the CO_2-acceptor, whilst the sixth molecule appears as hexose.

Recent authors have a rather different conception from CALVIN's of the position of sedoheptulose in the cycle, and its participation is after all somewhat hypothetical, as also the participation of a C_4 compound (DUYSENS 1956). This scheme of the fate of carbon dioxide is indeed not fully matured in other ways also; this much however is certain, that the total process can be split up into a series of individual reactions;

and this makes possible a gradual ultilisation of the photosynthetic reduction products stored in coenzymes and ATP for hexose formation.

The photochemical conversion of phosphoglyceric acid into hexose diphosphate takes place also in isolated chloroplasts, when the appropriate enzymes and co-factors of the glycolysis are available (VISHNIAC and OCHOA 1952). It can be thought of as a reversal of glycolysis. Reduced pyridine nucleotide and ATP collaborate as suppliers of energy, and also in the bacterial chemosynthesis of CO_2, as has been shown by WOOD and WERKMAN (1935, 1938).

(e) *The Transformers of Light Energy*

It has been shown (VISHNIAC and OCHOA 1952, ARNON and HEIMBÜRGER 1952) that in isolated chloroplasts pyridine nucleotides (PN) including coenzymes I (NAD) and II (NADP) act in the Hill reaction as hydrogen acceptors. In the absence of hydrogen acceptors photolysis may give rise to molecular hydrogen, as was observed in purple bacteria (GEST *et al.* 1950), and in certain circumstances in *Scenedesmus* and *Chlorella* (GAFFRON 1942, SPRUIT 1954). A quantity of YOH (cf. above), corresponding to the amount of HX used, produces the oxygen developed in photosynthesis. It was found later that the reduced coenzyme (PNH) together with ATP supplies the energy for the key reaction

$$\text{phosphoglyceric acid} \xrightarrow[\text{ATP}]{\text{PNH}} \text{phosphoglyceraldehyde} \tag{19}$$

as outlined in the previous section (RACKER 1954, VISHNIAC 1955). Progress experiments have shown that on illumination oxygen is evolved at once, whilst the products of the hydrogenation (HX) are accumulated to a certain extent. According to JOLIOT (1957) some secondary inhibition of the reaction may thus be introduced.

The photoperoxide $Y(OH)_2$ gives rise to ATP from ADP and inorganic phosphate (P_a) in a reaction which is reminiscent of the oxidative phosphorylation which proceeds in all respiring cells. The formation of ATP in the dark assumes consumption of oxygen (that is, oxidative phosphorylation). In the photosynthetic formation of ATP oxygen is neither consumed nor formed.

There are, however, other differences as well. In the photosynthetic formation of ATP, according to ARNON (1957), nicotinamide-adenine dinucleotide phosphate (NADP) serves predominantly as the first electron- and proton-acceptor but in the dark reaction nicotinamide-adenine dinucleotide (NAD) so serves. There are also certain differences of sensitivity towards inhibitors. According to WINTERMANS (1955), in the absence of carbon dioxide, that is in default of the photoformation of energy-rich phosphates, polyphosphates are formed, since ATP cannot be consumed in the CO_2-reduction chain.

The central chemosynthetic system for dark production of energy-rich phosphate is the *cytochrome system*, which in a controlled 'combustion' oxidises the hydrogen from the decomposition of glucose with free oxygen to H_2O. In this way ATP is formed from $ADP + P_a$ at three or four points of the reaction chain (see Chap. 4).

It has not yet been decided whether a complete cytochrome system collaborates in the photosynthetic formation of ATP where the photoperoxide $Y(OH)_2$ takes over the role of free oxygen. It seems in any case to lack cytochrome oxidase. Of the

$$H_2C-O-P\begin{smallmatrix}\nearrow OH\\=O\\\searrow OH\end{smallmatrix}$$
$$|$$
$$CHOH$$
$$|$$
$$COOH$$

$+ ATP \rightarrow$

$$H_2C-O-P\begin{smallmatrix}\nearrow OH\\=O\\\searrow OH\end{smallmatrix}$$
$$|$$
$$CHOH$$
$$|$$
$$C-O-P\begin{smallmatrix}\nearrow OH\\=O\\\searrow OH\end{smallmatrix}$$

$+ ADP$

3-Phosphoglyceric acid   Diphosphoglyceric acid

$$\underset{\text{dehydrogenase}}{\overset{\text{Phosphoglyceraldehyde}}{\xrightarrow{\hspace{3cm}}}} + NADH \rightarrow$$

$$H_2C-O-P\begin{smallmatrix}\nearrow OH\\=O\\\searrow OH\end{smallmatrix}$$
$$|$$
$$CH$$
$$|$$
$$CHO$$

$+ NAD + PO_4$

3-Phosphoglyceraldehyde

Some partial reactions in photosynthesis (see RACKER 1954, VISHNIAC, 1955)

remaining cytochromes, cytochrome f (see Chap. 4) has been found in leaves and in green algae (HILL and SCARISBRICK 1951, DUYSENS 1954, 1956, KOK 1956). LUNDE-GÅRDH (1954) observed an oxidation of cytochrome f on illumination of green algae and of isolated chloroplasts of wheat which reverted on darkening.

A dependence of the oxidation-reduction state of the cytochrome system on the equilibrium $ADP + P_a \underset{-e}{\overset{+e}{\rightleftharpoons}} ATP$ has been detected for cytochrome b in wheat roots (LUNDEGÅRDH 1955). Corresponding investigations with chloroplasts have not yet been carried out, but in principle there is nothing against assuming that, in the photosynthetic formation of ATP, cytochromes available in the chloroplasts take part in the reaction chain.

ARNON further assumes that pyridine nucleotide, flavoproteins (flavin mononucleotide, FMN), vitamin K and ascorbic acid are brought into the reaction chain. In this one can imagine, by analogy with the respiration sequence, that the flavoprotein splits the hydrogen atom from the HX, which is formed by photolysis of water, into a proton, H^+, and an electron. The electron reduces the flavoprotein, whilst the proton remains in the surrounding medium. From the flavoprotein the electron goes via the cytochrome system to the oxygen of the photoperoxide $Y(OH)_2$. The eliminated oxygen then forms water with protons. The potential difference between the individual steps of the electron conductor (about 0·9 volts between FMN and oxygen) makes possible the transfer of electron energy from one or more points of this reaction chain to the $ADP \rightleftharpoons ATP$ system.

Thus equivalent quantities of 2HX and $Y(OH)_2$ are used in the formation of ATP, and no excess of free oxygen arises. Free oxygen is formed only by those amounts of HX which correspond to the quantity of hydrogen transferred to pyridine nucleotides (see above).

The idea that energy-rich phosphate is involved in photosynthesis was put forward by EMERSON et al. (1944), KOK (1947), KANDLER (1950), STREHLER and TOTTER (1952),

VISHNIAC and OCHOA (1952) and others. Many workers are of the opinion that pyridine nucleotide also enters into ATP formation as the first hydrogen-acceptor (dehydrogenase). According to ARNON, however, flavoprotein would have this function.

CALVIN et al. (1933) introduced thioctic acid into the discussion and expressed the opinion that it might take part as a redox body. Nothing further, however, is known about this. GUNSALUS, REED, JUKES et al. (cf. CALVIN 1953) believe that coenzyme A and acetyl-coenzyme A are also active in intermediate processes and that, in general, intermediate substances of the photosynthetic reaction chain are connected with the respiration cycle and thus also with the nitrogen cycle. There are also somewhat indefinite ideas about partial re-oxidation of intermediate components of the CO_2-reduction, that have misled some workers (WARBURG and BURK) into assuming a partial recovery of the energy quanta used. This would of course be possible only if it abolished the energy barriers otherwise met with, about which nothing is known.

A direct collaboration between photosynthesis and respiration is rather unlikely. Photosynthesis and respiration usually take place at sites which are completely separated structurally, that is on the one hand in chloroplasts and on the other hand in the small cytoplasmic particles (mitochondria, etc.) or surface layers. The substances common to the two processes are also subject to numerous diffusion and membrane barriers, which allow in vivo a regulated exchange both of intermediate and end products, but which also give the experimenter the means for studying the two processes separately. The accurate detailed biochemical study of isolated chloroplasts and isolated mitochondria is, however, at present only being commenced.

As regards the collaboration of *ascorbic acid* (AA) postulated by ARNON, it may be mentioned that this substance occurs generally in leaves, a fact which had already led to the idea that it was in some way concerned in photosynthesis. It may be noted in passing that the coenzymes and adenosine phosphates also concerned in photosynthesis occur in cytoplasm. A strict connection with the chloroplast structure therefore can be ascribed, so far as is known at present, only to chlorophyll, cytochrome f and the special enzymes active as acceptors and reaction centres. On homogenisation the coenzymes, probably partly also flavoprotein, vitamin K and ascorbic acid, are more or less easily dissolved or ripped away from the chloroplast structure, and can then be supplied again experimentally from outside. The same applies to the effect of flavoprotein and coenzymes on the respiration chain structurally anchored in the cytoplasm (Chap. 4). The part that may be played by ascorbic acid in photosynthesis has not yet been made clear.

The presence of ascorbic acid both in cytoplasm and in the chloroplasts was demonstrated by microchemical reduction of silver nitrate in the dark (TUBA et al. 1946).

Ascorbic acid (AA)   Dehydroascorbic acid (DAA)

The reversible equilibrium between AA and DAA allows this system to operate as an oxido-reduction system (SZENT-GYÖRGYI; see Chaps. 4-5). A collaboration of AA as a transporter of electrons and protons was suspected by BUKATSCH (1940). The reduced form is very unstable at biological pH-values.

The close connection between ascorbic acid and the hexoses formed in photo-synthesis was interpreted by several workers (e.g. WEISSENBRÜCK 1940) as indirect, i.e. lying outside photosynthesis. A series of observations has, however, shown the importance of light for AA formation (MOLDTMANN 1939, KOIZUMI and KAKUKAWA 1940, HAMNER et al. 1942, BERNSTEIN et al. 1945, ÅBERG 1945). In the dark AA is removed from the leaves. AA synthesis can, however, obviously take place also in the dark, e.g. during the germination of seeds. ISHERWOOD et al. (1954) suggest the following sequences:

1. D-glucose→D-glucuronic acid→L-gluconic acid→L-ascorbic acid;
2. D-galactose→D-galacturonic acid→L-galactonic acid→L-ascorbic acid

The relationships between light and the final stages of chlorophyll formation were mentioned on p. 36. Carotene formation, on the other hand, appears to be unaffected by light. Carotene, unlike ascorbic acid but like chlorophyll, is strongly influenced by mineral nutrition, particularly by the supply of nitrogen (CRIST and DYE 1931).

Vitamin K_1

Vitamin K_1 (α-phylloquinone, 2-methyl-3-phytyl-1, 4-naphthoquinone), which like chlorophyll has a hydrocarbon tail, is apparently synthesised in the chloroplasts. It has, however, not yet been possible to determine clear relationships between the formation of vitamin K_1 and the leaf pigments (DAM et al. 1947).

As an illustration of the many unsolved problems which photosynthesis still offers may be mentioned the discovery by SHIAN and FRANCK (1947) that certain organic acids which take part in the tricarboxylic acid cycle take part in the regulation of the speed of photosynthesis.

(f) The Quantum Yield of Photosynthesis

As photosynthesis is the only process by which energy from outside is taken into the green autotrophic cell, it is of exceptional interest to know with what degree of effici-ency the process operates, in other words to find the percentage ratio

$$\frac{\text{energy taken up}}{\text{energy content of the carbohydrate formed}}.$$

Very many workers (first WARBURG and NEGELEIN 1922, 1923) have been occupied with this problem in the last forty years.

As the intensity of photosynthesis is measured as a gaseous exchange of CO_2 or O_2, respiration is of course always concerned, and an important part of the discussions on the reliability of the methods of measurement refers to the problem of 'light respiration', i.e. whether and to what extent respiration intensity is directly altered by illumination (KOK 1949). If light respiration occurs, the CO_2 production of the plant in the dark cannot of course serve as the measure of respiration. In calculating the share of photosynthesis in the gaseous exchange observed, the dark respiration measured before and after illumination is subtracted (cf. below).

Difficulties also arise because the material investigated can react in various ways. TAMIYA et al. have shown that Chlorella cultures produce at least two different cell types, which show great differences in quantum yields. Finally it makes a difference whether one counts only the energy necessary for the photolysis of water or includes the extra energy necessary for the synthesis of reduced pyridine nucleotide and adenosine triphosphate.

The net energy necessary for the reduction of a mole of CO_2 to carbohydrate amounts to about 112 kg-cal. A mole quantum of red light (cf. above) supplies about 43 kg-cal. Theoretically, therefore, 3-4 quanta would suffice to effect the reduction of one molecule of CO_2. Taking into account the inevitable loss of energy in surmounting numerous reaction-barriers, a quantum yield of almost 100% seems extremely unlikely. A large number of investigations and discussions (EMERSON and LEWIS 1942, 1943, WASSINK and KERSTEN 1944, KOK 1948, 1949, FRANCK 1953, LUMRY et al. 1954, STREHLER 1954) have determined the numbers of quanta required as 6-8, or even 12.

Recent calculations of the quantum yield of the total course of the photosynthetic reactions are based on the energy values of the intermediate carriers, PNH and ATP. It is assumed that two PNH and three ATP are necessary to reduce a molecule of CO_2 to (CH_2O). As the reduction of a molecule of pyridine nucleotide requires about 4 quanta and the formation of a molecule of ATP from ADP about half a quantum, a total figure of 6-7 quanta would be given for the reduction of a molecule of CO_2, equivalent to the still high energy yield of 60%-70%. Most direct determinations of the quantum yield (EMERSON and CHALMERS) have, however, led to somewhat lower values.

D. Photosynthesis and Chemosynthesis in Bacteria

1 AUTOTROPHIC BACTERIA

The photosynthesis of the 'purple' bacteria (sulphur bacteria) was discovered by ENGELMANN (1883, 1888). The colour of these bacteria is caused by a combination of bacteriochlorophyll and carotenoids (MANTEN 1948), which makes photosynthesis possible in the shorter-waved infra-red (NAKAMURA 1937). VAN NIEL and his co-workers showed the occurrence of two types of purple bacteria, Thiorhodaceae and Athiorhodaceae, and also of green sulphur bacteria containing the pigment bacterioviridin. Most sulphur bacteria photosynthesise only under anaerobic conditions (MOTHES 1937).

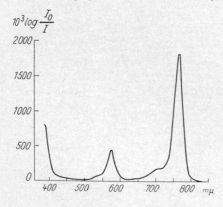

Fig. 67. Absorption spectrum of bacteriochlorophyll in ether solution (after KAMEN 1956).

The infra-red absorption spectrum of the purple bacteria, e.g. of *Chromatium*, usually shows three bands at 800, 850 and 890 mμ. In certain cases, e.g. *Rhodospirillum rubrum*, only a strong band at 880 mμ is shown. The differences may be caused by the different properties of the pigment carriers, which influence the molecular orientation (KAMEN 1956), or by changes in pH (THOMAS *et al.* 1956).

Fluorescence is also influenced by the pH. On illumination, irreversible changes are evoked in bacteriochlorophyll, which in these organisms has taken over the role of chlorophyll a in green plants. In this way the light energy is transformed into quanta in the shorter-waved infra-red instead of in the red. Other differences also occur such as the absence of the Hill reaction.

The course of photosynthesis in purple bacteria appears otherwise to be similar to that in green plants. FRENKEL (1956), who investigated the formation of energy-rich phosphates on illumination of cell-free preparations of *Rhodospirillum rubrum*, found that AMP and ADP were transformed almost quantitatively into ATP in the presence of orthophosphate.

The sulphur bacteria, as mentioned earlier, do not use water as the hydrogen donator, but chiefly H_2S. The green sulphur bacteria, e.g. *Chlorobium linicola*, oxidise this donator to molecular sulphur with H_2S_2 as an intermediate product (VAN NIEL 1931). The obligately anaerobic purple bacteria of the Thiorodaceae can also use other inorganic sulphur compounds, which are oxidised to sulphate. Sulphur can be exchanged for selenium (SAPOZHNIKOV 1947). Organic compounds also, especially simple fatty acids, can serve as H donators. Individual species utilise even molecular hydrogen or simply water. In the latter case hydrogen peroxide is first formed, which then produces sulphur from H_2S, according to the equation (NAKAMURA 1937):

$$H_2O_2 + H_2S \rightarrow S + 2H_2O \tag{20}$$

The group of purple-red or reddish-brown bacteria (Athiorhodaceae) does not select H_2S exclusively though some species oxidise it to sulphate. Besides hydrogen they can utilise a number of organic H donators. Carbon dioxide is reduced in the light anaerobically, and the necessary four hydrogen atoms are drawn from organic compounds. Some of these bacteria, however, are aerobic.

The fact that photosynthesis by green sulphur bacteria uses hydrogen donators other than water, forms, as mentioned above, the starting-point for VAN NIEL's theory of photosynthesis as an 'intra-molecular oxidoreduction'.

2 CHEMOSYNTHESIS IN BACTERIA

The *nitrate bacteria* discovered by VINOGRADSKIJ (1890) reduce CO_2 at the expense of the chemical energy which arises through the oxidation of ammonia to nitrite (in *Nitrosomonas*) and of nitrite to nitrate (in *Nitrobacter*). These exothermal reactions produce respectively 49 and 48 kg-cal. per mole of absorbed oxygen.

VINOGRADSKIJ (1887) also investigated the colourless sulphur bacterium *Beggiatoa*. It uses H_2S in the reverse way to the coloured sulphur bacteria. H_2S is oxidised to sulphur or, in case of shortage of material, to sulphate. The free energy, e.g. 126 and 98 kg-cal., is used for the reduction of CO_2.

Later, sulphur bacteria were discovered which are resistant to high acidity. The optimum pH of *Thiobacillus thiooxydans* lies between 3 and 4 and it is alleged that

I

these bacteria can live even in 5% sulphuric acid (WAKSMAN and JOFFE 1922). *Thiobacillus denitrificans* uses nitrate, which is reduced to nitrogen, and at the same time sulphur is oxidised to sulphate. *Thiobacillus thioparus* oxidises thiosulphate, a salt that is formed in the soil during the bacterial oxidation of sulphates to sulphur (TAMIYA *et al.* 1941).

Of special interest are the Knallgas bacteria, *Bacillus picnoticus*, which thrive exceptionally well in inorganic media. They utilise the high energy of the Knallgas reaction

$$O_2 + 2H_2 \rightarrow 2H_2O + 137 \text{ kg-cal.} \tag{21}$$

to reduce CO_2 (KLUYVER and MANN 1947). These bacteria take up as much hydrogen as corresponds to the amount of CO_2 reduced. This is certainly the simplest and at the same time the most effective solution of the problem of chemosynthesis.

Bacteria are also known which oxidise carbon monoxide (CO), methane (CH_4) or other hydrocarbons. There are even bacteria which oxidise solid carbon. KLUYVER and SCHNELLEN (1947) investigated the methane bacteria, which can also ferment CO, according to the equation

$$\begin{array}{c} 4CO + 4H_2O \rightarrow 4CO_2 + 4H_2 \\ CO_2 + 4H_2 \rightarrow CH_4 + 2H_2O \\ \hline 4CO + 2H_2O \rightarrow 3CO_2 + CH_4 \end{array} \tag{22}$$

The methane-producing bacteria can also use ethanol to reduce CO_2.

Leptomitus lacteus of the Saprolegniaceae oxidises fatty acids according to the equation

$$3CH_3COOH + 2O_2 \rightarrow 2CO_2 + 4(CH_2O) + 2H_2O \tag{23}$$

(SCHADE and THIMANN 1940).

All these micro-organisms play an important part in nature's economy, as they ensure the resynthesis of a number of products of decay, and thus maintain the necessary cycle of carbon, nitrogen and sulphur. The bacteria and fungi active in degrading organic residues ordinarily supply the autotrophic micro-organisms with raw materials, and very elaborately interwoven exchange relationships are often encountered. Thus the methane-consuming bacteria are fed by the methane-producing bacteria, which reduce CO_2 to CH_4 in presence of molecular hydrogen according to the equation

$$CO_2 + 4H_2 \rightarrow CH_4 + 2H_2O + 62 \text{ kg-cal.} \tag{24}$$

(SÖHNGEN 1910). Here therefore the CO_2 is used as an oxidising agent with a gain of energy. The 'half reduction' to carbohydrate would use more free energy and therefore cannot be carried out to any great extent. It has, however, been found that a fraction of the CO_2 taken up is reduced to carbohydrate, at the expense of the energy which is available according to the equation.

The chemosynthetically effective bacteria show that the reduction of CO_2 is a widespread process, which can also occur without light energy, but at the expense of chemical-reducing agents. The ability to reduce CO_2 chemosynthetically probably belongs to all cells. This property is certainly of importance for the development of the central cells of thick organs, which suffer from an insufficient supply of oxygen and yet maintain some synthetic activity. As a rule, however, reducible sugars are available for this purpose.

The utilisation of CO_2 as an oxidising agent is in effect the reverse of respiration (Chap. 4). For technical reasons it is very difficult to follow such a reversal experimentally, although radioactive isotopes supply valuable tools here, as also in research on photosynthesis. As hydrocarbons, such as carotenoids, are synthesised in the dark, e.g. in roots, it follows that there must be possibilities of reduction in the cells of higher plants, similar to those of the methane-producing bacteria.

E. Methods of Measuring the Intensity of Photosynthesis

The intensity of the assimilation of CO_2 can be measured by determining one of the components included in the overall reaction, for example the CO_2 taken up, the O_2 produced or the carbohydrates formed. Of these methods the weighing of the assimilation products is the simplest, but also the least certain.

According to the *half-leaf method*, one-half of the surface of a symmetrical leaf is removed before the experiment and dried and weighed. After the experiment the remaining half is treated similarly. The difference in weight per unit of area gives the net gain of assimilates. The values are quoted per 1 or 50 cm^2; more rarely the fresh weight is used. These weighing methods gain more certainty if one punches out a number of round discs with a cork borer. A twinning method has also been suggested (DENNY 1930), i.e. in plants with opposite leaves one is taken first and then the other. When these weighing methods are applied to attached leaves there is the danger that the value may fall because of translocation of the assimilates.

A favourite method of measuring photosynthesis in water plants is the *determination of the oxygen evolved*. Microscopic algae, e.g. *Chlorella* and *Scenedesmus*, are the favourite objects. The oxygen production is determined either chemically, e.g. by the well-known WINKLER method, manometrically, e.g. by the BARCROFT respirometer as modified by WARBURG, or polarographically. In this field there is an extraordinarily abundant literature, particularly about the manometric methods. HILL and WHITTINGHAM (1953) used haemoglobin as an indicator of the oxygen production of *Chlorella*: oxyhaemoglobin has a different spectrum from haemoglobin.

In manometric measurements it is all-important to provide for adequate stirring, as the measurements assume complete equilibrium between the air phase and the liquid phase. It is also very important to investigate whether volatile, non-absorbable materials are produced by the cells; this could completely spoil the results.

Formerly the so-called *bubble counting method* was a favourite. *Elodea canadensis* served as plant material. The oxygen formed in photosynthesis came from the cut stalks in the form of small bubbles. The speed of the gas stream gives approximately the intensity of the photosynthesis. The method is suitable for demonstrations in practical classes, but its value is strongly contested (GORSKI 1930, ARNOLD 1931).

With land plants, living in air rich in oxygen, determinations of O_2 give all-too-uncertain values. The CO_2 consumption is therefore usually measured. The CO_2 content of the air can be determined e.g. by a modified PETTENKOFER method, to an accuracy of about 0·005 mg per litre of air. The best method is to collect the air that has been in contact with the assimilating leaf in a large evacuated flask, into which a small amount of baryta solution is later introduced. After the absorption of the CO_2 the baryta is titrated, using a burette fitted to the flask. This method can be used with advantage for investigations of air with its natural CO_2 content. For the investigations which biochemists like, using higher concentrations of CO_2 (1%-5%), only the volumetric and manometric methods are suitable.

The CO_2 content of the air can also be measured physically, e.g. by means of its absorption band at 4,400 mμ or the radiation of heat of a dark body in presence of CO_2. On the basis of these principles apparatus has been constructed which registers the disappearance of CO_2 at short time intervals (AUFDEMGARTEN 1939, GAFFRON 1940, STRUGGER and BAUMEISTER 1951). These methods have been used especially for the study of the *induction period of photosynthesis*. In this period the diffusion rates of CO_2 and O_2 are also involved.

An initially high release of oxygen was ascribed by WHITTINGHAM (1956) to reductive amination and carboxylation of keto acids accumulated in the dark. An initial variation of the CO_2 factor has also been observed (see below). In general, one understands by the term 'induction period' a depression of the intensity of assimilation during the first minutes of illumination after a preceding dark period (summary by CLENDENNING and HAXO 1956). As mentioned on p. 107, these facts, which are connected with the complicated nature of photosynthesis and with diffusion phenomena, etc., must be carefully taken into account in evaluating the results of observation.

Plant-physiological studies of the dependence of photosynthesis on light, temperature and CO_2 content require a long series of experiments with graduated changes in the factors. It is technically inconvenient to work with intact plants or leaves. Especially because of temperature control it is essential to keep the object in a thermostat and to eliminate any disturbing rays of heat from the light source. The great advantage offered by working with water plants, viz. the absence of stomata, unfortunately is not available with land plants. With these one must arrange by suitable preliminary treatment (moisture, light) that the leaves are turgid and the stomata open. The latter

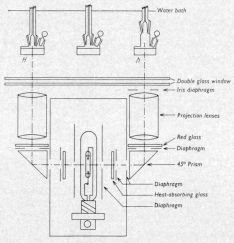

Fig. 68. Diagram of an experimental arrangement to measure photosynthesis by suspensions of algae. *H* and *h* are the experimental vessels connected to a Barcroft-Warburg-manometer, which are illuminated from below in a water-bath at constant temperature. The O_2-formation during photosynthesis can be measured by the changes in pressure of the manometer, if the CO_2 concentration is maintained constant by an excess of bicarbonate in the medium. Without bicarbonate the O_2 pressure as well as the CO_2 pressure changes during the photosynthesis. Measurements can in this case be carried out by using two parallel vessels, *H* and *h*, with different ratios between gas volume and liquid volume. For illumination a Hg-Cd-lamp is used. The filter transmits the red cadmium line (644 mμ) (after NISHIMURA, WHITTINGHAM and EMERSON 1951).

is important, as the uptake of CO_2 from the air depends on the width of opening of the stomata (STÅLFELT and JOHANSSON 1927, 1928), especially with sun plants.

It should be noted here that in many succulents the stomata remain closed after the leaves have been cut off; cut leaves of mesophytes show no alteration of photosynthetic capacity in comparison with intact leaves (BELJAKOV 1929, BAUER 1935, STOCKER et al. 1938). The process goes on mostly for hours at a time at a constant intensity.

A technical requirement of continuous photosynthetic experiments is a satisfactory mixing of the medium, so that the supply of CO_2 is not hindered. In research with leaves air is ordinarily allowed to flow at a constant speed through the receivers.

F. Photosynthesis and Respiration

Respiration is the reverse of photosynthesis. Both processes are directed by porphyrin enzymes (GRANICK 1950):

$$\text{Fe-Porphyrin}$$
$$-\Delta F$$
$$2H_2O \rightleftharpoons O_2 + 4H^+ + 4e \tag{25}$$
$$+u \cdot h \cdot v$$
$$\text{Chlorophyll}$$

The free energy (ΔF) of respiration is largely utilised for synthesis (see Chap. 4). It is the metabolic equivalent of the light energy accumulated in photosynthesis ($u \cdot h \cdot v$). Since no life is possible without respiration, this process must go on also in photosynthetically active cells. A part of the sugar produced in the chloroplasts diffuses into the cytoplasm and is available for respiration, which goes on outside the chloroplasts.

Since an experimental separation of photosynthesis and respiration is not possible with intact tissues, only the *apparent photosynthesis* can be determined (cf. p. 117). This difficulty has always hindered the researcher on photosynthesis (RABINOWITCH 1945), and it is not made any less by the fact that little is actually known about 'light respiration' (about the difficulties of the isotope method see STEEMANN NIELSEN 1955). The effect of the internal sugar concentration is also a question which has not yet been much discussed.

Since glucose represents the most usual starting material for respiration and glucose supplied from outside has the effect of increasing respiration, it must be assumed that respiration is accelerated by the photosynthetic production of sugar. Many workers (VAN DER PAAUW 1932, FÖCKLER 1938) have in fact found an increase in respiration immediately after illumination. Others have shown that the increase in respiration does not occur if the leaves have been previously fed with sugar. By interpolation between the respiration values before and after illumination the glucose quotient can be calculated approximately. Attempts have also been made to separate respiration and photosynthesis by means of inhibitors, e.g. cyanide or hydroxylamine (GAFFRON 1939).

Even though these experiments showed no effect of light on respiration, it still remains uncertain whether there is a possible influence of photo-oxidation of chlorophyll (FRANCK and FRENCH 1941, KOK 1947). There is also the question of the effect of carotene, which absorbs ultra-violet light more strongly than chlorophyll (EMERSON and LEWIS 1943). As is shown in Chapter 5, photoprocesses also contribute to the formation of nitrogenous compounds.

G. The Influence of External Factors on the Intensity of Photosynthesis

Because of its central position in the metabolism of green plants photosynthesis dominates growth and development. For these reasons light and temperature are the dominant ecological factors.

1 THE LIGHT FACTOR

The absorptions pectrum of chlorophyll (Fig. 20, p. 36) affords an indication of the value of different wavelengths; but it cannot be assumed that there is a complete parallel between light absorption and photosynthetic ability, even if there is a striking agreement, especially in the red and yellow regions (NODDAK and EICHHOFF 1939). Considerable photosynthesis also takes place in green light, that is in the region of minimum light absorption (HOOVER 1937).

Different plants give rather variable results. WARBURG found with *Chlorella* a light utilisation of 59% in the red-orange (610-690 mμ), 54% in the yellow (578 mμ), 44% in the green (546 mμ) and 34% in the blue (439 mμ). GABRIELSEN (1935) found with *Sinapis alba* a utilisation of 26% in the red (600-705 mμ), 19% in the whole region from 480 to 640 mμ and 13% in the region 400-510 mμ. Later GABRIELSEN found a photosynthesis in the green which amounted to two-thirds of that in the red, whilst blue light was used only to the extent of one-third (see also EMERSON and LEWIS 1943).

The maximum of light utilisation falls generally at the characteristic red absorption band (655 mμ; HOOVER 1937), but a second maximum occurs in the blue (440 mμ), even if green light has about the same effect (BURNS 1942). Infra-red appears not to be used by higher plants. This applies also for those Cyanophyceae which live in the surface layer of the soil (BAATZ 1939). As mentioned on p. 115, purple bacteria, however, assimilate in the infra-red. For the ultra-violet BURNS (1942) states that higher plants assimilate at 365 mμ. The failure of certain leaves, e.g. the needles of pines, to utilise the ultra-violet is probably due to the presence of pigments that shield the chlorophyll. Short-wave rays, 320-340 mμ, are however, in general, photosynthetically ineffective.

Detailed investigations on the spectral sensitivity of photosynthesis assume, of course, exact methods for determining the incident light energy. The absorption of a black surface is best measured bolometrically or thermoelectrically. The results are, of course, strongly affected by the extent of absorption and reflection of the object. The varying values for energy yields which are found in nature often depend on losses of light by reflection or conversion to heat in the photosynthetic organs or cells (see on this also SCHANDERL 1931; SEYBOLD 1932, 1933). GABRIELSEN states e.g. that the occurrence of anthocyanin in the epidermis can reduce the total light yield by 43% (cf. Fig. 69; discordant data about anthocyanin effects are given by KUILMAN 1930 and KOSAKA 1933). The cell sap, according to METZNER (1930), absorbs the ultra-violet strongly in the region 350-400 mμ. Tannins also exercise a similar protective effect (PÉNZES 1938).

In investigations of the light yield the technical difficulties of getting monochromatic light of a sufficient intensity are considerable. Light sources such as the mercury lamp, which give a spectrum with few sharp lines, are naturally to be preferred and are frequently used. Of monochromatic filters, which, however, only separate out narrow regions, those of CHRISTIANSEN-WEIGERT (MCALISTER 1935) may be mentioned and particularly the interference filters prepared by Schott. With monochromators the quartz prism apparatus is to be preferred because of the purity of the spectrum, unless one uses double monochromators, the only really reliable ones.

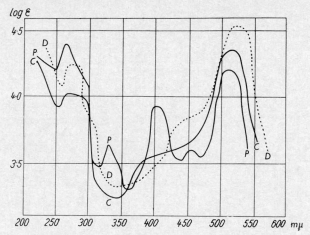

Fig. 69. Absorption spectra of three anthocyanidin pigments: D-Delphinidin, C-Cyanidin, P-Pelargonidin (after GILMAN 1944).

Red and brown algae possess pigments which by means of light-transformations (p. 103) make possible a fuller utilisation of infra-red and green-blue-violet rays. *Phycoerythrin* absorbs more green light than chlorophyll; *phycoxanthin*, and *phyco-cyanin* even more, absorb blue-violet rays in particular (MONTFORT 1933, 1934).

Ecologically these colour variations indicate an adaptation to the screening off of certain regions of the spectrum in water. Ontogenetic adaptations also occur (HARDER *et al.* 1936). SEYBOLD describes changes of concentration between chlorophyll a and b in plants which live in 'green shade' or in 'blue shade'. Similar differences also occur among green water plants.

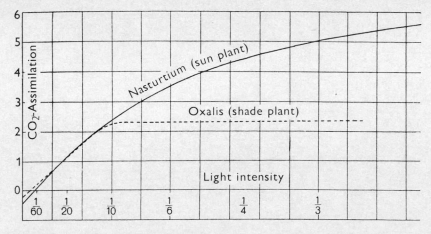

Fig. 70. Apparent (ecological) assimilation curves of a sun plant and a shade plant (after LUNDEGÅRDH 1921).

The relation between intensity of photosynthesis and light-intensity follows a 'logarithmic curve', i.e. it rises initially almost in a straight line and gradually turns parallel to the abscissa (Fig. 70). WASSINK and KERSTEN (1944) found in Diatomaceae a direct proportionality between photosynthesis and light-intensity up to a value $1 \cdot 5 \times 10^4$ erg per cm^2 per second.

The curve of apparent CO_2-assimilation begins at a point below the abscissa, because at the light-intensity *nil* only respiration would take place. At a definite low light-intensity as much CO_2 is used in photosynthesis as is formed in respiration. This is the so-called *light-compensation point*, whose position depends also on temperature. In general, the light value of the compensation point drops with temperature (MÜLLER 1928, RUSSEL 1940). The difference between the courses of the light-assimilation curves usually observed for shade leaves and sun leaves (Fig. 70), which is treated in ecological handbooks, is allied to the general problems of limiting and minimum factors.

The minimum law introduced by LIEBIG in the first half of last century was applied by F. F. BLACKMAN (1905) to photosynthesis. BLACKMAN spoke of limiting factors.

Light and carbon dioxide are both absolutely necessary for photosynthesis. Both therefore control the speed of the process: with weak light only a little assimilate is formed, even when the CO_2-supply is at a maximum; with a low CO_2-content photosynthesis proceeds slowly, even when the light-factor is at a maximum. The factor occurring at the minimum thus limits the process; if it is increased the photosynthetic yield rises until one or other essential factor becomes minimal, and so on. These easily understood relationships can also be expressed as a collaboration or balance between the production factors. The ecological application of these facts is expressed in the *biological relativity law* (LUNDEGÅRDH 1957), which is referred to here.

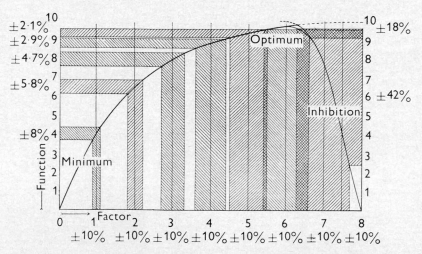

Fig. 71. Graphic representation of the biological relativity law. The shaded vertical columns indicate a $\pm 10\%$ variation of the factor. The horizontal fields show the corresponding variation of the biological function dependent on the factor.

According to the ideas of LIEBIG and BLACKMAN the retarding effect of the minimum factor should set in suddenly, so that the curves would show a sharp bend between the rising and the asymptotic branches. Shade leaves approach this type (cf. Fig. 70), but ordinarily the curves bend down very gradually. This fact is explained by interaction of the factors. Consider for example carbon dioxide: it is supplied from the air, but must be dissolved in the protoplasm and taken up by its buffers (see p. 107) before it passes over into the chloroplasts. An adequate surplus of CO_2 thus means that all these intermediate processes can keep pace with the CO_2-consumption regulated by the light. If now the supply of CO_2 to the chloroplasts follows a strictly constant speed, its retarding effect must of course set in suddenly at a definite light value. But the speed is dependent on the diffusion gradients between the air and the chloroplasts, which can reach the peak value only if the internal concentration is nil. The limit set by the retarding effect depends on a number of circumstances, e.g. the length of the transport path, the character of the intermediate processes, protoplasmic streaming, etc. It is pointless, under these conditions, to speak of a greater or lesser correctness of the various types of curve. The chemical reactions which co-operate in photosynthesis naturally follow curves of the first or higher orders only approximately, but they all show curves of convex form.

The difference between the light-assimilation curves of sun and shade leaves can be connected with the various leaf thicknesses. In shade plants, because of the thinness of the leaf, all chloroplasts are illuminated equally and thus reach the maximum light intensity at about the same time. In sun leaves the chloroplasts shade each other, and as a result the upper ones reach the maximum illumination much earlier than the lower; this causes a prolonged transition between the minimum and maximum areas of light. The cell dimensions also are different. In the sun plant *Nasturtium palustre* the ratio between the effective surface of the cells and the mass of the chloroplasts is five times greater than in the shade plant *Oxalis acetosella* (LUNDEGÅRDH 1922). The ratio between the surface of the chloroplasts and their mass is also more advantageous in sun leaves than in the shade leaves, so that there is an abundant supply of CO_2 per unit of chlorophyll. The problems touched on here should also be considered in discussing the photosynthesis of polyploids. This is usually somewhat weaker than that of the corresponding diploid forms (STÅLFELT 1943; cf. p. 81).

The small mass in proportion to the surface area makes for better ventilation in shade leaves than in sun leaves. The respiration on the other hand comes out weaker, if it is calculated per unit of leaf area, which explains the lower light-value at the compensation point. In a number of shade plants the compensation point is as low as 0·3%-1% of the maximal daylight, whilst some sun plants show a corresponding light value of 1·3%-7·5% (LUNDEGÅRDH 1924, p. 89). Thus, in minimal light intensities, the carbohydrate economy is better in shade than in sun plants, while the latter make better use of the maximal light range.

The individual adaptation of shade plants to varying light relationships also appears to be more flexible. In especially shady locations the compensation point of the shade plants is considerably lowered, but not that of sun plants (DAXER 1934). The seedlings of many trees behave like shade plants. Here a direct relation between light-intensity and dry weight has been found experimentally (SHIRLEY 1929), an illustration of the limiting effect of the light-factor.

In the crown of mature trees various types of leaf are mixed according to the local illumination. It has been found, for example, that the individual pine needles attain optimal photosynthesis at one-third of full daylight, but that twigs carrying all their leaves under similar illumination show at most 60% of the maximal value (KRAMER and CLARK 1947). In apple-leaves also optimal photosynthesis is reached at a quarter to a half daylight, but because of mutual shading they approach this optimal value only at midday on quite clear days (HEINECKE and CHILDERS 1937).

English workers especially have drawn attention to the relationship between the total increase of a plant and the extent of the total leaf area. This 'net assimilation rate' (HEATH and GREGORY 1938, WILLIAMS 1946, WATSON 1947), which is an ecological term for the food production (both for C and N assimilates), shows striking consistency when different plants are compared. This agrees with the approximately equal CO_2-assimilation intensity of the leaves (see below). These problems are connected also with the theory of 'leaf analysis' (cf. Chap. 7).

A much-discussed question is the possible *inhibition of photosynthesis in strong light*. The light-assimilation curve for sun plants still rises, although less steeply, when the light approaches the maximal value; in certain cases, however, one obtains an optimum curve, i.e. the CO_2-assimilation decreases again in strong light. If the decrease is not due simply to the closing of the stomata (strong light increases transpiration), either light-damage of the chlorophyll apparatus or light-respiration could be the cause.

STÅLFELT (1939, 1945) is of the opinion that both light-respiration and light-inhibition of photosynthesis can occur. Sudden illumination sometimes evokes an increase of respiration, whilst this effect does not occur with long-continued illumination (GRONER 1936). Other complicating processes are ascorbic acid synthesis and nitrate assimilation. BURSTRÖM (1945) found e.g. in strong light a competition between carbohydrate formation and nitrogen assimilation. An inhibition of photosynthesis caused by the storing of assimilates in the cells has never been definitely shown.

Direct light inhibitions, due either to photo-oxidation of the chlorophyll or to light-effects in the protoplasm (cf. STÅLFELT 1939), undoubtedly occur. Injuries caused by the short-wave rays of the sun's spectrum are of special concern (MONTFORT 1941, 1942). Observations on *photo-oxidation of chlorophyll* were carried out by MYERS and BURR (1940).

Isolated chlorophyll is generally much more sensitive to light than the chlorophyll found in the chloroplasts, and it has thus been thought that a protection against light is afforded by the combination with proteins and lipids (cf. p. 102). The normal tendency for chlorophyll to be photo-oxidised is therefore probably balanced by a reverse reaction. The carotenes also, according to STOLL, afford protection against photo-oxidation.

Taking into account the frequently very high temperatures in leaves (see LUNDE-GÅRDH 1957, pp. 157, 239), there probably exist in chloroplasts alternative reaction chains, some of which are more resistant to heat, though less efficient. Chlorophyll is of course, like all chemical components of protoplasm, subject to a steady state between anabolic and catabolic processes, a state which can be shifted by changed conditions. Here again a reference may be made to the scattered data in the literature referring to the inhibiting materials arising in photosynthesis, which are removed only in a subsequent dark period (cf. above). In autumnal leaves catabolism predominates; but seasonal variations have been observed also in evergreen leaves, e.g. in needles of pines and firs. According to STÅLFELT, a minimum that lies 30% below the winter maximum is reached in September.

The intensity of photosynthesis and the utilisation of light are dependent on the concentration of chlorophyll in the leaves; but on account of the many 'protoplasmic factors' present (WILLSTÄTTER and STOLL 1918) differences due to variations of chlorophyll content are often less obviously important under physiological conditions. A number of other physiological factors, e.g. turgescence (SIMONIS 1948) are also concerned. Experiments of EMERSON (1929) with *Chlorella* showed, however, a close connection between chlorophyll content and intensity of photosynthesis. STÅLFELT (1922), in a comparison of sun and shade leaves of conifers, was able to show that the chlorophyll-rich shade leaves assimilate more strongly at half maximal daylight than the sun leaves which are poorer in chlorophyll.

Calculated per 10 g of fresh weight, leaves of maple, lime, oak, elder, etc., contain 20-50 mg chlorophyll, whilst conifers (*Taxus, Pinus* and *Picea*) contain 10-18 mg and seaweed only 1-7 mg. The chlorophyll content varies, however, with the stage of development of the individual leaves. On the other hand, there does not appear to be a direct connection between the amount of chlorophyll and the intensity of illumination, with the exception of the minimum region which is important for the transition from protochlorophyll to chlorophyll (p. 36).

Chlorophyll formation is also, in a way not yet sufficiently understood, dependent on the presence of certain heavy metals, especially iron (BENNET 1945), but also zinc (NOACK *et al.* 1940) and manganese (BUKATSCH). The last metal apparently is effective in the chemical stages of photosynthesis. The chlorophyll content is strongly influenced by the supply of nitrogen. Potassium also is an important component of the chloroplasts (MENKE 1939), but on the other hand magnesium seldom occurs as a direct limiting factor. It is however known (p. 108) that Mg and Ca ions form a buffer system important in the fixation of CO_2.

In spite of the great differences of leaf construction, chlorophyll content, etc., the intensity of photosynthesis measured with good illumination and normal CO_2 content turns out to be fairly uniform in the majority of land plants. The evergreen plants and shade plants, however, show lower values throughout (see Table 2). Arctic plants behave similarly to plants from the temperate zones.

Table 2

CO_2-assimilation at 18°C—20°C, with Full Daylight and 0·03% CO_2-content in the Air (CO_2-assimilation in mg CO_2)

Plant	Per 50 cm² leaf area per hour	Plant	Per g fresh-weight per hour
Potatoes	9·6	Pine	3·0
Tomatoes	8·4	Spruce	2·0
Sugar beet	9·3	*Pinus cembra*	2·3
Spinach	9·8	*Rhododendron ferrugineum*	5·5
Horse beans	8·8	*Vaccinium uliginosum*	4·4
Dwarf kidney bean	9·3	*Vaccinium myrtillus*	3·0
		Loiseleuria procumbens	2·0
		Oxalis acetosella	2·4
		Dryopteris austriaca	2·4

An ecological idea of photosynthesis is given by calculations of wood-production in forests. According to MÜNCH (1930), one hectare of beech wood produces 10,000 kg of organic matter in a growing season. This comes to 2·22 g of assimilates per square metre per 24 hours, if one reckons with five months of photosynthesis and a total leaf area three times the size of the 'standing room', i.e. 3 m² per 1 m² of soil area. A calculation of the production by the ground flora of meadows is given for comparison. Table 2 gives, after re-calculation as sugar, a production of 0·2-1·2 g per m² of leaf area per hour. If one assumes six hours of full CO_2-assimilation per day, this makes 1·2-7·2 g of carbohydrate formed per square metre. From this must be deducted the respiration losses during the dark period; so the differences between the results for the net photosynthetic product adduced by MÜNCH for forests and those given by us here for ground vegetation are hardly significant.

2 THE CARBON DIOXIDE FACTOR

On account of its low concentration, carbon dioxide readily affects photosynthesis as a limiting factor. This has been shown by numerous physiological investigations (LUNDEGÅRDH 1921, 1924, 1957, STOCKER 1938) in which the increase in the intensity of photosynthesis on raising the CO_2-content of the air above 0·03% was determined. The effect of the CO_2-factor is of course dependent on light; an increase in the region where light is the limiting factor has only an unimportant, though measurable, effect which increases many-fold with optimal light (Fig. 72).

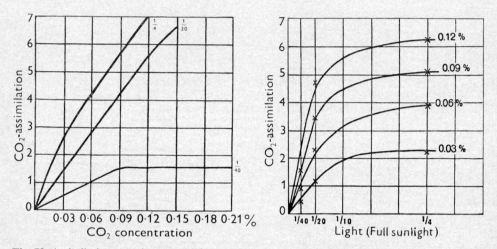

Fig. 72. Assimilation experiments with leaves of *Oxalis acetosella*. *A*-Variation of the CO_2-concentration with three light intensities (1/40, 1/20 and 1/4 of maximum daylight).
B-Variation of the light intensity with four CO_2-concentrations (0·03%, 0·06%, 0·09% and 0·12% by volume) (after LUNDEGÅRDH 1924).

The interaction between the CO_2-factor and the light-factor is influenced in its turn by temperature, as shown below. At 18°C-20°C and with strong light (1/4—1/1 of full daylight) a three-fold increase of the CO_2-content (from 0·03% to 0·09%) caused an increase of apparent photosynthesis by 2·1 times in *Oxalis*, 2·8 times in *Phaseolus* and 2·6 times in *Solanum*. Some experiments with *Chlorella* (WHITTINGHAM 1952) illustrate the effect of the CO_2-factor on photosynthesis (Table 3).

Table 3
Photosynthesis of *Chlorella* (after WHITTINGHAM 1952)

CO_2 (%)	0·0013	0·0035	0·007	0·0089	0·0108	0·030
Photosynthesis	6·8	11·5	14·6	16·3	16·8	18·0

A further increase in the CO_2-concentration raises photosynthesis still higher, but individual plants react in different ways. It was mentioned earlier (p. 123) that CO_2

has to travel a long way before it arrives at the interior of the chloroplasts. According to CLENDENNING and GORHAM (1952) the CO_2 taken up by the cells distributes itself quickly in the cytoplasm and cell sap. The abundance of buffers already mentioned of course facilitates the uptake. In this way a local concentration far above the external concentration is attained; which is undoubtedly very important for the result produced by the chlorophyll apparatus. The pervasive CO_2-enrichment in the cytoplasm and cell sap probably explains isolated statements that the CO_2 concentration of the environment is, on the whole, unimportant. With experiments of long duration, however, the external concentration must finally be decisive.

With very high contents the effect of the CO_2 on the protoplasm, respiration, etc., becomes more important on account of a CO_2-inhibition or poisoning. STEEMANN NIELSEN (1955) reports for *Chlorella* that at CO_2-concentrations over 1% an unknown enzymatic process is blocked, so that photosynthesis decreases. Investigations on the respiration system of wheat roots have shown that CO_2 inhibits the oxidation of cytochrome b. This must undoubtedly cause an inhibition of respiration which, if green cells behave similarly, could secondarily influence the chloroplast mechanism.

The CO_2-inhibition can work out in various ways, and even the root-systems of different plants can show differences in this respect. For short periods leaves seem to tolerate 20%-50% CO_2 or even higher concentrations. BALLARD (1941), however, states that, with low temperatures and strong light, leaves of *Ligustrum* already suffered an inhibition of photosynthesis at 2%-$2\cdot5\%$ CO_2. A complicating factor in the leaves is the reaction of the stomata to CO_2. The investigations of BALLARD already mentioned also show that CO_2-inhibition increases at low temperatures.

As the CO_2-content of free air only exceptionally rises above about $0\cdot1\%$ (see LUNDEGÅRDH 1924, 1957), the upper limit of the positive effect of an increase in concentration is of practical interest, particularly for plant culture under glass. Comprehensive investigations on 'CO_2-fertilisation' (see LUNDEGÅRDH 1924, 1928, 1957) have shown, however, that optimal effects are attained with a moderate increase to about $0\cdot1\%$. This is probably connected, among other things, with the fact that the conducting tissues of the leaf stalk and of the stem in general are not large enough for the transport of a great excess of assimilates. The same morphological-anatomical obstacles may also explain the different reactions of different species of plants to CO_2-fertilisation.

The gradual transition between the minimum and the maximum regions of the external assimilation factors discussed above is undoubtedly important in the life of shade plants. With normal CO_2 supply most shade plants attain their optimal assimilation intensity at about 1/10 of full daylight. At this light-intensity (about 10-20 kilolux) the normal CO_2-content ($0\cdot03\%$) is limiting, as may be seen from the strongly positive reaction of photosynthesis to an increase in concentration (Fig. 72). But at low light-intensities, e.g. 1/40 of daylight, an effect can still be detected, although it is naturally smaller than in the maximum region of light. This means that with light-intensities of 1/10 or more the photosynthesis is controlled almost exclusively by the CO_2-content of the air. At lower light-intensities both light and CO_2 are minimal, and probably very low light-intensities must be used if a CO_2-increase is to remain ineffective.

The above relationships have led to comprehensive investigations of the variations of the CO_2-content in the lower layers of air (bibliography in LUNDEGÅRDH 1957). It has been shown that the CO_2-content at the level of the leaves depends on three factors: (1) the intensity of photosynthesis; (2) CO_2-production in the soil (*soil respiration*); (3) exchange with the atmosphere above the level of the vegetation, as illustrated in Fig. 73. Factor 3 is considerably less dominant than is usually supposed,

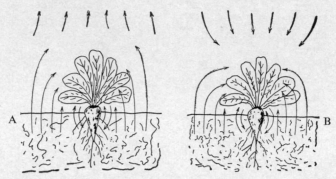

Fig. 73. Diagram of the 'local CO_2-cycle'. The arrows indicate how the carbon dioxide escapes from the soil and is (*A*) partly or (*B*) wholly absorbed by the leaves. In (*A*) the soil-CO_2 is given off in excess and part escapes into the atmosphere. In (*B*) the atmosphere and the soil-respiration together satisfy the CO_2-consumption of the assimilating leaves.

since wind is very much retarded near the ground. Similar results have also been obtained for transpiration (see Chap. 8). Thus it is that on sunny days the CO_2-concentration of a cornfield can sink far below its normal value in open air.

In the laboratory the CO_2-supply can of course be adjusted as desired. It is then found that some CO_2 always remains in the air, since a steady state is set up between photosynthesis and the air concentration to which respiratory CO_2 contributes (GABRIELSEN 1948, EGLE and SCHENK 1952). This equilibrated CO_2-value lies considerably below the normal value of the CO_2-content of the air (Fig. 74).

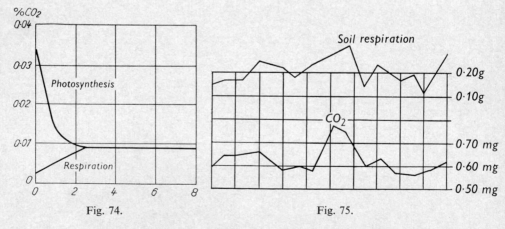

Fig. 74.   Fig. 75.

Fig. 74. If an assimilating leaf is enclosed in a restricted volume of air, a steady state is set up at an equilibrated value of the CO_2, which in this case is at 0·009% by volume (after GABRIELSEN).

Fig. 75. The parallel variations of soil-respiration (in g per m^2 per hour) and the CO_2-content of the atmosphere (in mg per litre) 5 m above the ground (after LUNDEGÅRDH 1924).

Soil respiration, i.e. the total CO_2-production of the micro-organisms living in the soil, is the largest source of CO_2 in nature, since the decay of dead organisms keeps roughly in balance with the photosynthesis in green plants. The magnitude of soil-respiration in Swedish soils lies between about 1 and 25 kg of CO_2 per hectare per hour, according to the composition of the soil (American workers, however, found higher values; SMITH *et al.* 1932). Soils low in humus produce less and soils rich in humus more, but a suitable humidity also plays an important part, which explains the high values of atmospheric CO_2 which can be found in the undergrowth of deciduous woods. The supply of nutrients also stimulates bacterial life. In the total soil respiration the respiration of roots is included. Mycorrhiza can increase the root respiration of trees 2-4 times (ROUTIEN 1943).

The influence of soil respiration extends through the whole of the lower air up to about 5 m in height. Variations in the bacterial life of the soil due to season, rainfall, temperature, etc., are reflected, although to a reduced extent, in the CO_2-content of the atmosphere (Fig. 75; JOHANSSON 1929 observed even a diurnal variation). This is understandable if one remembers that an average soil respiration of 10 kg per hectare per hour corresponds to the total CO_2-content in a layer of air 40 m high. On the coast of southern Sweden (Hallands Väderö) the mean variation during six summers amounted to $\pm 7\cdot1\%$ to $\pm 21\cdot0\%$ of the mean value of the CO_2-concentration, which lay between $0\cdot028\%$ and $0\cdot033\%$.

In high mountains, the mean concentration may be lower; according to CARTEL-LIERI (1940) and BLAGOVESTSJENSKIJ (1935) $0\cdot022\%$-$0\cdot015\%$ at 2,600 and 4,000 m height respectively. Here the limiting effect of the CO_2-factor is very striking. The ultra-violet radiation may also influence the protoplasm unfavourably (MÖNCH 1937).

In tropical rain-forest there is no increase in the CO_2-content of the air, since the universally rapid decay is compensated by the photosynthesis of the enormous mass of leaves (STOCKER 1935, EVANS 1939). During the night CO_2 is accumulated, but the content decreases quickly after sunrise.

The stems and branches of trees participate in the CO_2-cycle; their total respiration can even equal the soil respiration (JOHANSSON 1934). The chlorophyll layer in the bark, e.g. of the ash (LARSEN 1936), apparently regains by photosynthesis about one-third of the respiration loss. The roots contribute considerably to soil respiration (HÜBER 1934), and their expired CO_2 either enriches the air or in part directly benefits the leaves by way of the transpiration stream (OVERKOTT 1939; on the contrary LUNDEGÅRDH 1943, 1945).

The CO_2 in water is naturally subject to variations (Fig. 76) according to salt-content, temperature and pH concentration (JAMES 1928, PRÁT 1929, ÅBERG and

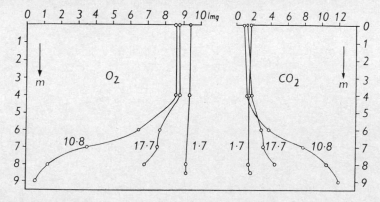

Fig. 76. Distribution of oxygen and carbon dioxide at various depths of an inland lake. Observations on three days—1st and 17th July and 10th August (after ÅBERG and RODHE 1942).

RODHE 1942). ARENS (1930-6) proposed the hypothesis that water plants take up $Ca(HCO_3)_2$ as molecules on the underside of the leaves, work up the bicarbonate ion photosynthetically and then separate off $CaCO_3$ or another calcium salt on the upper surface (see also STEEMANN NIELSEN 1952). Objections have been raised against this (GESSNER 1930, RABINOWITCH 1945, p. 197) and, on the whole, one must assume that the CO_2 molecules normally present as well are also taken up, probably chiefly through the upper side of the leaves.

Reference has been made earlier to the fact that, since CO_2 penetrates more quickly into the cells than HCO_3^-, the concentration of the undissociated carbonic acid in the main determines the intensity of the photosynthesis. It can scarcely be doubted, however, that HCO_3^-, which is taken up by means of active anion respiration (Chap. 5), can also be worked up in photosynthesis (MOMMAERTS 1940, STEEMANN NEILSEN 1944, 1947). Some water-plants, such as *Fontinalis* (STEEMANN NIELSEN 1952) and *Vallisneria* (VAN LOOKEREN CAMPAGNE 1955) appear, however, to reject bicarbonate ions.

3 THE TEMPERATURE FACTOR

The controlling effect of temperature on photosynthesis, for the reasons mentioned on p. 101, applies more to the chemical than to the purely photoprocesses; but the close interconnections of the partial reactions make analysis difficult. It may be remembered that the reception of light-energy at the reaction-centre of the photo-synthetic units (p. 104) itself entails the co-operation of biochemical reactions. Actually only the rapid energy transformation between the pigments is purely photochemical and therefore little dependent on temperature. As, however, the slower biochemical processes govern the measurable components of photosynthesis, i.e. CO_2-consumption, O_2-production and sugar formation, a high sensitivity of overall photosynthesis to temperature results. Together with the chemical partial processes physical processes also come into play, such as the solution of CO_2 and O_2, their speed of diffusion, etc.; these take place mostly with lower Q_{10}-values than the chemical processes.

Investigations of the dependence of photosynthesis on temperature are made difficult by *shock effects*, which in some circumstances may occur with a fall, but not with a rise, of temperature (BELJAKOV 1930) and which are certainly due to changes in the protoplasmic structure (cf. Chap. 1). Other complicating circumstances are the induction period (p. 114) and, especially at critical temperatures, the varied resistances to heat of the enzymes collaborating in the overall reaction.

The respiration proceeding simultaneously becomes increasingly dominant at higher temperatures. The destructive processes in protoplasm especially characterise the high temperature regions. With falling temperatures, on the other hand, respiration sinks more quickly than photosynthesis. According to ANDERSON (1944) in the range $2°C$-$12°C$, cereals have Q_{10}-values of 2-3 for respiration, but of only $1\cdot2$ for photo-synthesis. Most plants seem to be able to show a positive net assimilation at $0°C$, and cold-resistant species apparently even at temperatures below freezing point.

The *temperature curve* of apparent photosynthesis is always of the *optimum type*, i.e. it rises from a zero point, the minimum, to the highest point, the optimum, and sinks again, as the temperature rises still further, to a second zero point, the maximum. The experimental determination of the cold minimum encounters great difficulties.

The maximum is usually not sharp, since time factors come increasingly to the fore (cf. Chap. 4). The maximum of apparent photosynthesis is a point where the curve cuts the abscissa; with still further rise of temperature the curve becomes negative.

As first described by DUCLAUX and F. F. BLACKMAN, an optimum curve can be split up into two opposite components, one positive the other negative, and the two show various values of the temperature coefficient (cf. Fig. 77). In the present case, positive carbohydrate formation dominates in the lower temperature region, but respiration and other negative processes in the higher. As the positive component of apparent photosynthesis is dependent also on light and the CO_2-factor, a whole system of temperature curves arises when these factors also vary. The analysis of the dependence of apparent photosynthesis on temperature has not yet been finally made, but the facts so far available are indicated by the curves of Fig. 77.

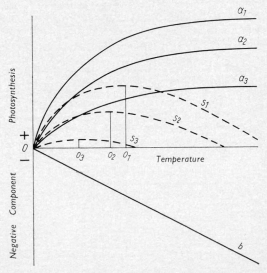

Fig. 77. Diagrammatic representation of the sliding temperature optimum. The abscissa shows rising temperature. a_1, a_2 and a_3 are absolute assimilation curves with increasing influence of the two factors light and CO_2. The falling curve b shows the negative (destructive) effect increasing as temperature rises. The curves s_1, s_2 and s_3 resulting from the combination of b with a_1, a_2 and a_3 show the sliding optima o_1, o_2 and o_3.

When light is varied, one realises that the positive component of apparent photosynthesis follows a family of curves whose convex curvature is shifted progressively towards higher temperatures as the light-intensity rises. The negative component (chiefly respiration) would show a straighter course independent of light. The resultants of these curves, that is each positive curve minus its negative curve, appear as a system of optimum curves, in which the optimum lies at higher or lower temperatures according to the intensity of the light. This is the principle of the *sliding temperature optimum*.

Similar relationships obtain if instead of light the CO_2-content is changed. In the experimental investigations based on this principle (see LUNDEGÅRDH 1924, 1957) there were found e.g. for leaves of potatoes, cereals and other plants with a normal CO_2-concentration (0·03%) and strong light (1/1) an optimal temperature of 20°, whereas with weak light (1/40) it was shifted to about 10°, and with strong light and high CO_2-content (1·2%) it was shifted to about 30°. The sliding optimum of the Egyptian plant *Zygophyllum* is illustrated by the researches of TADROS (1945) (Fig. 78). In *Chlorella* also the temperature optimum increases with the intensity of illumination (KOPP 1942). It is a general rule that the temperature optimum of apparent photosynthesis is shifted upwards on increase of light- and CO_2-factors, but moves downwards when these fall.

K

Changes in the illumination can be counterbalanced by alterations of the CO_2-concentration, and vice versa. EHRKE (1934) found in *Cladophora* no increase of the temperature optimum on increase of the CO_2-factor. The highest position of the temperature optimum was reached with a combination of strong light and high CO_2-concentration. If the temperature optimum of apparent photosynthesis is quoted, the values of the light and CO_2-factors must also be indicated. As various species, or

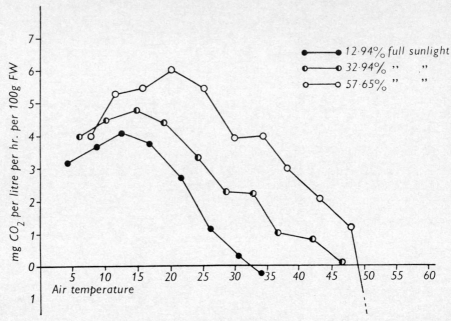

Fig. 78. The apparent photosynthesis in *Zygophyllum coccineum* at three different light intensities, showing the sliding temperature optimum (after TADROS 1945).

even breeds, show specific differences with respect to the dependence of photosynthesis on external conditions, it is advisable to take as *normal optimum* that temperature optimum which is attained at normal atmospheric CO_2 (0·03%) and maximal daylight (1/1). The term *low optimum* would then be suitable for normal CO_2-content and low light (1/10-1/100), with *high optimum* for high CO_2-concentration and strong light (1/1). The high temperature optimum thus corresponds to the ideal optimum for the respective species, though it can hardly ever be effective in nature, but may well be effective e.g. in cultivation under glass (cf. above).

The position of the normal optimum is an important physiological-ecological characteristic of the species. It is low (10°C-15°C) in northern spring plants, e.g. *Anemone nemorosa* (arctic plants were investigated by WAGER (1941)) and northern varieties of barley (BELJAKOV 1930); medium high (about 20°C) in mid-Scandinavian cereal and potato varieties; somewhat higher (20°C-25°C) in sugar beet, and relatively high (27°C) in dwarf beans (see the data and bibliography in LUNDEGÅRDH 1957). The typical desert plant *Zygophyllum coccineum* has a relatively low temperature optimum (Fig. 78) but still assimilates positively at 45°C (TADROS 1945).

The form of the temperature curves can also vary. Sugar beets give a flat optimum (though varietal differences have been observed (DE ROUBAIX (1941)), and this also appears to be true for deciduous trees of the tropics (STOCKER 1935), whilst tomatoes and especially potatoes show a sharp optimum. The photosynthesis of water-plants seems similarly to reflect their adaptation as 'cold plants' or 'warmth plants' (HARDER 1924), although EHRKE (1934) found none with low optima. Shade plants usually show lower temperature optima than sun plants (HENRICI 1921, LUNDEGÅRDH 1924, 1957, JOHANSSON 1926). On the other hand there are reports of fairly concordant temperature curves in related breeds and species (GASSNER and GOEZE 1934, WAGER 1941). In thermophile Cyanophyceae, which live in hot springs, the respiration increases with temperature more slowly than in other plants, whilst photosynthesis increases uninterruptedly almost up to the maximal temperature (BÜNNING and HERDTLE 1946).

A peculiarity of the temperature curves of apparent photosynthesis is their often irregular course. A number of research workers (BELJAKOV 1930, NEYDEL 1930, EHRKE

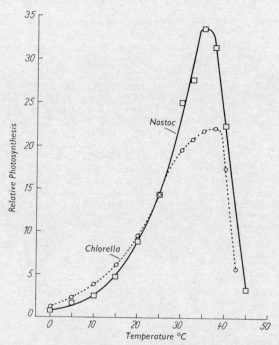

Fig. 79. The dependence of photosynthesis on temperature in *Nostoc muscorum* and *Chlorella pyrenoidosa* (after CLENDENNING *et al.* 1956).

1931, STOCKER 1935) describe undulating or multiple-peak curves, where the peaks often indicate those temperatures at which the various sliding optima occur. The fact that in the study of algae smoother curves have been obtained (e.g VAN DEN HONERT 1930) does not diminish the value of these observations. They cannot be ascribed to errors on the part of the observers. A slightly undulating course of the assimilation curve undoubtedly reflects alterations in the steady state of the partial processes.

Many workers have confirmed the fact that the Q_{10}-values of apparent photosynthesis are different in different sections of the rising branch of the temperature curve. The Q_{10}-values are mostly high at low temperatures, and then sink to the normal value of about 2. Near the optimum the values are inverted. As the data on induction processes show, individual reactions differ from others in their time-course, and this must cause new steady states when the temperature is changed. Short-period and long-period experiments, as already mentioned, cannot be compared directly with each other. If, however, the component reactions have different Q_{10}-values, one may expect temperature curves which are not quite uniform even when all experiments are of equal duration.

This discussion of the undulating nature of temperature curves of apparent photosynthesis affords examples of the danger of schematising biological observations. Still more uncertain, of course, is a generalisation of ecological facts. The negative component of the temperature curve in the diagram is actually compounded of respiration and other processes which have something to do with protoplasmic structure. Respiration is also subject to variations in the course of the day.

If one calculates from field results the net yield of photosynthesis for longer periods, the dark respiration is also of course included. An example will illustrate this. STÅLFELT (1936, 1939) determined the daily net gain by photosynthesis for mosses and lichens and found a temperature optimum moving downwards with increasing daylength, that is a different kind of optimum from that in short-period physiological investigations, since in these a time factor also is involved.

In extreme cases, as so many individual processes take part, even negative values can arise, when, for example, stomatal movements affect the picture. Experiments carried out under ecological conditions thus give little indication of the course of photosynthesis under laboratory conditions, in which all factors are maintained constant. Conversely, laboratory results can be transferred to ecological conditions only with caution.

Calculations of the 'substance-production' (LUNDEGÅRDH 1928, BOYSEN-JENSEN 1932) can however yield an interesting insight into life processes and especially the ecological adaptations of plants. A similar object is aimed at by the method of 'net assimilation rate' previously mentioned on p. 124. This method of transferring the results of plant-physiological experimental research to ecological questions is part of the programme of experimental ecology, which has been dealt with in detail elsewhere (LUNDEGÅRDH 1957). The understanding of the plant-physiological mechanism of CO_2-uptake is, however, made easier by the discussion of the morphological-anatomical facts described in the following section.

4 MORPHOLOGICAL-ANATOMICAL PRECONDITIONS FOR THE PHOTOSYNTHETIC UPTAKE OF CO_2 AND FOR GASEOUS EXCHANGES IN GENERAL

The structure of the photosynthetic organs is directed towards good exposure to light and effective gaseous exchange. These problems have been solved phylogenetically in various ways, especially with respect to a third factor, viz. the need for arrangements to restrict transpiration.

It is easy to demonstrate that air can pass through all parts of a plant (GLEASTONE 1942). It is stated that in water-plants, e.g. Nuphar, oxygen formed in the photosynthesis of floating leaves, or coming from the air, is transported through the stalk into the roots, whilst, conversely, the carbon dioxide formed in the roots escapes through the air passages into the atmosphere. LAING (1940) states e.g. that in Nuphar up to 7% of O_2 has been found in the air spaces of the rhizome, whilst the CO_2-content can amount to 5% or more. Part of the CO_2 escapes with the rising transpiration stream.

The leaves of hydrophytes usually have large air chambers and passages, between which thin layers of assimilating tissue are stretched, e.g. in Potamogeton (Fig. 80).

In this way an internal atmosphere is formed in which CO_2 accumulates during the night and O_2 during the day. These air chambers fulfil the double function of gas spaces and floats. By the exchange of dissolved gases with the surrounding water the higher water-plants, as well as the algae, can provide for photosynthetic and respiratory metabolism, as there is no intervening cuticle to prevent it. They dispense with stomata. For the transport of assimilates water-plants have available a well-developed phloem and, conversely, the small need for water conduction is reflected in the weak development of the xylem.

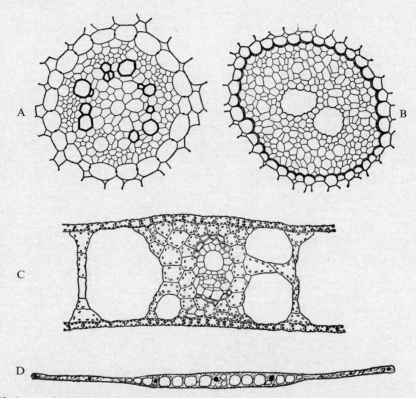

Fig. 80. Anatomical construction of some hygrophytes. A and B—Cross-sections from the vascular bundles in the stem of *Elatine alsinastrum* and *Potamogeton pectinatus*. The xylem is much reduced but the phloem is developed normally. C and D—Section of a water leaf of *Potamogeton* with air chambers, no xylem and no stomata (after EAMES and McDANIELS).

The stomata of land plants fulfil the important functions, on the one hand, of providing the photosynthetically active mesophyll cells with CO_2, and on the other hand of preventing too much evaporation in times of water shortage. The width of the stomata pores and their number per unit of leaf area generally allow unrestricted gaseous exchange with the surrounding air (BROWN and ESCOMBE 1900).

HUBER (1930) found with artificial perforated membranes that 72% of the diffusion through a free area could take place through pores of 50 μ diameter, which amounted to only 3·2% of the total area. The size of the stomatal pores varies between about 7×3 μ in beans and 38×8 μ in oats. Lengths greater than 40 μ and widths greater than 12 μ have seldom been observed. The number of stomata rises to several thousand per cm^2 of leaf surface; usually the upper side of the leaves bears few stomata. As the speed of diffusion is proportional to the circumference, not the diameter, of the stomatal pores, long openings offer greater advantages than round ones.

For this reason the CO_2-supply decreases notably only when the elliptical openings are almost closed, and this is confirmed by experiments on CO_2-assimilation (JOHANSSON 1926, 1929). The fact already mentioned, that open stomata provide for almost

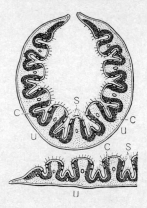

Fig. 81. Cross-section through a leaf of *Stipa capillata* ($\times$ 25). S stomata, C assimilation tissue, U lower side.

unhindered gaseous exchange through an epidermis covered with cuticle, was also confirmed by transpiration experiments. The full capacity of the stomata can, however, be developed only if there is an adequate intercellular volume (NIUS 1931).

As well as the closing of the stomata there are other protective devices against excessive transpiration. e.g. the rolling up of leaves of *Psamma arenaria*, *Festuca rubra* and other species (VREDE 1930), whereby the evaporation of water is restricted to about one-third, but the photosynthetic uptake of CO_2 on the other hand is restricted to a scarcely perceptible extent (Fig. 81). The purely anatomical arrangements for the restriction of transpiration are dealt with elsewhere (cf. Chap. 8). This field of research, including both purely physiological and more experimental-ecological problems, reveals surprisingly individual solutions of the ventilation problem, peculiar to each species. It has been found, for example, that the stomata of apple trees in the eastern states of the USA are opened only in the morning (MAGNESS 1934), whereas those of oak trees (YOCUM 1935) and tomatoes (LUNDEGÅRDH 1924, WENT 1944) are open during the whole day. The fact that many xerophytes keep their stomata open is remarkable in view of their great resistance to wilting (GRADMANN 1923, STOCKER 1928). The high sensitivity of the stomata of the Liliaceae makes it difficult to conduct research on photosynthesis with excised leaves (p. 117).

The CO_2-supply to the leaves is also complicated by the *colour-sensitivity of stomata* (PYRKOSCH 1936). Their opening movements are more than twenty times as sensitive to blue light as to red; and infra-red has no effect (SIERP 1933).

A special type of CO_2-supply has been developed by the succulent xerophytes. The daily variation in acidity of their tissues was noted early (bibliography in BENNET-CLARK 1932, 1933). It was found later that the succulents formed large amounts of acid, viz. malic acid, during the night, and sometimes also citric acid or other acids of the Krebs cycle (see Chap. 4). These acids are to a large extent used up again during the day. MEYER (1887) proposed the theory that the acid formation assists CO_2-supply, in that during respiration the oxidation of the acids is discontinued but on renewed photosynthesis they are again degraded to CO_2. It was found that acids are produced at the expense of carbohydrates (BENNET-CLARK 1932).

It has, however, also been considered that during the night the acids are chemo-synthetically re-formed from the accumulated CO_2 (THURLOW and BONNER 1948).

Data are also available to show that acids are accumulated under anaerobic conditions (BENDRAT 1929).

This working-up of acids in the light, which is found in succulents, can be thought of either as a photo-oxidation to CO_2, which is again reduced in photosynthesis, or as a direct utilisation of the acids in the chain of biochemical processes which lead to hexoses via phosphoglyceric acid. Malic acid is indeed a member of the same acid cycle as pyruvic acid, an acid which assumes a key position in carbohydrate metabolism. According to THODAY and JONES (1939), the break-down of malic acid to CO_2 takes place also during the night, thus the possibility of photo-oxidation appears to be excluded.

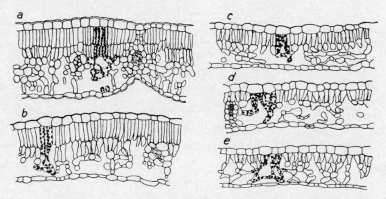

Fig. 82. Cross-sections through hazel leaves: (a) from the south side, (b) from the north side of a bush (sun leaves), (c)-(e) shade leaves with the relative light-factors 1/20, 1/33 and 1/50 respectively (after HESSELMAN 1904).

As malic acid, etc., always occur in the cycle in non-succulent plants also, it is conceivable that the decisive factor for the storage of considerable quantities of acids may even be the accumulation of respiration-CO_2, and that the phenomenon is found especially in succulents because of their more difficult ventilation. If the chemosynthesis of carbohydrates from CO_2 is a general property of almost all cells, there must be a steady state between CO_2 and intermediate products of hexose formation, which normally lies towards CO_2 but which is driven in the opposite direction by increases in CO_2-concentration. In addition, as mentioned above (p. 127), CO_2-accumulation influences certain enzymes of the respiration cycle.

Diurnal variations of the osmotic value are fairly often observed (LUNDEGÅRDH 1957, p. 249); and investigations of the acid content of roots (ULLRICH 1942, BURSTRÖM 1943) have shown that the steady state in which the malic acid is converted is easily shifted by the pH values and the cation balance. From a general point of view the acid balance of succulents should therefore be considered as a special case.

The *osmotic state* of plants also influences photosynthesis. Apart from the already mentioned regulation by stomatal movements governed by water uptake, the state of hydration of green cells also has an effect (WALTER). This is naturally best studied in land plants without stomata, such as lichens. Here ELLÉE (1939) found that the maximal photosynthesis was attained only on full water-saturation, although more light was wasted because of transmission through a moist gonidial layer (a diminution of 20% as compared with 10% in a dry layer). Long-continued drought evoked an inhibition as an after-effect.

That specific differences in the state of hydration involve no notable differences in the absolute intensity of photosynthesis, follows from the fact that halophytes (salt-plants) form about as much assimilate per unit of leaf area or unit of dry weight as ordinary mesophytes (NEUWOHNER 1938, BEILER 1938; *re* succulents see GABRIELSEN and LARSEN 1935). The increased concentration of Na^+ and Cl^- ions in halophytes thus seems to have little photosynthetic effect.

Chapter 4

RESPIRATION AND FERMENTATION. ENZYME CHEMISTRY

A. General

The phenomena of life are always connected with the development of energy, and since the available supplies of energy are predominantly of chemical type, life is dominated by the oxidative metabolism of cells and organs. The driving force is the energy-capital stored up in the organic reserves. Green plants utilise sunlight to build this energy-capital, which is utilised not only for their own life processes but also for those of the heterotrophs.

Metabolism includes *exergonic* and *endergonic* processes, i.e. those which give out or take up free energy respectively. A chemical reaction in which only small quantities of energy are released can be shifted in one or the other direction even by the kinetic energy of the molecules, e.g. by changes in concentration. Precipitation or crystal-formation are factors controlling concentration. If large amounts of energy are necessary in order to carry out endergonic processes, these must be coupled with exergonic processes. Such *combined reactions* are characteristic of the metabolism of growing cells.

The French chemist LAVOISIER towards the end of the eighteenth century discovered the secret of respiration as a slow combustion of organic substance, with the consumption of oxygen and the formation of carbon dioxide and water. The idea gradually developed that the heat of combustion also had something to do with the phenomena of life. Respiration was regarded as the energy-supplying process.

PASTEUR (1857) led the development a stage further by demonstrating the existence of organisms which live anaerobically, i.e. without oxygen. These anaerobic organisms also use chemical energy, and PASTEUR developed the idea that the fermentation studied by him in yeast could be utilised to maintain organisms living anaerobically. In alcoholic fermentation a molecule of sugar is split without consumption of oxygen into two molecules of alcohol and two molecules of carbon dioxide. In this way a restricted amount of energy is liberated. PASTEUR considered that *fermentation* might be a substitute for *oxygen respiration* and thus make possible a life without oxygen. In alcoholic fermentation the oxygen in the molecule of sugar is transferred to one-half of the molecule, which is thus oxidised to CO_2, while the other half is reduced to C_2H_5OH. For this reason the expression *intramolecular* respiration is often used for this type of internal oxidation. The terms anaerobic respiration, intramolecular respiration and fermentation are usually not sharply differentiated. The term *anaerobic respiration* is very wide and includes any transfer of atomic oxygen or of hydrogen between two molecules or two halves of a molecule whereby free energy arises.

The term *intramolecular respiration* is restricted to oxidoreductions within individual molecules, in which this process, however, proceeds mostly step by step through intermediate stages.

The term *fermentation* is associated with the reaction products, e.g. alcoholic fermentation, lactic fermentation, acetic fermentation, etc. Alcoholic fermentation is not only a characteristic of yeast, but occurs extensively in higher plants also as anaerobic respiration.

The physiological importance of respiration is not quite clear. The synthesis of compounds with higher energy content than the sugars formed in photosynthesis naturally requires the co-operation of exergonic processes. It is not obvious, however, why a mature 'resting' cell must respire, for no syntheses are taking place, since protoplasm, cell walls, etc., are already there. None the less, respiration continues in every living cell, even in organisms such as plants which normally remain at the same temperature as their surroundings.

It is generally assumed that the protoplasmic structure is 'used up' and must be continually renewed. Investigations with radioactive isotopes usually show a lively internal rearrangement of the atoms, e.g. of N or P, in mature organs. This, however, may be due to the system of reversible equilibria which holds together a multiplicity of chemical building-stones of protoplasm; in these dynamic equilibria the atoms move to and fro without external loss of energy. The general high reactivity of protoplasm naturally involves a danger of unavoidable losses, which must be overcome by release of a certain basal quantity of 'idling energy'.

To live means change and movement, and it is generally difficult to combine the idea of absolute rest with that of life. Even in resting seeds, processes are usually taking place which facilitate germination. Apparently-resting parenchyma cells are often concerned with transport which uses energy, and so on. From the biochemical point of view it should be remembered that in every living cell oxidisable materials are present which cannot remain completely screened off. Thus without stored reserves even 'resting' cells would be destroyed as a result of autolysis, in which first the soluble carbohydrates, and finally the proteins, disappear. It may thus be surmised that the basal energy turnover protects a number of sensitive building materials and enzymes from decomposition. The general tendency to a lowering of the energy level is thus overcome.

The 'luxury respiration' observed when the cell has a large excess of respirable material at its disposal, may be regarded as the counterpart of the basal respiration which is a last resort. If, for example, mature leaves are allowed to float on sugar solution their respiration is markedly increased without anything being anabolised in consequence. A similar luxury respiration can be evoked in most tissues and is evidence of the high capability of the respiratory mechanism. If the anabolic possibilities are blocked, the free energy disappears as heat, as shown for example by seedlings.

According to DOYER (1915), during the first active germination stages only a minor part of the respiratory energy is lost as heat, but later the loss may rise to 50%. Similar calculations on the utilisation of energy were later made with fungi. It appears doubtful whether the germination can derive any appreciable benefit from the heat developed, since the greater part is lost to the medium. On the other hand it is not unlikely that the temperature increase of 10°C or more in *Arum* spadices hastens their growth.

Measurements in various zones of root tips have shown that the intensity of respiration is increased with the degree of new formation of building materials for the cells (LUNDEGÅRDH 1940, WANNER 1944). In the lower zone of wheat roots, 30 mm long and partly covered with root hairs, the respiration is three times as fast per unit of dry weight as in the upper zones. An investigation of the whole plant and its organs shows likewise that the intensity of respiration decreases with increasing age, that is with diminishing growth (KIDD et al. 1921). As indicated above, active transport in mature organs still requires a certain expenditure of energy (see also Chap. 6).

With the exception of the very rarely encountered obligate anaerobic bacteria, growth and multiplication are universally connected with oxygen respiration. This applies even to yeast, which can of course live without oxygen, but in these circumstances ceases growth and multiplication.

The first stages of germination of many seeds can proceed without oxygen, but oxygen is necessary for further development. The same applies to roots and root hairs, which do not continue to grow if the oxygen supply is cut off, even though the cells can still live for a considerable time. Usually the growing point dies first, since its oxygen requirement is the greatest.

Mature organs appear to withstand oxygen deficiency longer. Apples and pears, for example, can be preserved for months in pure hydrogen without damage. It has often been supposed that the inner parts of fleshy fruits, cacti, etc., also normally lead an anaerobic life. Considering the rapid mobility of O_2 and CO_2 in aqueous media (cf. p. 107), however, these data are somewhat doubtful. In marsh plants a certain amount of gaseous exchange is in fact provided for by air channels. If parts of plants survive periods of anaerobic existence, this is usually linked with an ability to eliminate harmful fermentation products. It is certainly biochemically possible to direct anaerobic respiration along paths which end in less poisonous products.

B. Enzymes and Enzyme Reactions

1 THE PROPERTIES OF ENZYMES

(The enzymes mentioned in this section are treated in greater detail in sections 2 and 3.)

(a) *General Chemical Characteristics*

As mentioned above, there is in every living cell a certain unavoidable tendency towards autoxidation, which however is reduced to a minimum by the protection of the oxidisable components of the biochemical mechanism by *energy barriers*. These are effectively overcome only with the collaboration of special catalysts, the oxidative enzymes. In open combustion the material requires to be heated until the kinetic energy of the molecules overcomes the barriers. In the laboratory the wet combustion which is characteristic of life can be managed by the addition of inorganic catalysts. In cells the *oxidising and reducing enzymes* produce this result.

A second large group of organic catalysts is the *hydrolysing enzymes*. They facilitate the numerous processes which serve to introduce water into or remove it from organic compounds. Examples of such processes are the combining of amino acids to form peptides and proteins, the condensation of glucose to starch and cellulose, and the inversion of these processes. Whereas the oxidising and reducing enzymes mediate in processes that are connected with considerable transfers of energy, with hydrolytic processes the energy transfers are smaller. Whilst the oxidising and reducing enzymes supply metabolism with energy, the hydrolysing enzymes are more concerned with the formation of cellular structure and shape.

The enzymes are thus catalysts which reduce the activation energy of a substrate so that even at ordinary temperatures the processes go on with measurable speed. The enzyme is not used up by the reaction catalysed by it, but can take part in the chemical equilibria as an intermediary, according to the following scheme:

$$A + enzyme \rightleftharpoons A \cdot enzyme$$
and   (26)
$$A \cdot enzyme + B \rightleftharpoons A \cdot B + enzyme$$

Here A and B are two substrates which because of the energy barrier cannot react directly but only through the intermediary of the enzyme. The phenomenon is mostly explained by reactive groups on the surface of the enzyme molecule having affinity both for A and for B and thus bringing them into closer contact with each other.

As WILLSTÄTTER (1928) showed, an enzyme molecule consists of a larger carrier, the *apoenzyme*, ordinarily a protein, and a smaller *prosthetic* group, or *coenzyme*. The prosthetic group is the actual activator or accelerator of the enzyme, whilst the apoenzyme seems to have the function of attracting the substrate and holding it fast during the reaction. Specificity is usually so pronounced that only one of several stereoisomeric forms is selected. The coenzyme then attacks the firmly held substrate. Apoenzyme and coenzyme together form the *holoenzyme*.

Just as little is known with certainty about the molecular configuration of an enzyme as about other protein molecules. Enzymes, however, have often been isolated in a crystalline state, first by SUMNER (1926; urease) and NORTHRUP (1930; pepsin). Later a number of enzymes such as trypsin, amylase, papain, peroxidase, cytochrome c, etc., have been crystallised.

Unlike the apoenzymes, the coenzymes have been studied in detail. Their chemical constitution is often known and the number of coenzymes is typically much more restricted than the number of apoenzymes, i.e. one and the same prosthetic group can be the activator of a number of different enzymes. Thus *protohaem IX* is the prosthetic group of catalase, peroxidase and cytochrome b, and *phosphopyridine nucleotides* are the prosthetic groups of a number of enzymes which transfer protons and electrons in the first stages of respiration and fermentation, as well as in photosynthesis (Chap. 3). Similarly versatile coenzymes are the *flavins*, which also co-operate in a number of oxidising and reducing enzymes. In these cases one can speak of *enzyme families*. Thiamine pyrophosphate (TTP) (in carboxylases), ergosterin (in sucrase), etc., have somewhat more restricted functions.

Metal atoms can also occur as prosthetic groups, e.g. copper in polyphenol oxidases (tyrosinase, ascorbic oxidase). In other cases metal atoms appear to play an activating role together with organic activators, e.g. molybdenum together with flavin in nitrate-reducing enzymes. Manganese is well known as an activator of arginase and, together with magnesium, of various other enzyme processes.

The method of operation of the inorganic ions is still a little-investigated sphere of enzyme research. There may, for example, be a general activating effect of cations and anions and this may be partly connected with transitory linkages similar to those between enzymes and substrates. In addition, ions may facilitate electro-chemically the transfer of electrons between two molecules (cf. Chap. 6). The effect of metal ions

as activators of enzymes makes an interesting background for the long known phenomenon of 'trace elements' (see Chap. 7).

Linkages, Dissociation and Sensitivity to pH

The linkage between the protein and the coenzyme is usually dissociatable. An early
example of this is the 'old yellow ferment' that THEORELL (1935) was able to split by
electrodialysis into the protein and the flavin group. When mixed together, the
components recombine. Similar splittings and recombinations were later achieved
with protohaematin enzymes. Cleavage into apoenzyme and coenzyme can also be
carried out with concentrated ammonium sulphate at a low pH (2-3).

Compounds of apoenzyme and coenzyme, which are held together by bivalent metal
atoms as 'cement', are also usually dissociatable. The carboxylases e.g. have been
shown to be TPP–magnesium–proteins. BERGER *et al.* (1946) give the dissociation
constant of the hexokinase, a magnesium protein, as $2·6 \times 10^{-3}$. A similar cementing
effect is shown by calcium ions on the pectins in the primary cell wall (Chap. 2). Toxic
effects of heavy-metal ions on the protoplasm (SEIFRIZ and URAGUCHI 1941) may also
often be connected with similar, but in these cases harmful, compounds of protoplasmic
components which during life are freely mobile.

The linkage between apoenzyme and coenzyme is not always ionic. SH-groups of
apoenzymes often appear to serve as links. Single or multiple linkages between protein
and prosthetic groups can also be made through carboxyl groups. In the covalent
linkage between apoenzyme and coenzyme the electrolytic dissociation of the holoenzyme is ordinarily an important characteristic and usually determines the activity.

In the enzyme families mentioned, where a prosthetic group is combined with different
proteins, one finds a range of different dissociation constants and correspondingly
a varying sensitivity to changes in pH. As regards the oxidising and reducing enzymes

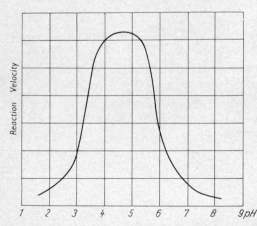
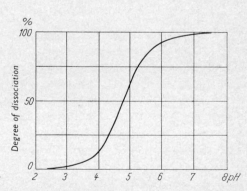

Fig. 83. The pH curve of sucrase activity.   Fig. 84. The dissociation curve of β-indolyl-
                                                     acetic acid (pK = 4·75).

one must reckon usually with two dissociation constants, one for the oxidised, the
other for the reduced, state. The ratio between these constants determines the oxidation-reduction potential of the enzyme. These relationships have been studied with
Fe-porphyrin enzymes, phosphopyridine enzymes and flavin enzymes. As regards the
first-mentioned, the oxidation-reduction potential increases in the following order:
(1) haemoglobin (no transfer of electrons, only oxygenation by addition of O_2);

(2) cytochrome c (electron transfer between two intermediary systems); (3) cytochrome oxidase (electron transfer to molecular oxygen).

The general form of an activity curve of an enzyme determined by the pH value is reproduced in Fig. 83 for sucrase. It can be related to the ionisation of acidic and basic groups and is obviously due to the fact that the reactivity of the enzyme is reduced by ionisation. Similar dissociation curves also give proteins a similar relationship between pH and solubility. The pH-sensitivity extends also to the stability of the enzyme, a fact that finds its expression in the many arrangements of the living cell for keeping the pH value constant. The stability mostly diminishes in the ionised form of the enzyme, which is thus less suitable for the determination of activity.

The hydrogen-ion concentration also influences the linkage between enzyme and substrate, as was first shown by SÖRENSEN. Most hydrolytic enzymes have their maximum activity in the acid region (pH 4-7; cf. Fig. 83), whilst the oxidoreducing enzymes have their highest activity in the alkaline region or at the neutral point. The link between apoenzyme and coenzyme has already been mentioned as a pH-sensitive point. The transitory linkage between the holoenzyme and the substrate can also be pH-sensitive.

In certain circumstances cation exchange at the surface of the protein carrier can displace an equilibrium. It has been shown that proteins combine preferably with large anions (LARDY and ELVEHJEM 1945). In this way the dissociation of the amino and carboxyl groups is changed, whereby the attack of hydrolytic enzymes can be made easier or more difficult according to the pH prevailing. Since within the range of 2 pH units the dissociation can vary by 70%-90% (cf. Fig. 84), it is understandable that even small changes in acidity can greatly influence enzymatic processes. In experiments with dried yeast, in which the enzyme system is not protected, alcoholic fermentation shows a sharp optimum at pH = 6·3. Living yeast, on the other hand, shows a broad optimum, at pH 2-8. The difference is connected with the strong buffering ability of the living cell which has already been emphasised several times. Hence the suggestion that the pH value may be a determining factor in the differentiation of tissues (PFEIFFER 1925).

Very important for the maintenance of enzymatic activity is of course also the preservation of the correct linkage between apoenzyme and coenzyme. As already mentioned, SH-groups often take part in this linkage. This confers on many enzymes an important sensitivity towards oxidation, which converts the sulphydryl groups into S—S linkages. The biochemical mechanism of the cell usually has available compounds which screen off these sensitive points of the enzyme molecule. One such protective compound is the tripeptide from glutamic acid, cystëine and glycine, viz. *glutathione*:

$$HOOC \cdot \underset{\underset{\displaystyle NH_2}{|}}{CH} \cdot CH_2 \cdot CH_2 \cdot CO \cdot NH \cdot \underset{\underset{\displaystyle HS \cdot CH_2}{|}}{CH} \cdot CO \cdot NH \cdot CH_2 \cdot COOH$$

Glutathione

Many enzymes which participate in carbohydrate metabolism are inhibited by materials which react with SH-groups and can be reactivated by addition of glutathione or cystëine. According to BARRON and SINGER (1945), the following enzymes are sensitive towards oxidation of SH-groups: (1) enzymes which oxidise or decarboxylate pyruvic acid; (2) dehydrogenases which are active in the Krebs cycle (see below);

(3) phosphorylases; (4) hexokinases; and (5) transaminases. Cytochrome c apparently contains six sulphur atoms, two as methionine and the others probably as cystëine. Less sensitive with respect to SH-groups are *inter alia* cytochrome oxidase, catalase, pepsin, trypsin and carbonic anhydrase. The inactivation of enzymes with sensitive SH-groups takes place according to the following equation:

$$\text{2 enzyme—SH} \underset{\text{reduction}}{\overset{\text{oxidation}}{\rightleftharpoons}} \text{enzyme—S—S—enzyme} + 2H \qquad (27)$$

active   inactive

The oxidation can take place in various ways, e.g. by quinones, and the reduction, as already mentioned, by cystëine or glutathione. To avoid inactivation of the enzymes these substances are therefore usually added when homogenising tissues.

Cystëine may, however, inhibit certain necessary syntheses, e.g. of pantothenic acid in *Escherichia coli*; in this way an enzyme is blocked which takes part in the decarboxylation of aspartic acid to β-alanine (RAVEL and SHIVE 1946). Most investigators who have worked on the effect of antibiotics are of the opinion that many of them inactivate key enzymes by oxidising SH-groups (HOFFMAN-OSTENHOF 1947).

The *molecular weight of enzymes*, like those of most proteins, is very high, although there are notable differences. Only a few examples are given here. Adenosine triphosphatase, which cleaves phosphate from ATP, has a weight of more than 1 million. According to GLICK *et al.* (1945), such an enzyme is contained in wheat germ. Crystalline phosphorylase, which condenses D-glucose to starch, has a molecular weight of 340,000-400,000, whilst enolase (a magnesium protein) weighs only 62,000 and horseradish peroxidase 44,100. Very low molecular weights are shown by cytochrome c (13,000-15,000) and ribonuclease (15,000), whose apoenzyme is a protein of the albumin type. The molecule of ribonuclease has a remarkably symmetrical construction. Otherwise the spiral structure given for certain proteins may occur also in enzymes although most data indicate more compact forms.

(b) *Speed of Reaction of the Enzymes*

According to the law of mass action the speed of a reaction is dependent on the concentration (activity) of the reacting components. If two components A and B react with each other and the components C and D result, the speed of reaction can be represented as follows:

$$A + B \rightleftharpoons C + D$$
$$K = \frac{[C] \cdot [D]}{[A] \cdot [B]} \qquad (28)$$

where the square brackets indicate concentrations and K is the equilibrium constant. With a large excess of one of the components of the reaction, e.g. A, the speed of the reaction in the direction towards $C + D$ is determined exclusively by variations in the concentration of B. This gives a straight-line relationship between the concentration of B and the speed of reaction, or, as it is usually expressed, the reaction is 'of the zero order'. This occurs in enzyme reactions, when e.g. the substrate is present in great excess. The speed is then determined exclusively by the concentration of the enzyme. Concentration of the enzyme and reaction products vary, then, according to a straight line.

If, however, the components are present in limited amounts which diminish during the reaction, the speed of reaction changes into a convex curve; which shows that the speed at any moment is proportional to the decreasing concentration of the reaction components. If the original concentration of the reacting components is shown as a, and the concentration of the reaction resultants as x, the following equation of a reaction of the first order is obtained:

$$\frac{dx}{dt} = K\,(a-x) \tag{29}$$

in which K is the reaction constant and t is the time.

After integration one gets the algebraic equation:

$$K \cdot t = \ln \frac{a}{a-x} \tag{30}$$

From this equation it follows that the half-value, i.e. the time for a 50% diminution in a, is in inverse proportion to the speed of reaction, which facilitates exact measurements of the reaction constants.

Most enzyme reactions roughly follow a reaction of the first order. If the substrate concentration is initially very high, the reaction begins with zero order, and changes gradually to a reaction of the first order. At times, if several components participate in the reaction, the reactions are of the second or higher orders.

MICHAELIS and MANTEN (1913) proposed to take as a measure of the speed of reaction those concentrations of substrate at which the reaction reaches 50% of its maximum speed. This value is called the Michaelis constant or K_m and is expressed in moles per litre. From the definition it follows that the activity of individual enzymes can be expressed in values of this constant. Very active enzymes are thus characterised by low Michaelis constants and less active enzymes by higher values, as shown in Table 4:

Table 4

Michaelis Constants of some Enzymes

Enzyme	Substrate	K_m (moles per litre)
Maltase	Maltose	$2 \cdot 1 \times 10^{-1}$
Urease	Urea	$2 \cdot 5 \times 10^{-2}$
β-Glucosidase	Salicin	$2 \cdot 6 \times 10^{-2}$
Sucrase (Saccharase)	Sucrose (Saccharose)	$2 \cdot 8 \times 10^{-2}$
Phosphatase	Glycerophosphate	$3 \cdot 0 \times 10^{-3}$
Zymase	Glucose	$6 \cdot 0 \times 10^{-3}$
Lipase	Ethyl-D-mandelate	$5 \cdot 0 \times 10^{-4}$
Xanthine oxidase	Adenine, Xanthine	$3 \cdot 0 \times 10^{-5}$
Lactic dehydrogenase	Pyruvic acid	$3 \cdot 5 \times 10^{-5}$

Oxidoreducing enzymes generally give lower values for K_m than hydrolytic enzymes. For glucose dehydrogenase, which operates with the coenzyme NAD, $K_m = 1 \cdot 5 \times 10^{-5}$. The practical determination of the Michaelis constants is usually troublesome, since the activity curves, as already mentioned, follow a mathematical formula only approximately. Correct pH values are of course indispensable. To the experimental difficulties of measuring the speed of enzyme reactions are also added the inactivation of the enzyme which usually increases in the course of the reaction. In enzymatic oxidation the oxidase itself is gradually inactivated. This inactivation may be caused by oxidation of active SH-groups (cf. above), which appears to happen much more easily *in vitro* than in the living cell. Apparent deviations from the law of mass action can also occur due to the formation of an irreversible complex between enzyme and substrate.

Our knowledge of enzyme reactions is largely restricted to observations *in vitro*, and how far the processes studied by biochemists play a part *in vivo* is a delicate point. Only among oxidising and reducing enzymes, whose degree of oxidation can be followed by direct spectrophotometric measurement on the living object, have numerous enzyme reactions been studied *in vivo*. This is possible because the oxidised and reduced states of all the enzymes taking part in aerobic respiration (that is, phosphopyridine nucleotide, flavoprotein and haem enzymes) are distinguished by different characteristic absorption spectra. All these enzymes, their concentration and their state of oxidation, can thus be identified in the living cell and followed quantitatively.

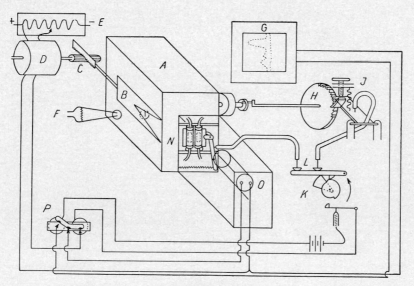

Fig. 85. A recording spectrophotometer. Diagrammatic. *A*. Grid monochromator, *B*. Triangular iris, which is regulated by the balancing motor *D* and the crank *C*, *E*. Compensation arrangement for *D*, *F* Light source, *G*. Recording millivoltmeter, *H* and *J*. Arrangement for automatic change of wavelengths, which is driven by the synchronous motor *K* and the lever *L* driven by it, *N*. Slide holder for the sample under investigation and the control substance, which change places synchronously with the arrangement *HJ*, *O*. Photomultiplier, *P*. Relay for automatically changing switching of the compensation arrangement *B C D* and the recording millivoltmeter.

The instrument records in 1-4 seconds the control substance and the sample in turn for distinct intervals of wavelength (e.g. 1 or 2 mμ), and the compensating arrangement eliminates the spectral sensitivity curve of the photocell (after LUNDEGÅRDH 1956).

On the other hand it is surprising how resistant many enzymes are against homogenisation of the cells as well as against techniques for extraction and purification. Another surprising fact is the good agreement between data on the speed of enzyme

L

reactions *in vitro* and in the living tissues. This applies to the reaction speed of cyto-chrome oxidase (LUNDEGÅRDH 1952, 1954; cf. earlier data in BARRON 1943).

One may perhaps express the view that the enzymes in this case maintain their reactivity at about the same level and that after homogenisation they do not lose their molecular structural integrity. Usually, however, structural degradation takes place on homogenisation of the enzyme systems which in the living cell co-operates closely. The total activity of the aerobic respiration in homogenates may sink to one-tenth on this account. Studies of enzyme systems dependent on structure lead to the conclusion that certain enzymes, e.g. cytochrome oxidase and cytochrome b (cf. LUNDEGÅRDH 1958), are contained as multimolecular groups within the protoplasmic or mito-chondrial structure and so lose much of their activity in true solution. This does not happen with easily soluble enzymes, less strongly bound to the cell structures, e.g. cytochrome c, peroxidase and some flavoprotein enzymes. The solution of these interesting questions about the dependence of enzyme action on structural organisa-tion is, however, only now being tackled.

Fig. 86. A complete instrument assembly for automatic recording of the absorption spectrum of living objects. A. Recording millivoltmeter, B. (In the middle) a grid monochromator with connected cabinet for the object-holder and photomultiplier cell (at D), (above) an extra tube intensifier for very strongly light-absorbing objects, E. Protected carriage with the batteries necessary for the photo-cell operation, F. Oscilloscope with a camera for ultra-fast recording.

The mechano-electric drive necessary for moving the wavelength screw and the object slide can be seen to the right of C (after LUNDEGÅRDH 1958).

Another property characteristic of 'living enzyme systems' is the ontogenetically regulated activation and inhibition of individual systems. Many seeds have *zymogens*, which become active only on germination. There is e.g. in *Ricinus* seeds a zymogen of lipase. In sea-urchins the respiration system inhibitable by cyanide becomes active only after fertilisation (RUNNSTRÖM 1930). In the development of the germinating roots of barley the initially active cytochrome system partly loses its activity after a few days although the amount of enzyme is maintained.

Certain insectivorous plants give examples of enzyme (e.g. pepsin) activation by external stimulation. The name *exoenzyme* has been proposed for such excreted enzymes. The exoenzymes hemicellulase and amylase are excreted from the scutellum of cereal seeds and influence the mobilisation of carbohydrates in the endosperm.

In connection with zymogens the formation of *adaptive enzymes* may be mentioned. The fungus *Botrytis cinerea* secretes the enzyme pectinase, which cleaves the pectin chains found in the middle lamellae of the cell membranes. The enzyme pectase, which removes the methyl groups from the molecular chain, is on the other hand formed only in the presence of pectin (PHAFF 1947, GAUMANN and BÖHM 1947).

A means of expressing the speed of an enzyme reaction is given by the 'turnover number' i.e. the number of substrate molecules which are converted per minute (or second) by an enzyme molecule. Some approximate values are given in Table 5.

Table 5

Turnover Numbers of some Enzymes

Enzyme	Coenzyme	Substrate	Turnover number $\dfrac{\text{moles substrate}}{\text{moles enzyme}}$ per minute
Carbonic anhydrase	Zn	$HCO_3{}^-$	9×10^2
Yeast carboxylase	Thiamine pyrophosphate (TPP) $+$ Mg	Pyruvic acid	$1 \cdot 3 \times 10^3$
Alcohol dehydrogenase	Coenzyme 1	Alcohol	2×10^4
Hexokinase	Mg	Glucose $+$ ATP	$1 \cdot 4 \times 10^4$
Polyphenol oxidase	Cu	Catechol	7×10^4
Phosphorylase	Adenylic acid	Glucose phosphate & glycogen	4×10^4
Cytochrome c	Fe-porphyrin	Cytochrome b	$1 \cdot 4 \times 10^3$
Cytochrome oxidase	Fe-porphyrin	Cytochrome c	7×10^3
Catalase	Fe-porphyrin	H_2O_2	$2 \cdot 5 \times 10^6$

The turnover number is of course not a physical constant but only an expression of the speed of an enzyme process under the conditions of the determination. The intensity of an oxidation is dependent on the oxidation-reduction level at which the enzyme is working. If cytochrome oxidase e.g. is completely reduced, the initial speed of electron transfer to oxygen (cf. below) is about ten times as fast as when the enzyme is 80% oxidised as in normal respiration. The turnover figure is depressed in normal respiration by the greater inertia of the dehydrogenating systems.

A factor regulating the speeds of reaction in living protoplasm is the distribution of the reacting components into different phases or in monomolecular layers. The reactive groups of an enzyme can e.g. be adsorbed on a surface and thus set aside, hindering contact with a freely mobile substrate. A restricted location can of course in other cases have an exactly opposite effect, i.e. favouring reaction.

The distribution of different enzyme systems among different structures or molecular groups is obviously the best method for the cell to isolate reaction chains in such a way that opposed processes can proceed undisturbed. It is known e.g. that materials of high energy value are built up inside a cell, although the surface is surrounded by oxygen. CANNON (1926) found that in photosynthetically active cells of *Mercurialis perennis* hermidine was reduced to the extent of 95%, a state which corresponded to an O_2 pressure of only 10^{-60} atm.

If two reactive components are adsorbed at different surfaces, reaction does not take place. Reaction can, however, be mediated by a third component, which moves freely between the boundary layers. From this point of view it is interesting to find that various enzymes are anchored in the protoplasmic structure. It is found that dehydrogenases and hexokinases are anchored in the surface layer of bacteria. The activity of sucrase (saccharase or invertase) in the surface of wheat roots is influenced by conditions of the surroundings which alter the surface potential. MYRBÄCK and VASSEUR (1943) give examples of the structural localisation of different enzymes in the yeast cell. It has been found that ascorbic oxidase, peroxidase and other enzymes are anchored in the protoplasmic surface (cf. GODDARD and STAFFORD 1953) whereas, according to the results of many workers, the cytochromes of higher organisms are located in the mitochondria. It has already been mentioned that cytochromes a_3 and b are closely combined with the structure.

The quantity of the enzymes or prosthetic groups necessary for the normal functions of a cell is usually very small. It has been calculated that in particular cases a few molecules of a hormone or of a trace element are sufficient. The term *ergones* has been suggested for enzymes, hormones or vitamins which are effective in extremely low concentrations. For this it has been suggested that the cell acts as an amplifier of ergone effects (JORDAN 1938). About 0·000,005 mg of vitamin B, i.e. about a hundred thousand to a million molecules, can build up 1 mg of dry substance of *Phycomyces* (WASSINK 1946). In bacteria which can themselves synthesise vitamin B_1 a molecule is built up in one second. The formation of nicotinic acid occurs 500 times more quickly (MCILVAINE 1946). According to KUHN, androthermon is active even in a quantity of 10 molecules per cell; these data are for the alga *Chlamydomonas*. One or several molecules of crocin suffice. The intensification factor of most ergones varies between 10^5 and 10^9. By comparison, the hormone auxin is less active. It has been calculated that about 100,000 molecules of auxin are necessary to induce a weak tropic curvature (Chap. 10).

(c) *Enzymes, Hormones and Vitamins*

The fact that many enzymes are easily split into apoenzyme and coenzyme suggests that the latter, having a considerably smaller molecular volume than the holoenzyme, may circulate in organs and organisms. The high molecular weight of apoenzymes limits them more to one location.

A transportable coenzyme is called a *hormone*; for example, *thiamine pyrophosphate* (cocarboxylase), which is formed in green leaves and is transported thnce through the phloem to the roots, where it acts as a growth regulator. The *auxins* (see Chaps. 9 and 10) are widely distributed hormones which are likewise transported over considerable distances partly in the stele and partly in the parenchyma. Little is yet known about the method of action of auxins. At present it cannot be stated whether they are combined with proteins at the place of action to form true enzymes or whether they intervene as isolated activators at important points in carbohydrate metabolism.

Vitamins are prosthetic groups which are transferred from one organism to another. Many vitamins are identical with prosthetic groups of enzymes in plants. A few may be mentioned here. WILLIAMS and CLIVE (1936) identified vitamin B_1 as thiamine. Nicotinamide, which WARBURG (1934) recognised as a component of coenzymes I and II, was identified by ELVEHJEM *et al.* as the anti-pellagra vitamin. The *riboflavins* are components of enzymes which co-operate in oxygen respiration of almost all organisms. They were recognised by KUHN and KARRER (1935) as part of the vitamin B_2 complex. Vitamin B_6 is identical with pyroxidine (FOLKERS, KUHN *et al.* 1938) and is closely related to pyridoxal (SNELL 1944), whose phosphate represents the prosthetic group of glutamic transaminase and carboxylase (SCHALES *et al.* 1946). Biotin (vitamin H) may be effective (according to SHIVE and ROGERS 1947) in the reversible carboxylation of pyruvic acid to oxalacetic acid. Folic acid (pteroylglutamic acid or vitamin B_c; ABDERHALDEN 1947) has been less investigated. Vitamin K_1 (α-phylloquinone) has been quoted as a coenzyme in photosynthesis (cf. p. 113).

(d) *The Importance of Molecular Configuration for Enzyme Activity*

Because of the specific linkage between apoenzyme and the substrate, the speed of the conversion, as explained above, is dependent on a number of factors, e.g. changes in pH. The review given in Chapter 1 of the probable structure of a protein molecule explained the denaturation of a globular protein as an unravelling of the fibrous molecules. On account of this unravelling the side-chains are exposed to the influence of the environment. It has been shown that proteolysis, i.e. the hydrolytic decomposition of a protein, usually begins with a denaturation. Through this the reactivity of the polar groups increases and the balance between them and the peptide linkages is altered. In the undamaged state the protein molecule is relatively well protected; but after injury to the cell the degradation of protein spreads quickly, preceded by partial coagulation. The enzymes are of course included in this process.

Some denaturation results from the surface forces in monomolecular films, and consequently the activity of a number of enzymes decreases rapidly when they are spread out on a water surface. Some of the active groups are more resistant, however, e.g. sulphydryl and the phenylhydroxy groups. In pepsin the active tyrosine groups are relatively stable; but a partial denaturation can occur. This is the case e.g. in the globular protein, actin, in muscle (SZENT-GYÖRGYI), which on addition of KCl assumes a fibrillar structure. Globular proteins in their natural state are usually more slowly attacked by hydrolytic enzymes than they are after denaturation, whereas fibrillar proteins are always quickly degraded.

Large enzyme molecules, prosthetic groups and hormones all illustrate the great importance of molecular configuration. Particularly striking is the phenomenon of *chemical antagonism*, i.e. the fact that a substance can be competitively exchanged for another substance having a similar molecular configuration. Then sooner or later the process 'goes off the rails' when the wrong substance enters into a reaction chain in which it cannot be worked up.

The *ionic antagonism* (see Chaps. 6 and 7) which is so important in plant physiology is due to competitive displacement of ions from adsorption linkages and the harmful alterations thus caused to the physical condition of proteins and other high-molecular substances. Examples of competitive displacement of organic substances are given by antibiotics, i.e. compounds which are produced by one organism and release inhibitive effects in another organism (cf. HOOGERHEIDE 1944, ETTLINGER 1946, GÄUMANN *et al.* 1947).

A classical example of such an exchange is the biochemical antagonism between sulphonamides and *p*-aminobenzoic acid, which is an essential nutrient for many bacteria (BRADBURY and JORDAN 1942). As the uptake mechanism of bacteria is unable to distinguish between *p*-aminobenzoic acid and sulphonamide, a sufficient concentration of the latter stops nutrient uptake, and the bacterium remains inactive. A similar antagonism is observed between 3-pyridine sulphonic acid and nicotinic acid, as well as between thiopanic and pantothenic acid. In thiopanic acid a COOH-group is exchanged with an SO_3H-group.

In all these cases a hydroxyl or carboxyl group has been exchanged with an amino or sulphonic acid group. The exchange has, of course, serious consequences if it is concerned e.g. with a prosthetic group or with a part of the enzyme molecule that combines with the substrate. Detailed studies on 'false enzymes' will certainly help to explain the connection between molecular configuration and physiological effect. Similar researches on the action of auxins have gone a fair way (see Chap. 9).

Some further examples of exchanges are given here. The replacement of an —S— with a —CH=CH-group in the ring system of thiamine blocks the catalytic activity of the enzyme, in which thiamine represents the prosthetic group. N— can also be exchanged with C—, e.g. in a benzene or a thiophen ring. In the latter case certain reactions in which biotin is active are blocked. Desthiobiotin is an intermediate stage in the synthesis of biotin, e.g. in *Escherichia coli* (ROGERS and SHIVE 1947). Desthiobiotin is blocked by 2-hydroxy-imidazolidylcaproic acid, which therefore hinders the synthesis of biotin.

The great importance of molecular configuration for the chemical reactions taking place in the cell is clear in that the position of a group, e.g. the *ortho-*, *meta-* or *para-*position in a benzene ring, is usually more decisive than its chemical character. For example, amino-, methyl-, chloro- and hydroxyl-groups are mutually exchanged, without great biological differences resulting at first, provided that they have the correct steric position as the side-chains of an active compound. Only if a special chemical reaction is involved do competitive inhibitions arise.

(e) *The Effect of Inhibitors on Enzyme Reactions*

A favourite method of separating the individual members of a reaction chain governed enzymatically is the addition of specific inhibitors. The best known is the inhibition of oxygen respiration by *cyanide*, a phenomenon which was explained by WARBURG as the blocking of the 'respiration enzyme', i.e. of cytochrome oxidase. In this the cyanide is combined with the active iron atom of the prosthetic haem group in such a way that the valency change between di- and tri-valent Fe, which is essential for the activity of the enzyme, is stopped.

Among other so-called specific inhibitors may be mentioned: *malonic acid*, which blocks succinic dehydrogenase, *arsenate*, which can take the place of phosphate and inhibits phosphotransacetylase, *dialkylhalogenphosphates* which inhibit esterases and certain proteolytic enzymes, *fluorides*, which block enolases, etc.

Unfortunately amazingly few inhibitors are quite specific; the effects are mostly spread over several enzymes, even though one of these may show an especially sensitive reaction. Cyanide, for example, is a very sensitive indicator through its blocking of cytochrome oxidase, and even in concentrations of 10^{-7}—10^{-5} M it blocks respiration, but also it inhibits peroxidase with equal intensity which in plants also participates in oxygen respiration (LUNDEGÅRDH 1954, 1958). Cytochrome c also reacts with cyanide, but much more slowly (HORECKER and KORNBERG 1946) and only under certain conditions of pH.

It can be said that among the iron-containing enzymes under normal biological conditions cyanide blocks only cytochrome oxidase and peroxidase (also catalase). The fact, however, is important that CN combines also with other heavy metal ions, e.g. Cu. Copper is present in a number of oxidising enzymes, e.g. tyrosinase and ascorbic oxidase (AMES *et al.* 1946, DAWSON and TARPLEY 1951). Cyanide also partly influences phosphorylation and reacts chemically with ketones.

Carbon monoxide is a more specific inhibitor of cytochrome oxidase than cyanide, since the iron carbonyl compound, through which the enzyme is blocked, is decomposed in strong light. CO combines also with Cu and thus also blocks copper oxidases, but this effect can be separated from haem blocking by the dissociation of iron carbonyl by light. For *copper* there are also more specific inhibitors, e.g. dithiocarbamate, thiourea and glutathione. An inhibitor which, like cyanide, blocks cytochrome oxidase and also peroxidase is *azide* (sodium azide, NaN_3). But this inhibitor also shows side-effects, in that it influences phosphorylating enzymes and forms a complex with the Zn atom of carbonic anhydrase. An inhibitor of iron-containing enzymes is *α-dipyridyl* (bipyridine, $(C_5H_4N)_2$).

For the study of the cytochrome system, which is indeed a universal mechanism of oxygen respiration in living organisms, inhibitors have also been utilised, which influence the intermediate enzymes catalysing the electron transfer from and to cytochrome b. A number of substances, e.g. *urethane* and *amytal*, hinder the release of electrons, i.e. the oxidation of cytochrome b. The most useful example is the inhibition of the oxidation of cytochrome b by the antibiotic *antimycin A*, which combines with cytochrome b almost equimolecularly. *BAL* (2, 3-dimercaptopropanol) is another inhibitor used for the study of cytochrome b.

One of the few specific inhibitors is *malonic acid*, which competitively inhibits the oxidation of succinic acid to fumaric acid by succinic dehydrogenase. Pyrophosphate or *p*-carboxyphenylarsinoxide (POTTER and REIF 1952) have a still stronger effect. The specificity depends apparently on the similar molecular configuration of succinic acid and malonic acid:

$$HOOC \cdot CH_2 \cdot CH_2 \cdot COOH \qquad HOOC \cdot CH_2 \cdot COOH$$

succinic acid   malonic acid

The latter displaces the former in the formation of a compound with succinic dehydrogenase which cannot react with malonic acid and so the process is blocked. Competitive phenomena can of course occur also at any point where an inhibitor is displaced by another substance. It has been found e.g. that the poisonous effect of cyanide on respiration is dependent on the oxygen concentration: with increasing O_2 concentration the poisonous effect diminishes. Oxygen here probably displaces CN from an active position on the surface of the cytochrome oxidase. This is therefore a different kind of competitive inhibition from that of malonic acid—succinic acid.

Organic inhibitors which combine chemically with the enzyme and disturb its molecular configuration of course act specifically. Such a substance has been identified in soya beans (KUNITZ 1947). It combines with trypsin in a peptide-like linkage between COOH- and NH_2-groups. An inhibitor of carboxylase is 1-amino-2-naphthol-4-sulphonic acid.

Among inhibitors which attack stages of glycolysis, *monoiodoacetic acid* and *fluoride* may be mentioned. The former inhibits the phosphonucleotide enzymes with little specificity; fluoride inactivates especially enolase which splits phosphoenolpyruvic acid. Enolase contains an active magnesium atom, which is inactivated by fluoride as magnesium fluorophosphate.

More information about inhibitors is given in the description of individual enzymes.

2 HYDROLASES, LIPASES AND PHOSPHATE-TRANSFERRING ENZYMES

The extensive group of *hydrolysing enzymes* causes hydrolytic cleavage of those linkages which unite the building elements of polysaccharides, fats and proteins. These processes occur usually with a small expenditure of energy and mostly show reversible equilibria, so that the hydrolysing enzymes also participate to a large extent in the synthesis of condensation products, e.g. high-molecular carbohydrates and fats. Table 6 shows the most important hydrolysing enzymes.

The chemical character of these enzymes has been little investigated and even the nomenclature is variable. Further research has often shown that a newly discovered enzyme actually consists of a mixture of two or more individual enzymes. Examples of this are amylases, proteases and phytophosphatases (cf. GREENBERG and WINNICK 1940, FLEURY and COURTOIS 1946).

The *specificity of enzymes* with respect to the stereochemical structure of the substrate may vary. Usually the structural specificity is related to details of configuration. As a result, substances of different chemical natures can be attacked if they possess only similar specific groups.

Emulsin (a β-glycosidase) is a very unspecific enzyme, since it attacks a number of substrates, but it is specific with respect to β-glycoside linkages, which occur in a number of different substances.

The *proteolytic enzymes* are similarly specialized for certain links or molecular configurations which occur in proteins of various origins. The same degree of specificity recurs in the synthetic activity of the enzymes. It is remarkable that the synthetic action of proteinases can lead to the formation of true peptide links and that the synthetic specificity is generally identical with the hydrolytic specificity. A crystallising proteinase was prepared by OKUNUKI *et al.* (1956) from *Bacillus subtilis*. It has a fairly wide specificity and chiefly attacks both the nitrogen and the carbon ends of neutral and acid amino acids of proteins.

It can be said that the biochemistry of the cell is satisfied with a relatively restricted

Table 6

Enzyme	Reaction
I *Hydrolysing Enzymes*	
A. *Carbohydrases*	
Sucrases (invertase=glyco- and fructosucrase)	Hydrolysis of sucrose from the glucose or fructose end
α-D-glycosidases (yeast maltase)	Maltose → glucose. Cleavage of the α-glycoside linkage in α-D-glycosides
β-glycosidases (β-glycosidase + mandelo-nitrilase (emulsin))	β-glycoside → sugar + other substances (*e.g.* HCN)
Amylases	
β-amylase, saccharogenic or exoamylase	Cleavage of 1,4-α-glycosidic linkages in starch and
α-amylase, dextrinogenic or endoamylase	glycogen.
Cellulase	Cellulose → cellobiose (glucose 4-β-glucoside)
Protopectinase	Hydrolysis of 'protopectin'
Pectin-polygalacturonase (pectinase)	Hydrolysis of pectinic acids
Pectin-methylesterase (pectase)	Hydrolysis of the methyl ester groups of pectinic acids
B. *Esterases*	
Lipase	Fat → glycerol + fatty acids
Phosphatases (adenosine triphosphatase, nuclease, nucleotidase)	Splitting off H_3PO_4 from phosphate esters
Phytophosphatases	Phytin (inositol hexaphosphate) → inositol + $H_3PO_4^{-}$
Phosphorylases	Conversion and liberation of H_3PO_4
II *Deaminating Enzymes*	
Arginase	Arginine → urea + ornithine
Urease	Urea → $CO_2 + NH_3$
Asparaginase	Asparagine → aspartic acid + NH_3
Glutaminase	Glutamine → glutamic acid + NH_3
III *Proteolytic Enzymes*	
Exopeptidases (aminopeptidase, carboxypepti-dase)	Cleavage of end peptide linkages
Endopeptidases (proteinases), for example: Pepsin, trypsin, chymotrypsin, papain (from the latex of *Carica papaya*), bromelin (a papain from the sap of the pineapple fruit), asclepain and solanain	Cleavage of central peptide linkages

choice of group combinations, which make the structural units of living matter. Each type of linkage has its specific enzyme, and the cell is consequently able to control a multiplicity of chemical reactions with a relatively restricted number of enzymes.

Of the enzymes mentioned in Table 6 the *carbohydrases* generally work more quickly than the proteolytic enzymes. They cause a complete decomposition of the molecules attacked. Their function in carbohydrate metabolism and in the transport of sugars is extraordinarily important (about the microbiological degradation of cellulose see NORKRANS and RÅNBY 1956, and others).

Other important cell regulators are the *phosphatases*, which cleave phosphoric acid from ester linkages. An adenosine triphosphatase splits inorganic phosphoric acid from adenosine triphosphate (ATP) so that adenosine diphosphate (ADP) is formed. We shall refer to these reactions again in the treatment of intermediate energy transfers. Binding and liberation of phosphoric acid are two of the key processes of living cells. The phosphatases are considered as fairly unspecific, since phosphate ester linkages occur in the most varied organic compounds.

The term *phosphorolysis* was proposed by PARNAS (1937). It follows from what has been said about phosphatases that this process is similar to hydrolysis. Whereas in hydrolysis a molecule of water is transferred, in phosphorolysis phosphoric acid is transferred instead:

$$\text{Hydrolysis} \qquad R^1R^2 + H \cdot OH \rightleftharpoons H \cdot R^1 + R^2 \cdot OH$$
$$\text{Phosphorolysis } R^1R^2 + HO \cdot PO_3H \rightleftharpoons H \cdot R^1 + R^2 \cdot O \cdot PO_3H_2 \tag{31}$$

The corresponding enzymes are named *phosphorylases*. They are particularly important for carbohydrate metabolism and in the respiratory degradation of sugars. They catalyse the reversible reaction:

$$\alpha\text{-glucose-1-phosphate} \rightleftharpoons \text{starch} + \text{phosphoric acid} \tag{32}$$

(HANES 1940). This reaction consequently leads to the synthesis of starch (by exchange of an ester linkage with a glucoside linkage) or the reverse process, that is the first step of glycolysis.

Hexokinase takes part in the phosphorylation of glucose (and thus the formation *inter alia* of the α-glucose-l-phosphate ester), by transfer of a phosphoric acid group from ATP. Fructose and mannose can also be phosphorylated similarly (BERGER *et al*. 1946). It has further been assumed that NAD (coenzyme I) can participate in the transfer of phosphoric acid (LINDAHL *et al*. 1946).

Reversible phosphorylation, as said above, mediates the polymerisation of simple types of sugar. A phosphorylase isolated from *Pseudomonas saccharophila* catalyses the reaction

$$\alpha\text{-glucose phosphate} + \text{fructose} \rightleftharpoons \text{sucrose} \tag{33}$$

This reaction has an important function in intermediate carbohydrate metabolism. The α-glucose phosphate is also a preliminary stage in the formation of amylose, one of the components of starch, which on breaking down yields again α-glucose phosphate. This phosphate ester is accordingly an important member in the equilibrium of the carbohydrates.

These reactions are examples of the various means of synthesis and decomposition. In synthesis phosphorylases are always active, whereas decomposition can also take the path via hydrolysis. In this α- and β-amylases are active, which introduce H_2O instead of H_3PO_4 into the glycoside link.

Of the two components of starch the amylase has a straight, unbranched molecule, whereas the chain molecules of the amylopectin are branched. For the breakdown of amylopectin the activity of the phosphorylase must therefore be combined with the effect of a second enzyme, which catalyses another type of glycoside linkage, viz. branching. It has been found that for the synthesis of polysaccharides, 'primers' are necessary, i.e. traces of already formed chain molecules. The participating phosphorylase is a very active enzyme, with a turnover number of 4×10^4 per minute. The reaction can be written as follows:

$$\text{glucose phosphate} + \text{end glucose units} \rightleftharpoons \text{maltose chain units} + \text{phosphate} \tag{34}$$

The phosphorylases have active SH-groups which must be protected by the presence of reducing substances. For this cystëine or glutathione (see p. 144) are suitable. The chief difference between hydrolases and phosphorylases lies in the fact that the former destroy the glycoside link, whereas the exchange between glycoside link and phosphate ester link is reversible. As the energy value of the two linkages is approximately the same (about 3 kg-cal) the transfer works with only small amounts of free energy. A striking contrast is afforded by the formation or utilisation of high-energy phosphate linkages which convert large amounts of energy (about 9-16 kg-cal) that can only be raised in combination with oxidation processes (see further below).

From what has been said about phosphorylases it follows that the formation of cane sugar and starch are closely related processes, both of which are connected with a-glucose-l-phosphate, as the following scheme shows:

$$\text{glucose} \leftarrow \overset{\displaystyle H_3PO_4}{\underset{\displaystyle \updownarrow}{+}} \text{sucrose} \rightarrow \text{fructose}$$

$$a\text{-glucose-1-phosphate} \rightleftharpoons \text{starch} - \left\{ \begin{array}{c} \text{amylose} \\ + \\ \text{amylopectin} \end{array} \right\} + H_3PO_4 \qquad (35)$$

a-Glucose-1-phosphate or $D(+)a$-glucopyranose-1-phosphate, also termed Cori ester, is also, as will be shown later, the starting-point for the respiratory degradation of sugar.

The discovery of the effect of phosphorolysis both in the formation and the degradation of carbohydrates throws new light on the function of the hydrolytically separated hexose molecules glucose and fructose. They seem now to be fairly inactive, a fact that agrees with the observation that the concentration of free monosaccharides depends less on respiration than that of starch and cane sugar, which are quickly utilised.

Here, however, hexokinase comes in. This enzyme assists the direct entry of glucose into the respiration cycle. It appears to be located in the surface layer of yeast cells (ROTSTEIN 1953), where it supposedly mediates the uptake of glucose by transporting the molecules as glucose phosphate through the surface layer.

Wheat roots also have a mechanism for absorbing glucose actively (LUNDEGÅRDH and BURSTRÖM 1944), but they do not depend on hexokinase. Just as this enzyme can in certain circumstances co-operate in the uptake and transport of glucose, so it may conversely catalyse the uptake of phosphoric acid in the presence of glucose. Experiments on this have been carried out with potatoes (LUNDEGÅRDH 1958); wheat roots behave anomalously (cf. also Chap. 6).

Whilst hydrolysis and condensation of di- and polysaccharides go partly by different ways—even though reversible equilibria are available in phosphorylation—the *lipases* catalyse both the formation and the degradation of fats (lipids), processes which transfer little free energy. The equilibrium may be written as follows:

$$\text{glycerol} + \text{fatty acid} \underset{}{\overset{\text{lipase}}{\rightleftharpoons}} \text{fat} \qquad (36)$$

Fats usually have a much higher energy level than carbohydrates: 1 g of carbohydrate yields on combustion about 4·1 kg-cal. but 1 g of fat about 9·3 kg-cal. The ease with which the living cell carries out the reversible conversion of carbohydrate into fat is surprising when one considers the large amount of energy transferred and how complicated the intermediate reactions are (cf. p. 100). It has been suggested that high-energy phosphates take part (KAPLAN 1951). In addition to coenzyme A (cf. p. 183) ATP, NAD and magnesium appear to be involved in the synthesis and the oxidation of fats (GREEN 1955). The rapid conversion of fat to starch and vice versa can be observed in the germination and the drying of fatty seeds, such as those of cucumbers and pumpkins.

The proteolytic processes also are, as emphasised above, usually reversible, in that the hydrolysing enzymes also catalyse syntheses. The collaboration of proteases, particularly papains, in protein synthesis has been observed, and the specificity of the enzymes is usually pronounced. The energy requirement for a peptide linkage is about the same as for a phosphate ester linkage, about 3 kg-cal. In an equilibrium: protein $\rightleftharpoons$ amino acids, the energy difference, however, causes a strong shift to the right. Synthesis, i.e. a shift to the left, is therefore mostly brought about by combination with an exergonic process e.g. cleavage of a high-energy phosphate linkage (cf. C below).

Most of the proteolytic enzymes also have active SH-groups, which require protective substances such as cystëine, glutathione, etc. The end-products of protein hydrolysis, the amino acids, are easily transportable and can be moved from cell to cell.

Through *deaminases* the amino acids are decomposed further into their components, organic acids and ammonia. A commonly occurring deaminase is *asparaginase*, which splits asparagine into aspartic acid and ammonia. Aspartase leads a step further, and from aspartic acid makes fumaric acid and ammonia. Aspartase is related to the group of enzymes which catalyse additions to double bonds. To these belong *fumarase* and *aconitase*. Fumarase converts fumaric acid into L-malic acid by addition of a molecule of H_2O and plays a large part in the intermediate processes connected with oxygen respiration. Aconitase fulfils a similar function between isocitric acid and aconitic acid.

To the same group belongs also *carbonic anhydrase*, which catalyses the equation:

$$CO_2 + H_2O \rightleftharpoons H_2CO_3$$

Aldolase (*zymohexase*) accelerates the cleavage of fructofuranose 1,6-diphosphate into two molecules of triose phosphate.

There may also be mentioned here the *carboxylases* which catalyse the very important conversion between CO_2 and the carboxyl group –COOH. Those carboxylases which effect the decarboxylation of pyruvic acid have Mg–thiamine pyrophosphate as the prosthetic group.

A number of phosphatases and phosphorylases occur as 'transferring enzymes' (*transferases*); in intermediary metabolism they exchange phosphate ester linkages against glycoside linkages. Other examples of transferring enzymes are the *transaminases*, which bring about the exchange of amino groups between amino acids and keto acids. Glutamic transaminase has a prosthetic group which consists of a phosphorylated derivative of pyridoxal. Pyridoxal is one of the B_6-vitamins (for formula, see p. 177).

Isomerising enzymes (*isomerases*) catalyse conversions between isomers. One of the longest-known is *triose phosphate isomerase*, which accelerates the transfer between 3-phosphoglyceraldehyde and phosphodihydroxyacetone. The prosthetic group of *phosphoglucomutase*, which catalyses the reversible conversion of α-glucose-1-phosphate into glucose 6-monophosphate, is glucose 1,6-diphosphate. These enzymes, as also phosphoglyceric mutase, whose prosthetic group is 2,3-diphosphoglyceric acid, are active in glycolysis.

3 OXIDATION-REDUCTION ENZYMES (REDOX ENZYMES)

The most important function of these enzymes is the control of the reactions which accompany the important energy transfers of oxidative metabolism. According to the extent to which these processes occur reversibly or are connected with reversible intermediate reactions, the redox enzymes work in both directions, thus both oxidising and reducing. The degradation of an organic substance, containing carbon, hydrogen and oxygen, to a higher stage of oxidation can take place by addition of oxygen or the loss of hydrogen or by a combination of both processes. The following examples illustrate the possible methods of oxidation of a substrate:

1. Loss of electrons:

$$\underset{\text{reduction}}{\overset{\text{oxidation}}{Fe^{++} \rightleftharpoons Fe^{+++} + (e)}} \tag{37}$$

2. Loss of hydrogen:

$$+ (2\,H) \tag{38}$$

Examples of apparently irreversible oxidation are the following:

1. Consumption of oxygen:

$$CO + \tfrac{1}{2}\,O_2 = CO_2 \tag{39}$$

2. Addition of water and loss of hydrogen:

$$CCl_3 \cdot CHO + H_2O \rightarrow CCl_3 \cdot CHO \cdot H_2O \rightarrow CCl_3 \cdot COOH + (2H) \tag{40}$$

The brackets indicate that electrons or hydrogen are not scattered freely in the surroundings of the reacting system, but are captured by acceptor substances, which occur chiefly as intermediate members in the reaction chain. Molecular oxygen is the final acceptor of electrons. In special cases, e.g. in cellulose-decomposing bacteria, molecular hydrogen emerges on the reducing side of the equation.

There are of course no sharp dividing-lines between reversible and irreversible redox processes, since this depends on the amount of energy involved in each stage. Large jumps in energy require connection with other systems which make available the energy necessary for the endergonic process. It may be mentioned, as an example, that a reversible electron transfer between cytochromes b and c is possible, but not between c and a_3 (cytochrome oxidase).

The free energy of the oxidation can be calculated from the equation

$$\Delta F = -nF\Delta E \tag{41}$$

where n is the number of electrons taking part in the reaction, F is the Faraday constant or 23,068 cal. and ΔE is the potential difference in volts (KAPLAN 1951). For the spontaneous occurrence of a reaction (that is, an exergonic reaction) it is necessary that the free energy (ΔF) should be negative. An exergonic reaction can be reversed if the same amount of energy is supplied by a coupled exergonic reaction. As previously mentioned, only small values of ΔF allow reversal of reaction by the energy sources which are always available such as differences of concentration between substrate and products, heat of crystallisation, etc.

The oxidation-reduction enzymes are ordinarily divided into two chief groups, the *dehydrogenases* and the *oxidases*. The former catalyse the removal of hydrogen, and the latter direct oxidation by oxygen. The distinction between these groups is not sharp however, since there are enzymes which both split off hydrogen from a substrate and oxidase the hydrogen by oxygen. Molecular oxygen, however, is not the natural acceptor for most dehydrogenases.

Certain reactions which at first sight seem fairly simple, e.g. the microbiological dehydrogenation of cellulose, are in reality probably more complicated and require the participation of *hydrogenases* (WARING and WERKMAN 1944), i.e. of enzymes which catalyse reduction via molecular hydrogen:

$$H_2 + A \rightarrow AH_2 \qquad (42)$$

Such enzymes are usually active in micro-organisms and it is believed that on account of the high reduction potential, -0.445 volts, they also serve as protection for enzymes liable to oxidation (STEPHENSON 1947).

The mechanism of enzyme reactions, e.g. those of peroxidases, is often complicated, and this has helped to put the nomenclature of the redox enzymes on a less categorical basis. They are now characterised more with respect to their chemical properties. This method is helped by the fact that we are better informed about the prosthetic groups of the redox enzymes than about those of the hydrolases.

A special task of many oxidation-reduction enzymes is the transfer of chemical energy to phosphate groups of high energy content, a process that is termed *oxidative phosphorylation*, which is discussed in Section C.

(a) *Iron-porphyrin Enzymes*

I. *Cytochromes*

MACMUNN discovered in the 1880s the red pigments in animal cells which he called *histohaematins*. He supposed that they had something to do with respiration. Only after the re-discovery of these pigments by KEILIN (1925; cf. KEILIN and HARTREE 1939 and 1949), who introduced the term *cytochromes*, was the attention of biochemists directed to their central position in oxidative metabolism.

The prosthetic group of the cytochromes is *haematin*. At least three types of cytochromic haematin are known, which are distinguished by different spectral bands. For the observation of the haemochromogen bands the respective enzymes are treated with pyridine and dithionite. The prosthetic group of cytochrome b is protohaem IX, which occurs also in peroxidase and catalase (cf. p. 35).

To the cytochromes belong also the '*respiration ferments*' described by WARBURG (1928). The cytochromes are very widely spread, not only in animal tissues, but also in micro-organisms (cf. ROWLINSON 1949, SMITH 1954) and in higher and lower plants (review in ZEILE 1949-50; HILL and HARTREE 1953, HARTREE 1956). Characteristic of these enzymes is their occurrence in groups of several individual cytochromes, some of which are so closely combined with the structure of the protoplasm that one can speak of an *organised cytochrome system*. Different groups of organisms, however, show different types, combinations and mass ratios of the individual cytochromes. These group differences, e.g. between animals and plants and between types of micro-organisms, are reflected in the reaction of oxygen respiration towards certain enzymatic inhibitors such as cyanide. Cyanide normally inhibits animal respiration almost totally, whereas in higher plants one must distinguish between a fraction readily inhibited by cyanide and a 'basal respiration' which is inhibited only with difficulty.

The haem group has a very characteristic absorption spectrum in the visible region. Especially valuable for biochemical work is the fact that oxidised and reduced cyto-chromes show characteristic spectral differences.

All cytochromes show a very intensive band in the blue-violet, the so-called Soret- or γ-band. On reduction this band is shifted about 10–20 mμ towards higher wave-lengths, and the extinction usually is somewhat increased. The γ-band causes the red colour of most cytochromes.

Oxidised cytochromes show only weak indistinct absorption bands in the blue-green, but on reduction sharp bands occur in this region and in the bright red (see Figs. 87, 88). These bands are termed β and α. Thanks to the characteristic change on

Fig. 87. Absorption spectrum of cytochrome c in aqueous solution (recorded at intervals of 1 mμ with the instrument pictured in Fig. 86). On the ordinates, molar extinction. The lines represent: —— oxidised, . . . reduced (after LUNDEGÅRDH 1956).

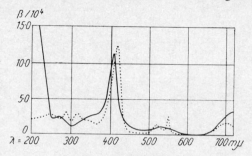

reduction or oxidation one can calculate the *difference spectrum*. For this purpose the extinction value of the oxidised is deducted from that of the reduced cytochrome. According as the differences are positive or negative, the difference spectrum lies above or below zero, i.e. the position at which it is unaffected by oxidation and reduction.

The difference spectrum is very valuable for the calculation of the stage of oxidation or reduction in the cytochromes found in the living cell. If the extinction e.g. of the α-band of a pure cytochrome is known, then one can calculate from the extinction measurements on living objects the concentration of the enzyme in them. It must be noted, however, that on account of the cloudiness and light dispersal in living tissues and suspensions, certain corrections must be introduced which become larger, the smaller the wavelength concerned (LUNDEGÅRDH 1956, DUYSENS 1956). For the calculation of concentration the basis is the *molar extinction*, which for cytochrome c in the α-band (reduced) amounts to $2 \cdot 5 \times 10^4$ per cm per litre.

The different cytochromes have very varying molecular weights; the lowest is that of cytochrome c at about 15,000 (ATLAS and FARBER 1956). This cytochrome is the only one that goes into solution without much difficulty and that can also be crystal-lised (HAGIHARA et al. 1956). Cytochrome b has a much higher molecular weight and has only recently been isolated from ox-heart tissue (KIESE et al. 1954, OKUNUKI 1957). A high molecular weight (apparently about 80,000) is also shown by cytochrome oxidase (cytochrome a$_3$), which however has not yet been fully purified. One usually gets a mixture of two cytochromes, a and a_3, which can be analysed only spectro-photometrically (LUNDEGÅRDH 1957); but only a_3 is a true oxidase.

In addition to the cytochromes a_3, c and b there are other cytochromes which generally occur with them, e.g. cytochromes c_1 (or e), a and b_3; others are observed in more specialised connections, e.g. b_2 (lactic dehydrogenase of yeast; see below) and f, which appears to occur only in green leaves or in algae. In addition a number of less well-known cytochromes have been described from the abnormal placing of the bands, e.g. a number of b cytochromes (b_4 to b_7) and 'modifications' of cytochrome oxidase in certain micro-organisms.

It is also known that one and the same haem e.g. that of cytochrome c, can occur with different apoenzymes (NEILANDS 1953, KAMEN and TAKEDA 1956); such cases have been described for micro-organisms. For higher plants and animals the differences in the construction of the cytochrome systems are qualitatively unimportant, but on the other hand quantitative differences occur, viz. higher plants have about twice as much cytochrome b as animals and yeasts have. In plants there are also, as shown below, the *peroxidases*.

In the investigation of the enzymatic properties of the cytochromes, especially with reference to their collaboration in the terminal electron transfer to oxygen, various means have been used. The most important are the specific inhibitors. Kinetic studies also throw light on the organisation of the system.

All observations indicate that the cytochromes together form a system or a 'multienzyme' that is firmly anchored in the structure of the protoplasm. The location in the cell has not yet been definitely established and may be different in different organisms. It is stated, for example, that in certain micro-organisms the cytochrome system is anchored in the surface layer of the protoplasm. For higher

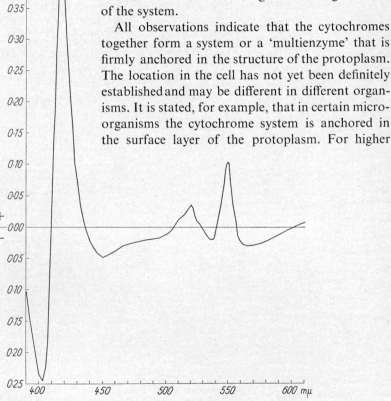

Fig. 88. Difference spectrum (extinction of the reduced minus extinction of the oxidised preparation) of cytochrome c in aqueous solution.

organisms fixation in the surface layer of mitochondria is usually alleged (p. 7). In homogenising plant tissue one finds cytochrome a_3 and b (as well as b_3) in almost all particulate fractions, whilst cytochrome c goes partly into solution (see above). Cytochrome c_1 also is less structurally bound than b and a_3.

As well as cytochromes, flavoprotein enzymes (FP; see below) occur as a rule in the first particle (mitochondrial) fraction, but also go partly into solution. Nicotinamide-adenine dinucleotide (NAD) has been found in mitochondria, but likewise mostly goes into solution. It can also be said that *the cytochromes together with flavoprotein form a part of the protoplasmic structure.* The individual enzymes are, however, bound with differing degrees of firmness, and the system thus becomes more or less destroyed on isolation. The disablement of isolated cytochrome systems in particulate fractions is also recognisable from the strong reduction in their ability to oxidise. In mitochondria of wheat roots, for example, respiration sinks to a few per cent of the normal value, but rises after addition of the enzymes removed in the homogenisation (LUNDEGÅRDH 1958).

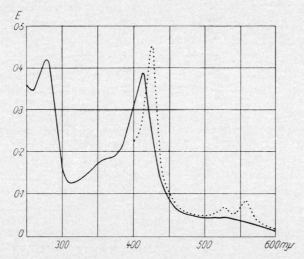

Fig. 89. Absorption spectrum of cytochrome b from the heart muscle of the ox. ———— oxidised ...... reduced (after SEKUZU and OKUNUKI 1956).

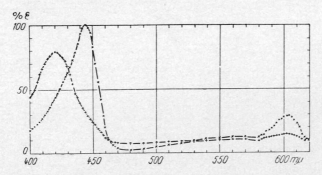

Fig. 90. Absorption spectrum of oxidised (. . . . .) and reduced (— . — . —) cytochrome oxidase $(a+a_3)$ (after LUNDEGÅRDH 1957).

M

The cytochromes form together with NAD and FP an *'electron conductor'* from dehydrogenases to oxygen. An important dehydrogenase in higher organisms is succinic dehydrogenase (see below), which dehydrogenates succinic to fumaric acid. This enzyme is an iron flavoprotein. The reduced succinic dehydrogenase is oxidised by cytochrome b. The reduced cytochrome b is oxidised by cytochrome c, and so on, according to the following plan:

$$
\begin{array}{l}
\text{H}^+\text{————————————→}\text{H}^+ \\[2pt]
\text{succinic}\uparrow\downarrow \\
\text{succinic acid}\text{H}| \\
\updownarrow\xrightarrow{}\tfrac{1}{2}\,\text{H}_2\xrightarrow{\ e\ }\text{cyt. b}\to\text{cyt. c}\to\text{cyt.a}_3\to\tfrac{1}{2}\text{O} \\
\text{fumaric acid}\downarrow \\
\text{dehydrogenase}\tfrac{1}{2}\text{H}_2\text{O}
\end{array}
$$

The succinic dehydrogenase is reduced by the two H atoms of the succinic acid. In co-operation with FP (see below) each H atom is oxidised to a proton (H^+) that is given up to the surroundings, whilst the electron is captured by the b-haem with reduction of F^{+++} to Fe^{++}. Electron exchange then follows between b and c, between c and a_3, and finally between a_3 and oxygen, which is thereby activated ($2e + \tfrac{1}{2}\text{O}_2 \to \tfrac{1}{2}\text{O}_2^{--}$). The activated oxygen reacts spontaneously with a proton of the surroundings to form water. As an equivalent amount of protons arises at the beginning of the electron conductor (see plan above), the pH of the surroundings remains unaltered.

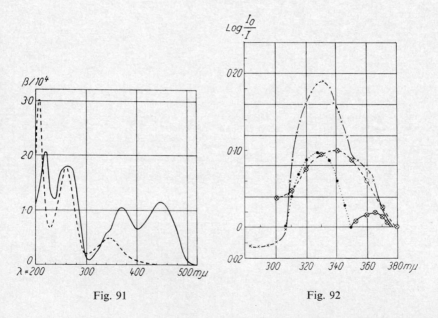

Fig. 91   Fig. 92

Fig. 91. Absorption spectra of riboflavin (solid line) and of reduced coenzyme I (NADH) (after LUNDEGÅRDH 1956).

Fig. 92. Absorption spectrum of NAD and of its enzyme combinations in living baker's yeast. The washed yeast was aerated with 2·5% glucose one-and-a-half minutes before the recording. × — × recorded total curve; ⊗—⊗ enzyme combination of triosephosphate dehydrogenase and Co I ox; ..... enzyme combination of alcohol dehydrogenase and Co I red; ⊗ — — — ⊗ Co I red (after LUNDEGÅRDH 1956).

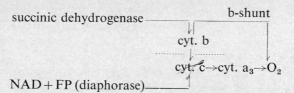

Plan of the two dehydrogenase systems connected with cytochrome c. The dotted line shows the electron transfer between the cyt. b and c which is sensitive to antimycin and other inhibitors. Both dehydrogenase systems operate e.g. in yeast. The 'b-shunt to oxygen' is characteristic of higher plants. The effects of cytochromes a, c_1, b_3, etc., still inadequately known, are omitted here.

In addition to cytochromes b, c and a_3, cytochromes c_1 and a are also active in the electron conductor. Of these, c_1 appears to assume a position between b and c. An electron transporter between b and c, sometimes called the Slater factor (SLATER 1950), must also be mentioned. It is influenced by various inhibitors, and controls the branching of the electron path into the two different dehydrogenase systems, succinic dehydrogenase and a NAD-enzyme.

In the studies of the equilibria of cytochrome b, antimycin A has played a large part. It inhibits electron transfer from b to c, and is an antibiotic of N-phenolic character

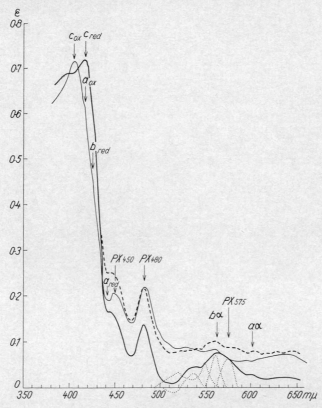

Fig. 93. Absorption spectrum of a bundle of wheat roots 14 mm thick. ———— aerated in 0·05 mole KCl; ———— anaerobic in O_2-free KCl; - - - - in water saturated with CO. c_{ox} and c_{red} oxidised and reduced γ-band of the cytochromes + peroxidase; a_{ox} and a_{red} oxidised and reduced γ-bands of cytochrome a_3; PX 450—riboflavin bands; PX 480—unknown bands (probably complex-bound carotene); b—cytochrome b; PX 575 — dh-complex of peroxidase, a—reduced bands of cytochrome a (after LUNDEGÅRDH 1952).

with the empirical formula $C_{28}H_{40}O_9N_2$ and a molecular weight of 548 (POTTER and REIF 1951). The conjecture has, however, been made that the electron conductor sketched in the above plan does not consist of simple molecule chains, but that at least the strongly structurally-bound enzymes form more or less 'crystalloid' multi-molecular groups, which similarly to chlorophyll (p. 104) are connected with a 'factor' or a 'reaction centre', which mediates the electron transfer.

Every cytochrome contains only one iron atom whose linkage in the centre of four pyrrole groups situated circularly in a disc follows from the formula on p. 35. The charge of this iron atom oscillates between bi- and trivalency as an electron is alternately captured or given up. The tendency to take up electrons, thus with the oxidation of a donator to be itself reduced, increases with the oxidation-reduction potential, which for oxygen amounts to $+0.83$, for cytochrome c 0.25 and for succinic dehydrogenase something below 0 volts. The values for the remaining cytochromes have not yet been determined, but it is known that the potential of cytochrome b is low, and that of cytochrome a_3 is higher than $+0.25$. The potential of cytochrome f (HILL and SCARISBRICK 1949) is stated to be 0.35 volt (DAVENPORT 1952).

Large differences in the oxidation-reduction potential naturally have a strong tendency to shift the equilibrium in one direction, which e.g. makes impossible the simple reversal of the reaction $a_3 \text{ e } O_2$. The equilibria between the cytochromes b and c and between these and cytochrome c_1, however, are reversible. The electron conductor provides a smooth-running system, suitable for the transfer of electron energy to systems which come into action at different points, e.g. in high-energy phosphate formation.

Universal inhibitors for the cytochrome system are HCN and CO, which block the cytochrome oxidase (a_3), since they form CN- or carbonyl-compounds with the iron atom. Especially characteristic is the dissociation of the CO-linkage in light. WARBURG (1928) utilised this reaction for his elegant identification of cytochrome oxidase as a haem enzyme. LEMBERG (1953) isolated from heart muscle the protoporphyrin A of cytochrome oxidase. He believes that it is provided with a long lipophile chain, which according to him may determine the close combination of this enzyme with the cell structure. Cytochrome oxidase, according to MARINETTI et al. (1957), may contain 33% of lipids, of which 14.7% are phospholipids. The haemochromogen of cytochrome oxidase has an α-band at about 585 mμ.

If cytochrome oxidase (a_3) is inhibited by cyanide, the electron transfer to oxgyen diminishes sharply and the intensity of respiration sinks correspondingly. The inhibition is dependent on the oxygen tension (LUNDEGÅRDH 1957) which suggests, as well as the chemical blocking of Fe, a competitive depression of the $CN \rightleftharpoons O_2$ equilibrium at the surface of the enzyme. The cytochrome oxidase of baker's yeast reacts with O_2 according to a reaction of the first order and thus extensively affects the reaction kinetics of the whole system, since because of the intensive dehydrogenase activity, the oxidase remains partly reduced, even with good ventilation. Since a_3 is a specific cytochrome c oxidase, cytochrome c is also indirectly blocked by HCN, although in itself it reacts only weakly with CN on account of the protected position of its iron atoms. The other cytochromes, e.g. b, b_3 and c_1, are also fairly insensitive towards cyanide inhibition.

All cytochromes are, at least at certain pH values, autoxidisable, but it has been found that this property is of practical importance only where cytochrome b is concerned. In wheat roots and other plant organs only about half of the aerobic respiration is inhibited by cyanide. A 'ground respiration' remains, and it has been found that in this cytochrome b enters as a substitute oxidase (LUNDEGÅRDH 1955). On account of the reversible equilibria this 'b-shunt' effects some secondary oxidation of cytochrome c, but the effect of this ground respiration remains very modest relative to the salt accumulation (see Chap. 6) and the growth. The fact that the CN-inhibition of root respiration gradually falls off (LUNDEGÅRDH 1950) indicates, however, that the cell has ways of modifying the configuration of the effective oxidases.

II. *Peroxidase and Catalase*

(A) *Peroxidase* was first described by WILLSTÄTTER (1928). Later KEILIN and HARTREE (1951), THEORELL (1951) and others studied its properties. The prosthetic group, protohaem IX, is the same as in cytochrome b. It is fairly loosely bound and can e.g. be split off by HCl in cold acetone. The molecular weight of horseradish peroxidase is 44,100, and each molecule contains a haematin group and an atom of Fe, which normally is oxidised and *in vitro* can be reduced only by dithionite. The spectrum is then greatly changed, and the high Soret (γ) band of the brown pigment at 404 mμ is shifted to 437 mμ and instead of the diffuse raising of the extinction at about 500 mμ an α-band occurs at 556 mμ.

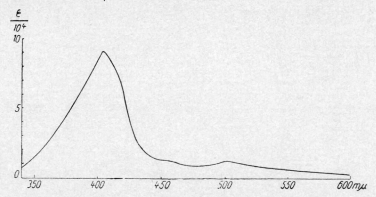

Fig. 94. Absorption spectrum of horseradish peroxidase in aqueous solution.

Peroxidase is especially characteristic of plants; in animal tissues it occurs only seldom. It occurs usually in amounts which considerably exceed those of the cytochrome present. One of the best-known sources for peroxidase preparation is horseradish, in which the absorption spectrum of the reduced enzymes can be observed directly with a hand spectroscope. But cereal roots also contain considerable quantities, amounting to 12-20 μmole per kilogram in wheat.

The presence of peroxidase can be determined qualitatively by the brown coloration of phenols, e.g. catechol, in presence of H_2O_2. The purpurogallin method of WILLSTÄTTER (formation of yellow purpurogallin from pyrogallol) can be utilised also as a semi-quantitative method.

Peroxidase readily forms complexes, and many of them have been studied spectrophotometrically. The CN- and F-complexes are formed in living tissues even at very low concentrations of cyanide and fluoride (Figs. 95, 96).

Special interest has been shown in the complex with H_2O_2, since this transfers oxygen very easily to a number of acceptors. It has for some time been believed that this reaction chain, which occurs somewhat as follows:

$$\text{peroxidase } H_2O_2 + \text{acceptor } H_2 \rightarrow \text{peroxidase} + 2H_2O + \text{acceptor} \qquad (43)$$

also represents the main reaction of the enzyme in living tissues. Hydrogen peroxide, in the opinion of many biochemists, is formed in certain oxidations, e.g. the autoxidation of flavoprotein, and it has been imagined that in this the peroxidase has a protective function, since H_2O_2 is an extremely poisonous substance.

The H_2O_2-complexes of peroxidase are distinguished by characteristic absorption spectra, but, because of the high reactivity of the compound, it is difficult to use them as indicators of possible H_2O_2 reactions in living tissues. Hydrogen peroxide has never been found with certainty in living cells. In the above-mentioned series of reactions it has mostly been assumed that the peroxidase remains in the oxidised state. Some workers, e.g. KEILIN, are of the opinion that the iron atom of peroxidase, like that of the cytochromes, suffers a change of valency in certain reactions.

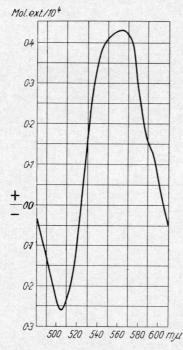

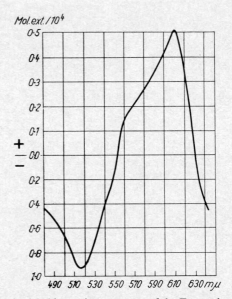

Fig. 95. Absorption spectrum of the CN-complex of peroxidase (after LUNDE-GÅRDH 1955).

Fig. 96. Absorption spectrum of the F-complex of peroxidase (after LUNDEGÅRDH 1955).

The long-unsolved question of the function of the peroxidase, which is found almost everywhere, has been considerably clarified in recent years. KENTEN and MANN (1953) showed that some organic acids are oxidised by peroxidase in the presence of manganous ions (Mn^{++}). The process may possibly be connected with an electron exchange $Mn^{++} \underset{e}{\rightleftharpoons} Mn^{+++}$. A considerable stimulation of the respiration of wheat roots by manganous ions had already been observed (LUNDEGÅRDH 1939). Another possible use for the peroxidase in the cells might be the oxidation of ascorbic acid and flavanones, which are almost always present (HUSZAK 1938, LUNDEGÅRDH and STENLID 1944). Tryptophan, tyrosine, histidine, catechol and other phenols are also oxidised by peroxidase.

MASON et al. (1957) speak of 'hydroxylation', i.e. a peroxidic activation of oxygen. THEORELL and SWEDIN (1939) had already found an oxidising effect of peroxidase on dihydroxyfumaric acid. In this a molecule of oxygen is consumed per molecule of fumaric acid. In this reaction peroxidase is inhibited by CO, similarly to cytochrome oxidase. The peroxidase thus behaves in many respects like a cytochrome, and the complexes show cytochrome-like absorption spectra. This originally led to the assumption of a new cytochrome 'dh' of the b-type (with protohaem IX as the prosthetic group), which later however proved to be a peroxidase complex occurring under anaerobic conditions (LUNDEGÅRDH 1957). In wheat roots apparently fumaric acid and probably also flavanones behave as complex-formers. The peroxidase · dh-complex is extraordinarily easily oxidised and appears only on extensive removal of oxygen and after the reduction of cytochrome. Absorption bands are found at 424 (γ), 540 (β), and 571 (α)mμ. Simultaneously with the appearance of the dh-complex the bands of oxidised peroxidase disappear.

Peroxidase possibly reacts with the cytochrome system, somewhere near the b-stage, but the easy autoxidation of the complex suggests a direct oxidation which, like that of cytochrome oxidase, is very easily inhabited by CN. Peroxidase cannot therefore take part in ground respiration.

According to data of RAY and THIMANN (1956), STUTZ (1957) and others, peroxidase complexes may cause the oxidative inactivation of auxin (β-indolylacetic acid). It has also been suggested that peroxidase may be effective in the formation of lignin (LYR 1957); coniferyl alcohol might be oxidatively polymerised to lignin-like products.

Peroxidase may occur in certain fungi as an ectoenzyme. The peroxidase of wheat roots is brought into solution fairly easily and shows no close structural affinity with the cytochrome system. The strong stimulation of formation of peroxidase · dh-complex by ATP probably indicates a collaboration of the peroxidase in oxidative phosphorylation (cf. below).

All haem enzymes show peroxidase activity to a limited extent (LEMBERG and LEGGE 1949; cf. KEILIN and HARTREE 1951). In baker's yeast a 'cytochrome peroxidase' has been mentioned (cf. also LENHOFF and KAPLAN 1953). In milk a 'lactic peroxidase' and in leucocytes a 'verdi- or myeloperoxidase' occurs.

(B) *Catalase*, unlike peroxidase, is present mostly in animal tissues. Its prosthetic group is also protohaem IX (ZEILE and HELLSTRÖM 1930), with the difference that four Fe-porphyrin groups are present per molecule of catalase. The molecular weight, about 250,000, is also much higher than that of peroxidase.

Chemically there is no great difference between catalase and peroxidase, which suggested to THEORELL (1951) the term 'hydroperoxidases' for both. Catalase has a distinctive behaviour towards hydrogen peroxide, which gives up oxygen in this case without the help of an acceptor, according to the equation:

$$2H_2O_2 \rightarrow O_2 + 2H_2O \qquad (44)$$

It was primarily this 'catalytic reaction' that gave rise to the hypothesis already mentioned of an intracellular 'guard' against H_2O_2. Catalase however, like peroxidase, can also utilise substrates other than H_2O_2, e.g. secondary alcohols. The activity is then dependent on the length of the chain of the substrate molecules. This fact suggested the idea that the active centre of the catalase molecule is not so easily accessible as it is in peroxidase, where it lies on the surface.

Catalase is one of the most effective enzymes known. A milligram of catalase produces from H_2O_2 at 0°C no less than 2,749 litres of oxygen per hour. A trace of oxygen must however be present initially. The function of catalase in the living cell is still largely unknown. A direct collaboration in photosynthesis has been deduced from the preferential occurrence of catalase in green leaves. Since the original view about the formation of H_2O_2 in the photolysis of water has been dropped (cf. Chap. 3), no definite interpretation of the function of catalase has been reached.

III. Other Iron-porphyrin Compounds

A compound very widespread in nature is haemoglobin, whose prosthetic group, protohaem IX, is closely related to that of cytochrome b and the hydroperoxidases; but its haem iron occurs in the reduced form as Fe^{++}. Haemoglobin compounds have been found in the nodules of Leguminosae and in certain micro-organisms (KEILIN 1953).

Haemoglobin is not an enzyme, but is only a carrier of oxygen molecules. Whether similar carriers occur also in plant cells appears doubtful since it has been found that oxygen diffusion from an air-saturated solution is quite sufficient for normal respiration e.g. of cereal roots. Some adsorption of O_2 may take place at the surface of cytochrome oxidase (cf. above).

The synthesis of the porphyrin nucleus is a fairly simple process, which may be carried out in all young cells. The starting materials are glycine and succinic acid (cf. p. 37). It is therefore suspected that many cells have a porphyrin reserve which can be used as required for the synthesis of cytochromes, peroxidase, etc. It has been found that in wheat roots the cytochrome content is dependent on the salt nutrition, and that an optimum is reached at the concentration which is best suited for growth (LUNDE-GÅRDH 1954; cf. Fig. 93). The previous history of seeds, e.g. the conditions of harvest, also influences the effectiveness of the cytochrome system. In yeast also the formation of iron-porphyrin enzymes has been found to be dependent on external conditions such as ventilation. In animal tissues and in certain micro-organisms there are un-specific haems, iron proteins, ferritin or ferrichrome (NEILANDS 1955). Such iron reserves have not been found in higher plants.

(b) Other Enzymatically-active Metalloproteins

The fundamental importance of iron in oxidation-reduction enzymes depends on valency changes. Other heavy metals also show valency changes connected with electron transport, and it has been suspected that, in the activity of peroxidase, there is a reversible change from $Mn^{+++} \underset{e}{\rightleftharpoons} Mn^{++}$. It seems, however, that free metal ions are involved rather than a manganese enzyme.

As activators of arginase, manganous ions can be replaced partly by copper or nickel ions. This activates can be written as follows:

$$\text{Proarginase} + Mn^{++} \rightleftharpoons \text{arginase} \cdot Mn^{++} \tag{45}$$
$$\phantom{Proarginase + Mn^{++} \rightleftharpoons} \text{(inactive)} \text{(active)}$$

Free copper ions also seem to evoke catalytic effects in living cells. Such effects can often occur in homegenates and inactivate the enzymes. To fix the interfering traces of heavy metal the homogenate is treated with cystëine or ethylenediamine tetraacetic acid (EDTA). Copper ions can, however, occur also as prosthetic groups of important enzymes, which are termed *copper oxidases*. The copper atom here is mostly combined directly with the apoenzymes. From animal tissues, however, haematocupreins are also known (DAWSON and TARPLEY 1951).

The phenol oxidases (*tyrosinase, laccase*) catalyse the oxidation of monohydric and *ortho*dihydric phenols to their corresponding quinones according to the following equations:

1. $2\,Cu^{++} +$ [Pyrocatechol (catechol)] $\underset{+\,2\,H}{\overset{-\,2\,H}{\rightleftharpoons}}$ $2\,Cu^{+} +$ [o-Quinone (*ortho*benzoquinone)] $= O + 2\,H^{+}$ (46)

Pyrocatechol
(catechol)

o -Quinone
(*ortho*benzoquinone)

2. $2\,Cu^{+} + 2\,H^{+} + \tfrac{1}{2}O_2 \rightleftharpoons 2\,Cu^{++} + H_2O$

The process is reversible and represents the transfer of hydrogen to oxygen. The enzyme is most simply prepared from fungi, e.g. *Agaricus campestris*, or from *Solanum tuberosum*. KUBOWITZ (1937, 1938) observed a linear relationship between the copper content and the activity of the enzyme preparations. The molecular weight is estimated at about 100,000 with a copper content of 0·25%, equivalent to four atoms of Cu to one enzyme molecule.

In agreement with the equation (46) it is believed that through the activity of the phenol oxidases Cu^{++} is reduced to Cu^{+} by transfer of an electron from the substrate which in this way is oxidised to a quinone. The reduced copper atom may then be oxidised by oxygen. It must, however, be remarked that the assumption of the transport of an electron is still hypothetical (cf. BONNER 1957).

One of the enzymes longest known (since 1895) is *laccase*, which occurs in the Indochinese lacquer tree *Rhus vernificera* or *Rh. succedana*. The yellow sap of the tree is converted by laccase into black lacquer. The polyphenols urushiol and laccol act as substrates.

According to MASON (1955) the phenol oxidases fulfil important functions in the life of plants e.g. in the formation of flavonoids, tannins, etc. The well-known browning of seeds, fruits, barks, etc., may also be caused by the phenol oxidases. L-Tyrosine is oxidised to 3,4-dihydroxy-L-phenylalanine ('dopa') which can then be further oxidised to brown melanins.

Little is yet known about the possible collaboration of phenol oxidases in respiratory processes, although various hypotheses have been suggested. Most data about the supposed respiratory properties of copper enzymes involved neglect to apply methods which would show the collaboration of the cytochrome system. On account of the relatively slow autoxidation of the phenyl oxidases (see also below) it may be supposed that their most important function is an intermediary electron transport in anaerobic metabolism.

Ascorbic oxidase, which was discovered by SZENT-GYÖRGYI in 1931, catalyses the oxidation of ascorbic acid (AA) by oxygen. Very active preparations were obtained from cabbage, pumpkins, etc., and in general this enzyme seems to be widespread in plants. It is a copper protein. Its marked specificity limits the reaction to substances with a dienol structure, similar to L-ascorbic acid. JOSELOW and DAWSON (1951) state that the molecular weight is about 150,000. The copper atom is exchangeable only in active, not in resting enzymes. On oxidation dehydroascorbic acid (DAA) and water are formed (p. 112). The oxidation of AA by free cupric ions on the other hand yields H_2O_2.

Ascorbic oxidase is inhibited by cyanide like other copper enzymes. Soluble ascorbic oxidase is, however, insensitive towards CO. Complex-formers such as diethyldithiocarbamate inhibit. It is found that NADH and NADPH are oxidised by ascorbic systems with the collaboration of glutathione reductase (MAPSON and GODDARD 1951) and also by triosephosphate, malic acid and alcohol, but the possible collaboration of this copper enzyme in normal respiration is still incompletely understood (cf. W. D. BONNER 1957).

According to THIMANN, YOCUM and HACKETT (1954) ascorbic oxidase, because of the slow course of the oxidation, can hardly be considered as a normal respiration enzyme. JAMES, however, states that ascorbic oxidase may partly replace cytochrome oxidase in ageing barley roots. In summary it may be said that ascorbic oxidase, which appears to be located not in mitochondria but in the surface of the cell, can be utilised for oxidations when the oxygen supply is abundant. This is possibly also the reason why copper enzymes are most energetically effective in cut surfaces or in homogenates. In addition there is of course the possibility that ascorbic oxidase, like the flavoproteins, collaborates in the intermediary transfer of electrons.

Ascorbic oxidase has a molecular weight of 146,000, with 0·26% Cu. The colour of the oxidised enzyme is bluish-green, but on reduction it assumes a light yellowish-brown hue.

(c) *Flavoprotein enzymes*

The 'yellow ferment' discovered by WARBURG and CHRISTIAN (1932) in Lebedew sap of yeast has been found to be a lacto- or flavoprotein (KUHN, KARRER *et al.*). The prosthetic group, which THEORELL (1934) separated from the protein by electrophoresis, is a flavin monophosphoric acid or a *flavin mononucleotide* (FMN).

The majority of flavin enzymes contain as prosthetic group *flavin adenine dinucleotide* (FAD; see below). One of the enzymes is D-*amino acid oxidase* (KREBS 1933), others belong to the group of 'cytochrome c reductases' or *diaphorases*, of which one representative was isolated from yeast.

Flavin adenine dinenucleotide (FAD) (CHRISTIE *et al.*, 1953).

The molecular weight of the flavoproteins is estimated at 68,000 to about 80,000 (MAHLER *et al.* 1952). From the low dissociation constant (about $1\text{-}250 \times 10^{-9}$) it can be concluded that the flavin, in itself inactive as a catalyst, is very strongly attached to the protein. The kind of linkage influences the characteristic fluorescence of the flavin, which is chiefly used as the analytical criterion. Spectrophotometrically the flavins are identified by absorption bands at 275, 355-380 and 440-470 $m\mu$, which disappear on reduction. The position of the bands is somewhat variable in the different flavo-protein enzymes (Fig. 91, p. 164).

At least seven different flavoproteins have been isolated. Most of them are reduced by pyridine nucleotides (NAD or NADP), and the reoxidation occurs via the cytochrome system, at first cytochrome b or cytochrome c_1. The flavoproteins are also autoxidis-able, but the reaction appears not to be quick enough for an independent oxidase.

Although *succinic dehydrogenase* is also a flavoprotein (cf. below), many observa-tions suggest that a diaphorase or second flavoprotein closely collaborating with NAD collaborates in the respiration cycle. The flavoproteins usually appear to be very closely connected with cytochrome b, e.g. in yeast, in equimolecular combination. Each flavoprotein molecule contains a flavin group, or about 0.5% of flavin. Through rapid spectrophotometric recording it has been possible to ascertain in the oxido-reduction of flavoprotein the formation of semi-quinoidal intermediate stages (BEINERT 1956, 1957).

Glucose dehydrogenase or *notatin* is an enzyme discovered by D. MÜLLER (1928) in *Aspergillus niger* and *Penicillium glaucum*. It catalyses the oxidation of glucose by oxygen with the formation of gluconic acid and H_2O. It owes its name notatin to the occurrence of the enzyme in *Penicillium notatum* where it acts like an indirect anti-biotic on account of H_2O_2 formation. *Xanthine oxidase* from milk behaves similarly in this respect (GREEN and PAULI 1943). Notatin acts as a dehydrogenase and is very specific for glucose (KEILIN and HARTREE 1948).

A tendency of the flavin enzymes to associate with metal ions and thus to acquire new specific properties has recently been discovered. Succinic dehydrogenase, which for a long time could not be separated from cytochrome b, has been found by recent investigations with baker's yeast (SINGER, MASSEY and KEARNEY 1957) to be a yellowish brown protein, which contains four iron atoms with one molecule of flavin. Succinic dehydrogenase therefore contains no haem, but it is oxidised by the cytochrome system. *Fumaric dehydrogenase* also may be a ferroflavoprotein.

A green *copper-containing protein* collaborates in the initial oxidation of saturated fatty acids (CRANE *et al.* 1955). Butyryl-coenzyme A-dehydrogenase is stated also to be a copper flavoprotein. In combination with *molybdenum* a flavoprotein enzyme forms a *nitrate reductase*, which has an important function in the nitrogen economy of green plants (see Chap. 5).

Riboflavin (*lactoflavin* or *vitamin* B_2) is very widespread in plant tissues. According to WATSON and NOGGLE (1947), leaves of oats contain nine times as much flavo-protein as the stalk. The roots synthesise riboflavin independently. The presence of this yellow pigment has been shown to be connected with growth- and tropistic reactions (see Chap. 9). There seem to be also certain relationships between flavin formation and auxins and antiauxins (GUSTAFSON 1955). In wheat roots flavin forma-tion appears to be competitively influenced by cytochrome formation (LUNDEGÅRDH 1954).

The tendency of the flavoproteins to combine actively with metal atoms can be considered, in view of their close association with cytochromes of the b-type, as the expression of a general tendency to complex formation. It has already been mentioned that in baker's yeast cytochrome b and flavoprotein react in about equimolecular combination (LUNDEGÅRDH 1956). Whether in this case there is a direct multi-enzyme formation between succinic dehydrogenase and cytochrome b is not known with certainty.

In baker's yeast there is a cytochrome b_2 which also occurs in equimolecular combination with flavin as *lactic dehydrogenase*. This multi-enzyme, according to BOERI and TOSI (1956), has a molecular weight of about 230,000 and one molecule of FMN and one molecule of haem, together with 8 iron atoms not bound with haem. Lactic dehydrogenase is insensitive to cyanide and does not oxidise NADH. Here also the haem enzyme has been isolated as a cytochrome b_2 from the flavoprotein (YAMASHITA *et al.* 1957).

(d) *Pyridine Nucleotide Enzymes* (*Codehydrogenases*)

The prosthetic groups of these enzymes consist of adenine, nicotinamide, pentose and phosphoric acid (see formula). There are two groups of enzymes, according to whether two or three phosphate groups are esterified with the pentose. Codehydrogenase 1 (formerly termed diphosphopyridine nucleotide, DPN, now NAD), also called coenzyme I or cozymase, has two phosphate groups, whereas codehydrogenase II (formerly termed triphosphopyridine nucleotide, TPN, now NADP), also called coenzyme II, contains three.

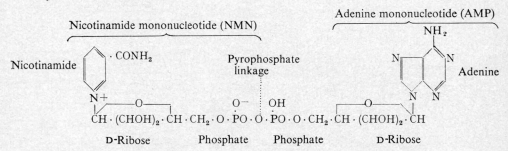

Diphosphopyridine nucleotide (NAD) (Codehydrogenase I or Cozymase).

NAD was discovered in yeast by HARDEN and YOUNG (1906), and NADP was first isolated from horse erythrocytes (WARBURG *et al.* 1935). NAD is more widely distributed than NADP, but conversion of the coenzymes into each other can be carried out under the influence of ATP.

The codehydrogenases are white, amorphous, readily water-soluble substances. They are excellently characterised spectrophotometrically by a strong absorption band at 340 mμ. The molar extinction of this band amounts to $6\text{-}7 \times 10^3$ per litre; it appears only in the reduced state (NADH) and is therefore usually utilised for measurements of the oxidation-reduction state.

The codehydrogenases take up hydrogen from various substrates and are reoxidised by enzymes of a more positive potential, e.g. flavoproteins. The hydrogen transfer $(2H^+ + 2e)$ probably goes through intermediate stages of a semi-quinoidal character (formulae below; SCHLENK 1951).

Oxidoreduction of the pyridine group of codehydrogenases. For R_2 and R_1, see the formula on page 174; R_1=ribose residue; R_2=phosphate radical(s) [one in codehydrogenase I (NAD), two in II (NADP), plus ribose residue and adenine.

The codehydrogenases can be combined with a number of apoenzymes. In this way many key enzymes of the intermediate hydrogen transfer in glycolysis and oxygen respiration are formed. Because of the transferability of the coenzymes from one protein to another the term 'mobile coenzymes' was coined (PARNAS 1943). Thus NAD takes part in numerous systems with lactic acid, malic acid, α-glycerophosphoric acid, etc. Among the reaction components may be mentioned also acetaldehyde and glyceraldehyde.

Glyceraldehyde-3-phosphate dehydrogenase in yeast and muscles catalyses an important reaction in glycolysis:

$$\text{D-3-phosphoglyceraldehyde} + \text{phosphate} + \text{Co I} \rightleftharpoons$$
$$\rightleftharpoons \text{D-1,3-diphosphoglyceric acid} + \text{Co I} \cdot H_2 \tag{47}$$

Lactic dehydrogenase governs the reaction:

$$\text{L-lactic acid} + \text{Co I} \rightleftharpoons \text{pyruvic acid} + \text{Co I} \cdot H_2 \tag{48}$$

Alcohol dehydrogenase governs the reaction:

$$CH_3 \cdot CH_2 \cdot OH + \text{Co I} \rightleftharpoons CH_3 \cdot CHO + \text{Co I} \cdot H_2 \tag{49}$$

Aldehyde dehydrogenase governs the reaction:

$$R \cdot CHO + H_2O + \text{Co I} \rightleftharpoons R \cdot COOH + \text{Co I} \cdot H_2 \tag{50}$$

Malic dehydrogenase governs the reaction:

$$\text{L-malic acid} + \text{Co II} \rightleftharpoons \text{oxalacetic acid} + \text{Co II} \cdot H_2 \tag{51}$$

In equation (51) NADP thus serves as prosthetic group. Coenzyme II is also active in *glucose-6-phosphate dehydrogenase*, the so-called 'intermediate ferment' of WARBURG and CHRISTIAN, which converts glucose-6-phosphate to 6-phosphogluconate. A further enzyme, which oxidises D-isocitric acid to oxalosuccinic acid, also contains NADP.

Glutamic dehydrogenase catalyses one of the stages which lead from L-glutamic acid to α-ketoglutaric acid $+ NH_3$. Here NAD as well as NADP appear to be effective. The oxidoreduction of glutathione ($2 SH \rightleftharpoons 2S + 2H^+ + 2e$) and cystëine $\rightleftharpoons$ cystine are also governed by NADPH and NADH respectively.

Certain pyridine nucleotide enzymes have very high molecular weights, whereas those of the alcohol dehydrogenases amount to about 70,000-140,000.

The activity of the pyridine nucleotide enzymes (cf. SCHLENK 1951, SINGER and

KEARNEY 1954) appears to be very dependent on the presence of intact sulphydryl groups. The coenzyme is combined in the reduced state with the apoenzyme, but it is clear that the linkage is not specially firm. Through the enzyme linkage the 340 mμ absorption band is shifted, viz. with NADH in alcohol dehydrogenase to 325 mμ, and with NAD in glyceraldehyde-3-phosphate dehydrogenase to about 360 mμ. These shifts facilitate the study of the kinetics of the linkage between apoenzyme and co-enzyme (see Fig. 92, p. 164).

(e) *Thiamine-protein Enzymes*

After the identification of vitamin B_1 as the hydrochloride of thiamine chloride; (formula on p. 237) by WILLIAMS *et al.* (1936) there followed the discovery of the identity of cocarboxylase with thiamine pyrophosphate (TPP) (LOHMANN and SCHUSTER 1937). *Keto acid decarboxylases* can be defined as enzymes which catalyse the abscission of CO_2 from keto acids. One of the longest-known of these reactions is the conversion of pyruvic acid into acetaldehyde by the reaction:

$$CH_3 \cdot CO \cdot COOH \rightarrow CH_3 \cdot CHO + CO_2 \qquad (52)$$

Decarboxylases are widespread in plants. The apoenzyme is activated by a number of divalent cations, of which Mg^{++} and Mn^{++} are especially effective; but the trivalent Al^{+++} and Fe^{+++} show no effect. Another enzyme of this group is *α-ketoglutaric decarboxylase*.

Thiamine pyrophosphate (TPP) catalyses also the oxidative decarboxylation of pyruvic acid to acetic acid, a process that is probably connected with the formation of high-energy phosphate. The oxidative decarboxylation of α-ketoglutaric acid to succinic acid is one of the stages of the citric acid cycle (see below, p. 196).

(f) *Other Oxidation-reduction Enzymes*

The enzymes described above are predominantly active in oxidative breakdown of carbohydrates. There are, however, also examples of direct oxidation of fatty acids.

A *lipoxidase* from soya beans causes the oxidation of unsaturated fatty acids. This enzyme has a molecular weight of about 100,000, and neither metal atoms nor other dissociatable prosthetic groups have been found in it. This soya-bean lipoxidase is specialised on methylated unsaturated systems, in which the double bonds are in the *cis*-position (HOLMAN and BERGSTRÖM 1951). Several types of unsaturated compounds are oxidised, e.g. carotenoids, chlorophyll, haematin, ascorbic acid and amino acids.

One of the numerous hypotheses about the course of fatty-acid oxidation predicates that the oxygen molecule in an active —O—O— configuration is 'cloven', and destroys a double bond of the substrate with the formation of peroxide. After the breakdown of the peroxide oxygen can be transferred to another substrate molecule. This idea may be valid, e.g. for the oxidation of carotene. By lipoxidase the lipoids can thus be involved in oxidative breakdown.

An oxidation starting at the double bond between two carbon atoms occurs also in simpler organic acids, e.g. fumaric acid—maleic acid ($HOOC \cdot CH = CH \cdot COOH$). The oxidation can go e.g. via addition of water and subsequent dehydrogenation through an H-acceptor. A reversible oxidation of double bonds can also take place by phosphorylation and subsequent dehydrogenation

The *oxidative deamination* of amino acids is catalysed by D-*amino acid oxidase* (see p. 172).

1. Alanine + oxidase→pyruvic acid + NH_3 + reduced oxidase
2. Reduced oxidase + O_2→oxidase + H_2O_2 (53)

Pyridoxal phosphate is the prosthetic group of the *amino acid decarboxylases* and *transaminases* (see formula). Bivalent cations (Mg^{++}, Mn^{++}, etc.) serve as activators

$$CHO$$
$$HO \cdot \quad \cdot CH_2 \cdot O \cdot PO_3H_2$$
$$H_3C \cdot$$
$$N$$

Pyridoxal phosphate (a codecarboxylase *inter alia*).

(OCHOA 1951). Transaminases are abundantly present in leaves (LEONARD and BURRIS 1947) and also in yeast and bacteria. They are specific for different substrates. The effect of pyridoxal phosphate has been studied in tyrosine, lysine and arginine.

The oxidation of ascorbic acid, which occurs in almost all plant tissues, is carried out by copper oxidases (p. 170) but the part of this reaction in oxidative metabolism is still incompletely known.

It has already been mentioned that some workers (e.g. JAMES *et al.* 1943, 1944, WAYGOOD 1950) ascribe to ascorbic acid an important function in respiration, whereas others believe that it is not an indispensable member of the respiratory reaction chain. Dehydroascorbic acid is unstable at pH values higher than about 5, but it may be supposed that the oxidation of ascorbic acid is protected e.g. by glutathione, probably also by α-hydroxyacids (JAMES and CRAGG 1943). It is stated (BOSWELL and WHITING 1940) that ascorbic oxidase is less widespread than ascorbic acid. Because of its low molecular weight AA is otherwise very suitable to function as a mobile hydrogen carrier, which could participate as a regulator in metabolic oxidation-reduction (see also below).

C. The General Course of the Oxidation Processes

1 THE METHOD OF OPERATION OF RESPIRATORY ENZYMES

Oxidation processes working with oxygen as the end-acceptor are combustions of the hydrogen of organic compounds occurring in small stages. Oxygen respiration can be considered as a modified or 'tamed' Knallgas reaction. HABER, WILLSTÄTTER, MICHAELIS *et al.* have referred to the importance of a stepwise electron transfer, by which reaction barriers can be more easily overcome, and an opportunity be given to capture the high total combustion energy of hydrogen in smaller doses at different places along the electron conductor.

With the carbon of the respiration material the behaviour is somewhat different. A direct oxidation of carbon comparable with that of hydrogen does not occur. Usually the organic carbon is oxidised indirectly to CO_2 by a number of dehydrogenations of oxygen- (and hydrogen-) containing compounds, including water. The CO_2 appears in respiration. This is illustrated for glucose, by far the most usual respiratory material, by the following model reactions:

$$1. \ C_6H_{12}O_6 + 6H_2O \rightarrow 6CO_2 + 24H$$
$$2. \ 24H + 6O_2 \rightarrow 12H_2O$$

$$\overline{\qquad\qquad\qquad\qquad\qquad\qquad\qquad\qquad\qquad\qquad\qquad}$$ (54)

$$3. \ C_6H_{12}O_6 + 6O_2 \rightarrow 6CO_2 + 6H_2O$$

The final separation of carbon as CO_2 proceeds usually via the carboxyl group —COOH of the organic acids and takes the form of a *decarboxylation*. This decarboxylation, which we will consider in greater detail below, occurs with only a small turnover of energy. The greater part of the energy gain, about 113 kg-cal per mole of CO_2 released, thus originates from the oxidation of hydrogen. Oxygen respiration is thus a dehydrogenation with subsequent stepwise oxidation of the hydrogen, as has been elucidated especially by THUNBERG and WIELAND.

WARBURG's term 'oxygen-transferring enzyme' for cytochrome oxidase is thus not correct. Cytochrome oxidase does not transfer oxygen to the respiration material, but activates the oxygen, so that it can take up hydrogen atoms already half-oxidised as protons.

True aerobic respiration occurs in the oxidation systems, but a release and conversion of the respiration material must precede it. In this complicated mechanism, which we term *glycolysis*, hydrogen comes into a steric position appropriate for dehydrogenation and carbon is separated out as CO_2.

Of the oxidative systems so far discovered, only the cytochrome system occurs generally and can be considered as universally dominant in both higher and lower plants. It should not, however, be overlooked that other systems, such as peroxidase complexes and copper proteins, can also in certain circumstances co-operate in respiration at least in the oxidation stages, as mentioned above. It is, however, still not clear whether and how these substitute oxidases are supplied with protons and electrons by special dehydrogenases.

For the cytochrome system there are two sources of supply of protons and electrons, viz. succinic dehydrogenase and the pyridine nucleotide (PN) enzymes. Succinic dehydrogenase, which is a ferroflavoprotein, takes up hydrogen from succinic acid, which in this way is oxidised to fumaric acid. These two acids are members of a cyclic transformation of the pyruvic acid appearing as the end product of glycolysis and are important for the transfer of organically combined hydrogen.

The pyridine nucleotides take up hydrogen in combination with various apoenzymes (see above, p. 174), and the mobility of the coenzyme facilitates the transfer of hydrogen to flavoproteins, through which the splitting into protons and electrons probably follows. In yeast, which also has succinic dehydrogenase, the pyridine nucleotides are much more dominant than in higher plants. Baker's yeast contains about 40 times as much NAD as cytochrome b, but in wheat roots the amount of NAD is also 5-30 times more than that of cytochrome. Table 7 shows some interesting comparisons of the relative quantities of the cytochromes in yeast and in wheat roots; the double concentration of cytochrome b in roots is particularly striking.

Table 7

Relative Molar Concentration of the Respiration Enzymes, calculated on the Quantities reacting in the Change of Oxidation and Reduction

Enzymes	Cyt. a_3	Cyt. a	Cyt. c	Cyt. c_1	Cyt. b	Cyt. b_3	FP
Baker's yeast	1	1	2	(1)	2	—	4—6
Wheat roots	1	1	2	1	4	1	8

Cytochrome b is most abundant in the roots, a fact which is connected with its ability to act as a substitute oxidase as already mentioned. The ground respiration still remaining after blocking of cytochrome oxidase by cyanide probably proceeds mostly through this b-shunt to oxygen (cf. the respiration plan on p. 165).

The intensity of oxygen respiration is dependent partly on the absolute content of enzymes, and partly also on the ratio between dehydrogenases and oxidases. As may be seen from Table 8, the average concentration of cytochrome a amounts to about 9×10^{-6} mole per kg of dry weight in wheat roots, whereas yeast contains about eight times as much. Animal tissues, e.g. heart muscle, contain more cytochrome than plants. The intensity of respiration per unit of cytochrome oxidase is, however, about the same in yeast and wheat roots (see Table 8). The turnover number, i.e. the number of electrons transferred to oxygen per minute, is also about the same in animals and plants, i.e. about 1,700 at 19°C (LUNDEGÅRDH 1952).

Table 8

Respiration and Concentration of Respiratory Enzymes in Yeast and Wheat Roots (dry weights)

	Cytochromes in 10^{-6} mole per kg			NAD	Cyanide-inhibitable respiration in moles per 10 mg per hr
	a	b	c		
Yeast	70	70	70	2800	5·0—7·5
Roots	9	34	17	30—250	1·0—2·0

The balance between dehydrogenases and cytochromes reveals itself as follows: with a high content or high effectivity of the dehydrogenases the cytochromes in normal respiration remain more reduced than with more weakly effective dehydrogenases. In yeast fed with glucose or alcohol the cytochrome system remains mostly reduced. The oxidation of cytochrome oxidase consequently becomes the respiration-regulating process (LUNDEGÅRDH 1956, 1957).

This strong shift of the balance in fed yeast towards a predominant reduction of the cytochrome system is due not only to the high concentration of NAD (Table 8) but also to the high turnover number of the NAD-enzymes. The electron transfer proceeds in $NAD \overset{e}{\underset{e}{\rightleftharpoons}} NADH$ more than ten times as fast as in cytochrome oxidase.

Because of the weaker activity of the dehydrogenases, in normally-respiring wheat roots the cytochromes remain oxidised to the extent of 60%-80%. This is the case also

N

with the flavoproteins, which co-operate also in the b-shunt, that is in ground respiration (LUNDEGÅRDH 1954).

A relatively high effectiveness of the dehydrogenases as compared with the oxidases is shown reaction-kinetically in the high speed of reduction of the cytochrome system, as compared with the course of the oxidation. The ratio speed of oxidation/speed of reduction is accordingly low in normally-respiring yeast, but high in wheat roots (see Table 9). High values of the ratio can, however, also be obtained in yeast by reducing the influence of the dehydrogenases by the inhibiting factor antimycin A (p. 165), which blocks cytochrome b.

Table 9

Ratio of speed of oxidation/speed of reduction

Enzyme	Normal yeast	Yeast + antimycin A	Wheat roots
cyt. a_3	0·34	3·9	2·7
cyt. c	0·50	5·7	2·3
cyt. b	2·00	blocked	5·2
FP	1·20	3·5	10·7

MICHAELIS (1940) assumes that all oxidations occur in two univalent steps. This means that an intermediate stage, i.e. a free radical, is passed through. This radical (S) is usually short-lived and is reversibly related to the reacting components, according to the equation

$$2S \rightleftharpoons red + ox \tag{55}$$

This may be expressed as follows: the free radical and the co-operation of the enzyme divide the available energy in a lower (ox) and a higher (red) stage, a process which is comparable with a *dismutation*. A substance is dismuted when it is decomposed without access of energy from outside into a higher and a lower state of oxidation. The classical example of dismutation, the Cannizzaro reaction, is the formation of an alcohol and a carboxylic acid from an aldehyde:

$$2R \cdot CHO + H_2O \rightarrow R \cdot CH_2OH + R \cdot COOH \tag{56}$$

In the above discussion the importance of the activation energy for the starting of an irreversible reaction has been mentioned several times. It can be assumed with MICHAELIS that the instability of the free radical acts like a brake. MICHAELIS sees the function of the enzyme as a stabilisation of the radical, whereby the speed of reaction is increased. This goal can be reached e.g. by the combination of the enzyme protein with the substrate, whereby the electron transfer is facilitated. The apposition of two closely fitting molecules also lowers resistance to reaction.

For the speed of reaction it is not only the oxidation-reduction potential of the components that is decisive (see p. 166), but also the reaction constants of the formation and decomposition of the radical.

How the electron transfer takes place between the individual cytochromes is not yet known. For the transition between b and c SLATER (1950) has assumed a 'factor' not chemically characterised in detail, which may occur as an intermediate enzyme or stable radical. Other workers believe that competitive inhibitions have an effect.

The fact that on exclusion of oxygen a 'latent stage' exists between the reduction of cytochrome c and cytochrome b (i.e. that c is largely reduced, before the reduction of b begins), supports the view that the molecules of the individual cytochromes are not arranged directly one after the other like pearls on a string. It is more likely that the individual enzymes are organised as multi-molecular complexes, which through the intermediary of a 'reaction centre' transmit the electron stream somewhat as in an impulse generator. It may also be noted that the diversion, actually found, of the electron stream to energy-rich compounds, e.g. ATP (see below), would scarcely be understandable without the activity of intermediary factors.

2 OXIDATIVE PHOSPHORYLATION

The organic ester linkages with phosphoric acid play a great part in the cleavage of the carbon skeleton of glucose, with the result that on further breakdown by dehydrogenation and carboxylation less resistance is encountered. This ester linkage $(R \cdot O \cdot PO_3H_2)$ corresponds to about 3kg-cal. The high-energy phosphate linkages, which, following LIPMANN, are indicated with $\sim$ph, on the other hand show an energy storage of 9-16 kg-cal. (KALCKAR 1942, 1947, 1951). The ester linkages are fairly strong and are hydrolysed only with difficulty. The $\sim$ph linkage is less stable and therefore more readily transfers its energy content to other processes.

The high-energy content of the $\sim$ph linkage depends on the molecular configuration, which in acyl phosphates is as follows:

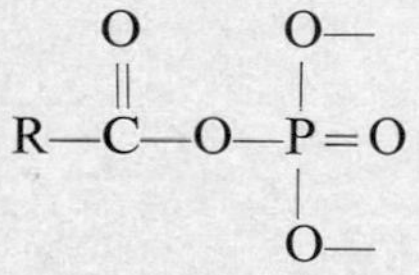

$$R-\overset{\overset{\displaystyle O}{\|}}{C}-O-\overset{\overset{\displaystyle O-}{|}}{\underset{\underset{\displaystyle O-}{|}}{P}}=O \tag{57}$$

High-energy phosphates, which can also show the pyrophosphate configuration, have been described by LOHMANN, LIPMANN, WARBURG and NEGELEIN, and others.

The adenosine phosphates have (in ADP) one or (in ATP) two $\sim$ph groups. The individual phosphate group of adenosine monophosphate (AMP, also called adenylic acid) is of the ester type (indicated by LIPMANN as —ph). The phosphate groups are in a side-chain, somewhat as in the following diagram:

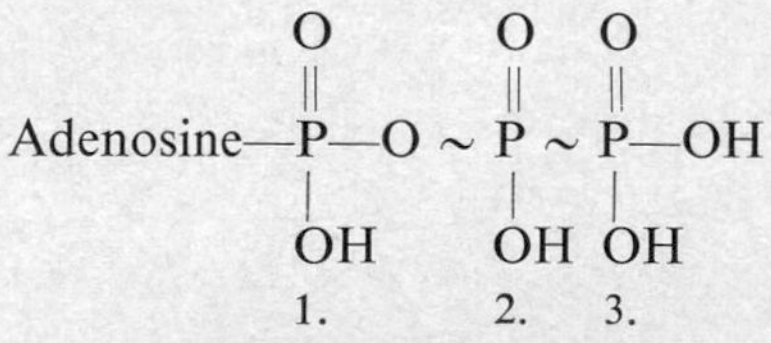

$$\text{Adenosine}-\overset{\overset{\displaystyle O}{\|}}{\underset{\underset{\displaystyle OH}{|}}{P}}-O \sim \overset{\overset{\displaystyle O}{\|}}{\underset{\underset{\displaystyle OH}{|}}{P}} \sim \overset{\overset{\displaystyle O}{\|}}{\underset{\underset{\displaystyle OH}{|}}{P}}-OH \tag{58}$$

$$1. \qquad\qquad 2. \qquad 3.$$

The end phosphate group is readily hydrolysed, releasing about 12 kg-cal. The second group, which shows a similar energy value, can be split off in a similar way. The first phosphate group can be removed only with difficulty, and yields only 2-3 kg-cal. In Table 10 are given (according to KAPLAN 1951, p. 92) some examples of reactions which are supplied with phosphate linkage energy.

Table 10

Reactions supplied with the Energy from Phosphate Linkages

Reaction	Free energy (ΔF° kg-cal.)	Syntheses
1. Formation of glycoside linkages	$+3$—4	Sucrose
2. Ester formation	$+3$	Acetylcholine
3. Peptide linkage	$+3$	Glutathione
4. Amide linkage	—	Arginine
5. Keto acid formation	$+16$—17	Pyruvic acid, acetoacetate
6. β-Carboxylation	$+5\cdot28$	Oxalacetic acid
7. Fatty acid synthesis	-10	Butyric acid
8. Aldol condensation	$+4\cdot68$	Citric acid
9. Transmethylation	—	Creatine
10. Carboxyl reduction	$+16$	Reduction of phosphoglyceric acid to phosphoglyceraldehyde

As far as known at present many reactions in which $\sim$ph is formed (an exception is the enolase reaction in glycolysis—see below) are combined with oxidation processes. This is *oxidative phosphorylation*, by which an important part of respiration energy is supplied.

$$\sim P(1) \qquad\qquad\qquad\qquad \sim P(2) \qquad \sim P(3) \qquad\qquad \sim P(4)$$

$$\alpha\text{-Ketoglutaric acid} \rightarrow \text{Lipoic acid} \rightarrow \text{NAD} \rightarrow \text{FP}_1 \rightarrow \text{Cyt. b} \rightarrow \text{Cyt. c} \rightarrow \text{Cyt. a}_3 \rightarrow O_2$$

$$\uparrow \qquad\qquad\qquad \uparrow$$

$$\text{Glutaric acid} \qquad \text{FP}_2$$

$$\uparrow$$

$$\text{Succinic acid}$$

Diagram of oxidative phosphorylation in the aerobic respiration chain (after SLATER 1957).

The P/O ratio in an oxidative phosphorylation is an expression for the efficiency of the process. In the oxidation of pyruvic acid to CO_2 and H_2O, a process which occurs naturally via a series of intermediate steps, five electron pairs are transferred to oxygen. These five electron pairs yield a total of 6 volts, which corresponds to a change in free energy of $277\cdot5$ kg-cal., an amount theoretically equivalent to $17\cdot3$ $\sim$ph linkages. The calculated P/O ratio for a conversion into phosphate energy would theoretically amount to about $3\cdot5$. OCHOA found experimentally the value 3, not far from that calculated. Thus in the total oxidation of pyruvic acid practically the whole of the free energy is stored in high-energy phosphate.

According to LIPMANN (1948, 1949) *coenzyme A* (CoA) (formula below, cf. NOVELLI 1953) plays the part of a carrier of activated acetyl groups, e.g. in the conversion of α-ketoglutaric acid into succinic acid as follows (LITLEFELD and SANADI 1952):

$$1.\ \alpha\text{-ketoglutaric acid} + \text{NADH} + \text{CoA} \underset{\text{oxylase}}{\overset{\text{cocarb-}}{\rightleftharpoons}} \text{succinyl} \cdot \text{CoA} \tag{59}$$

$$2.\ \text{Succinyl} \cdot \text{CoA} + PO_4 + \text{ADP} \rightleftharpoons \text{succinate} + \text{CoA} + \text{ATP}$$

CoA can also collaborate in the condensation of 2 C-fragments (acetic acid) to oxalacetic acid. Another example of the collaboration of $\sim$ph and CoA is given by the conversions of pyruvic acid. Pyruvic acid can occur as a donator of acetyl groups for CoA. Acetyl phosphoric acid ($CH_3 \cdot COOPO_3H_2$) is easily formed by dismutation

$$\underset{\substack{\quad\\ \text{Pyrophosphate} \mid \text{linkage}}}{\underset{\substack{| \\ O=P-OH \\ | \\ O}}{\underset{\substack{\\ \cdots\cdots O \cdots\cdots \\ }}{\underset{\substack{| \\ O=P-OH \\ | \\ O}}{\underset{\substack{| \\ CH_3}}{\overset{\substack{CH_3\;\; OH \;\;\;\; O \\ | \quad\; | \quad\;\; \| \\ CH_2-C-CH-C-N-CH_2-CH_2-C-NH-CH_2-CH_2-SH \\ | \qquad\quad H}}{}}}}}}$$

CH₃ OH O ... O
| | || ||
CH₂—C——CH——C—N—CH₂—CH₂—C—NH—CH₂—CH₂—SH
| | H
O CH₃   Pantothenic acid   Thioethanolamine
|
O=P—OH
|
·············O················   OH
Pyrophosphate | linkage |
O=P—OH   O=P—O⁻
| |
O   O
| |
CH₂——CH————CH—CH—CH— Adenine
                    |
                   OH
                    |
          ————— O —————

Adenylic acid

Coenzyme A

of pyruvic acid in presence of NAD, in which lactic acid is formed at the same time. On the other hand, with the supply of energy from ATP, pyruvic acid can be formed from acetic acid and formic acid.

To summarise, it can be said that high-energy phosphate may be formed in two ways, by intra-molecular energy transfer or by oxidative phosphorylation.

A further example of the first way is given by ATP-formation in the transfer of D-glyceraldehyde-3-phosphate into 3-phosphoglyceric acid and in the transfer of succinyl-CoA into succinic acid + CoA. These reactions are not inhibited by dinitrophenol.

The path requiring free oxygen is of course directly combined with aerobic respiration and is stopped both by dinitrophenol and by a number of other inhibitors which block cytochrome b.

It can be calculated that in the oxidation of glucose theoretically 688/11 = about 63) high-energy phosphate molecules can be formed. Experimental investigations give the value 38-40 $\sim$ph for the total oxidation of a molecule of glucose to CO_2 and H_2O. This gives a yield of 60%-64%, which is a good efficiency in comparison with man-made machines. The remaining 36%-40% is lost in plants as heat, but in warm-blooded animals would also be of use. Of the 38 $\sim$ph mentioned the majority are associated with the electron transfers in the oxidation chain.

The $\sim$ph groups formed by anaerobic processes can therefore fix only a small part of the full energy content of the glucose molecule, since these processes always end in an incomplete oxidation, that is, they do not go fully to CO_2 and H_2O. This is the reason why almost all living organisms are so greatly dependent on oxygen respiration for 'creative activity', i.e. growth and reproduction.

Examples of the importance of the $\sim$ph groups as 'energy-stores' in anabolism have already been given above, and further examples are mentioned in later sections. In general it may be said that endergonic reactions can also go on without energy supplied by $\sim$ph, provided that the equilibrium constants are not too unfavourable (not larger than 10^4) and that a coupling with a reduction process is available. There may be other energy-yielding groups besides phosphate (SLATER 1953).

Large concentration differences between reactants and products can also be effective in smaller energy transfers, e.g. in peptide formation (about 3 kg-cal.); but the $\sim$ph energy is undoubtedly the most convenient and most utilisable energy transport medium. It is known that it can be utilised also for mechanical purposes, e.g. in muscular work of animals. Plants do not require to make any rapid mechanical movements, but growth and the maintenance of turgor are also mechanical effects. A very important synthetic activity, in which $\sim$ph probably co-operates, is the synthesis and maintenance of the protoplasmic structure, which provides for all metabolic work and the uptake and transport of dissolved compounds (more on this in Chap. 6).

D. Alcoholic Fermentation

Alcoholic fermentation by yeast requires the co-operation of twenty or more apoenzymes (proteins), at least three or possibly as many as eight soluble coenzymes and in addition a number of activators, e.g. NH_3, K, Mg, Mn and Cu. About a dozen intermediate reactions can be investigated with the help of suitable inhibitors.

The end-products of alcoholic fermentation are CO_2 and C_2H_5OH. No enzyme system has been investigated in greater detail, and the results obtained have yielded a relatively complete picture of the whole process. The enzymes *phosphorylases* and *phosphatases* as well as transferring and isomerising enzymes (*mutases* and *isomerases*) take part. A number of them have been isolated and their prosthetic groups identified (see Section B). Modern investigations on alcoholic fermentation began with the discovery by HARDEN and YOUNG of the fructose 1,6-diphosphate, which occurs as an intermediate product, the so-called Harden-Young ester.

Glycolysis (i.e. the anaerobic degradation of sugar) begins with the formation of the previously mentioned Cori ester, α-glucose-1-phosphate (see Fig. 97). The Cori ester arises either through the exchange of a glucoside group in starch or cane sugar with a phosphate group, or by a direct transfer of a phosphate group from ATP to a glucose molecule. The intervening enzyme here is *hexokinase*. ATP is formed continuously during alcohol fermentation (see below). The direct introduction of a phosphate ester linkage into glucose corresponds to about 3 kg-cal., whilst the exchange with a glucoside linkage is connected with only a small energy change.

Through phosphorylation the sugar molecule is prepared for a split into two fragments. The position of the ester linkage in the molecule is of decisive importance.

The Cori ester is reversibly converted to fructofuranose 6-phosphate by the enzyme *oxoisomerase*. A second phosphate group is then supplied from ATP by the enzyme *phosphohexokinase*, and fructofuranose 1,6-diphosphate (the Harden-Young ester) arises. There is probably also a side conversion, catalysed by *isomerase*, of glucose 6-phosphate into fructose 6-phosphate, the so-called Neuberg ester.

The sugar molecule is now prepared for a split into two halves. These 3-C-fragments or trioses are 1-phosphodihydroxyacetone and 3-phosphoglyceraldehyde. The enzyme concerned, *aldolase*, was isolated and crystallised by WARBURG and CHRISTIAN (1943). By inhibition of the glycolysis with monoiodoacetic acid the trioses can be made to accumulate. They are inter-converted by the efficient enzyme *phosphotriose-isomerase*.

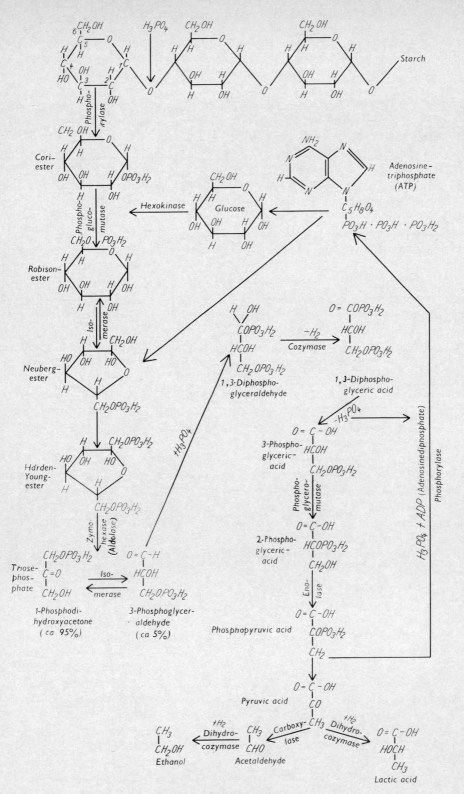

Fig. 97

The equilibrium between the two triose phosphates at normal temperature (20°C) is strongly (about 95%) towards the side of phosphoglyceraldehyde. This compound is the starting point for further reactions. No metabolic derivatives of phospho-dihydroxyacetone have been discovered.

After the original hexose has been split without noteworthy energy losses into phosphorylated hexoses, the next stage is an oxidoreduction. As a preliminary 1,3-diphosphoglyceraldehyde is formed by the introduction of a second phosphate group. Whether an enzyme is concerned in this is not yet known.

The 1,3-diphosphoglyceraldehyde now undergoes a dehydrogenation, whereby 1,3-diphosphoglyceric acid is formed. The effective enzyme is the previously mentioned NAD-enzyme *triose phosphate dehydrogenase*. This reaction is the one that is inhibited by monoiodoacetic acid which blocks the SH-groups of the enzyme. By the intra-molecular oxidation the phosphate group in position 1 is raised to a higher energy state. This reaction is one of the phosphorylations in which dinitrophenol is ineffective as an inhibitor (cf. above).

The ~ph group in the 1-position is now transferred to ADP, and thus 3-phospho-glyceric acid is formed together with ATP. The process is catalysed by *phosphoglycero-kinase* and the 3-phosphoglyceric acid is then converted into 2-phosphoglyceric acid by *phosphoglyceromutase*. All these reactions are reversible.

The energy level of the glucose fragments now sinks further, as 2-phosphoglyceric acid passes by the second dehydrogenation in the series into phosphoenol pyruvic acid. The phosphoric acid group in this is raised to the high energy level (~ph). The active enzyme is *enolase*, with Mg as activator. The enzyme is easily inhibited by fluoride with the formation of magnesium fluorophosphate. The enol form of the pyruvic acid may also go over into the more stable keto form, but the enol form is probably more directly concerned.

The new ~ph group of the phosphopyruvic acid is now transferred to ADP, whereby ATP (the second in the series) and pyruvic acid are formed. The dephospho-rylation is catalysed by a *phosphokinase* together with Mg or Mn^{++} and K (on which Ca has an antagonistic effect).

Pyruvic acid occupies a central position in metabolism. From it radiate a number of biochemical reaction chains, some of which have already been dealt with above. In alcoholic fermentation pyruvic acid is decarboxylated by the agency of carboxylase (see p. 158) to acetaldehyde. Carboxylase is also widespread in higher plants. Alcohol is then formed by dehydrogenation of the acetaldehyde. The enzyme *alcohol dehydro-genase* (p. 175) here utilises NADH (reduced Coenzyme I) as the prosthetic group, which was reduced in the dehydrogenation of diphosphoglyceraldehyde. The hydrogen atoms are now transferred to $CH_3 \cdot CHO$, which is hydrogenated to C_2H_5OH. In the muscles of animals pyruvic acid is reduced to lactic acid. Lactic acid is also formed in plants under anaerobic conditions (JAMES and CRAGG 1943, JAMES 1946, 1957).

A sideline of glycolysis of technical importance is the formation of *glycerol*. In the fermentation of sugar normally about 3% of the sugar is converted into this triol (tri-basic alcohol). Glycerol is formed by dephosphorylation and reduction of phosphoglyceric acid. In industry the yield of glycerol is increased by adding bisulphite to the fermenting mash. The bisulphite fixes the acetaldehyde and thus hinders its function as an acceptor for the hydrogen of the reduced coenzyme I. In its place as hydrogen acceptor phosphodihydroxyacetone now comes in and is reduced to phosphoglycerol which is hydrolysed to glycerol by yeast-phosphatase. A molecule of glucose yields a molecule of glycerol, a molecule of the aldehyde bisulphite compound and CO_2. There are also two other routes to the formation of glycerol. With lipase and condensation products of acetaldehyde and acetic acid it finally forms fats (cf. p. 100).

The scheme sketched here for alcoholic fermentation is based on intensive experimental work by EMBDEN, MEYERHOF and many other workers (see OPPENHEIMER 1939, MANN 1944, NORD and WEISS 1951 et al.). There are, however, still uncertainties, e.g. about the function of the various hexose phosphates. Hexose diphosphate is formed in comparatively large quantities in the initial stages of fermentation, but is fermented further only slowly. If, however, triose formation proceeded from glucose monophosphate, one of the halves formed by the cleavage would have to remain without phosphoric acid, and such a product has not yet been found.

The fact that the initial stage of fermentation occurs either by substituting a glucoside linkage with phosphoric acid or by direct phosphorylation of simple hexoses, is of considerable physiological interest. With starch as respiration material the process is regulated by amylase, an enzyme which, however, is not present in yeast. The amylases are formed in the germination of starch-containing seeds. They are previously formed in seeds and are activated by the removal of an inhibitor (KNEEN and SANDSTEDT 1943). Certain salts and ascorbic acid may also co-operate in the activation of amylase.

From the point of view of energy, alcoholic fermentation liberates about 50 kg-cal. as free energy (KAPLAN 1951). The summary reaction is:

$$C_6H_{12}O_6 \rightarrow 2CO_2 + 2CH_3CH_2OH \tag{60}$$

glucose   ethanol

Two ~ph linkages, having about 23 kg-cal., are formed at the expense of each glucose molecule. This corresponds to about 46% of the total free energy, a rather lower efficiency than in oxygen respiration. The loss as heat (54%) causes the well-known spontaneous heating of the fermentation mash. As the alcohol formed by the cells is not changed further, there is only a small net yield of energy, which amounts to only about 7% of the theoretical value of oxygen respiration. Thus in intramolecular respiration the sugar reserves of the tissue are quickly expended.

E. Other Types of Fermentation

Alcoholic fermentation is the usual type of anaerobic degradation of carbohydrates, and the enzymes involved are present also in higher plants. In higher plants the formation of alcohol and the accumulation of acetaldehyde have been observed under anaerobic conditions. The expected ratio of $C_2H_5OH : CO_2 = 1$ has also been observed, e.g. in carrots. Wheat roots give for alcohol formation the characteristic ratio

glucose used/CO_2 formed $= 1/2$, and the ratio CO_2 aerobic/CO_2 anaerobic $= 1/3$.

As already mentioned, *lactic acid* can also occur as end-product of glycolysis. The general scheme for the formation of lactic acid probably applies also for the lactic acid bacteria, which cause acidification of milk and silage. The decarboxylation of pyruvic acid is absent in lactic acid formation, and the reaction takes the following form:

$$CH_3 \cdot CO \cdot COOH + 2H \rightarrow CH_3CHOH \cdot COOH \tag{61}$$

pyruvic acid   lactic acid

The conversion of a mole of glucose into two moles of lactic acid is combined with an energy gain of about 36 kg-cal., i.e. less than in alcohol formation. The amount of energy stored is however relatively higher as, just as with alcohol formation, two molecules of ATP are formed, which corresponds to about 64% of the free energy.

Butyric acid (butanoic acid, $CH_3 \cdot CH_2 \cdot CH_2 \cdot COOH$) is formed by a number of bacteria which take part in the degradation of cellulose in the humus layer of the soil. Some of these bacteria fix molecular nitrogen. The formation of butyric acid probably follows the general scheme of glycolysis as far as pyruvic acid, but from there proceeds via acetic acid and its recombination with CO_2 to butyric acid (BARKER *et al.* 1945).

Acetic acid can be formed from ethanol according to the following equation:

$$CH_3 \cdot CH_2 \cdot OH + O_2 \rightarrow CH_3 \cdot COOH + H_2O + 117 \text{ kg-cal.} \tag{62}$$

The alcohol is dehydrogenated to acetaldehyde. After hydration with H_2O and a second dehydrogenation acetic acid is formed. The hydrogen transfer is catalysed by dehydrogenases which are then oxidised by oxygen with the formation of H_2O_2. The H_2O_2 is finally catalytically decomposed (by catalase?) into H_2O and O_2. The high energy yield thus results from the oxidation of hydrogen. Oxygen can be replaced by an organic acceptor, and the reaction chain can then proceed anaerobically.

Other routes to acetic acid formation have also been observed. According to BARKER and KAMEN (1945) a species of *Clostridium* splits hexose into three molecules of acetic acid:

1. $C_6H_{12}O_6 + 2H_2 \rightarrow 2CH_3 \cdot COOH + CO_2 + 8H$
2. $8H + 2CO_2 \rightarrow CH_3 \cdot COOH + 2H_2$ \hfill (63)

Nett: $C_6H_{12}O_6 \rightarrow 3CH_3 \cdot COOH$

The accompanying chemosynthesis of CO_2 is widespread among micro-organisms (WIKÉN 1948). Fats are also formed by condensation of the initial products.

Methane fermentation usually implies the reduction of a fatty acid to methane, but the methane bacteria can also utilise CO_2 as the acceptor of hydrogen, which comes from alcohol. The alcohol is thus oxidised to fatty acid.

The study of micro-organisms thus brings to light a large number of redox processes, which often take other routes than via carbohydrates, and differ from the biochemical events in higher plants (see KLUYVER 1933, 1934, VAN NIEL 1953, UMBREIT, 1953).

F. Aerobic Respiration

1 THE RELATIONSHIPS BETWEEN AEROBIC RESPIRATION AND GLYCOLYSIS

Biochemical investigations of recent decades (viz. KLUYVER 1934 *et al.*) have confirmed the view that aerobic respiration, ending with complete oxidation and the liberation of the whole of the chemical energy of sugar, coincides in the initial stages leading to pyruvic acid with the initial stages of alcoholic fermentation.

The oxidase system which is dominant in almost all organisms, and which leads from pyruvic acid to CO_2 and water, is the flavoprotein-cytochrome system, that we have already depicted above in detail. About the point of attack of other oxidases, copper enzymes and peroxidase, there is considerable uncertainty and it has not yet been decided to what extent they take part in the biochemical transfer of energy.

An important side of respiration research is the study of the numerous related synthetic processes, e.g. amino acid and protein formation. We have already dealt with the intermediary function of the ∼ph linkages as 'packets of energy'.

Oxygen respiration is, as we have learnt, dependent on the equilibria round α-glucose1-phosphate. Through these equilibria the consumption of respiratory material (sugar and starch) is guided. The free pyranoses (that is hexoses with a six-membered ring made up of five C plus one O) are, however, brought into the respiration cycle through the intermediary of the ∼ph groups formed in glycolysis. In the condensed sugars there is generally a competitive balance between phosphorylation and hydrolysis (by invertase, amylase, phosphatase, etc.). The transport relationships in higher plants probably influence these enzyme equilibria since the free hexoses and cane sugar belong to the mobile carbohydrates.

The supply of inorganic phosphate is also of course one of the conditions for respiration, and it has sometimes been possible to discover a direct connection between respiration and phosphate uptake (JAMES 1946). In a similar way a direct relationship between the intensity of respiration and the concentration of glucose phosphate has often been found. Such observations have been made both in germinating roots and in leaves.

In barley embryos an inhibition of carboxylase evokes an accumulation of pyruvic acid. There is thus no doubt that the higher plants, like yeast and animals, have available a phosphorylation mechanism, which phosphorylates sugar and polysaccharides via phosphoglyceric acid to pyruvic acid. The glycolysis continues anaerobically also in higher plants as far as alcohol. This can also happen to some extent in the presence of oxygen.

The point of divergence between oxygen respiration and alcoholic fermentation seems to lie at the end of the glycolysis, thus approximately at the pyruvic acid, or possibly also at the acetaldehyde stage.

From pyruvic acid a transformation goes on to 2- and 4- C-acids and to amino acids. Via acetaldehyde a line also goes to acetic acid and fat formation. As the most usual end-product of anaerobic glycolysis, ethanol, is respired by most plants only with difficulty, the switching to oxygen respiration from here on should be excluded. Acetaldehyde is even more poisonous than alcohol for most of the higher plants, and it is therefore difficult to imagine it as a normal intermediate in respiration. Everything thus indicates a key position for pyruvic acid, although alternative routes are conceivable, e.g. via a system of triose phosphate, coenzyme I and dehydrogenases (WAYGOOD 1950), that could be directly connected to the cytochrome system (cf. pp. 182-3).

2 VARIOUS AEROBIC RESPIRATION SYSTEMS

Growing and salt-accumulating tissues, e.g. in roots (LUNDEGÅRDH and BURSTRÖM 1935, HOAGLAND and BROYER 1942, ROBERTSON 1944), seedlings, young leaves (JAMES and HORA 1940), embryos (GODDARD 1944), also yeast, etc., show a subdivision of aerobic respiration into two parts, which are distinguishable by different degrees of inhibition by cyanide. One part of the respiration, about 50% of the total respiration in wheat roots, but more in potato tissue, is inhibited at cyanide concentrations as low as $10^{-8} - 10^{-6}$ M. Almost as strong an inhibition of respiration is found with a mixture of 95% CO and 5% O_2, but this is overcome by strong light (SUTTER 1950, ROBERTSON and WILKINS 1951). The conclusion may be drawn that the part of the respiration inhibitable by cyanide is governed by the cytochrome system (cf. p. 153).

As peroxidase is also inhibited by extremely low cyanide concentrations (LUNDE-GÅRDH 1954, 1955) and this enzyme has been shown to occur in wheat roots (LUNDE-GÅRDH 1958), it might be considered that a certain fraction of the cyanide-inhibitable respiration proceeds via peroxidase (cf. p. 166).

In the part of the oxygen respiration which is almost unaffected by high concentrations of cyanide (0·01-0·05 M) probably neither cytochrome oxidase nor peroxidase takes part. On the other hand cytochrome b and $c + c_1$ can co-operate here, and the possibility of a b-shunt to oxygen, i.e. a cyanide-resistant cytochrome b oxidase combined with flavoprotein, has been suggested (p. 165). In wheat roots there is a positive relation between the intensity of the cyanide-resistant respiration and the flavoprotein concentration (LUNDEGÅRDH 1954).

An indication of the intensive collaboration of the cytochrome system in aerobic respiration is given by the amount of cytochrome found, which in wheat roots amounts to 22 mg of cytochrome c per kg of fresh weight or 240 mg per kg dry weight (LUNDE-GÅRDH 1952). The typical reaction for cytochrome oxidase with CO also excludes a comprehensive collaboration of phenol oxidases and ascorbic oxidases. The cytochrome system may, in addition, react with a cyanide more quickly than the copper oxidases (COMMONER 1940). The inhibiting effect of HCN on root respiration proceeds in fact extraordinarily quickly.

On the basis of the fact first demonstrated by LUNDEGÅRDH and BURSTRÖM (1935), that the cyanide-inhibitable part of oxygen respiration shows a quantitative connection with active salt accumulation, whilst the cyanide-resistant part of the respiration does not show this connection, one ordinarily distinguishes between *ground respiration* (i.e. the cyanide-resistant part) and *salt respiration* (i.e. the cyanide-sensitive fraction) (cf. Chap. 6). As salt respiration is combined with an active uptake of anions, the term *anion respiration* is also used (LUNDEGÅRDH 1958).

A distinction between ground respiration and salt- or anion-respiration should not be taken to indicate two sharply separated biochemical reaction chains. Much more probable is the assumption, already mentioned, of a shunt by way of flavoprotein and cytochrome b, which can maintain a more or less diminished respiration which provides little utilisable energy.

It has already been mentoned that in certain objects cyanide inhibition becomes still stronger at higher concentrations; which suggests attacks at places other than cytochrome oxidase. There may further be mentioned the peculiar adaptation to cyanide (LUNDEGÅRDH 1949) which suggests an important but as yet little-investigated multiplicity of respiratory enzyme chains. Similar internal reversals in the flavoprotein-cytochrome system are also observed in the effect of dinitrophenol and fluoride (p. 153). These inhibitors cut out cytochrome b, whilst the cytochrome oxidase with the help of cytochrome c and flavoprotein now supports a respiration which, however, on account of the interference of the system is apparently able to form little high-energy phosphate.

Riboflavin has been found in many tissues, e.g. in *Avena* coleoptiles (BONNER 1948) and wheat roots (LUNDEGÅRDH 1953, 1954). In ground respiration and also in peroxidase respiration manganese appears to be concerned as a co-factor (KENTEN and MANN 1949, 1951). Early statements of the absence of the cytochrome system from certain tissues are based mostly on inadequate methods of investigation. Renewed investigations with good biochemical and spectrophotometric methods have often corrected such ideas. This applies e.g. to potatoes (LEVY and SCHADE 1948, GODDARD and HOLDEN 1950, LUNDEGÅRDH 1958).

As early as 1909 PALLADIN suggested the idea that hypothetical 'chromogens' could be effective as hydrogen-carriers in respiration. He believed that further oxidation of hydrogen could result via phenols and quinones. WAYGOOD (1950) developed these ideas by asserting the presence in wheat roots of a system of ascorbic oxidase, an unknown pigment, and coenzyme.

For reasons already mentioned the collaboration of ascorbic oxidase in normal respiration is doubtful. On the other hand PALLADIN's hypothetical pigments may well be connected with the abundant occurrence of flavone compounds, since it has been found that these are conceivable as participants in an oxidation governed by peroxidase (LUNDEGÅRDH 1958). It may, however, be that only side lines of aerobic respiration are concerned. The same applies to the system constructed by MAPSON and GODDARD (1951), in which the hydrogen from carbohydrates passes via malic acid to glutathione $\rightarrow$AA$\rightarrow$O$_2$ and would have as enzymes glutathione reductase, ascorbic oxidase and flavoproteins.

An equilibrium or 'steady state' between alternative reaction chains may possibly be regulated by shifts in equilibrium or variations in activity of individual enzymes. The apoenzymes of many catalysts are sensitive towards shifts in the oxidation-reduction balance, particularly where enzymes with active SH-groups are concerned. The importance of protecting systems, e.g. glutathione, has already been emphasised several times. As an example carboxylase may be mentioned. The large increase of aerobic respiration on germination of *Neurospora* spores is connected with the activation of carboxylase by which the cytochrome system is also indirectly stimulated (GODDARD and SMITH 1938). A similar activation of respiration takes place after the fertilisation of ovaries (WHITE 1907).

Other aspects of activation are discussed in connection with enzyme synthesis. A mobilisation of the cytochrome system from haem reserves is observed during the sporulation of *Bacillus subtilis* (KEILIN and HARTREE 1947). Similar observations have been made on baker's yeast.

3 THE PASTEUR EFFECT

Since in anaerobic respiration (alcoholic fermentation) a molecule of glucose yields only two molecules of CO_2—as against six in aerobic respiration—an experimentally determined ratio

$$\text{anaerobic } CO_2/\text{aerobic } CO_2 = 1/3 \qquad (64)$$

means that the degradation of glucose is taking place in both with equal speed. Ordinarily, however, the ratio is found to be higher. In growing wheat roots, for example, the rate of CO_2 formation with and without oxygen is about equal.

In certain storage organs also ratios greater than 1/3 have been observed (APPLEMAN and BROWN 1946). This means that in the presence of oxygen relatively less glucose is used up. The phenomenon is known as the 'Pasteur effect', since as early as 1861 Pasteur made the observation that alcoholic fermentation of yeast was inhibited by oxygen (PASTEUR 1876). This effect has been much discussed. The various opinions can be summarised as follows (BURK 1939):

1. The so-called unitary theory, which was put forward by PFLÜGER and PFEFFER and their school, states that the intermediate products formed in the degradation of carbohydrates are either oxidised to CO_2 and H_2O, or are fermented to alcohol. This theory admittedly maintains the connection confirmed by later investigations between anaerobic and aerobic respiration, but it does not explain the fact that glycolysis is inhibited in presence of oxygen, with the result that the CO_2 quotient assumes values greater than 1/3.

2. The theory of MEYERHOF (1930) asserts that the intermediate products of glucose degradation are partially re-synthesised, according to the scheme:

(a) Carbohydrate→intermediate product;

(b) Intermediate product$+O_2$→carbohydrate$+CO_2+H_2O$.

According to this interpretation part of the combustion energy of the carbohydrates would be utilised for the reversal of the glycolysis. WARBURG also agrees with this idea in principle since he assumes a reaction which combines respiration and fermentation, that is a 'Pasteur reaction'.

The reason for this interpretation may well be the desire to be able to apply the scheme propounded by MEYERHOF to the muscle theory of the same investigator. According to this scheme, in resting muscle a re-synthesis of lactic acid to sugar takes place.

A chemosynthesis of carbohydrates is probably possible not only from lactic acid but also from other intermediate products (see under Section G). According to the investigations of BENNET-CLARK and BEXON (1943) it is conceivable that malic acid is re-formed via oxalacetic acid and pyruvic acid to phosphoglyceric acid and finally to carbohydrates. The equilibrium pyruvic acid$+CO_2\rightleftharpoons$oxalacetic acid is reversible and is activated by manganese.

F. F. BLACKMAN (1928) had already been led by his experiments on apples to the idea of an 'oxidative anabolism', i.e. a partial re-synthesis of carbohydrate from intermediate products of glycolysis. Presence of oxygen (i.e. the Pasteur reaction), according to THOMAS and FIDLER (1941), prevents the glycolysis from going too far. According to these authors the full oxidation of a molecule of hexose should protect two other molecules against degradation. A considerable oxidative anabolism has been found in carrots (APPLEMAN and BROWN 1946). In storage organs the anaerobic and oxidative paths of glucose degradation usually proceed in parallel during variations in the external conditions, but treatment with narcotics, e.g. ethylene bromide, accelerates the aerobic process more.

3. The hypothesis of LIPMAN (1941) lays down that oxygen through an intermediate factor inhibits one or several enzymes in the later stages of glycolysis. The points of view mentioned above for the switching of anaerobic to aerobic respiration agree in the main with this theory.

Some workers suggest that the inhibiting effect of oxygen on anaerobic glycolysis must depend on cytochrome oxidase. The activity of this enzyme in plants is not very dependent on the partial pressure, since a considerable reduction in respiration becomes noticeable only at about one-third of the normal oxygen content of air. It has been observed that the speed of glycolysis is influenced by variations of oxygen pressure which have little effect on the activity of cytochrome oxidase. From this it may be concluded that cytochrome oxidase does not enter directly into the Pasteur effect, but that the effect is dependent on other processes sensitive to oxygen.

Even though anaerobic glycolysis is inhibited by oxygen, there are still numerous examples both in yeast and in higher plants of 'aerobic fermentation' in growing cells. RUHLAND and RAMSHORN (1938) observed aerobic fermentation in meristematic tissues. In many mature tissues, however, fermentation is completely suppressed at normal oxygen pressure, which is expressed in the ratio $CO_2/O_2 \simeq 1$.

In growing wheat roots values of about 1·6 for this ratio are usually observed (LUNDEGÅRDH and BURSTRÖM 1935, LUNDEGÅRDH 1945), and they increase still further when the oxygen pressure diminishes. Aerobic glycolysis is an expression of the synthetic activity of the meristem in which materials are formed that have a higher energy value than the carbohydrates.

An intensive aerobic glycolysis has been observed in animal cancerous tissue (WARBURG), which might well be connected with the intensive cell multiplication. In non-growing plant tissues, on the other hand, little aerobic glycolysis is present. A further example of a low intensity of aerobic glycolysis is given by carrots, where appreciable fermentation first occurs only with a 50% inhibition of the oxygen respiration (MARSH and GODDARD 1939). Similar results were obtained by inhibiting aerobic respiration with HCN and CO. This therefore supports again the influence of the cytochrome system on the glycolytic enzymes (cf. above).

The monoiodoacetic acid technique introduced by LUNDSGAARD (1933) which inhibits triose phosphate dehydrogenase, according to TURNER (1938) failed when carrots were used. The exact position of the Pasteur reaction in the glycolysis chain thus cannot be very easily determined. One can imagine that carboxylase and alcohol dehydrogenase are possible key enzymes. Both contain active SH-groups, and are thus easily inactivated by oxidation.

G. Intermediary Systems in Aerobic Respiration

Although peroxidase, phenol oxidases and ascorbic oxidase undoubtedly participate to a certain extent in the oxidative metabolism of living plant tissues, the results available up to the present suggest that the cytochrome system is the most important in aerobic respiration.

The chief interest of the biochemist has always turned towards animal tissues and homogenates, and yeast and micro-organisms are also standard objects for respiration research, whereas detailed biochemical investigations on plant respiration were undertaken only more recently (review in BOSWELL and WHITING 1940, STILES 1945, 1946, BONNER 1951, JAMES 1953, 1957, etc.). The idea has, however, become more and more widely accepted that a considerable number of enzymes is common to all organisms and that the general course of the respiration reactions is also fairly universal, even if variations occur with respect to apoenzymes. The micro-organisms here again exhibit their role as the 'trial ground of nature', and among them are found special types of glycolysis, which have been suppressed in phylogenetic development. The agreement, or at least similarities, between the metabolic processes of animals and plants include the intermediary processes of respiration with their carboxylic acids and the amino acids linked with them.

1 THE GENERAL IMPORTANCE OF INTERMEDIARY SYSTEMS

One of the most important general results of biochemical research is undoubtedly the recognition of the importance of chain reactions. The speed of a redox reaction, i.e. the transfer of a proton and an electron to an acceptor, is partly determined by the oxidation-reduction potential. The collaboration of different redox systems is made difficult by too high potential differences. An example of the importance of an 'electron conductor' in the bridging of the large potential difference between dehydrogenases and oxygen has been mentioned earlier (cf. also OPPENHEIMER and STERN 1939). Free radicals also co-operate here.

Because of the easier passage of the intermediate stages of a chain reaction the individual members do not require to be present in measurable quantities. Isolation of intermediate products results mostly from the method by which specific inhibitors are added; the products behind the inhibited reaction can then be collected. On account of the shortness of the life of many of the compounds occurring as intermediate members of the chain, those isolated in measurable quantities are the more stable of them, whereas free radicals, e.g., were first revealed by oscillograph spectrophotometry. Paper chromatography and paper electrophoresis have, however, facilitated the isolation of many intermediate products occurring in small quantities.

The visible and submicroscopic organisation of the protoplasm is very important for the separation and independent progress of reaction chains, which act partly in opposite directions. Localisation of enzymes in various structures has often been found, the best known being the localisation of the cytochrome system in mitochondria. Peroxidase appears to work in other locations and certain copper oxidases and also transferring enzymes of glycolysis (invertase, hexokinase) have been found in the surface layer of cells (cf. also GODDARD and STAFFORD 1954).

Macromolecular enzymes of course tend to be bound to structures, whereas enzymes and coenzymes of smaller dimensions more easily fulfil the functions of transporters between different systems. Migratory activity of coenzymes, such as coenzyme I and II and probably to a certain extent also of riboflavin, greatly facilitates hydrogen transfer and oxidoreduction at different stages of glycolysis. It may thus often happen that the apoenzyme is bound to a structure, whereas the coenzyme remains mobile (soluble). In dry tomato seeds for example the protein part of carboxylase is pre-formed, whereas the coenzyme (thiamine pyrophosphate) is formed only during germination (BARTLETT 1942). Examples of long-distance transport of coenzymes are given also by vitamins.

2 THE TRICARBOXYLIC ACID (KREBS) CYCLE

The two dominating processes during the fermentative and respirative degradation of sugar are decarboxylation and dehydrogenation (THUNBERG 1933), which is expressed in the overall equation

$$C_6H_{12}O_6 + H_2O \rightarrow 6CO_2 + 24H \tag{65}$$

The hydrogen is taken up by a series of dehydrogenations from the sugar molecule, and the protons and electrons are transported by the cytochrome system to oxygen.

When the stage of pyruvic acid ($C_3H_4O_3$) is reached, a third of the hydrogen has already disappeared, whereas the C : O ratio is still the same as in glucose. Up to this stage no carbon has yet been separated.

The first loosening of the carbon skeleton is through the formation of a carboxyl group in the dehydrogenation of 1,3-diphosphoglyceraldehyde to 1,3-diphospho-glyceric acid. This carbon atom is then thrown off during the decarboxylation of the pyruvic acid to acetaldehyde. A shortage of hydrogen acceptors in glycolysis hinders the complete break-up of the carbon skeleton and consequently a complete decarb-oxylation. In contrast to this, the end-stages of aerobic respiration open up the opportunity for complete decarboxylation, through the fact that from the pyruvic acid there stem a number of organic acids which are decarboxylated one after another. The acids are bound together in a unique cycle by reversible equilibria. One speaks of the *tricarboxylic acid cycle* (TCA cycle) or citric acid cycle, or calls it after its discoverer the 'Krebs cycle'.

The formulae of the tri-, di- and mono-carboxylic acids concerned are set out side by side below (p. 197), following Fig. 98, which illustrates the TCA cycle; the inter-conversions by loss or gain of water, hydrogen, oxygen and/or CO_2 are thus more easily shown.

THUNBERG had discovered as early as 1920 that a number of acids, e.g. citric, tartaric, malic and fumaric acids, are oxidised by methylene blue by transfer of hydrogen. SZENT-GYÖRGYI (1935, 1937), KREBS (1937) and others continued THUNBERG's in-vestigations and showed that in animal tissues the end-oxidation was governed by a cycle of acids with two or three carboxyl groups. The individual members of the cycle are formed by a number of hydrations and dehydrogenations. The acids involved, which are all well-known 'plant acids'. were first recognised as intermediates in aerobic respiration in animal tissues, but later also in plant tissues.

In the original scheme of SZENT-GYÖRGYI two molecules of acetic acid were formed from two molecules of pyruvic acid. Two molecules of acetic acid were 'condensed' to succinic acid, with acetaldehyde as an intermediate. SZENT-GYÖRGYI then assumed a series of dehydrogenations and hydrations, which led from succinic acid via fumaric acid and malic acid to oxalacetic acid. Oxalacetic acid would then after decarboxyla-tion yield pyruvic acid again. SZENT-GYÖRGYI regarded fumaric acid as a catalyst. During a circuit of the Szent-Györgyi cycle a molecule of pyruvic acid would thus be degraded to CO_2 and H_2O, whilst the oxidation of the hydrogen would be provided for by the cytochrome system.

KREBS elaborated and extended the ideas of SZENT-GYÖRGYI and identified a number of further members of the cycle, especially *cis*-aconitic, isocitric and oxalosuccinic acids. In this way it was possible to explain, e.g. the formation of citric acid in animals and plants as well as the position of α-ketoglutaric acid as one of the most important constituents of protein metabolism (see Chap. 5). Other links with the formation of amino acids are pyruvic acid (to alanine) and oxalacetic acid (to aspartic acid). Not all details of the TCA cycle are yet completely clarified, but the present position can be summarised in Fig. 98.

Contrary to the earlier idea that acetic acid is an intermediate between pyruvic acid and the TCA-cycle, LIPMAN holds that *acetylphosphate* ($CH_3 \cdot COOPO_3 \cdot H_2$) or *acetyl CoA* (p. 100) come in as intermediates. It is imagined that coenzyme A acts as a bearer of '*active*' *acetic acid* radicals, and that this 'active acetate' is the starting point of the TCA-cycle. It reacts with the enol form of oxalacetic acid

O

and thus forms citric acid; coenzyme A and ATP collaborate. By successive dehydration and hydration citric acid is converted into *cis*-aconitic acid and isocitric acid, the effective enzyme being aconitase. Isocitric acid is converted by isocitric dehydrogenase (with Co II) into oxalosuccinic acid, which is decarboxylated with the aid of a Mn-decarboxylase and yields α-ketoglutaric acid. Oxidative decarboxylation via succinyl CoA yields CO_2 and succinic acid which is dehydrogenated by succinic dehydrogenase (cf. p. 173) to fumaric acid. Fumarase catalyses the hydration to malic acid, which is converted by malic dehydrogenase (with Co I) into oxalacetic acid, which after spontaneous enolisation again enters the cycle.

Each transit of the cycle thus effects the complete breakdown of a molecule of pyruvic acid into carbon dioxide and hydrogen according to the equation

$$C_3H_4O_3 + 3O \rightarrow 3CO_2 + 4H \tag{66}$$

The complete combustion of a molecule of pyruvic acid thus requires three oxygen

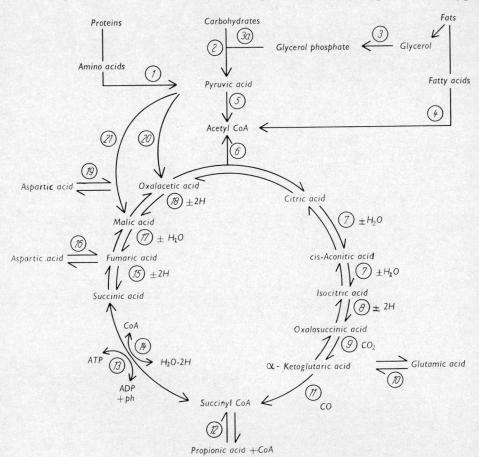

Fig. 98. The tricarboxylic acid (TCA) cycle. (1) Aminases. (2) Glycolysis system. (3) Glycerol kinase. (3a) α-Glycerol phosphate dehydrogenase. (4) Degradation of fatty acid. (5) Pyruvic oxidase. (6) Condensing enzymes. (7) Aconitase. (8) Isocitric dehydrogenase. (9) Oxalosuccinic decarboxylase. (10) Glutamic dehydrogenase. (11) α-Ketoglutaric oxidase. (12) Succinyl CoA carboxylase. (13) Succinyl CoA transphosphorylase. (14) Succinyl CoA deacyclase. (15) Succinic dehydrogenase. (16) Aspartase. (17) Fumarase. (18) Malic dehydrogenase. (19) Transaminases. (20) Oxalacetic decarboxylase. (21) Malic enzyme.

The formulae of these acids are:

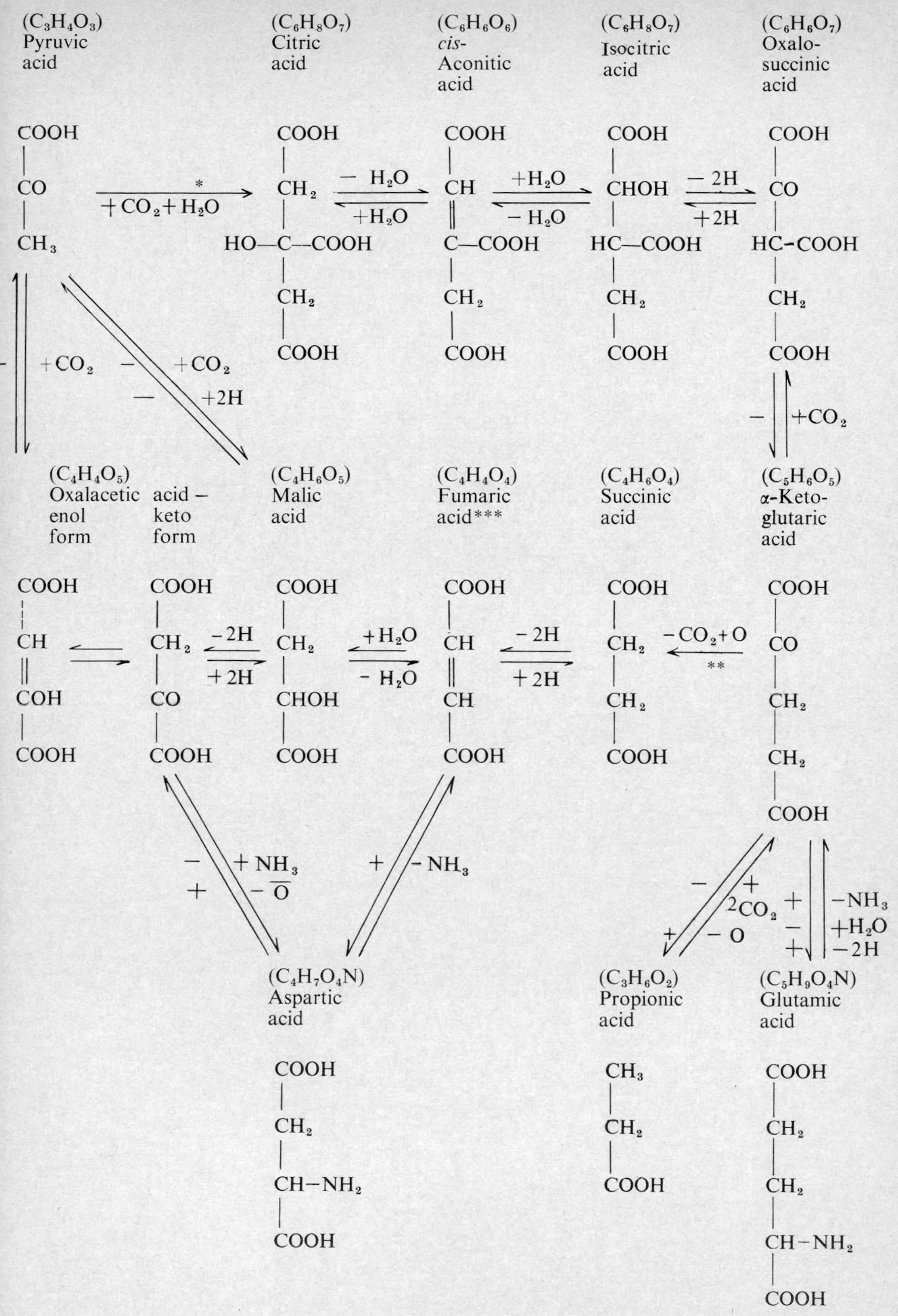

* With acetyl CoA [$CH_3 \cdot CO \cdot (CoA)$]

** Via succinyl CoA [$COOH \cdot CH_2 \cdot CH_2 \cdot CO \cdot (CoA)$]

*** Fumaric acid is the *trans* form, *i.e.* $HOOC \cdot CH = CH \cdot COOH$ (The *cis* form would be maleic acid).

atoms. Since molecular oxygen does not enter into the cycle, three molecules of water are used as the source of oxygen (see Fig. 98) equivalent to the uptake of six H atoms. Together with the four H atoms from the pyruvic acid this gives five pairs of hydrogen atoms that must be removed by H-acceptors and oxidised by oxidase systems.

The TCA cycle is a very efficient mechanism for the complete oxidation of any substance which can be converted into one of the acids concerned. On account of the side reactions, which lead to amino acids and fats (via Co A; see p. 183), the TCA cycle dominates large sections of the whole metabolism of the cell. Most of its individual reactions are reversible, probably with the exception of the oxidative decarboxylation of pyruvic acid and α-ketoglutaric acid. The latter reactions occurring only in one direction therefore determine the direction of rotation of the TCA-wheel (see, however, p. 200).

Several plant physiologists (see JAMES 1953) have identified most of the substrates and enzymes of the TCA cycle in plant tissues. The effect of certain inhibitors has been explored and it has been found that the state of dissociation is very important, since most substances enter into the protoplasm most rapidly in the form of molecules. The inhibition of succinic dehydrogenase by malonic acid thus occurs only at low pH values, e.g. with 0·1 M malonate at pH 3·2 (values below 3 are usually harmful; see p. 47, also TURNER and HANLY 1947, HANLY *et al.* 1952). The inhibitory effects of monoiodoacetic acid, fluoride and dinitrophenol are also strongly dependent on pH (STENLID 1947, LUNDEGÅRDH 1949, 1952).

The TCA cycle is responsible for the breakdown of the carbon skeleton of carbohydrates. The hydrogen concerned is mostly transferred by coenzymes and flavoproteins (succinic dehydrogenase) to the cytochrome system. Because of the labile equilibria between the participating systems, the final removal of hydrogen can be restricted to one or two points such as succinic dehydrogenase (POTTER 1946, KREBS 1951).

3 THE ENERGY YIELD OF CARBOHYDRATE OXIDATION

The dissipation of energy on complete combustion of a mole of glucose to CO_2 and H_2O amounts to about 688 kg-cal., and for each individual stage can be calculated from the differences in the oxidation-reduction potentials; but as these are known exactly only in a few cases, the calculation remains approximate. The supply of energy as $\sim$ph groups (see p. 181) is of special importance.

The direct measurement of the P : O ratio in the oxidation of pyruvic acid (cf. p. 182) suggests that a considerable percentage of the total energy is transferred to high-energy phosphate. In the oxidation of pyruvic acid five pairs of electrons and protons are transferred to oxygen. The potential jump amounts to about 6 volts; this corresponds to a free energy (ΔF) of 277 kg-cal., or about 17 $\sim$ph groups of 16 kg-cal. each (see Table 11).

OCHOA found the P : O ratio to be about 3·15 $\sim$ph, i.e. a utilisation of about 87%. Passing from glucose to pyruvic acid 8 $\sim$ph are formed. As the glucose molecule gives two molecules of pyruvic acid, the total yield is $8+30=38$ $\sim$ph, which corresponds to about 70% of the total energy. The storage as $\sim$ph of the energy contained in the glucose thus takes place anaerobically only to a rather unimportant extent. For effective $\sim$ph production oxygen is absolutely necessary.

Table 11

Energy Transfer in Oxygen Respiration

Hydrogen donator	$\Delta F°$ kg-cal. per electron pair	Maximum number of $\sim$ph
Pyruvic acid	$-72\cdot5$	$4\cdot5$
Isocitric acid	-51	$3\cdot2$
α-Ketoglutaric acid	$-72\cdot5$	$4\cdot5$
Succinic acid	-36	$2\cdot3$
Malic acid	-45	$2\cdot8$
Total	-277	$17\cdot3$

The decisive importance of aerobic respiration for 'creative metabolism' is shown by the fact that a number of organic acids, which are raw materials for amino acids and proteins, are members of the TCA cycle. The fundamental importance of oxidative phosphorylation has been explained above; in this ATP and acetyl-coenzyme A are the most important transporters of energy. The metabolism of the fats branches off from glycolysis (glycerol formation) and from oxidative carboxylation of pyruvic acid (cf. p. 195 and Fig. 98).

The reversibility of most TCA and glycolytic reactions allows them to go in the reverse direction for synthetic purposes. A number of heterotrophic bacteria utilise CO_2 for the formation of organic acids, beginning with the basic equation:

$$CO_2 + CH_3 \cdot CO \cdot COOH \rightleftharpoons COOH \cdot CH_2 \cdot CO \cdot COOH \qquad (67)$$
$$\text{Pyruvic acid} \qquad\qquad\qquad \text{Oxalacetic acid}$$

By means of this process the CO_2 produced in respiration can be brought back again into the synthetic activity. The butyric acid bacteria utilise CO_2 for the formation of acetic acid and butyric acid (BARKER *et al.* 1946; p. 188).

To what extent a similar inversion of respiration and glycolysis occurs in higher plants is not yet fully known. The principle, however, is clear, and the partial recovery of respiratory CO_2 has been observed e.g. in roots.

For an effective re-assimilation (chemosynthesis; see p. 115) a reversal of the formation of $\sim$ph is of course necessary, and has in fact been observed. It has long been believed that the difference of free energy between phosphopyruvic and enolpyruvic acid, about 8 kg-cal., could not be overcome, and that on this account it might serve as a valve that would allow only a downward flow of energy. The reversal of the reaction was however successfully carried out by CORI (1946) and other biochemists.

Oxidative carboxylations, which were often considered to be similar valves, are also probably similarly reversible. The utilisation of added ATP for the reversal of the electron stream to and from cytochrome b can be followed spectrophotometrically (LUNDEGÅRDH 1955). It is of course not certain that all such reversals of processes in which high-energy phosphate is concerned take place in true equilibria. Degradation and synthesis can follow different paths, which maintain a steady state between the components. Such complex systems then serve as important switch-points for metabolism.

4 THE ORGANIC ACIDS AND THEIR IMPORTANCE FOR THE REGULATION OF pH IN CELLS

The TCA cycle active in aerobic respiration does not cause any appreciable accumulation of the participating acids, which behave merely as intermediate stages. A simple running of the cycle would result mainly in acetic acid and its condensation products as well as pyruvic acid. There are, however, also other paths leading to acid formation. Through investigations on leaves, e.g. of tobacco (VICKERY 1955, 1956), it has been shown that glycollic acid ($CH_2OH \cdot COOH$) is as active as succinic acid. Glycollic acid can be considered as a source for the formation of oxalic acid. There is a special enzyme system that oxidises glycollic acid and other α-hydroxyacids e.g. L-lactic acid (CLAGETT et al. 1949, TOLBERT et al. 1949). Formic acid also occurs in the metabolism of tobacco leaves.

A synthesis of considerable amounts of organic acids can result from carboxylation of pyruvic acid or phosphoenolpyruvic acid ($CH_2=CO \sim PO_3H_2 \cdot COOH$). Three such carboxylases occur in higher plants: the 'malic enzyme', which catalyses the reductive carboxylation of pyruvic acid to malic acid (OCHOA 1948; Fig. 98); oxalacetic carboxylase, which catalyses the equilibrium between oxalacetic acid + ATP and phosphopyruvic acid + ADP + CO_2; and finally β-carboxylase, which catalyses the carboxylation of phosphopyruvic acid to oxalacetic acid + orthophosphate (BANDURSKI 1955).

Acids can thus be accumulated in various ways, and they can disappear again. One of the conditions affecting this reversible storage of acids is the pH value of the medium (VICKERY 1955), and one can consider this fact as a mechanism of internal pH regulation of the cells. The acid balance also plays a considerable part in the daily increase and decrease of the acid content of leaves connected with photosynthesis, the so-called 'Crassulacean acid metabolism'. In this case it seems that illumination causes the formation of a specific intermediate product, which in the dark is re-formed into acids. The acids formed may not arise directly in photosynthesis (STUTZ and BURRIS 1951).

A number of workers have confirmed the fact that the pH value of the plant cell is remarkably difficult to change. Data are available for roots (HOAGLAND and DAVIS 1923), leaves (HAAS 1941) and water-plants (STEEMANN NIELSEN 1942). An automatic buffering is of course exercised through the weak acids stored in the cell sap, phosphates, etc. In larger alterations of the external pH value however these are not sufficient but must be supported by metabolic mechanisms of the type indicated above.

In roots a steady state operates in such a way that with increase of the pH value of the medium, e.g. through an excess of metallic cations, the formation of plant acids is stimulated (ULRICH 1942, BURSTRÖM 1943). If the pH value of the medium drops, the organic acids are partly catabolised by respiration. In this way the roots for example can maintain their internal pH value between about 6·0 and 6·2, even when that of the medium varies by several units.

Metallic cations are concerned as well as acids in the regulation of acidity. If the pH value is lower in the cell than in the environment, it promotes an uptake of metallic cations on account of the membrane equilibrium (cf. p. 49). A higher pH value in the cell sap similarly increases the tendency to release metallic cations and absorb anions. It may be thought that the distribution of ions between medium and protoplasm determined by the membrane equilibrium directly affects the activity of the acid-forming or acid-degrading enzymes. This would in any case be probable for the enzyme systems located in the peripheral layer of the protoplasm. The metabolic regulation of pH discussed above occurs very quickly and in wheat roots takes only a few minutes.

It has already been mentioned above that systems other than the TCA cycle also take part in the acid balance. The kind of acids preferentially accumulated can also change. In rhubarb, whose cell sap shows the low pH value of 3, oxalic acid predominates. In tobacco leaves also oxalic acid is abundant, whereas it occurs only as traces in succulents, e.g. *Bryophyllum* (PULCHER *et al.* 1947). Otherwise malic acid seems to predominate. Acidities near the neutral point are shown e.g. by *Helianthus*, clover, peas and cucumbers (HURD-KARRER 1939).

According to BENNET-CLARK (1943), acids which pass from the cell sap again into the protoplasms are caught up in the system of 'oxidative anabolism' (cf. p. 192), On the other hand it is found that malic, fumaric, succinic and citric acids added from outside are quickly oxidised with the formation of CO_2. Some acids, e.g. maleic acid, may according to VICKERY inhibit amino acid formation. Abnormal increase of respiration is of course obtained also by feeding with glucose. In these circumstances, however, usually no great changes in pH are evoked, although addition of glucose to wheat roots lowers the pH value. That the activity of the TCA cycle is involved in the combustion of surplus acid is seen from the competitive behaviour of acids and glucose. On feeding with acids the glucose consumption falls, and vice versa.

5 FINAL POINTS ON AEROBIC RESPIRATION IN HIGHER PLANTS

In spite of the great advance in recent decades, the part played in aerobic respiration by systems other than the cytochrome system is still largely unknown. Of special interest of course are the regular occurrence of peroxidases and copper oxidases, and the presence of suitable substrates for these enzymes in the form of pigments, e.g. flavone and flavanone derivatives.

In bean leaves one finds much quercetin, a flavanol derivative which with a molecule of glucuronic acid forms querceturone, which according to ENDRES *et al.* (1939) may occur as a cellular transporter of H (cf. WILHELM 1930 on the chromogens in *Vicia faba*). Querceturone is dehydrogenated by phenol oxidase and reduced again by ascorbic acid. The tannin occurring in tea-leaves could possibly also function as an H-transporter, since it is oxidised by quinones (ROBERTS and SARMA 1940).

The majority of such observations, however, refer to researches with extracts and homogenates, which give little insight into a possible collaboration of copper oxidases in normal aerobic respiration (cf. p. 177). Numerous substances serve as substrates for peroxidase, which undoubtedly takes part to a certain extent in plant respiration. They include the yellow pigment occurring in wheat roots, which is probably a flavanone derivative (LUNDEGÅRDH and STENLID 1944), together with a number of other compounds which occur chiefly in cell sap e.g. catechol and other phenols. Further investigation of such systems is needed for a fuller knowledge of them and also of how far they supply the cytochrome system with protons and electrons through side lines other than the TCA cycle (perhaps through cytochrome b).

One can also imagine that special oxidases, e.g. the copper oxidases, keep in operation reaction chains which have special cellular functions. The occurrence of copper as a trace element needs an explanation. According to WOOD and WOMERSLEY (1946), in the absence of copper the chloroplasts of oat leaves degenerate and the cells die. The copper is incorporated into the living structure and must therefore be supplied during the whole course of development.

Glycolysis can be blocked by various inhibitors, but hardly any of these are specific for only one reaction. Fluoride inhibits enolase (p. 154) and consequently the formation of pyruvic acid with the further result that the TCA cycle is slowed down. Fluoride however influences the normal protoplasmic structure very little and does not change the surface potential of the protoplasm. This may be connected with the lack of accumulation of acids. Malonic acid on the other hand, which competitively interferes with the dehydrogenation of succinic acid, does not hinder the accumulation of the preceding acids of the TCA cycle—and this probably explains the enormous vacuolisation of the protoplasm under the influence of this inhibitor.

Fluoride also interrupts the cytochrome system because, by the formation of peroxidase $\cdot F^-$, it inhibits the electron transport from the peroxidase complexes to cytochrome b. Cytochrome b in the presence of fluoride remains strongly oxidised, but a cytochrome respiration inhibitable by CN and CO remains in existence via cytochrome oxidase and cytochrome c (LUNDEGÅRDH 1952, 1954, 1955, 1958). The fact that growth and salt accumulation are strongly inhibited by fluoride is evidence for an important function of the electron path to cytochrome b in the synthesis of ~ph compounds (LUNDEGÅRDH 1949, 1955). Similar effects are, as mentioned above, evoked also by a number of other inhibitors. Electron transfer to cytochrome b (i.e. the oxidising effect of this cytochrome) is one of the more sensitive key points in the whole aerobic metabolism.

Apart from cereal roots, which have been studied in particular detail, the presence of a cytochrome system has been ascertained in a constantly increasing number of plant tissues (cf. p. 160). The oxidation and reduction of the cytochromes can be studied with modern spectrophotometric methods (see LUNDEGÅRDH 1951-8) in living tissues under natural conditions, and also in isolated mitochondria, in which the system mainly occurs. According to HUMPHREYS and CONN (1956), lupin mitochondria catalyse the oxidation of NADH in presence of cytochrome c; cytochrome b is fixed in the mitochondria (cf. also LUNDEGÅRDH 1958). A component of the cytochrome system in plants that is seldom lacking is peroxidase, which also can be spectrophotometrically studied in living objects (LUNDEGÅRDH 1955, 1958).

The presence of a complete cytochrome system of course makes most plants very sensitive towards cyanide and CO, but the sensitivity is reduced in comparison with the reactions of animals by the presence of the b-shunt to oxygen (p. 165). Characteristic, but still insufficiently explained, is the fact that the cyanide inhibition gradually diminishes with time (LUNDEGÅRDH 1949); which may be assumed to depend on the presence of alternative paths of oxidation. In certain tissues, e.g. in wild cherries (DALY 1954), the aerobic respiration of the leaves may even be stimulated by CO, although cytochrome oxidase is present. What happens in some of the lower organisms, which even contain free HCN, is still not properly known (MÜLLER 1944). It may, however, be mentioned that on account of the relatively high dissociation constants of the cytochrome oxidase $\cdot$ CN compound, the enzyme is never completely blocked (LUNDEGÅRDH 1957).

About the distribution of the various respiratory systems in growing organs, e.g. in roots, the data of individual workers are not altogether in agreement, which is partly due to inadequate methods for the determination of cytochromes. In wheat roots, for example, the cytochrome system is distributed fairly evenly up to a distance of 80-100 mm from the tip. The activity can however change, as has been observed e.g. in barley roots. As the respiration, due to the presence of the b-shunt, occurs by at least two ways, with which an unknown third way may be associated (cf. LUNDEGÅRDH 1949), there are many possibilities for variations and differences of activity between meristem and adult tissue. The intensity of the oxygen respiration usually decreases from the growing point upwards. BERRY and BLOCK (1946) found, for example in onion roots, the strongest cyanide inhibition in the tip zone (0-5 mm; about *Avena* coleoptiles see BOTTELIER 1939). MACHLIS (1944) also obtained similar results (Fig. 99). In wheat roots, however, the cyanide-inhibitable respiration is uniformly distributed. In cross-sections of tissues of trees the cambium respires the most intensively.

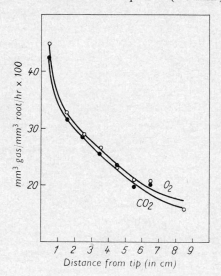

Fig. 99. The intensity of respiration in different zones of barley roots: consumption of O_2 and formation of CO_2 (after MACHLIS 1944).

H. The Physiology of Respiration

1 THE INFLUENCE OF O_2 AND CO_2 PRESSURE

CHONDHURY (1939) found no notable inhibition of the respiration of potatoes and carrots, when the oxygen pressure was decreased to $3\cdot5\%$-$6\cdot2\%$ of O_2. On the other hand artichokes were more sensitive. According to MARSH and GODDARD (1939), with a reduction of the oxygen pressure to 5% the respiration of carrots sank to three-quarters, and with a reduction to 1% it sank to one-fifth. DU BUY and OLSON (1940) state that in *Avena* coleoptiles with $0\cdot25\%$-$0\cdot45\%$ of oxygen there is a sudden onset of fermentation. In the experiments of LUNDEGÅRDH and BURSTRÖM (1935) the roots of intact wheat seedlings were enclosed in vessels which were filled with solutions with various oxygen pressures. The respiration followed the oxygen pressure almost rectilinearly at values of one atm ($1\cdot1$ millimole O_2 per litre of solution) down to about $1/10$ atm ($0\cdot1$ millimole per litre). TAYLOR (1942) reports similar results.

Investigations in higher plants thus show that the oxygen respiration of growing organs is fairly insensitive towards variations of the oxygen pressure, at least down to one-third or one-fifth of the normal pressure. Observations on the reduction state of the cytochrome system at different oxygen pressures showed that the oxidation of the cytochrome b and a_3 followed a reaction of the first order (LUNDEGÅRDH 1950,

1954, 1958). The entry of air into the organs may of course reduce the effective oxygen pressure. Even with good ventilation, oxygen deficiency may occur in thick tissues. (Concerning the gas content of tissues see DENNY 1946; the aeration in *Cyperus papyrus* was investigated by TADROS 1940). In the relatively thin roots of grasses (diameter about 0·5 mm) on the other hand the speed of diffusion of oxygen seems to suffice for normal oxygen supply of all cells.

Some investigations on yeast (LUNDEGÅRDH 1957) have shown that the dependence of the intensity of respiration (measured as oxygen consumption) on the oxygen pressure is markedly influenced by the state of nutrition and consequently of the initial speed of respiration.

Yeast fed with glucose respires 4-6 times more quickly than starving (washed) yeast. With starving yeast, with a reduction of the oxygen pressure to one-tenth of the normal ($2\% \ O_2 + 98\% \ N_2$), a reduction in respiration of only 25% was observed.

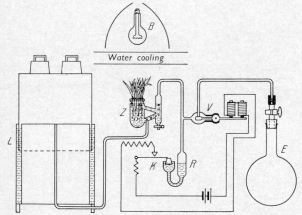

Fig. 100. Apparatus to measure CO_2-production in root respiration. *Z* circulation vessel with roots; *B* lamp to maintain normal photosynthesis of the leaves; *L* storage vessel for CO_2-free air, which circulates through *Z*; *KR* and *V* electric valves which control the transfer of air into the evacuated flask *E*. The CO_2 is absorbed by baryta solution introduced into *E*, and the titration is made in the flask (after LUNDEGÅRDH 1933).

Pure oxygen caused no increase over the respiration in air. In yeast which was fed with 1% glucose, however, the respiration increased by 40% in pure oxygen, compared with air, and fell by 68% in an oxygen-content of one-tenth of the normal. The ratio between respiration and oxygen concentration follows a logarithmic curve. A logarithmic ratio, i.e. a ratio of the first order, exists in yeast also between the intensity of respiration and the degree of oxidation of the cytochrome oxidase.

The different behaviour of starving and fed yeast is also reflected in the reaction to inhibitors, such as HCN, NaN_3 and CO. The starved yeast is much less affected by these poisons than the yeast fed with glucose. These investigations thus show that cyanide, etc., never effect a complete blocking of the cytochrome oxidase, but that a fraction remains unaffected, which suffices for the respiration of starved yeast but is quite insufficient for fed yeast. The only partial inactivation of cytochrome oxidase by CO and HCN has been followed spectrophotometrically. These facts are important in interpreting the resistance of cytochrome respiration towards cyanide mentioned on p. 202, since they suggest that with 'overloading' of the oxidase the inhibitability of respiration by cyanide decreases.

The onset of anaerobic respiration (fermentation) is usually observed before complete removal of oxygen (cf. p. 203). The limit may, however, be found at very different pressures. Certain plants or organs, e.g. rice roots, are better adapted to an anaerobic life than others. Oxygen, however, is probably often supplied through air canals (v. RAALTE 1940, LAING 1940). In the more sensitive wheat roots, in complete absence of oxygen, the meristem dies first and the mature cells survive longer. Alcohol poisoning is probably the cause of the damage to the meristem. Alcohol formation, however, does not occur before the oxygen concentration has sunk below about one-third of the normal.

A rise of the respiratory quotient, $R.Q. = CO_2/O_2$, above unity is ordinarily an indication of a switch to fermentation. It must, however, be remembered that values over 1 occur also in the normal growth of an organ, since reduction processes combined with liberation of CO_2 take part in the synthesis of the protoplasmic components. A unilateral consumption of oxygen on the other hand takes place in the formation and storage of certain plant acids. As reduction above the level of carbohydrates requires additional energy and this energy can be supplied in the main only by aerobic respiration and the $\sim$ph synthesis connected with it, a whole range of endergonic reduction processes is dependent on aerobic respiration.

Even at the normal oxygen content of the medium, wheat roots can show $R.Q.$ values up to 2·0 (LUNDEGÅRDH and BURSTRÖM). With increasing oxygen deficiency the $R.Q.$ rises still further, so that at one-third to one-quarter of the normal pressure values between 3 and 4 are obtained. This increase of $R.Q.$ refers entirely to the respiration inhibitable by HCN, since with cyanide poisoning the still existing ground respiration occurs with $R.Q. = 1$.

With $R.Q. = 1$ for the ground respiration and values higher than 1 for the cyanide-sensitive respiration, the quotient for total respiration must rise if the ground respiration is selectively inhibited. That the cyanide-sensitive fraction of the respiration shows a higher $R.Q.$ than the aerobic ground respiration is apparent without difficulty from what has been said above.

The switch of oxygen respiration to fermentation can of course be delayed by mobilisation of H-acceptors other than oxygen: quinoidal pigments come to mind. Nitrate ions can also serve as H-acceptors. YAMAGATA (1934) found in *Aspergillus* that was fed with nitrate an increase in $R.Q.$ to 1·57. The nitrate is reduced to NH_2.

It is quite conceivable that $\sim$ph linkages could act as substitute during a temporary shortage of oxygen. It has actually been observed that under anaerobic conditions the addition of ATP shifts the equilibrium of cytochromes b and c towards the side of oxidation (LUNDEGÅRDH 1955), so that the electron stream now flows in the reverse direction. As high-energy phosphate is used up and the protoplasmic structure suffers, this condition cannot be endured for long but may be of service as a temporary relief. At this point it is interesting to note that the rise in the respiratory quotient is delayed by the presence of mineral salts. This is probably due to the fact that salt ions activate electron transport in cytochrome systems (see Chap. 6).

The aerobic ground respiration insensitive towards HCN can be considered as a minimal performance, a 'blank run' of respiration. In this glucose is completely oxidised, and the intensity of respiration can be considerably stepped up by greater addition of glucose. An increase in respiration of 20%-60% has been observed, when wheat roots are fed with 0·003-0·020 mole of glucose per litre (LUNDEGÅRDH 1940, MILTHORPE and ROBERTSON 1948). With a deficiency of glucose the cyanide-sensitive respiration is of course also inhibited. It can be calculated that in the cyanide-inhibitable respiration of growing tissue only one-quarter to one-twentieth of the glucose consumed is fully oxidised, whereas the greater part increases the osmotic value of the cell sap as organic acids and is consumed in the synthesis of protoplasmic proteins. In luxury consumption of glucose much of it is accumulated in the cell sap. In a few hours under these conditions the glucose content of wheat roots can rise by 300% (LUNDEGÅRDH and BURSTRÖM 1944).

In mature tissues the synthetic processes have of course diminished, and $R.Q.$ sinks to about 1. An increase of $R.Q.$ with decreasing oxygen supply is therefore due chiefly to the onset of fermentation. A coupling of reduction processes and oxygen respiration has been observed in ripening fruits. HANSEN (1942) mentions a coupling between aerobic respiration and the production of ethylene. Ethylene itself stimulates respiration and, as is well known, is utilised, together with ethyl ether and other anaesthetics and warmth, for the early forcing of plants.

In comparison with the effect of reducing oxygen pressure, respiration is remarkably little influenced by varying CO_2 pressures; an inhibiting effect of higher CO_2 concentrations has however been observed. Similar effects have been mentioned in connection with alcoholic fermentation. The anaerobic release of CO_2 by wheat roots is about doubled, if the gas is removed from the immediate surroundings of the organ by stirring the medium. Aerobic respiration also increases in a streaming medium, but in this case the accelerated oxygen uptake also contributes. Higher CO_2 concentrations (above about 5%) inhibit the oxidation of the cytochrome system and increase the reduction of cytochrome b. The explanation for this phenomenon is not quite simple. An inhibition of decarboxylation would cause a slowing down of the TCA cycle and thus a higher oxidation level of the cytochromes. One can assume as a possible explanation of the CO_2 inhibition either a retardation of the electron transfer from cytochrome b to cytochrome c similar to that by narcotics, or possibly a competitive adsorption of CO_2 on the cytochrome oxidase reducing the reaction with oxygen. In this case CO_2 would have an effect similar to that of a weak poisoning with HCN. Resynthesis of carbohydrates from CO_2 seems to be a regular property of all cells. The observed inhibition of respiration and oxidation of the cytochrome system by CO_2 may therefore also be explained as an increased tendency to inversion of the decarboxylation of pyruvic acid and/or of phosphoglyceric acid with increasing partial pressure of CO_2. High CO_2 concentrations have been observed in the air chambers of many rhizomes (according to LAING 1940 up to 30%-40%). Ordinarily the CO_2 content of the intercellular air amounts to only a few per cent.

2 THE GLUCOSE QUOTIENT ($G.Q.$) AND $R.Q.$

Information about the progress of respiration can also be obtained by determining the consumption of glucose in relation to the CO_2 production. With complete oxidation of glucose the ratio is

$$G.Q. = \frac{C_6H_{12}O_6}{6CO_2} \times 6 = 1 \tag{68}$$

This value of $G.Q.$ is observed in wheat roots with inhibited growth e.g. when the pH value of the medium sinks to 3·1-3·2. The value of $G.Q. = 1$ applies generally to ground respiration, which is indeed functionally unimportant. At pH = 6-7, on the other hand, the roots grow remarkably, and $G.Q.$ then increases to about 1·6 (LUNDEGÅRDH 1937, LUNDEGÅRDH and BURSTRÖM 1944).

The excess of glucose consumed reflects the synthesis of substances such as pectin, cellulose, proteins, etc., which are synthesised wholly or mainly from carbohydrates, that is syntheses which are dependent on the activity of the cyanide-inhibitable fraction of oxygen respiration. Since this 'creative' respiration amounts to 50%-70% of the total respiration, it can be calculated that for the insertion of a molecule of glucose into the cell structure a further molecule must be completely oxidised, i.e. a yield of 50% is obtained. The yield is actually a few per cent higher, since the osmotic activities connected with the growth also have to be taken into account (see Chap. 6).

When oxygen is cut off both growth and osmotic processes are stopped, and the value 3 can be expected for $G.Q.$ according to the following equation:

$$C_6H_{12}O_6 - 2C_2H_5OH + CO_2; \quad G.Q. = \frac{C_6H_{12}O_6}{2CO_2} \times 6 = 3 \tag{69}$$

The value 3 has been found experimentally in wheat roots placed in oxygen-free distilled water. If instead of water as a medium an oxygen-free salt solution (KCl, KNO_3 or phosphate) is chosen, the $G.Q.$ sinks to 2 or still lower values. This discovery points to the operation of systems which favour a reversal of glycolysis. Here reference may be made to the possibility already mentioned that under anaerobic conditions high-energy phosphates can be utilised temporarily to reverse the electron stream of the catabolic processes. As salts generally serve as activators of electron transfer, the observed fall in $G.Q.$ caused by salts could be explained in this way. The presence of salts would thus stimulate the 'internal oxidation' caused by high-energy phosphate consumption, as a relief in time of need.

Alcohol formation during exclusion of oxygen has been found in a large number of tissues, e.g. in peas, potatoes, apples, etc. A very transient oxygen deficiency causes no serious damage, but a persistent lack of oxygen acts as a poison, which can be endured only transitorily by means of the above-mentioned reversal of the electron stream. The formation of alcohol and the release of CO_2 occur simultaneously in fruits maintained anaerobically, but sometimes a reduced alcohol production, as compared with the zymase fermentation, has been observed (THOMAS 1947).

Sugar is the universal respiration material. It is always preferred to other substances, even to fat reserves in oil-seeds. The conductive tissue of most plants is designed in such a way that all organs are assured of a sufficient supply of sugar, always provided that photosynthesis is maintained. In this the sugar serves also as a protective material for proteins which otherwise would be broken down in respiration (Chap. 5).

When fats pass over into sugar in order to serve as respiration material, the $R.Q.$ falls below 1, and in germinating castor-oil seeds even to 0·30. The oxidation of tripalmitin (p. 100) according to the equation:

$$C_{51}H_{98}O_6 + 72·5O_2 \rightarrow 51CO_2 + 49H_2 + 7590 \text{ kg-cal.} \tag{70}$$

gives $R.Q. = 0·70$. The sinking of the $R.Q.$ below 1 can be easily observed in germinating oil-seeds. After the disappearance of the fat and the adjustment of the respiration to glucose, which is delivered from the leaves now developed, the $R.Q.$ rises again to 1. A drop of the $R.Q.$ to 0·8-0·9 occurs also with destructive respiration of protein.

Detailed investigations on the effects of various nutrients on the $R.Q.$ were carried out by TAMIYA (1932) and YAMAGATA (1934) with *Aspergillus oryzae*. With carbohydrates as respiration material the $R.Q.$ amounted to 1·09-1·57, with glycerol 0·74-0·94, and with the less suitable ethanol 0·53-0·65. The variations were connected with the nitrogen nutrition, since NH_3 requires more oxygen and gives lower $R.Q.$ values than NO_3. The total 'combustion quotient' (that is, the ratio CO_2/O_2 for complete combustion) of the dry material of *Aspergillus* amounted to 0·911-0·953, and consequently the whole organism is somewhat poorer in oxygen than the carbo-hydrates. The normal *R.Q.* value of the growing fungus, must, therefore, lie above 1 as in higher plants.

In certain circumstances cells are compelled to oxidise compounds which contain more oxygen and less hydrogen than the carbohydrates, e.g. organic acids. The *R.Q.* then rises above 1 — with oxalic acid even up to 4 — according to the equation:

$$2(COOH)_2 + O_2 \rightarrow 4CO_2 + 2H_2O + 60 \cdot 2 \text{ kg-cal.} \tag{71}$$

Malic acid and other plant acids are accumulated by succulents during the night and disappear again during the day. This fact has been known a long time and is interpreted ecologically as an adaptation to a life with very narrow stomata (Chap. 3 and Fig. 101). In this way the balance between respiration and photosynthesis is improved. The diurnal variations of acidity are reflected in the varying *R.Q.* values. These are low in succulents during the night and increase during the day to $1 \cdot 3$-$1 \cdot 4$, or about the same as the value for malic acid (BENNET-CLARK 1932, RUHLAND 1934). The cacti endure a life

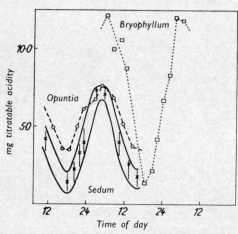

Fig. 101. Diurnal variations of the titratable acidity per 100 g of leaves of *Sedum* and *Bryophyllum* and pieces of stem of *Opuntia* (after BENNET-CLARK 1933).

without oxygen for several days and show a clear Pasteur effect (GUSTAFSON 1932). In prolonged dark periods the malic acid in *Kleinia* is again degraded (THODAY *et al.* 1944). The acid metabolism in ripening apples, etc., has been studied by British plant physiologists (THOMAS 1937; see also KROTKOV and HELSON 1946).

3 THE INFLUENCE OF pH, SALTS, ETC.

Like all enzymatic reactions, respiration is influenced by changes of pH in the immediate surroundings; for this, in fact, OGSTON (1947) proposed the term pH$_s$. From this results the necessity for the cell to maintain the internal pH value as constant as possible. The requisite mechanism has been described on p. 200.

BURSTRÖM (1943) mentions that the cell content of wheat seedlings varies only between pH $6 \cdot 0$ and $6 \cdot 5$, when the pH value of the medium moves between $3 \cdot 1$ and $7 \cdot 4$. For this reason the intensity of respiration of the wheat roots remains remarkably constant, even when the pH value of the medium varies from $3 \cdot 2$ to $10 \cdot 0$ (LUNDEGÅRDH and BURSTRÖM 1944). A somewhat higher oxygen consumption at pH 6-7 is caused probably by the increase in growth, etc., at this pH value which is optimal for wheat. A pH value of 3 is directly harmful; the surface of the protoplasm of the epidermal cells is discharged and the protoplasm is overwhelmed by acid anions (p. 47).

The internal pH value is then greatly altered, and the resultant strong shifts in the activity of the enzyme systems cause death within about half an hour. The cellular oxidations continue, usually with increased speed, amounting e.g. in 1mM HNO_3, to 130%-220%.

The *salt effect* may be due in various ways to the activation of the enzyme systems operating in electron transport. This question is considered in detail in Chapter 6. Ion exchange is certainly of importance; for example, cations which are exchanged at the surface of enzyme proteins can influence their reactivity. Many of these cation effects are specific, and cases are known, e.g. in connection with the copper oxidases (cf. also PETERSEN and WALTON 1943, BESZONOW and LEROUX 1945) and manganese, in which the cations, effective as prosthetic groups or as activators, are present in exchangeable unions. Here the pH value of the surroundings is of course important; on account of the high exchange power of H-ions these easily dissolve out metallic cations from their adsorption unions.

Among the *anions* phosphate occupies a special position on account of its relationships with glycolysis. The nitrate anion after uptake into the root is partly reduced and serves for the formation of amino acids and proteins. If sugar is supplied simultaneously with nitrate, the respiration intensity increases; which may be due partly to the salt respiration (cf. Chap. 6) and partly to increased activity of the TCA cycle.

The trace element boron is effective as the borate anion. This increases the surface potential of the protoplasm (LUNDEGÅRDH 1940). According to WINFIELD (1945) boric acid is combined with pyridoxin (vitamin B_6, a trihydroxy compound; formula p. 236), and via riboflavin accelerates respiration.

Among the specifically active *cations* potassium may be mentioned. BOYER *et al.* (1943) as well as LARDY and ZIEGLER (1945) state that potassium accelerates the transfer of phosphate from phosphopyruvic acid to ADP. Potassium appears to participate also in other phosphorylations, e.g. in the condensation of hexoses to cane sugar or starch (SIDERIS and YOUNG 1945). This fact can probably explain the positive influence of potassium on the transport of sugar between various organs (BARBIER 1945), since phosphorylations certainly participate regularly in the equilibria between mono- and polysaccharides.

The bivalent magnesium-, calcium- and manganous-ions usually have a function as 'enzyme cements' (cf. p. 143) and in this connection are interchangeable. Addition of manganese to manganese-free wheat roots stimulated the respiration (LUNDEGÅRDH 1939). Addition of 5×10^{-5} mole per litre of $MnCl_2$ increased the respiration by 150%-500%. Addition of similar amounts of iron were without effect, probably because the minute quantities necessary for haem synthesis were already present in the seeds. The catalytically effective manganese is exchangeable. As mentioned on p. 168, the action of manganese appears to be connected with the oxidative effect of peroxidase.

Copper, thallium and some other heavy metals are strong respiration poisons if they are supplied in doses above the optimal. Their effect on respiration is partly differentiating. A general effect of heavy-metal ions is the discharge of the protoplasmic surface, probably as a result of firm combination with the points where cations are exchanged (cf. p. 48). The toxic effects observed by SEIFRIZ (1947) *et al.* could also be due to the damage to enzymes caused by precipitation of proteins. Enzyme activity is affected even by normal non-harmful ion-exchange, as shown by the observed variations in respiration with the exchange between K and Ca. The respiration of roots generally remains lower in potassium salt solutions than in calcium salt solutions. Positive effects of calcium ions have been observed also with *Azotobacter* (ENDRES 1934). The antagonistic effects of Ca and Na are also clear in respiration. The effects of electrolytes on the respiration of algae have been studied by SHIBATA (1929) and HOFFMANN (1929).

Zinc appears to influence the oxidation-reduction balance (REED 1944). It is known that zinc is a component of carbonic anhydrase (KEILIN and MANN 1944). A participation of zinc in protein metabolism has also been suggested.

An important factor in the regulation of respiration is the *water content* of the organs. Increase in respiration with plasmolysis has been observed; but on the other hand respiration decreases when seeds dry and increases when they swell in water. In fungi also a positive correlation has been observed between the degree of hydration and the intensity of respiration (RICHARDS 1927). The greatly varying length of life of seeds (CROCKER 1938) is probably connected with the power of suspending respiration on drying out. BOUILLIENNE (1926) has reported on the relations between root respiration and osmotic conditions. On the other hand, no effects of varying transpiration on respiration have been observed (LÖWENECK 1930).

The influence of the osmotic state on respiration may well be connected with variations in the 'free water' which surrounds the colloid structure. There are numerous examples of a close connection between the condition of the protoplasmic structure and the intensity of physiological processes connected with enzyme activity. We may limit ourselves to one example, the effect of bending or stretching leaves on their aerobic respiration. This is increased by such mechanical influences up to 180% (AUDUS 1940-1) but anaerobic respiration remains unaffected.

4 RESPIRATION AND TEMPERATURE

Like all chemical processes, respiration is subject to the influence of temperature. In the first place, the viscosity of protoplasm depends on temperature (BĚLERHÁDEK 1929-35) and must induce changes in speed. The temperature coefficient (Q_{10}) varies ordinarily between 2·0 and 2·5. Different physiological processes are, however, often observed in different temperature ranges. The age of the organs also plays a part. Because of the shock effects of sudden temperature changes, which are often encountered, and which may be connected with hydration changes (NAVEZ 1931), due care must be exercised in carrying out the investigations.

Respiration follows a typical optimum curve. The position of the optimum is, however, strongly dependent on time (F. F. BLACKMAN 1905, KUIJPER 1910). At high temperatures the negative component of the optimum curve (cf. p. 131) has an ever-increasing effect. As this causes gradual destruction of the protoplasm, the optimum decreases with time, and is widened and transferred to lower temperatures (Fig. 77). In short experiments the optima can appear very steep and sharp (LUNDEGÅRDH 1924), and Q_{10} increases steadily in the rising branch of the curve (Fig. 103).

The increase in Q_{10} with rising temperature is probably due to the fact that certain processes connected with respiration are accelerated e.g. the supply of respiration material, which is facilitated by decreasing viscosity, etc. The balance between anabolic and catabolic processes appears to be shifted by excessive temperature rises in favour of catabolism; which gives the whole phenomenon a character rather like autocatalysis. At higher temperatures the proteins indeed coagulate, and sensitive enzymes are inactivated. In the initial stage this denaturation is reversible, but it soon becomes irreversible, which leads to death.

Deviations from the 'chemical' Q_{10} values (2·0-2·5) are in fact appreciable at temperatures under $+5°C$ and over $+30°C$. Between these values the van 't Hoff rule is generally valid (STILES 1935, 1946, LUNDEGÅRDH 1957) although deviations occur. According to STOCKER (1927) lichens show a Q_{10}-minimum between $+10$ and $+20°C$. Certain soil bacteria on the other hand show very high Q_{10} values between $+10$ and $+20°C$ (EIDMAN 1943).

The dependence of respiration on temperature has a considerable ecological importance, since the life of autotrophic plants on the whole depends on the balance between the carbohydrates formed in photosynthesis and those used up again in respiration. Since photosynthesis and respiration usually show different temperature curves, each change in temperature must involve a shift in the total carbohydrate balance. This fact is clear in the course of apparent photosynthesis. Respiration in general shows a higher temperature optimum than photosynthesis. During the night, respiration alone continues; which often makes the night temperature of decisive importance.

The equilibrium starch⇌sugar also shifts with temperature, usually towards the right with cold, a circumstance which can also have importance for cold resistance. To the extent to which respiration is dependent on sugar concentration a change in equilibrium at low temperatures brings with it a relative increase in respiration, a fact which can be observed, e.g. in the winter storage of potatoes. In arctic plants also a relatively high respiration in comparison with photosynthesis has been measured (WAGER 1941). The changes in the balance between carbohydrates and nitrogen assimilation with temperature were studied by NIGHTINGALE (1933) in tomato plants. At $+13°$ with low nitrate assimilation many carbohydrates are accumulated, at $+21°$ the former rises and at $+35°$ the net amount of carbohydrate is much diminished largely because of the increased respiration.

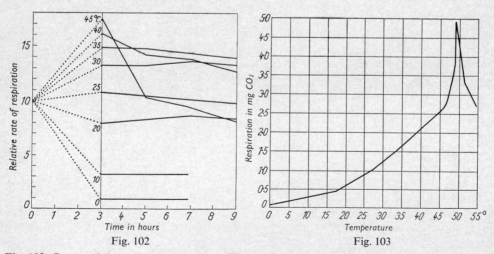

Fig. 102   Fig. 103

Fig. 102. Course of the respiration of pea seedlings with time at various temperatures. Germination began at $+10°$ C and the temperature was regulated in the course of three hours to the values given (after FERNANDES 1923).

Fig. 103. Dependence of respiration on temperature. Short-period experiments with potato leaves (after LUNDEGÅRDH 1924).

P

As so many enzymes collaborate in respiration, the activation or inactivation of individual enzymes can operate as a limiting factor. It has already been mentioned that the usually rapid alteration of the intensity of respiration in the germination of spores or seeds is due to the activation of the carboxylase or of the cytochrome system, perhaps because the prosthetic groups are formed at points other than the apoenzymes and the two combine only at a particular stage of development. The increase of the intensity of respiration in germination may be connected also with changes in hydration (Fig. 104). Similar fluctuations in respiration are observed in the ripening and in the storage of apples, potatoes,

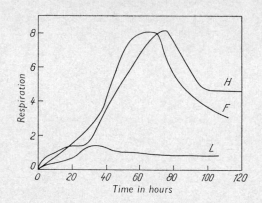

Fig. 104. The course of respiration during germination of *Fagopyrum esculentum* (F), *Lathyrus odoratus* (L) and *Helianthus annuus* (H) (after STILES and LEACH).

etc. Such changes occur both at constant temperature and on sudden temperature changes.

One sometimes speaks of a 'climacteric' in the cold storage of apples and potatoes, corresponding to the strong increase of respiration during ripening (KIDD *et al.* 1940, KROTKOV 1941). Such relationships, as also the dependence of respiration on the storage temperature, on the CO_2 concentration and on stimulating gases, e.g. ethylene, have practical importance for the technique of storage.

Chapter 5
NITROGEN METABOLISM

The nitrogen cycle in nature is similar to that of carbon, in that both materials occur in the atmosphere. Unlike carbon, however, nitrogen does not usually occur in rocks and minerals (exceptions being Chile nitrate and the nitrogen compounds in coal) and in fossils it occurs only in unimportant amounts. Even though the atmosphere represents the largest reservoir of nitrogen, there is no simple cycle between atmospheric nitrogen, higher plants and the soil. Ammonia and nitrate quantitatively restrict the cycle which runs by way of these compounds from soil to plants. Only the special N-assimilating (N-fixing) micro-organisms utilise atmospheric nitrogen directly.

In plants the percentage content of nitrogen is considerably less than of carbon, but nitrogen is never absent from the building materials of protoplasm. The heterocyclic pyrroles, pyridines, pyrimidines and purine derivatives are preferential components of the coenzymes and other active groups, while the protein chains build up the structural skeleton of the protoplasm and serve as specific carriers of prosthetic groups. Biological research has worked intensively on the formation and breakdown of proteins, but the most striking advances up to the present have been in the study of coenzymes and activators. Among reviews of nitrogen metabolism may be mentioned those of LUGG (1946), McKEE (1949) and WOOD (1953).

A. Formation and Turnover of Proteins

1 THE NITROGEN METABOLISM OF SEEDLINGS

The connection between carbohydrate metabolism and nitrogen metabolism is by way of the keto acids, pyruvic, α-ketoglutaric and oxalacetic acid (see Chap. 4 G and the diagram on p. 196). KNOOP early showed that amino acids are formed by catalytic reduction of a mixture of keto acids and ammonia or other amines. In this, cystëine can also serve as a hydrogen carrier. STICKLAND (1935) investigated from the purely chemical point of view the amination of a keto acid by ammonia e.g.

$$\underset{\substack{\text{Pyruvic} \\ \text{acid}}}{\overset{\displaystyle \text{CH}_3}{\underset{\displaystyle \text{COOH}}{\overset{\displaystyle |}{\underset{\displaystyle |}{\text{CO}}}}}} + \text{NH}_3 + 2\text{H} \rightleftharpoons \underset{\substack{\text{alanine}}}{\overset{\displaystyle \text{CH}_3}{\underset{\displaystyle \text{COOH}}{\overset{\displaystyle |}{\underset{\displaystyle |}{\text{CH·NH}_2}}}}} + \text{H}_2\text{O} \tag{72}$$

(cf. also transamination, p. 232)

This process of amination is endergonic and requires a supply of about 31 kg-cal. (OPPENHEIMER 1933). It must therefore usually be coupled with an exergonic process in the organism, e.g. with the reaction $ATP \rightarrow ADP + PO_4 +$ about 16 kg-cal., or with other oxidative reactions. Amino acid formation in the organism is a reversible process; the direction of the equilibrium shift is determined among other things by the supply of ammonia and keto acids. The latter are formed in aerobic respiration or in connection with photosynthesis.

Early experimental work on amino acids, amides and proteins was directed especially towards the behaviour of nitrogen compounds in germination and the development of seedlings. After the investigations of BOUSSINGAULT, PFEFFER et al., the pioneer work of SCHULZE (1877-1906) in particular laid the firm foundation for our present knowledge. SCHULZE asserted that in germinating seeds the stored protein is catalytically broken down into peptides and amino acids. The breakdown continues to ammonia or other N-rich compounds. The end products have low molecular weight and are therefore easily transported to the sites of germinating growth. When they have reached the right site, the fragments are again synthesised to amino acids.

Amination often goes a stage further, so that amides are formed by addition of one or more molecules of ammonia to the amino acids. *Amidation* is also an endergonic process. SPECK investigated the amidation of glutamic acid to glutamine in kidneys and found that ATP took part:

$$
\begin{array}{ccc}
\begin{array}{l}
\text{COOH} \\
| \\
\text{CH}_2 \\
| \\
\text{CH}_2 \\
| \\
\text{CH} \cdot \text{NH}_2 \\
| \\
\text{COOH}
\end{array}
& +\,\text{NH}_3 + \text{ATP} \longrightarrow
&
\begin{array}{l}
\text{CONH}_2 \\
| \\
\text{CH}_2 \\
| \\
\text{CH}_2 \\
| \\
\text{CH} \cdot \text{NH}_2 \\
| \\
\text{COOH}
\end{array}
& +\,\text{ADP} + \text{PO}_4
\end{array}
\tag{73}
$$

glutamic acid   glutamine

According to ELLIOTT (1951) a similar system operates in lupin seedlings.

Amino groups accumulate especially as *aspartic* and *glutamic acids,* and their amides, *asparagine* and *glutamine,* of which the former seems to be the commoner. The soluble amino compounds in seedlings and also e.g. in the spring sap of trees include a number of other amino acids in smaller amounts. One of the first discovered in recent times is γ-aminobutyric acid, also α-aminopimelic acid. Similar to glutamic acid in having a 5 C-skeleton are ornithine, citrulline and arginine which differ in the terminal N-substituent (see formulae on p. 233).

The method of synthesis of the amino acids present in the protein molecules is still uncertain. Attention has recently been drawn to the fact that in higher plants the mixture of amino acids occurring free in the cells is quite different from that found in proteins. From this it is to be concluded that the amino acids occurring free are not combined directly to form the protein. Electric discharges in a mixture of methane, ammonia, hydrogen and water vapour give rise to α- and β-alanine and glycine, and this has been suggested as a model of their primeval production.

The synthetic processes in germinating plants are regulated to a considerable extent by the availability of carbohydrates. The fundamental results of SCHULZE and PRIANISJNIKOV have been confirmed by later work (cf. CHIBNALL 1939). Urea ($NH_2 \cdot CO \cdot NH_2$) also appears to play an active part in seedlings (KLEIN and TAUBÖCK 1930).

BOUSSINGAULT early found that the seedling loses up to 50% of its dry weight before photosynthetically active leaves appear. These losses refer almost exclusively to carbohydrates or fats, which are consumed in respiration. Glutamine was found especially in germinating fatty seeds. Conifer seeds contain *arginine* (formula on p. 233) which is mobilised in germination. Other types of amide have been described by DAMODARAN *et al.* (1946) and DONE and FOWDEN (1951).

According to SCHULZE and PRIANISJNIKOV, at the end of germination a mixture of aspartic and glutamic acids and their amides together with a number of other amino acids is formed. From these by transamination and attachment of other molecular fragments protein is finally resynthesised. At the same time the carbohydrate reserves are mobilised and mono- and di-saccharides are set free. The rate of hydrolysis is determined by the rate of removal. As the fragments recombine at the final point to form more complicated molecules, the rate of growth thus indirectly exercises a control over the rate of hydrolysis.

An important process in the resynthesis of protein is *transamination*, i.e. the transfer of amino nitrogen from an amino acid to form another. The transamination taking place in hydrolysis in predominantly directed towards the formation of aspartic acid and glutamic acid, which play a fundamental role. Since many different transaminations take place, proteins can be built up in the growing zones with different compositions from those in the supply organs.

SCHULZE believed that transamination might take place preferentially in seedlings (cf. also ALBAUM and COHEN 1943); it is now, however, thought to occur universally (MOTHES 1940), although the number of cases investigated in detail is rather restricted (cf. WOOD 1953, PAECH 1955). It is generally assumed that the amino groups of each amino acid, possibly with the exception of glycine, can be reversibly transferred to α-ketoglutaric acid ($HOOC \cdot (CH_2)_2 \cdot CO \cdot COOH$) (PETRIE) 1943. The enzymes concerned, the *transaminases*, were mentioned in Chapter 4 (p. 158). It is sometimes stated that transamination is inhibited by the presence of amino acids which do not take part in the process. Specific inhibitory effects on the growth of seedlings are also alleged. According to AUDUS and QUASTEL (1947) glycine, tryptophan and tryptamine inhibit, but α-alanine and L-glutamic acid do not.

The transamination includes two reaction steps: the abscission of the amino group from one acid and the combination of this with a second keto acid. BUTKEVITSCH (1902) found that under the influence of narcotics (toluene) the second stage does not take place, and that, as a result, the amino group escapes as ammonia. This transaminase activity is regarded more and more as the general mechanism of *deamination*. Pyridoxal phosphate (p. 177) here plays the role of a coenzyme. The deamination occurs in two stages, via dehydrogenation to the imino acid and hydrolytic deimination, as the following example shows:

$$
\begin{aligned}
&1. \quad R \cdot CH{\Large\langle}_{COOH}^{NH_2} \;=\; R \cdot C{\Large\langle}_{COOH}^{NH} \;+\; 2H \;(\text{-Acceptor}) \\[2mm]
&2. \quad R \cdot C{\Large\langle}_{COOH}^{NH} \;+\; H_2O \;=\; R{\Large\langle}_{COOH}^{O} \;+\; NH_3
\end{aligned}
\tag{74}
$$

Besides this deamination occurring under the influence of dehydrogenases, an *oxidative deamination* (cf. p. 177) is known according to the equation

$$R.CH \big< \begin{matrix} NH_2 \\ COOH \end{matrix} + O \rightarrow R \cdot C \big< \begin{matrix} O \\ COOH \end{matrix} + NH_3 \qquad (75)$$

Both processes, especially the latter, can involve losses of nitrogen in connection with respiration (see below). The amino acids are thus reconverted to the initial products, but the same enzymes can also re-unite the components, if ammonia is still present. Resynthesis from keto acids newly formed in respiration and fresh ammonia taken up through the roots can also take place.

Ammonium ions, which are either taken up directly from the soil or arise from the reduction of absorbed nitrate ions, can thus quickly build up aspartic acid or glutamic acid. Leaves are able to synthesise asparagine from ammonia and aspartic acud. α-Keto acids are formed secondarily from newly formed photosynthetic products and are also aminated.

The formation of amino acids and amides can also be conceived in general as a process for rendering an excess of ammonia harmless. Thus it has been observed that storage of 5% of glutamine can be induced in mangold leaves by abundant addition of an ammonium salt. Young barley plants contain a transamination system that exchanges the amino groups between glutamic acid on the one hand and aspartic acid, alanine, serine, threonine, glycine, proline, methionine, cystëine, valine, arginine and histidine on the other (WILSON *et al.* 1954).

If sufficient energy-rich phosphates (ATP etc.) are available, the mitochondria can build up amino acids as well as amides and lower peptides (WEBSTER 1954). Methionine plays the part of transferer of methyl groups among the amino acids and a methyl-donator for all kinds of methylation processes (p. 231).

2 ACID PLANTS AND AMIDE PLANTS

Inhibited transamination, according to RUHLAND and WETZEL (1926, 1927, 1929), may characterise plants with very acid cell sap. The ammonia thus liberated may therefore be neutralised by plant acids, e.g. malic and oxalic acids. RUHLAND proposed for these plants the term *acid-* or *ammonia-plants*. In *Begonia semperflorens*, in which the pH value sinks as low as 1·53, abundant ammonium ions have been found.

In contrast to the ammonia plants the *amide plants* with a less acid cell sap form asparagine from ammonia. The surplus ammonia in this case is thus neutralised by extensive amination and amidation. ARENZ (1941) suggested that amide formation is favoured by pH values over 5, whereas at lower pH values ammonium salts occur. It is difficult here to separate cause and effect. RUHLAND's interpretation was criticised by SCHWABE (1932), since according to him ammonia plants can also produce many amides. This may be seen e.g. in the case of leaves of *Oxalis deppei* (pH 1·5) and *Pelargonium* (pH 0·73-1·7).

It cannot be denied, however, that the tendency towards the fixation of cations in plants with strong acid formation must favour a stronger concentration of ammonium ions than is necessary in plants with weaker acid formation. Part of the ammonia must be taken out of the amidation equilibria. These appear to be regulated primarily by the surplus ammonia, i.e. by those amounts which otherwise would have led to a dangerous rise in the pH value. This certainly agrees with the usual interpretation of the formation of asparagine as a buffer system against accumulation of free ammonia.

3 SYNTHESIS AND DEGRADATION IN PROTEIN METABOLISM

The balance between carbohydrates, ammonia and asparagine in lupin seedlings was investigated long ago by PRIANISJNIKOV. He supplied ammonium salts and, in certain cases, sugar and the results were investigated in plants kept in the dark or in light. When sugar was added, asparagine was formed independently of light, but with no sugar, amidation did not take place in the dark and ammonia accumulated, and ammonia detoxication only occurred in the light.

As the carbodydrates react with ammonia only after oxidative conversion to keto-acids there is no simple mass equilibrium between the internal sugar concentration and protein formation. A reversible equilibrium for the relationship between glutamic acid and $NH_3 + \alpha$-ketoglutaric acid (formula on p. 232) has been proposed, on the assumption that glutamic dehydrogenase and Co II $\cdot$ H_2 are present (ADLER et al. 1938). PETRIE and collaborators (WOOD and PETRIE 1942) were, however, unable to find any simple mass ratio between amino acids and proteins.

Undoubtedly a complex steady state exists, but facts have been adduced (PETRIE 1943) which suggest a partially specific sensitivity of the participating enzymes towards changes in the environment. It has been known for some time that the hydrolysis of starch is accelerated by decreasing water content of the tissues, and PETRIE showed a similar dependence of protein synthesis in leaves on the degree of hydration. The balance between amino acids and ammonia, on the other hand, was independent of variations in humidity. Among other regulating factors which determine the activity of the enzymes participating in protein synthesis, the oxidation-reduction balance may be mentioned, since many of the enzymes are provided with SH-groups. The import-ance of sugar concentration has already been mentioned.

As regards the mechanism of protein synthesis, the scheme mentioned above of a condensation of amino acid residues with the aid of high-energy phosphates becomes ever more important. About the details, however, there is still much discussion.

WOOD (1953) distinguishes two points of view, on the one hand the classic poly-peptide scheme of EMIL FISCHER, according to which preformed amino acids are con-densed in stages, and, on the other hand, the hypothesis put forward by LINDERSTRÖM-LANG (1939). According to the latter it is not essential that amino acids should be formed beforehand, but it is sufficient if keto aldehydes or keto acids condense with amino acids to keto peptides, which by transamination or further condensation finally yield proteins. This hypothesis was later further developed by STEWARD and THOMPSON (1950) and STREET (1949). They believe that amino acids are not building stones, but are mainly hydrolysis products of proteins, which serve for transport and storage. According to this hypothesis proteins may be built up round a nucleus in a single process in which sugar or intermediate products of respiration and photosyn-thesis together with nitrates, ammonia or other nitrogenous compounds are the components. An important part is ascribed in this hypothesis to glutamic acid or glutamine as a donor of carbon chains.

This *en bloc* hypothesis has not yet been established experimentally. The results already collected go towards showing that proteins are formed by condensation of amino acids, but that there is the possibility that some keto peptides arise which are aminated only later. Many workers have found that only the dicarboxylic acids are accumulated in considerable amounts, and that before the commencement of protein formation amino acids are seldom stored. This, however, can also be interpreted as showing that the amino acids formed are built up into the growing protein molecules so rapidly that no notable accumulation occurs.

The polypeptide theory is most strongly supported by those researches which prove conclusively that the formation and transformation of polypeptides are governed by the same enzymes that also catalyse protein hydrolysis. CHRISTIANSEN and THIMANN (1950) found the protein content increasing during the growth of isolated pea inter-nodes and the quantity of free amino acids decreasing simultaneously. The often observed fact that excised leaves cease protein formation (MOYSE 1950 et al.) has led to the idea that certain amino acid components are formed in other organs and are transported to the leaves before protein synthesis can begin.

The question of the collaboration of the hydrolytic enzymes in protein synthesis is, however, not finally settled. As in the polysaccharides—but to a still greater extent—the reversibility depends of course on the energy relationships. Because of the energy content of the peptide linkage, the equilibrium between amino acids and proteins is shifted towards hydrolysis. Only exceptionally, e.g. in storage organs and seeds, can free energy be introduced through a low solubility product. As a rule the free energy comes from acyl phosphate and coenzyme A, which are built up during respiration. In this cystëine may play the part of an activator.

A factor which supports the idea of the participation of proteinases in syntheses is their strict specificity for the substrate. They might be expected to be suitable for bringing the right components together at the right place. As hydrolases these enzymes preferentially attack denatured proteins, since the peptide linkages in the intact molecule are well screened. The last phase of protein synthesis should consequently be a reversal of denaturation. All hydrolytic equilibria, however, are probably re-versible. Among polysaccharides also synthesis sometimes takes a different path from hydrolysis.

Some workers (WRINCH, STANLEY et al.) have put forward views which are reminis-cent of the en bloc hypothesis mentioned above, in that they locate protein synthesis in an interphase, e.g. in the surface of mitochondria. According to this hypothesis a monomolecular protein layer may act as a matrix, on which corresponding layers of molecules are deposited, similar to the molecular layers in the growth of crystals, where the mobile molecules are attracted and arranged under the influence of the crystal grid. Difficulties, however, arise when one comes to the elucidation of the points of attack for enzymes and energy-yielding systems.

However one explains the mechanism of protein formation, it is at least certain that in the living cell there is a balance between hydrolysis and synthesis, in which shifts are induced by variations in respiration or in the supply of raw materials (sugar and NH_3). A minimum of carbohydrate supply is indispensable since otherwise oxygen respiration—and with that the level of high-energy phosphate and keto acids—could not maintain the balance with hydrolysis. With decreasing availability of carbo-hydrates and C_4-acids hydrolysis gains the ascendancy, and the proteins are consumed in respiration.

JAMES (1946) is of the opinion that hydrogen-transferring enzymes are held in the reduced state by the presence of soluble carbohydrates. With a shortage of carbohydrates the H-carriers are more easily oxidised, and can then, according to JAMES, oxidise amino acids via *ortho*quinones.

Other changes in the equilibrium could be caused by the influence of the oxidation-reduction potential of the sulphydryl compounds, e.g. cystëine and glutathione, on the active SH-groups of the proteolytic enzymes. The relatively high energy requirement for amination and peptide formation, which can be adequately covered only by the production of high-energy phosphate in the cytochrome system, makes protein synthesis, and thus growth as a whole, extraordinarily sensitive towards inhibitors such as fluoride, dinitrophenol, cyanide, azide, CO, etc., which wholly or partly prevent electron transport and the supply of free energy from the cytochrome system.

The greatest mystery of protein formation is still the regular arrangement of the individual amino acids. The tendency now is to consider protein formation in conjunction with nucleotide formation. As the nucleotides, ADP and ATP, bear the greatest burden of energy transfer, this is hardly surprising. Conversely there exists a close connection between protein formation and nucleotide synthesis, as the purine molecule seems to be built from amino acids such as glycine. Glycine yields $C_{(4)}$, $C_{(5)}$, and $N_{(7)}$ in adenine and guanine (ABRAMS 1951, SUTTON and WERKMAN 1954).

Concerning the location of protein synthesis it has been supposed that the most intensive synthesis is to be found in the microsomes, but protein formation has also been observed in mitochondria. In view of the uncertainty of conclusions drawn from fractionation of protoplasmic particles (cf. p. 7), these data should be assessed with care. In all considerations of protein synthesis one should always keep in mind that enzymes are themselves proteins, and that it is difficult to distinguish between protoplasmic proteins and enzyme proteins. As only the presence of a prosthetic group is necessary to evoke enzyme activity, one might consider the whole protoplasmic apparatus as a 'multicatalytic unity' (cf. SEVAG 1954, KRETOVIČ et al. 1954).

In nitrogen deficiency the constitutive enzymes are formed in the first instance, whereas the adaptive enzymes appear only with enriched nitrogen supply and parallel with the increased protein content (VIRTANEN 1952). A specially high content of certain amino acids often seems to be necessary for protein synthesis, as their presence furthers the appearance of certain enzymes, e.g. tyrosine, but not tryptophan (FÅHRAEUS and LINDEBERG 1953).

The chloroplasts contain 35%-40% of the total protein in leaves, and it has been maintained (HANSON 1941) that they have an independent N-metabolism. Protein syntheses, however, must also proceed in the cytoplasm, since the cytoplasmic protein has a composition different from that of chloroplasts. It has been stated that the chloroplastic protein has less lysine but more histidine than cytoplasmic protein and a higher sulphur content. An independent protein synthesis takes place in the cell nucleus (BENSLEY 1942). The microsomes are stated to contain phospholipids and phosphoproteins in a fixed ratio.

A number of scattered cytomorphological and biochemical observations indicate a continuous metabolic exchange between different organs and structures of the cell. Attention has been directed to the wide distribution of adenosine phosphates (ADP and ATP) as energy carriers and possibly also as carriers of amino groups. Enzymatic deamination of nucleotides has actually been observed in living cells. The pronounced mobility of the nucleotides in cells is indicated also by their considerable exudation from excised roots. Even if the various cell organs are provided with specific molecule-matrices (cf. above), yet the raw material (C_4-acids, amino-N, SH-groups, etc.)

and the energy carriers must circulate to bring protein synthesis to places which have no oxidative metabolism of their own.

The fact that intermediate products of photosynthesis can serve as substitutes for C_4-acids produced in respiration facilitates an intensive protein synthesis in green cells. It is consequently not surprising that there is a positive correlation in leaves between the percentage contents of chlorophyll and total protein. A similar ratio obtains between protein and carotene. In yellowing autumn leaves e.g., of *Tropaeolum majus*, there is a direct proportionality between protein catabolism and destruction of chlorophyll. When fully developed, green leaves are fed with nitrogen salts and they synthesise not only proteins for their own growth, but in addition deliver both C- and N-products (carbohydrates, acids and amino acids) into the downwardly directed phloem stream (WALKEY 1940). The mature leaf serves as a nutrient laboratory of the plant, a fact that is of interest for the theory of 'leaf analysis' (cf. Chap. 7).

4 NITROGEN TRANSFER BETWEEN ROOT AND SHOOT

The exchange of materials between root and shoot has been investigated in detail in recent times (see MOTHES 1956), and it has been shown that the root also functions as a chemical workshop in the plant. It has been found that the root is the chief site for the formation of some alkaloids. By special methods of investigation, e.g. grafting, analyses of bleeding sap and aseptic culture of isolated roots, it has been shown that certain coumarins are formed preferentially in the root. Phenols also rise upwards in exuded sap. In addition, the root frequently takes over the primary assimilation of nitrogen. Among amino acids and amides the universally predominant glutamic acid, aspartic acid, glutamine and asparagine, as well as others, are synthesised in the root. In certain plant families, e.g. Aceraceae, Boraginaceae and Papilionaceae, allantoin and allantoic acid (p. 236) occur, and in Betulaceae citrullin (p. 233). All these N-compounds are important storage materials in storage roots, rhizomes and stem parenchyma. They make new growth possible in the spring, in which they are mostly consumed. Because of this comprehensive synthetic activity an isolated greened root can grow autotrophically in the light and can feed shoots and darkened leaves. By rooting an isolated leaf can be made to propagate. Isolated leaves without roots show breakdown of protein and lose soluble N-compounds into the petiole, which do not return to the lamina.

The metabolic difference between leaf and root is illustrated by the fact that isolated leaves cannot metabolise ammonium salts or nitrates. Thus only after rooting can the life of the leaf be maintained. Experiments with isotopes by KURSANOW and ARONOFF have shown that the materials in the leaf cannot move from the removal tissues into these of supply. The root, however, allows such a transfer of materials. It still remains doubtful in all these investigations whether the root is a point of communication between the descending and ascending streams of N-compounds, or whether it manufactures specific materials for the growth of the shoot. Conversely, root growth is influenced by materials which come from the shoot. Cutting off the root at once reduces its speed of growth, but this more gradually occurring check to growth might be due to inadequate removal of newly formed materials normally intended for the shoot.

In   many plants the activity of the root is markedly checked at the onset of flowering which according to MOTHES is of great importance for the drying out of many culti-vated plants, for only in this way is the ripening of the fruit made possible. Flowering causes in general a complete change in metabolism.

5 THE N-METABOLISM OF LEAVES

The delivery of preformed organic N-compounds by the root to the shoot discussed in the previous paragraph refers of course only to part of the products needed by the shoot. In the exuded sap of germinating plants such as wheat, organic materials often cannot be identified with certainty, though large amounts of nitrate nitrogen are present if nitrates are supplied in the nutrient substrate. Of the nitrate taken up less than half is worked up further in the root, whereas the greater part is consumed in growth. Ammonium ions also go through the root and are removed by way of the xylem.

Organic nitrogen moves chiefly in the phloem, but can also utilise the tracheae when necessary, e.g. during the rise of the sap in trees in spring; the organic nitro-gen is then transported preferentially in the form of amino acids, whereas the amides have more the character of storage products.

CHIBNALL (1939) states that the leaf protoplasm has two types of proteins:
(1) proteins which at a pH of about 7 enter into ionic linkages with phosphates or K and N, whereas at lower pH they are completely dissociated;
(2) nucleoproteins or proteins closely combined with phosphates of Ca and Mg, which are insoluble in presence of the cell sap.

CHIBNALL counts the compounds mentioned under (1) as reserve proteins. With the application of modern electrophoretic methods BONNER and WILDMAN (1947) were able to distinguish in spinach leaves two different protein fractions. One fraction which amounted to 70%-80% of the total protein was electrophoretically homogene-ous and, on proteolysis, yielded auxin but few enzymes. The second fraction was electrophoretically non-homogeneous and contained most of the enzymes.

On starvation or ageing the protoplasmic proteins are catabolised, since they can no longer be protected by the carbohydrates (see above). This stage normally occurs shortly before leaf-fall, and the amino acids set free go back into the stem. In evergreen plants, e.g. *Hedera* and *Ilex*, this reversal of the sap stream does not occur, and the leaves show an N-maximum in winter (SATTLER 1929).

The proteolysis in excised leaves standing with their petioles in water was studied by DELEANO (1911), YEMM (1935) and MOTHES *et al.* (1956). SIDERIS (1947) reported on the metabolism of the pineapple plant. According to DELEANO, protein catabolism only begins in the leaf of vines 100 hours after cutting. YEMM found in excised barley leaves respiration intensity decreasing with the disappearance of the carbohydrates. After consumption of the carbohydrates the proteins are degraded, while the *R.Q.* sinks from about 1 to 0·80 (cf. Chap. 4, H 2 on p. 207). Simultaneously the content of insoluble nitrogen falls, whilst the soluble N-compounds increase. At the commence-ment of respiratory catabolism of proteins the liberated ammonia is detoxicated by formation of asparagine and glutamine; finally, in autolysis, the cells are unable to neutralise the ammonia, which collects in harmful concentrations, even when part of it escapes as gas into the air.

VICKERY and collaborators investigated the behaviour of malic, citric and oxalic acids in isolated tobacco leaves, which were kept in the light or in the dark. These acids, including acids not yet clearly identified, amount to 27% of the total organic material. With normal supply of carbohydrates, i.e. in illuminated leaves, no organic acids are consumed in respiration. In the dark also the total acidity remains approximately constant; considerable qualitative shifts, however, take place, in which the malic acid decreases strongly whilst the citric acid, for example, increases. These changes run parallel with the degradation of proteins, which however is somewhat retarded in illuminated leaves. The ammonia liberated on breakdown of protein is, especially in the dark, fixed in asparagine. On illumination the ammonia appears to be brought into the synthetic processes in a different way (see below) and is stored chiefly as glutamine. Finally under these conditions the organic acids are consumed in respiration. VICKERY and CHIBNALL suggest that in conformity with the TCA-cycle malic acid passes over via oxalacetic acid into citric acid.

The metabolic changes resulting from the absence of photosynthesis take place roughly in the following stages:

1. the carbohydrate phase, in which chiefly carbohydrates but also, in smaller amounts, organic acids and protein are broken down; $R.Q.$ is about 1;
2. the organic acid phase, in which breakdown is mainly directed on to acids, especially malic acid, and proteins are decomposed at increasing speed, but in which ammonia is neutralised as asparagine and $R.Q.$ rises to values over 1;
3. the final phase, in which the store of organic acids is exhausted, the proteins are decomposed with ever increasing speed and the $R.Q.$ value sinks below 1.

In the final stage the side-chains of the proteins which are important for the structure of protoplasm, e.g. fats and phosphatides, are split off and oxidised. Even though this increases the amount of keto acids, the reserves for the fixation of ammonia are insufficient, so that it accumulates in the free state and poisons the cells.

The time of entry into the final phase depends of course on the extent of the acid reserves, as these neutralise the ammonia. The acid plants of RUHLAND are probably more resistant in this respect. The low pH value indeed indicates the presence of a high basic buffering capacity. This is probably the cause of the high resistance of the succulents to times of restricted carbohydrate production, which occur in drought periods as the result of the closing of the stomata. The lupin also, according to ARENZ (1941), is an acid plant.

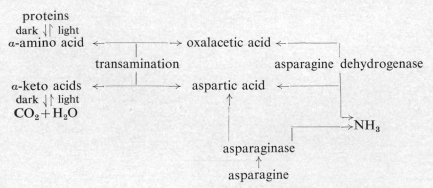

Nitrogen turnover in seedlings of *Lupinus luteus*.

According to recent investigations the amino acids are consumed during starvation in the following order:

cystine > glutamine > arginine > tyrosine > tryptophan.

This order of course exercises an influence on enzyme activity, since in different enzymes the active groups are combined with different amino acids.

6 RELATIONSHIPS BETWEEN RESPIRATION AND ENZYME SYNTHESIS

It has already been emphasised that no simple mass ratio exists between concentration of the protein components and the speed of protein formation. On the contrary, it is clear that proteolysis is stopped or in any case so much damped down by the presence of carbohydrates that synthesis outweighs it. The complicated nature of the balance between anabolic and catabolic processes becomes clear also e.g. from the observations of YEMM, VICKERY and MOTHES, that proteolysis may predominate even with rising carbohydrate content. Undoubtedly, however, there exists a positive relation between the concentration of α-keto acids plus ammonia and the rate between the formation of amino acids and amides.

We have already referred to the observations of PETRIE and MOTHES on the regulating effect of water content; with decreasing water content proteolysis and the removal of soluble N-products increase. According to GASSNER and FRANKE (1934), in wheat and rye temperature also has an effect on protein content which increases strongly with decreasing temperature; but the content of soluble N-compounds changes but little.

There is still some difference of opinion about the protein balance, since e.g. GREGORY (1937) and RICHARDS (1938) assume that aerobic respiration is stimulated secondarily by protein synthesis or protein concentration. Even if, as WOOD (1941) thinks, there is a positive correlation between the protein content of protoplasm and respiration, the causal connection behind this is by no means clear.

It is clear from what has been said above that protein reserves can regulate respiration in cases of carbohydrate deficiency. The correlation between respiration and protein content in growing organisms may on the other hand be due simply to the fact that the respiration occurs via the TCA-cycle and furnishes the raw material, i.e. the keto acids, and that a damming up of these substances is hindered by continuing protein synthesis. The positive correlation between respiration and protein formation is finally determined by the energy delivery through high-energy phosphates. These 'energy packets', however, are also used in other ways, e.g. in the synthesis of the cell wall, coenzymes, etc. Simple quantitative ratios between aerobic respiration and protein synthesis are therefore scarcely to be expected.

The complicated balance between synthesis and break-down of proteins, as well as between protein formation and respiration, naturally makes the economic quotient of the whole system rather variable. By 'economic quotient' is meant the ratio between dry matter produced and carbohydrate consumed in respiration. In Chapter 4 (p. 140) basal respiration was discussed, i.e. the minimum of free energy which is necessary as a brake or counterweight against unavoidable catabolism. It may be supposed that basal respiration yields just the minimum capacity for synthesis to maintain a metabolic steady state. Little is known about this; but organs which are exposed for several hours to cyanide poisoning do resume growth after elution or after the enzyme systems have become adapted (cf. p. 141). This suggests that the ground respiration not inhibitable by cyanide, like alcoholic fermentation, produces a certain amount of high-energy phosphates or acyl-coenzyme A compounds. The end oxidation by cytochrome oxidase would thus be unnecessary. On the other hand, all experience suggests that only cytochrome oxidase creates the high potentials necessary for growth, i.e. for protein synthesis.

It has been thought by various people (WAYGOOD 1950, JAMES 1953) that the cytochrome system disappears, e.g. on ageing of the root tissue; but this has been doubted by other other workers. It seems rather that the cytochromes are still present on ageing, but are less effective. In view of what has just been said, this would be quite comprehensible since an active cytochrome oxidation, in presence of the necessary raw materials, e.g. phosphate, undoubtedly produces many 'energy packets' which would find small outlet in mature tissue. Some synthesis of N-compounds, however, appears to take place also in mature root tissues, e.g. the formation of alkaloids (cf. p. 229), and these products migrate into the phloem. On the other hand, it is not known whether nucleotides and high-energy phosphates are also continuously produced in roots and made available for the parts above ground. The observed abundant exudation of nucleotides from cut-off roots could be explained in some such way, but here new experimental data are necessary. The synthesis of such high-level materials would probably require the collaboration of an active cytochrome system.

Calculations of the total chemical balance during growth have been made for certain fungi. HOOVER and ALLISON (1940) give the following equation for the synthetic activity of *Rhizobium meliloti*:

$$\frac{21}{12}C_{12}H_{22}O_{11}+2NH_4OH \rightarrow C_{19}H_{32}N_2O_9+2CO_2+\frac{99}{12}H_2O \qquad (76)$$

Respiration consumes one-third to one-quarter of the sugar available. The yield is therefore 67%-75%, which is fairly high. According to BUTLER (1946) the energy liberated from the oxidation of a molecule of glucose (688 kg-cal.) should suffice for the linking of about a hundred amino acid radicals into protein chains. About 7·5 kg-cal. are consumed in the synthesis of DL-leucylglycine from DL-leucine and glycine. To this must be added the fairly large amounts of energy consumed in the amination of keto acids. As the energy consumption in the formation of keto acids can be neglected, the amination of a molecule corresponds to about 1-2 ~ph or about one-fiftieth of the total amount of energy produced in the oxidation of a molecule of sugar. For the synthesis of a protein molecule a large number of sugar molecules must therefore be completely consumed; which makes the almost indispensable linking of protein synthesis and respiration comprehensible.

B. Fixation of Atmospheric Nitrogen (Nitrification)

The biological fixation of atmospheric nitrogen and its transformation into organic compounds has not been definitely shown in higher plants.

The experiments carried out by RUBEN *et al.* with the isotope ^{15}N, which were said to have shown N-fixation in rye leaves, were not confirmed (BURRIS 1941). Nitrification has been found only in unicellular lower organisms, e.g. blue-green algae (*Nostoc, Anabaena*), soil bacteria (*Azotobacter chroococcum, Clostridium pasteurianum*) and in the bacteria (*Bacillus radicicola* or *Rhizobium leguminosarum*; see WILSON

1939) living in symbiosis with the roots of plants, such as the Leguminosae. Certain data suggest the possibility that yeast and mould fungi may also fix atmospheric nitrogen (FREI 1942). Nitrification has been stated to occur in the parasitic fungus *Phoma betae* (BOSE 1943). Among mycorrhizal fungi (see below) an *Actinomyces* living in the nodules of alder is stated to be able to fix atmospheric nitrogen.

The nitrifying bacteria play an important part in the economy of nature, as in suitable soils they fix 20-100 kg of nitrogen per hectare per year. For comparison it may be mentioned that in Finland (VIRTANEN 1955) the nitrogen fixed by photochemical processes or electrical discharges in the atmosphere amounts to only about 3 kg per hectare. Part of this nitrogen originates in the ammonia given off from the soil.

Of the nitrogen-fixing soil bacteria *Azotobacter* prefers neutral or moderately acid soils, whereas *Clostridium* is less sensitive to variations in pH. *Clostridium* is predominantly anaerobic and *Azotobacter* aerobic, but symbiosis can occur between the two. Symbiosis has also been observed between *Azotobacter* and *Nostoc* or *Granulobacter*. The energy necessary for the reduction of the nitrogen to NH_3 is supplied in *Azotobacter* by the active oxygen respiration. *Azotobacter* is very adaptable as regards different sources of carbon (HARRIS 1946).

The symbiosis between *Bacillus radicicola* and the roots of Leguminosae, discovered by HELLRIEGEL and WILFARTH, is an example of the mutual advantages of two different metabolic systems working together. The bacteria, which do not fix nitrogen when living free in the soil, penetrate through the root hairs into the cortex (THORNTON 1947). The roots appear to secrete substances which stimulate bacteria in the soil. On the other hand the bacteria also seem to give out auxins, which evoke increased cell division and growth in the host tissue, from which the root nodules filled with bacteria finally arise. The form of the bacteria becomes changed ('bacterioids'), and they begin to fix atmospheric nitrogen energetically. The nitrogen compounds formed are absorbed equally intensively by the host plant.

The nodules contain a red pigment rather like haemoglobin (KUBO 1939, BURRIS and HAAS 1944, KEILIN and SMITH 1947, VIRTANEN et al. 1947). This 'leghaemoglobin' with decreasing activity, e.g. with a deficiency of oxygen, passes over into a brown and finally a green modification, which is related to the gall pigments. Pure leghaemoglobin has a molecular weight of 17,000 and, unlike animal haemoglobin, has only one haem group. The pigment is formed in the cytoplasm of the host cells. It seems to have nothing to do with absorption of oxygen, but apparently participates in the chemical process of nitrification, probably in the reduction of hydroxylamine (VIRTANEN 1955). Inhibition of leghaemoglobin is probably the main reason for the great sensitivity of nitrification towards carbon monoxide.

Different workers still hold different views about the biochemistry of nitrification (cf. BURRIS and WILSON 1946, VIRTANEN 1945, 1955). VIRTANEN (1945) maintains that nitrogen is converted to hydroxylamine by oxidoreduction, and that this compound with oxalacetic acid forms aspartic acid via oximinosuccinic acid. Hydroxylamine is said to be 'fixed' mostly as oxime nitrogen.

Investigations using ^{15}N on the other hand seem to show (BURRIS and WILSON 1946) that nitrogen, in conformity with WIELAND'S interpretation, is reduced to ammonia which is then built into aspartic acid and glutamic acid in the usual way. This idea is shared by other American workers.

Opinions are also divided about the secretion of nitrogen compounds from nodules into the soil. Equally unknown is the way in which the leghaemoglobin enters into the nitrification process. VIRTANEN (1955) has, however, emphasised that leghaemo-globin seems to be the sole factor which could effect a reduction of hydroxylamine. It has in fact been found that haemoglobin and leghaemoglobin quantitatively reduce hydroxylamine to ammonia.

$$
\begin{array}{l}
\text{CHO} \\
\text{|} \\
\text{HCOH} \\
\text{|} \\
\text{HOCH} \\
\text{|} \\
\text{HCOH} \\
\text{|} \\
\text{CH}_2\text{OH}
\end{array}
\quad \xrightarrow[-\text{CO}_2)]{(-\text{H}}
\begin{array}{l}
\text{COOH} \\
\text{|} \\
\text{CH}_2 \\
\text{|} \\
\text{CO} \\
\text{|} \\
\text{COOH}
\end{array}
\;+\;
\begin{array}{l}
\text{N}_2 \\
\text{|} \\
\text{(+H}_2\text{O} \\
\text{+H)} \\
\downarrow \\
\text{H}_2\text{N}\cdot\text{OH}
\end{array}
\xrightarrow[(-\text{H}_2\text{O})]{}
\begin{array}{l}
\text{COOH} \\
\text{|} \\
\text{CH}_2 \\
\text{|} \\
\text{C}=\text{NOH} \\
\text{|} \\
\text{COOH}
\end{array}
\xrightarrow[-\text{H}_2\text{O})]{(+\text{H}}
\begin{array}{l}
\text{COO} \\
\text{|} \\
\text{CH}_2 \\
\text{|} \\
\text{CH.N} \\
\text{|} \\
\text{COO}
\end{array}
$$

D-Glucose   Oxalacetic   Hydroxyl-   Oximino-   Aspa▸
(open-chain   acid   amine   succinic   acid
form)   acid

The nitrifying bacteria living free in the soil synthesise protein, which is degraded to ammonia after the death of the organisms. The ammonia is absorbed by nitrifying bacteria and oxidised to nitrate. Ammonium- and nitrate-ions dominate the nitrogen nutrition of green plants; but heterotrophic organisms and to some extent the roots of higher plants can also take up and metabolise organically-combined nitrogen.

C. Nitrate Assimilation

The nitrifying micro-organisms form a fairly specialised group of the organisms autotrophic for nitrogen. Most plants, lower as well as higher, also synthesise their organic N-compounds from inorganic substances, but are restricted to the strongly reduced or strongly oxidised N-forms (NH_3 and NO_3) (ROBBINS 1937). A strict subdivision into *nitrate plants* and *ammonia plants*, however, does not exist, since most can utilise both NH_3 and NO_3. A number of fungi, most species of yeast, certain bacteria and colourless flagellates are, however, better adapted to ammonia as a source of nitrogen.

In general, the ability to utilise one or other form of inorganic nitrogen seems to be present in every organism. It depends on external conditions, especially hydrogen-ion concentration, whether nitrate or ammonia is taken up and elaborated. As the nitrate, because of the strong dissociation of nitric acid, practically never occurs as a neutral molecule, its uptake and accumulation in the roots is less dependent on the hydrogen-ion concentration than on the intensity of the cyanide-inhibitable respira-tion (BURSTRÖM 1940).

Nitrate uptake into the hyphae of fungi is much [more strongly influenced by the ionic balance and is thus, in conformity with the DONNAN equilibrium, favoured by low pH values. *Aspergillus niger*, for example, absorbs the nitrate ion from NH_4NO_3 only at pH <3 and nitrate already taken up is in fact secreted at higher values. From KNO_3 the NO_3^- is taken up only at pH less than 6·5. Conversely, the uptake of NH_4 is favoured at higher pH values. This also applies to some extent to higher plants, in which a preference for NO_3^- or NH_4^+ can be influenced by the pH value and the ionic balance (PIRSCHLE 1929, 1931, RIBBERT 1931, PRIANISJNIKOV 1933; see Chap. 6). The uptake of ammonia on the alkaline side is favoured also by the molecular NH_4OH which occurs in greater concentration at high pH.

The uptake of ammonia because of its direct participation in amidation (see section A) only leads to the accumulation of ammonium and ammonia in typical 'acid plants' and dying organs; but in the presence of metallic cations nitrate can be accumulated without harm in the cell sap in amounts large enough to maintain a considerable part of the turgor pressure. The storage of nitrate and the elaboration of nitrate into protein do not, however, always proceed in step, and nitrate-accumulating plants are not necessarily limited to NO_3^- as a nitrogen source. The strongly nitrate-storing *Chenopodium album* is, for example, according to MARTHALER (1937), a typical ammonia plant, preferring NH_4 as nutrient. All typical high moor plants grow better on NH_4^+ than on NO_3^-, which they perhaps cannot utilise (MARTHALER 1939). These relationships depend of course, on a rather unspecific method of ion-uptake. Readily mobile nitrate ions are often involved in excess.

The only importance to the plant of the nitrate ion as such is that of being a means, together with other easily mobile ions and molecules, of rapidly increasing turgor. As one of the most important sources of nitrogen for the metabolism of higher plants, NO_3^- must be reduced to $NH_3(NH_4^+)$. The ability to reduce nitrate is biologically widespread, but two different physiological purposes may be distinguished: the provision of a suitable N-compound especially for amination, and the utilisation for oxidative purposes of the oxygen present in the nitrate. Higher plants, mould fungi and some species of bacteria use nitrate as a nitrogen source; certain organisms utilise it for the end-oxidation in energy-yielding respiration.

The role of nitrate in end-oxidation was first described by QUASTEL et al. (1925). Coli bacteria can grow anaerobically only in the presence of nitrate; the nitrate is reduced only as far as nitrite. In other examples of '*nitrate respiration*' (EGAMI 1957) reduction may go as far as NO, N_2O or N_2. Nitrate respiration can also be observed in higher plants, especially under anaerobic conditions. In nitrate respiration reduced phosphopyridine nucleotide is oxidised, and the cytochrome system, especially cytochrome b or b_1, may take part in the electron transfer. This co-operation of the cytochrome system, however, has recently been doubted. The data on the joint action of nitrate reductase and cytochrome b may be due to the two enzymes attaching themselves to the same particles in homogenates. In this way energy may be transferred also to phosphate.

The enzymes effective in nitrate reduction are termed *nitrate reductases*. They are metalloflavoproteins, and the metal is molybdenum (YAMAGATA 1940, MCELROY et al. 1952, NICHOLAS 1954). Flavin and molybdenum are conceived of as transitory electron carriers:

$$NADPH(or\ NADH) \rightarrow FAD\ (or\ FMN) \rightarrow Mo \rightarrow NO_3^- \rightarrow protein \qquad (77)$$

Details about the action of nitrate reductase are still insufficiently known. The complete reduction to ammonia must certainly take place through several stages, and this probably explains the findings of BURSTRÖM (1939, 1945) on wheat roots, of NOACK and PIRSON (1939) and ALBERTS-DIETERT (1941) on *Chlorella* and of STEINBERG (1937) on *Aspergillus*, according to which manganese (Mn^{++}) and to a smaller extent iron also take part. Calcium ions also seem to exercise a positive effect (NIGHTINGALE et al. 1931, SHOK 1941).

Q

This extensive dependence of nitrate assimilation on the ionic state of tissues suggests a link with respiration. It should be noted that, according to various data, the full assimilation of nitrate to amino nitrogen takes place only in the presence of oxygen and that under anaerobic conditions the process usually stops at the stage of nitrite. In certain algae which are provided with hydrogenases the further reduction of nitrite to NH_3 takes place with the co-operation of molecular hydrogen (KESSLER 1957); that is

$$HNO_2 + 3H_2 \rightarrow NH_3 + 2H_2O \tag{78}$$

A coupling between *nitrate assimilation*—that is the utilisation of nitrate nitrogen for synthetic purposes—and oxygen respiration is essential since the α-keto acids and hydroxy acids necessary for amino acid formation are formed only in the aerobic cycle. It is also evident from the increased *R.Q.* value in the presence of NO_3 (see section A) that the nitrate oxygen acts as a hydrogen acceptor during nitrate assimilation. WARBURG and NEGELEIN (1920) referred to the high energy yield (162 kg-cal.) of a complete utilisation of the nitrate oxygen, but it appears doubtful whether the theoretical gain can be fully utilised since the reduction under anaerobic conditions usually stops at the nitrite stage.

The supposition of ARNON (1937) that nitrate nutrition might compensate for deficient aeration of the root system appears doubtful. It should also be noted that the mere uptake of nitrate ions into the root requires the help of respiration (see Chap. 6). Thus in active nitrate uptake carbohydrates are consumed as respiratory material. YAMAGATA (1934), found an increased respiration during nitrate assimilation and a reduced production of heat; which suggests that the nitrate oxygen was partly transferred into newly formed organic substances. Here one may refer to the production of organic acids which is so important for the turgor of growing cells. LUNDEGÅRDH and BURSTRÖM (1944) found an increased oxygen consumption at pH values which favour root growth.

In higher organisms the complete reduction of NO_3 to amino groups apparently proceeds as a single sequence, but the process certainly forms a chain with many intermediate stages. It is in any case premature to think that complete nitrate assimilation represents only a continuation of the pure nitrate respiration which takes place in the denitrifying bacteria. In *Bacterium fluorescens*, *B. pyocyaneum* and *B. denitrificans* nitrogen oxides and nitrogen gas are given off. Various bacteria, on the other hand, show reduction from nitrate to nitrite and from nitrite to ammonia. One may assume as a hypothesis that reduction proceeds via nitrite and ammonia also in higher organisms and certain fungi and possibly via the NOH radical. Wheat roots maintained anaerobically reduce any nitrate taken up to nitrite, which does not accumulate but is again liberated into the environment. Nitrite can, however, be utilised under aerobic conditions and is, for example, an excellent source of nitrogen for maize. Nitrogen metabolism seems to be similar in this case to that in ammonium nutrition, since NO_3 is not accumulated in the cells (cf. above; MEVIUS and DIKUSSAR 1930). Hydroxylamine was also considered by MEYER and later workers (see STEPHENSEN 1947) as an intermediate stage, but this view was rejected by other workers.

In the colourless parts of plants, such as roots, nitrate assimilation proceeds with the consumption of sugar supplied through the phloem. The process is accelerated by supplying sugar from outside. Nitrate assimilation is probably a function of cortical cells and especially of the meristem. An indication of this is the rapid disappearance of accumulated nitrate in the tip zone. Certain observations suggest that an over-production of amino acids and other nitrogen compounds takes place in the root, and that the surplus is conducted upwards in the phloem. The preponderant part of nitrate assimilation appears to be located in the roots, especially in trees.

In wheat roots about half the nitrate taken up is at once assimilated (BURSTRÖM 1945, LUNDEGÅRDH 1945). In wheat seedlings two or three weeks old no measurable removal of amino nitrogen takes place, and the assimilated nitrate is thus consumed exclusively in the root's own growth. In tree roots, on the other hand, considerable over-production of combined nitrogen is found, which in spring is removed in the xylem sap. Similar relationships have been observed in herbaceous plants. The nicotine accumulated in tobacco leaves is synthesised in the roots and conducted upwards in the sap stream (DAWSON 1946).

The inorganic nitrate transported in the rising sap stream is distributed among the various aerial organs. The largest part goes to the leaves, but reserves are also deposited in the stem. During the growth of the leaf much nitrate is consumed, but nitrate assimilation continues parallel with photosynthesis also in mature cells and amino acids and proteins are formed. Some of the amino acids are conducted back into the stem and so to the growing shoots and inflorescences. The nitrate assimilation in the leaves seems to proceed wholly or partly in the chloroplasts or perhaps in their immediate environment. The positive influence of illumination on the protein content of leaves has long been known (see for example FUJITA 1931).

As regards *photosynthetic nitrate assimilation*, BURSTRÖM (1937-43) has shown that it is directly connected with photosynthesis, and that certain stages of the latter are linked with nitrate reduction. BURSTRÖM states that in the dark only traces of nitrates are reduced in the leaves, and he thinks that photosynthetic intermediate products are combined with light-activated derivatives of nitrate reduction. STEPKA et al. (1948) later showed that radioactive alanine and aspartic acid occur in leaves which have been supplied for thirty seconds with light and $^{14}CO_2$. BURSTRÖM's assumption of a specific photoreduction of nitrate in leaves was contested by WOOD (1953).

KESSLER (1957) maintains that the reduction of nitrate to nitrite is indirectly assisted by the photosynthetic formation of C-compounds in the presence of CO_2. The further reduction of the nitrite seems to be more closely connected with photochemical processes. KESSLER believes that, as well as the supply of H-donators, the formation of high-energy phosphates is of especial importance.

TOTTINGHAM et al. (1934) refer to the possibility that the photo-assimilation of nitrate depends particularly on the ultra-violet rays; this might be due to the special light absorption of the yellow-coloured nitrate reductase. BURSTRÖM found that at low light intensities the total yield of photosynthetic products rises in presence of nitrate, whilst in strong light the CO_2 assimilation and the nitrate assimilation compete against each other.

The *inversion of nitrate assimilation* i.e. the oxidation of ammonia to nitrate, as in the nitrifying bacteria, does not seem to occur normally in higher plants, although such an inversion has been observed under special conditions (PEARSALL and BILLIMORIA 1937). Here it consists probably of a steady state of $NH_2 + 2O_2 \rightleftharpoons NO_3 + H_2O$, which as a rule is shifted strongly to the left. With an abundant supply of carbohydrates the nitrate oxygen may behave preferentially as H acceptor and the ammonia formed may be quickly consumed in amination or amide formation. The oxidative deamination of amino acids is for this reason directed towards the NH_2-linkage; the ammonia is not oxidised.

Even in carbohydrate deficiency, the carbon skeleton of the amino acids seems to be attacked first. Observations on excised or dying leaves (VICKERY *et al.* 1933, PEARSALL and BILLIMORIA 1937) suggest that finally the ammonia is also oxidised. The consequent nitrate formation would be an autolytic or *post mortem* process.

D. The Interaction of Carbohydrate Metabolism and N-metabolism

We have dealt in detail above with the relationships between carbohydrate turnover and N-metabolism in protein synthesis and respiration. The synthesis of amino acids is dependent partly on the supply of ammonia nitrogen, partly on that of keto and hydroxy acids which in turn depends on the available carbohydrates. Variations in the supply of carbohydrates limit protein synthesis only when the supply is low. The relationships between respiration and protein formation in leaves are also influenced, for example, by the water content.

In the balance between anabolic and catabolic processes during the formation of new protoplasmic material, the most easily oxidisable amino acids are always important, since they limit protein production. A surplus of carboxylic acids is necessary because they partly determine turgor. It is at once clear that the general balance between carbohydrate supply, ultimately photosynthesis, and nitrogen nutrition represents an important factor in development. Some experiments of KRAUS and KRAYBILL (1918; see HICKS 1928) illustrate this fact. The experiments were carried out with varying nitrogen nutrition. With a low ratio of C : N, that is with a large surplus of N, the plants developed unsatisfactorily with respect to both growth and fruiting. Vegetative development was favoured, but fruit was not formed; which is a well-known phenomenon also in agriculture. With very high ratios of C : N, that is with an excess of carbohydrates, small leaves are formed and strongly lignified tissues.

Similar effects of changes in the ratio C: N can be observed in most plants. KLEBS (1896, 1903) has drawn particular attention to the shifts between vegetative and sexual development. According to TALLEY (1934) and HOWLETT (1936), the male sex organs are sensitive towards deficiency of carbohydrates, whereas the female organs of plants suffer more with nitrogen deficiency.

E. Conspectus of the More Important Organic Nitrogen Compounds in Plant Cells

Whether urea is synthesised biologically from carbonic acid and ammonia is uncertain; but the mobility of the amino-group in transamination (below, p. 232) suggests the theoretical possibility of the amination of carbonic acid.

Urea in small amounts occurs in a number of plants, e.g. spinach and potatoes. The enzyme *urease*, which catalyses the reaction

$$CO(NH_2)_2 + H_2O \rightarrow CO_2 + 2NH_3 \qquad (79)$$

occurs in plants, e.g. in soya beans.

The main process in nitrogen assimilation is usually the formation of α-amino acids by autotrophic plants. The simplest amino acids, shown below, are derivatives of acetic, propionic and butyric acids:

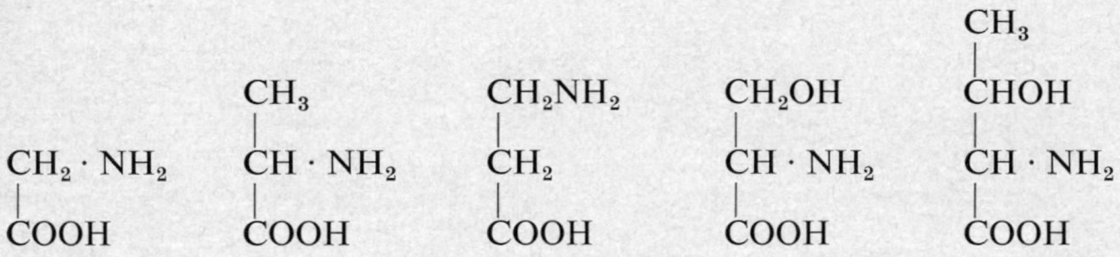

$$
\begin{array}{ccccc}
 & & & & CH_3 \\
 & CH_3 & CH_2NH_2 & CH_2OH & CHOH \\
 & | & | & | & | \\
CH_2 \cdot NH_2 & CH \cdot NH_2 & CH_2 & CH \cdot NH_2 & CH \cdot NH_2 \\
| & | & | & | & | \\
COOH & COOH & COOH & COOH & COOH \\
\text{Glycine} & \text{DL-Alanine} & \beta\text{-Alanine} & \text{Serine} & \text{Threonine} \\
\text{(glycocoll)} & & & &
\end{array}
$$

Glycine is one of the components in the synthesis of purines and porphyrins (p. 37 and of glutathione (p. 144). *Alanine* is the simplest of the optically active amino acids. In biological systems it is the L-alanine that is predominant. *β-Alanine* forms part of the molecule of pantothenic acid (p. 234). The next homologue to β-alanine, viz. *γ-aminobutyric acid*, has already been mentioned (p. 214). *Serine* is less common. It is believed that the phosphoric acid in phosphoproteins is attached to the amino acids such as serine and *threonine* which have hydroxyl groups.

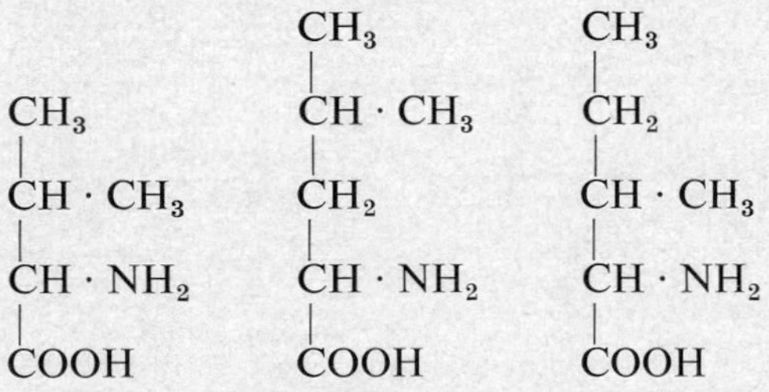

$$
\begin{array}{ccc}
 & CH_3 & CH_3 \\
 & | & | \\
CH_3 & CH \cdot CH_3 & CH_2 \\
| & | & | \\
CH \cdot CH_3 & CH_2 & CH \cdot CH_3 \\
| & | & | \\
CH \cdot NH_2 & CH \cdot NH_2 & CH \cdot NH_2 \\
| & | & | \\
COOH & COOH & COOH \\
\text{Valine} & \text{Leucine} & \text{Isoleucine}
\end{array}
$$

Valine, *leucine* and *isoleucine* have branched carbon chains (methyl side-chains), and from them originate the terpenoids.

Among the sulphur-containing amino acids three should be specially noted.

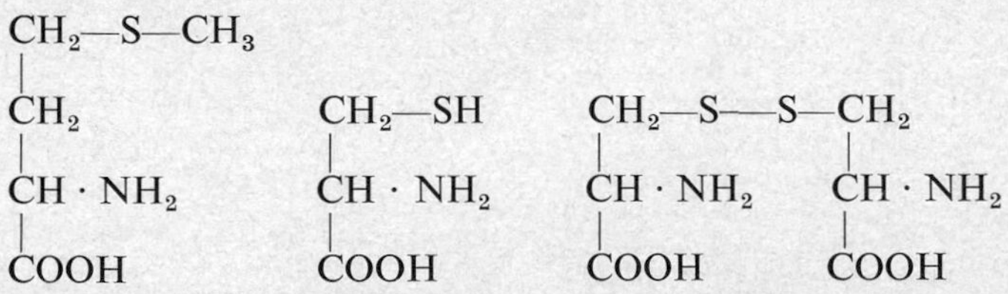

$$
\begin{array}{cccc}
CH_2\text{---}S\text{---}CH_3 & & & \\
| & & & \\
CH_2 & CH_2\text{---}SH & CH_2\text{---}S\text{---}S\text{---}CH_2 & \\
| & | & | & | \\
CH \cdot NH_2 & CH \cdot NH_2 & CH \cdot NH_2 & CH \cdot NH_2 \\
| & | & | & | \\
COOH & COOH & COOH & COOH \\
\text{Methionine} & \text{Cystëine} & & \text{Cystine}
\end{array}
$$

Methionine, as already mentioned (p. 216) is an important methylating agent; on demethylation it is converted to homocystëine, which can be remethylated, e.g. by choline (below, p. 234). Homocystëine is the next higher homologue to cystëine, that is, it has an extra methylene group—CH_2—in each of the carbon chains.

Cystëine and *cystine* are related through the sulphur atom(s); the former is the reduced and the latter the oxidised form. Because of this conversion between —SH and —S—S— they play an important part in the activation or inactivation of enzymes with active sulphydryl (—SH) groups. This role is usually taken over by the tripeptide glutathione which contains cystëine.

The aliphatic amino acids so far mentioned contain one amino group and one carboxyl group and are therefore sometimes called *neutral* amino acids. There are, however, also monoaminodicarboxylic acids, called *acid* amino acids; the chief o these are *aspartic acid* and the next homologue *glutamic acid*. By their dibasicity they play a decisive part in the amphoteric nature of the proteins (p. 11). With the collaboration of ATP these acids take up another molecule of NH_3 to form their amides,

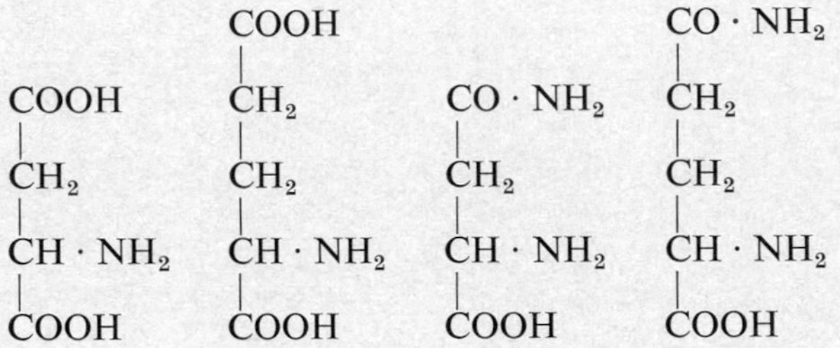

$$
\begin{array}{cccc}
 & COOH & & CO \cdot NH_2 \\
 & | & & | \\
COOH & CH_2 & CO \cdot NH_2 & CH_2 \\
| & | & | & | \\
CH_2 & CH_2 & CH_2 & CH_2 \\
| & | & | & | \\
CH \cdot NH_2 & CH \cdot NH_2 & CH \cdot NH_2 & CH \cdot NH_2 \\
| & | & | & | \\
COOH & COOH & COOH & COOH \\
\text{Aspartic} & \text{Glutamic} & \text{Asparagine} & \text{Glutamine} \\
\text{acid} & \text{acid} & &
\end{array}
$$

asparagine and *glutamine* respectively (p. 214). Another monoaminodicarboxylic acid already mentioned (also on p. 214) is *α-aminopimelic acid*.

Glutamic acid may be used as an example of the process of *transamination*:

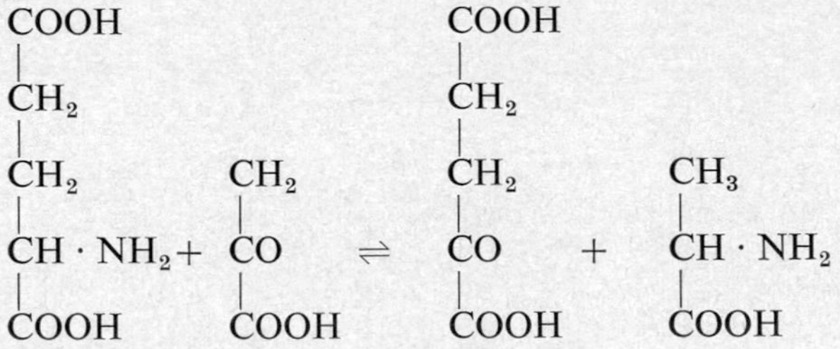

$$
\begin{array}{ccccccc}
COOH & & & COOH & & & \\
| & & & | & & & \\
CH_2 & & & CH_2 & & & \\
| & & & | & & & \\
CH_2 & CH_2 & & CH_2 & & CH_3 & \\
| & | & & | & & | & \\
CH \cdot NH_2 + & CO & \rightleftharpoons & CO & + & CH \cdot NH_2 & \qquad (80) \\
| & | & & | & & | & \\
COOH & COOH & & COOH & & COOH & \\
\text{Glutamic} & \text{Pyruvic} & & \text{α-Keto-} & & \text{Alanine} & \\
\text{acid} & \text{acid} & & \text{glutaric} & & & \\
 & & & \text{acid} & & &
\end{array}
$$

(cf. amination of pyruvic acid, equation (72), p. 213).

The next two amino acids, *lysine* and its next lower homologue *ornithine*, are examples of diaminomonocarboxylic acids, or *basic* amino acids. The former is a derivative of caproic acid and the latter of n-valeric acid. Ornithine, *citrulline* and *arginine* are shown here in a tripartite *ornithine cycle*, involving NH_3, CO_2, H_2O and urea; this has been found in *Neurospora crassa* and other plant organisms. The production of urea in the ornithine cycle requires 13·8 kg-cal. and therefore is probably supplied with energy by ATP. The conversion of arginine to ornithine takes place under the influence of the enzyme *arginase*. Arginine can be deaminated only with difficulty.

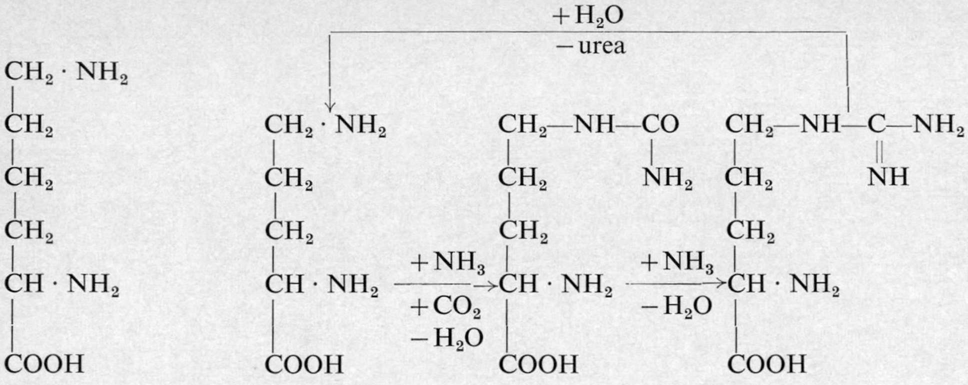

$$+H_2O$$
$$-\text{urea}$$

$$
\begin{array}{llll}
CH_2 \cdot NH_2 & & & \\
| & & & \\
CH_2 & CH_2 \cdot NH_2 & CH_2\!-\!NH\!-\!CO & CH_2\!-\!NH\!-\!C\!-\!NH_2 \\
| & | & | & | \qquad\quad \| \\
CH_2 & CH_2 & CH_2 \qquad NH_2 & CH_2 \qquad\;\; NH \\
| & | & | & | \\
CH_2 & CH_2 & CH_2 & CH_2 \\
| & | \qquad +NH_3 & | \qquad +NH_3 & | \\
CH \cdot NH_2 & CH \cdot NH_2 \xrightarrow[\substack{+CO_2 \\ -H_2O}]{} & CH \cdot NH_2 \xrightarrow[-H_2O]{} & CH \cdot NH_2 \\
| & | & | & | \\
COOH & COOH & COOH & COOH \\
\text{Lysine} & \text{Ornithine} & \text{Citrulline} & \text{Arginine}
\end{array}
$$

Further derivatives of alanine by substitution of aromatic or heterocyclic rings in the β-position are shown below:

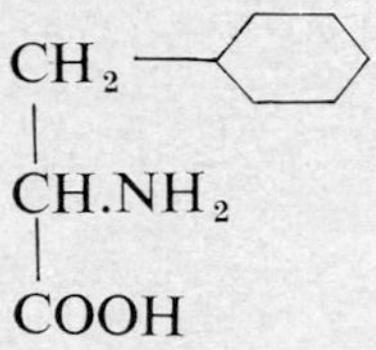

Phenylalanine

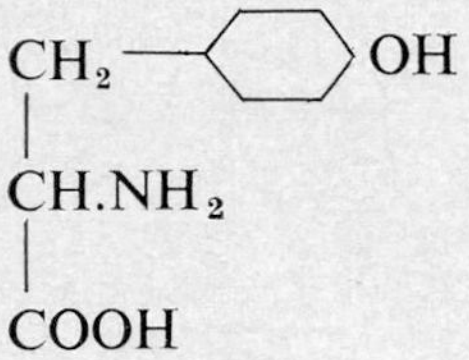

Tyrosine

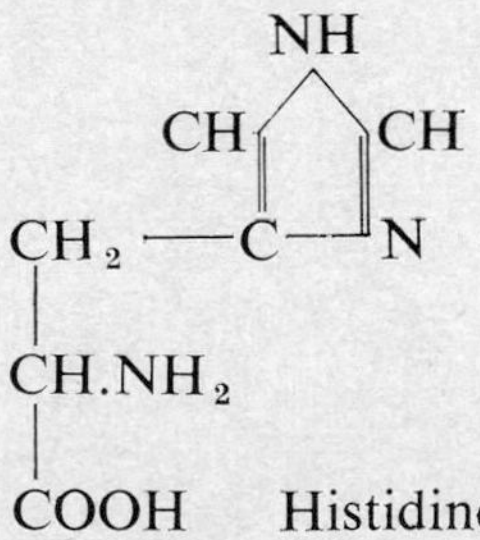

Histidine

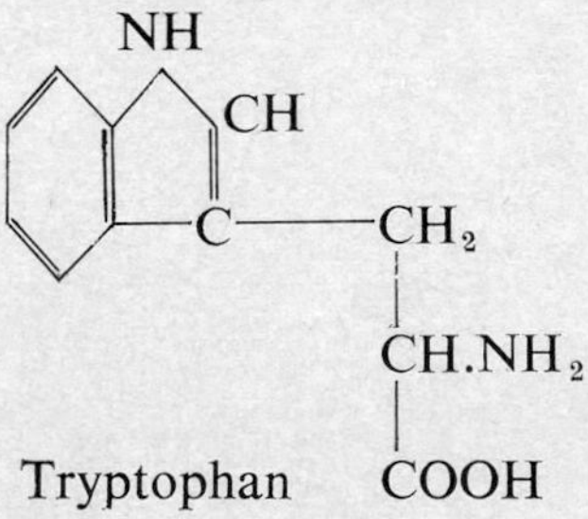

Tryptophan

Phenylalanine and *tyrosine* can by deamination and opening of the benzene ring pass over to *oxalacetic acid* (p. 225). Under the influence of *tyrosinase* tyrosine is converted *inter alia* into the quinone of *dihydroxyphenylalanine* ('Dopa'), which probably represents an intermediate stage in the formation of melanin. Tyrosine and phenylalanine under the action of various bacteria produce a number of poisonous compounds, e.g. phenol, *p*-cresol and tyramine.

Histidine is stated to be a component in the synthesis of *purine*. *Tryptophan* arouses plant-physiological interest because of its relationship to the heteroauxin β-indolyl-acetic acid (see p. 368). Bacterial decomposition of tryptophan leads to *indole* and *skatole*. The natural indigo dyestuff, formerly extracted from the indigo plant, consists of a β-glycoside of *indoxyl*, the hydroxy derivative of indole.

There is one acid, *proline*, which is not an amino but an imino acid; the N forms a ring with four of the carbon atoms:

$$\begin{array}{ccc}
CH_2 & \!\!\!\!-\!\!\!\! & CH_2 \\
| & & | \\
CH_2 & & CH \cdot COOH \\
& \diagdown N \diagup & \\
& H &
\end{array}$$

Proline (2-pyrrolidinecarboxylic acid)

The separation of the amino acids from hydrolysates of proteins has made great progress in recent years. Specially useful methods are adsorption analysis in columns or with filter-paper ('paper chromatography') and paper electrophoresis. The hetero-cyclic components of protein can be identified spectralanalytically (absorption spectra in the ultra-violet: LERNER and BARNUM 1946). The microbiological methods have also been improved; they are based on the usually strict specialisation of micro-organisms on particular amino acids as sources of food (DUNN 1949, STREET 1949).

From the amino acids a great number of complicated N-compounds are derived; but the ways in which the living cell utilises them are still largely unknown. A few examples of the synthesis of complicated substances from amino acid components have been mentioned above. From even the simplest amino acid, glycine, are formed *inter alia* the tertiary ammonium bases *betaine* and *choline*, which are important for the formation of phosphatides.

Betaine is recovered commercially from beet-sugar molasses after separation of the other crystallisable substances. Choline forms part of lecithin (cf. also p. 20):

$$\begin{array}{ccc}
\text{Betaine} & \text{Choline} & \text{Pantothenic acid}
\end{array}$$

Another derivative of aminopropionic acid is *pantothenic acid*, which is a factor in the vitamin B complex and also a component of coenzyme A (p. 183).

That amino acids, because of their active groups, enter into metabolism in different ways is known both from enzyme research and e.g. from studies of protoplasmic streaming. The special properties of pepsin and chymotrypsin are due to the presence in the substrate molecule of tyrosine and phenylalanine respectively (BERGMANN 1942).

As an example of the analysis of a protein for its content of the different amino acids lactoglobulin may be quoted; according to BRAND *et al.* (1946) it has the empirical formula $C_{1864} H_{3012} N_{468} O_{576} S_{21}$ made up of the following amino acids (the number of molecules of each in one molecule of the protein is shown by the subscripts): glycine $_8$, alanine $_{29}$, serine$_{20}$, valine $_{21}$, leucine $_{50}$, isoleucine $_{27}$, aspartic acid $_{36}$, glutamic acid$_{24}$, glutamine$_{32}$, lysine$_{33}$, arginine$_7$, phenylalanine$_9$, tyrosine$_9$, histidine$_4$, trypto-phan$_4$, proline$_{15}$, methionine$_9$, cystëine$_4$, cystine$_8$, plus H_2O_4.

Our knowledge of plant proteins is still very incomplete (VICKERY 1945, LUGG 1946).

The nomenclature is not unequivocal, as the most usual classification is based on solubilities which, because of the amphoteric nature of the proteins, their variable hydration and their tendency to denaturation, etc., do not give sharp differentiations.

The *albumins* are proteins soluble in water but precipitated by strong salt solutions e.g. ricin from *Ricinus* seeds, leucosin from cereals and legumelin from leguminous plants. They contain a considerable percentage of sulphur, but no glycine. *Globulins* are insoluble in water but soluble in dilute solutions of electrolytes, and are precipitated by half-saturated solutions of ammonium sulphate. They include edestin from flax, phaseolin from beans, and the cereal globulins. The *prolamins* (gliadins) are the only proteins soluble in alcohol, and include the gliadin of wheat, the zein of maize and the hordein of barley. The *glutelins* resemble the globulins but are soluble only in dilute acids and alkalis, not in neutral solutions; they include wheat glutelin and the oryzenin of rice. Little is known about the occurrence of the strongly basic *histones* in plants. They contain a high proportion of diamine acids. The *phosphoproteins* contain phosphoric acid as prosthetic group. The acid *glucoproteins* contain glucosamine, and the *nucleoproteins* nucleic acids. The nucleoproteins occur in cell nuclei (chromosomes) but also e.g. in viruses, and probably form part of the cytoplasm. Some 50% of the soluble proteins of leaf extracts consist of nucleoproteins (with ribonucleic acid), with a molecular weight of about 375,000 (EGGMAN et al., 1953).

A number of the N compounds which occur as prosthetic groups, growth substances or hormones are derivatives of pyrrole, pyridine, pyrimidine and thiazole and of purine.

Pyrrole   Pyridine   Pyrimidine   Thiazole

The formation of pyrrole and the porphyrins was mentioned on p. 37. Among the amino acids pyrrole groups are found in proline and in tryptophan. In the porphyrins the four pyrrole groups are arranged like a disc.

According to PICHET and ROBINSON (see KARRER 1939, p. 922) the alkaloids, even the most complicated ones, can be referred back to the amino acids as their components.

The imidazole nucleus of histidine occurs in many of the simpler alkaloids e.g. pilocarpine in the leaves of *Pilocarpus pennatifolius*. The growth substance *biotin* is a derivative of a fully reduced imidazolothiophene; its immediate precursor is *desthiobiotin*:

Desthiobiotin   Biotin

Another derivative of imidazole, *allantoin*, and the related *allantoic acid*, are shown below; their occurrence was mentioned on p. 220.

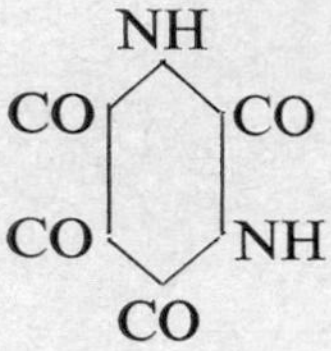

Alloxan 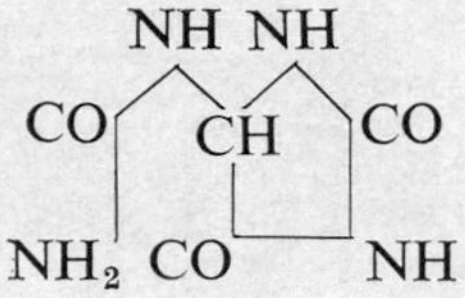   Allantoin 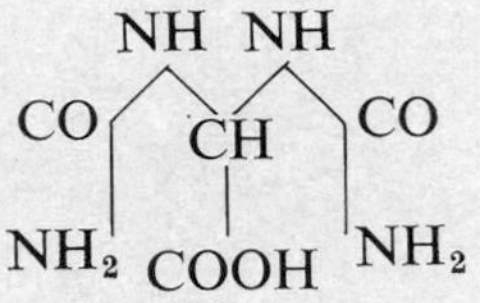   Allantoic acid

Some derivatives of pyridine are:

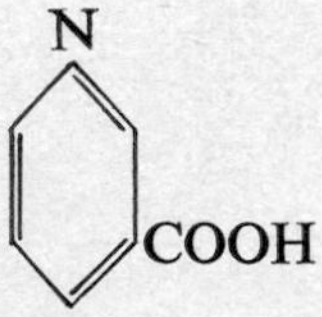

Nicotinic acid 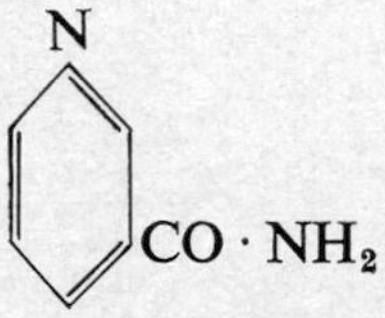   Nicotinamide 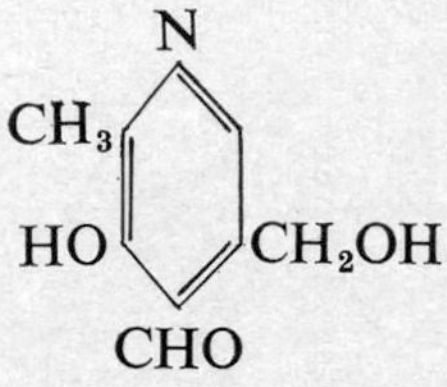   Pyridoxal

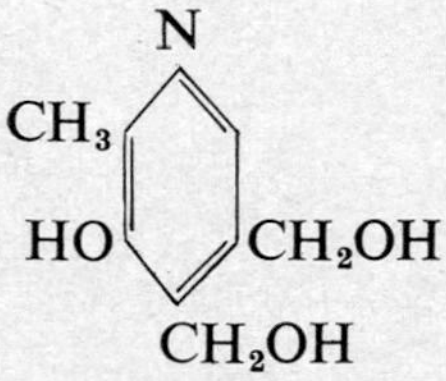

Pyridoxin
(vitamin B$_6$)

Nicotinamide is connected to two or three phosphate groups in *adenosine*. Pyridoxal phosphate forms the prosthetic group of *glutamic decarboxylase* (SCHALES *et al.* 1946). The prosthetic group of the flavoprotoids is a complex derivative of *alloxan*.
The purine bases include many important compounds, which are shown below:

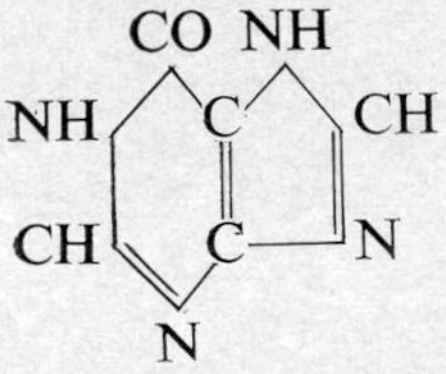

Hypoxanthine 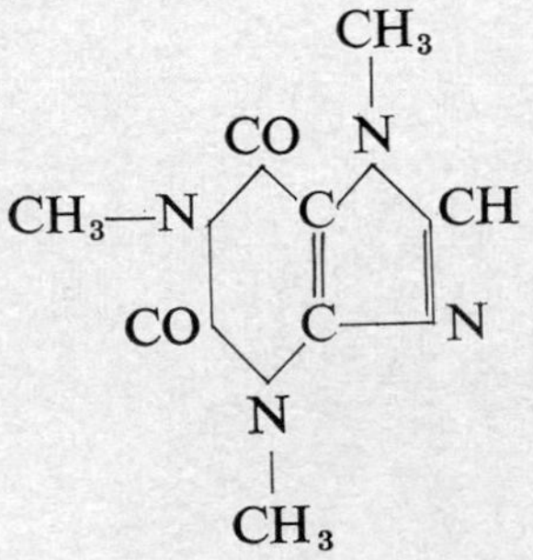   Caffeine (theine)

Uric acid   Adenine   Guanine

By amination of *hypoxanthine* is formed *adenine*, which with the pentose ribose forms the nucleoside *adenosine*, which when esterified with phosphoric acid yields the nucleotide adenylic acid (adenosine phosphate), whose central importance in fermentation and respiration processes has already been discussed. Other similar derivatives of hypoxanthine and *guanine* were mentioned on p. 22.

The occurrence of both a thiazole and a pyrimidine ring (not fused) in *thiamine* is shown by the formula below:

4-Methyl-5-ethoxythiazole   Methylene bridge   2-Methyl-6-amino-pyrimidine

Vitamin B$_1$ (thiamine chloride hydrochloride; aneurin)

The pyrophosphoric ester of thiamine forms the prosthetic group of cocarboxylase (p. 176).

Finally, a derivative of pteridine may be mentioned, viz. *folic acid*, which has been isolated from green leaves:

L-Glutamic acid   p-Aminobenzoyl   Methylene bridge   2-Amino-4 hydroxypteridine

Folic acid
(pteroyl-L-glutamic acid [PGA]; vitamin Bc)

F. Heterotrophic Plants

1 GENERAL PROPERTIES

Whilst the *autotrophic* plants, i.e. those that nourish themselves, form a physiologically fairly uniform group, the *heterotrophic* plants represent a mixed company. The autotrophs are satisfied with purely inorganic nutrition, that is CO_2 and salts; the nitrogen is taken up as ammonia or nitrate. The heterotrophs, on the other hand, are dependent for some necessary nutrients on organic substrates prepared by the activity of other organisms.

There is, however, no sharp dividing line between autotrophic and heterotrophic organisms. Among the unicellular algae one finds both autotrophic and heterotrophic forms. Also among the higher plants there are examples of parasites living heterotrophically. Partial *facultative heterotrophism* in which the organism is able to switch at will from inorganic to organic nutrition and conversely, is common. Sugar supplied from outside can be utilised by all autotrophic plants; and nitrogen also can often be utilised in organic combination. It has been found that maize thrives as well on phytin or nucleic acid as on inorganic phosphate, although with the former the plant's phosphorus content remains lower (WEISSFOLG and MENGDEHL 1933). According to PEARSON and PIERRE (1940) the surface of the roots secretes a phosphatase, which splits the phosphoric acid from the organic compound. Urea also can be taken up and elaborated by maize seedlings (YAMAGUCHI 1937). Nitrogen heterotrophism is very often present in fungi, but with a deficiency of organic N-compounds these plants can utilise also ammonia and nitrate, at times even nitrite.

The heterotrophic plants emphatically illustrate the mutual dependence of organisms. *Symbiosis* is the special case in which two organisms are bodily combined to mutual advantage, e.g. algae and fungi in the lichens or bacteria and cells of higher plants in the bacterial nodules of the Leguminosae. Here the autotrophic symbiont supplies special organic materials, especially carbohydrates, and receives from the heterotrophic symbiont other compounds, e.g. nitrogen compounds or salts, which facilitate the common existence, even though they could also be taken up directly from the soil. The boundary between a harmonious symbiosis and *parasitism* is, however, not sharply defined, but one can say that in pronounced parasitism the one symbiont has all the advantages. From a wider point of view autotrophic plants are always dependent on other organisms, such as the heterotrophic micro-organisms which by decay and putrefaction return the limited capital of carbon and nitrogen to the cycle. No living creature can exist completely independently of others.

2 FUNGI AND BACTERIA

(a) *The Micro-organisms of the Soil*

The micro-organisms, particularly the bacteria, as often emphasised, are to be considered as Nature's biochemical research field. A number of reaction sequences in which the elements C and N participate exist only in the world of micro-organisms (cf. for example 'Symposium on some aspects of microbial metabolism' in *J. Cell. Comp. Physiol.* 41, 1953, Suppl. 1). In other cases these processes do indeed occur in higher plants but are for experimental reasons most conveniently studied in micro-organisms. The means by which micro-organisms collect the chemical energy necessary for synthetic purposes are very various. Most micro-organisms are dependent on the utilisation of energy-rich products, e.g. carbohydrates, which they take over from other organisms, and thus live as *parasites* or *saprophytes*.

From the point of view of energy it is not surprising that the heterotrophic organisms preferentially use carbohydrates, since the reduction of CO_2 absorbs much more energy than, for example, the formation of amino acids from ammonia and keto acids. On account of the activity of the proteolytic enzymes in dead organisms, ammonia and carboxylic acids are available in close proximity in the soil.

Examples of the co-operation of micro-organisms in the supply and utilisation of materials have been given above. It often happens that one organism consumes substances which are secreted by others. Energy consumption by micro-organisms is large in comparison with the body volume, and the energy losses are considerable. VAN SUCHTELEN (1931) calculated that more than 50% of the free metabolic energy produced by soil bacteria disappears as heat.

Azotobacter secretes part of its fixed nitrogen into the soil; but the greater part is available for other organisms only after the death of the cells. The organic nitrogen compounds are first hydrolysed to ammonia and taken up by the roots of higher plants partly as such and partly, after nitrification by *Nitrosomonas* and *Nitrobacter* (ENGEL 1931, ROBERG 1935), to nitrate.

The nitrifying bacteria consume enormous amounts of carbohydrate and are therefore dependent to a high degree on the activity of the cellulose-decomposing bacteria, e.g. *Spirochaeta cytophaga* (FÅHRAEUS 1951). The cellulose-decomposers occupy a key position in the initial stages of humification, since cellulose forms the main component of dead plant residues. The cellulose, however, is so thoroughly decomposed that the ratio C : N finally assumes considerably lower values than in the living plants (see WAKSMAN 1952, LUNDEGÅRDH 1957).

Some soil bacteria, e.g. the nitrate-formers, build up their own carbohydrates. In *Nitrosomonas* the energy necessary for chemosynthesis originates from the oxidation of ammonia. About eighty molecules of NH_3 must be oxidised to NO_2 in order to build up one molecule of carbohydrate (ENGEL 1931). This example shows that the nitrogen turnover in the soil is not wholly driven by the oxidation of carbohydrates.

A counterpart to the cellulose-decomposers is provided by the protein-hydrolysing bacteria with their oxidative deamination, in which about 150 kg-cal. of free energy are produced for each ammonia molecule liberated. The exergonic character of this process makes these organisms independent of carbohydrate supply, since they can themselves chemosynthesise. They can, however, also utilise sugars, but proteolysis then decreases (DORYLAND 1916); which may help to explain the disadvantageous results of too much straw in farmyard manure. Fungi and Actinomycetes also participate in the ammonia production of the soil. *Aspergillus oryzae* cleaves most amino acids to NH_3 and CO_2 (TAMIYA and USAMI 1940).

The ammonia-bacteria and the nitrate-bacteria readily produce soluble nitrogen compounds, which are partly absorbed in the soil and thereby form an accessible nitrate reserve for roots. In the complete nitrogen cycle, however, *denitrifiers* also participate and their respiration consumes valuable nitrate (p. 227) which is converted into valueless nitrogen oxides and molecular nitrogen. These organisms can also live anaerobically by the utilisation of nitrate oxygen. The nitrate-bacteria, on the other hand, are typically aerobic organisms, whose growth depends on good aeration of the substrate.

The nitrifying organisms stand decidedly on the positive side of the nitrogen cycle; so that the net balance is usually a gain in nitrogen. This is made clear by considerable amounts of nitrogen being accumulated in fallow soils, although some of the nitrogen compounds are washed out by rain.

(b) *Humus Formation*

This more ecologically significant process can be only briefly touched on here (more detailed treatment e.g. in WAKSMAN 1932, 1936, 1951, LUNDEGÅRDH 1957). The surface layer of unworked soils consists of still undecomposed residues of dead plant parts (in Swedish *förna*). The förna is in fact attacked by fungi, e.g. species of *Marasmius* (NIETHAMMER 1937, LINDEBERG 1944), but cellulose-decomposers and Actinomycetes are also active. The ratio C : N, which in most living plants has the approximate value 40 (in Leguminosae about 25) is gradually brought to about 10 by this decomposition of förna.

With the cellulose-decomposers are associated a number of other micro-organisms which take over intermediate products, e.g. carboxylic acids. It was earlier thought that the brown humus represented a mixture of decomposition products of cellulose, lignin and protein; later experience, however, showed that it is rather a mixture of such decomposition products with resynthesised products (WAKSMAN 1936, PALLMANN *et al.* 1938). Very resistant components of humus are lignin and chitin (cf. p. 87 and formulae below), tannin, resin, etc. Dead micro-organisms are also naturally present.

The more resistant components are also finally decomposed. The chitin is attacked e.g. by Actinomycetes (JENSEN 1932) which are thereby abundantly nourished. Micro-organisms already attack the central wood of the living tree, but the host plant can successfully ward off these attacks in the trunk and in the bark by the production of bactericidal substances. Certain skeletal components of the living cell, e.g. lignin and chitin, have very resistant molecular combinations, which can be resolved only by special enzymes and organisms. For a complete breakdown of these substances several enzymes are necessary, which are produced by different organisms (CLAYSON 1942, 1943). Lignin hereby has the effect of an efficient protective wall against attacks by hydrolytic enzymes.

Chitin (unit = 2 molecules of N-acetyl-
D-glucosamine) cf. also cellulose, p.97

$$HO-\bigotimes^{OCH_3}-CH=CH-CH_2OH$$

Coniferyl alcohol
[3-(4-hydroxy-3-methoxyphenyl)-2-propen-1-ol],
a possible unit of lignin.

Humus-like substances, the so-called *phytomelans*, are also produced in living cells. They originate from the decomposition of carbohydrate and have the empirical formula $C_x(H_2O)_y$ (DE VRIES 1948). They occur e.g. as secretions in the pericarp of the Compositae.

During the humification process a number of resistant acids, e.g. phytic acid (p. 99) and other organic phosphoric acid compounds arise, as well as dicarboxylic acids. They lower the pH value if neutralising metallic cations, especially Ca^{++}, are not present in sufficient amount. This is one of the reasons why simultaneous mineral weathering prevents greater pH shifts during humification. Micro-organisms also participate in the weathering.

Hydrogen-ion concentration indeed determines the well-being of both higher plants and micro-organisms. Neutralising metallic cations are obtained by roots from the subsoil and after leaf-fall added to the humus layer. From this it follows that the geological composition of the subsoil to a certain extent governs the microbial decomposition of the humus later. Expecially important is the sensitivity of the nitrifying bacteria to a drop in pH, which also has to be taken into account in connection with crude humus formation which is also favoured (SILLINGER and PETRU 1937, HESSELMAN 1937).

Hydrogen-ion concentration, however, contrary to what was earlier thought, is not absolutely dominant. It must be considered in connection with the whole ion constellation in the medium. *Azotobacter* showed itself in later investigations to be in fact fairly pH-tolerant, and was found in the whole range between pH 3·6 and pH 7·6 (WILSON 1933), provided that metallic cations (neutral salts) were present. It is, on the other hand, absent from high moors deficient in salts (GAUGER and ZIEGENSPECK 1929, WENZEL 1934). The nitrifiers behave similarly (BÖMEKE 1939).

(c) *Annual Periodicity of the Soil Micro-organisms*

The annual periodicity is caused by periodic variations in temperature, humidity and nutrient conditions. These variations can be followed by recording the soil respiration (p. 127). The causal connections, however, are by no means clear, since the organisms partly collaborate with and partly compete against each other. A relevant example is given by the availability of nitrate. The nitrifiers and the denitrifiers compete by the formation and consumption of nitrate. In certain cases an organism produces growth substances, e.g. pantothenic acid, which stimulate the growth of others (NIELSEN and HARTELIUS 1945). Conversely, certain organisms produce bacteriostatic or bactericidal substances which inhibit growth or kill the organism. The *antibiotics*, e.g. penicillin and streptomycin, are such chemical-warfare agents. Many mould fungi and Actinomycetes secrete antibiotics (WAKSMAN 1942, 1947). Such phenomena can thus also be of importance in the periodic variations of bacterial life.

A further cause of annual periodicity is the annual cycle of the higher plants. Nitrification shows two annual maxima, one in spring and the second in late autumn or early winter. It has been found that all plants that utilise nitrate as the main source of nitrogen delay root growth until these periods (GAUGER 1929, LIMBACH 1929), but the phenomenon can also be interpreted conversely, i.e. as a stimulation of the bacteria by the root growth (STARKEY 1931). Other micro-organisms are inhibited by root secretions. RIPPEL found, for example, an inhibition of the growth of yeast cells by pea roots. The autumn maximum of the nitrifiers can also be related to the increased ammonia formation from the dead leaves. Some fungi secrete materials, marasmins, which induce withering of higher plants. *Fusarium lycopersici* produces a polypeptide, lycomarasmin (tomato-wilt factor) which damages the protein of the host plant (GÄUMANN and JAAG 1947).

(d) *The Rhizosphere*

The distribution of bacteria in the soil profile was studied by HANKE and WOZAK (1934) and others. On moors the highest bacterial count per gram may lie very deep, according to WAKSMAN at depths between 60 and 330 cm. The total count generally amounts to several million per gram of soil. Fungi give similar values, whereas the number of Actinomycetes is restricted to several hundred thousand (COBB 1932).

Especial interest attaches to the relationships between roots and bacteria. It has been observed (STARKEY 1931, 1937) that the micro-organisms abound in the immediate environment of roots, *Radiobacter* accumulating preferentially in this zone and *Actinomyces* less so. The roots of Leguminosae are particularly attractive. This zone round the root is named the *rhizosphere*.

It is an easy supposition that the bacteria are stimulated by special root secretions, e.g. thiamine, biotin, or simply amino nitrogen. These substances can originate from dead root hairs, sloughed-off cap cells, etc., but active substances are probably also secreted by the living root surface (LOCKHEAD 1940). It has in fact been observed that a high content of organic materials in the soil reduces the special root effect. STENLID (1948) showed that wheat and peas secrete numerous organic substances such as sugar (probably glucose) and purine derivatives (probably nucleotides). The exudation increases with oxygen deficiency, low pH, etc. As far as the effect of the roots on the soil structure is concerned, it is stated by D'HOORE and FRIPIAT (1948) that root secretions precipitate soil colloids.

According to TAPPING (1937) the root bacteria are usually rod-shaped and often branched ('Protoactinomycetes'). They are predominantly aerobic. As regards staining they are chiefly gram-positive. i.e. they adsorb basic dyestuffs. Thermophilic bacteria also occur in the soil (PRICKETT 1928), sometimes iron bacteria (NAUMANN 1930) and usually blue-green algae ('soil algae', QUISPEL 1938). The average number of bacteria in the soil has often been determined (THOM and HUMFELD 1932, ADACHI 1933, STILLE 1938, TIMONIN 1940). The rhizosphere can contain eight times as many fungi and five to seven times as many bacteria per gram as the surrounding soil. The ability to stimulate micro-organisms is different in different plants; e.g. fungi predominate in the rhizosphere of oats and bacteria in that of lucerne. Even red yeast (*Torula*) is stimulated by root excretions. The rhizosphere locally increases the soil respiration.

(e) *Mycorrhiza*

If the fungal hyphae accumulate round the roots in such a way that a weft of hyphae arises, the mycorrhiza is termed *ectotrophic*. When hyphae penetrate into the living cells and enter into symbiosis with them, an *endotrophic mycorrhiza* is present. Endotrophic mycorrhiza is widespread in Orchidaceae and Ericaceae, but otherwise ectotrophic mycorrhiza dominates in nature. Ordinarily Basidiomycetes are the fungi concerned (RAYNER 1926, MELIN 1936, BJÖRKMAN 1942, 1943); in alder, however, nitrogen-fixing bacteria live in special root nodules (KREBBER 1932, ROBERG 1934). The development of the mycorrhiza of coniferous trees is regulated by nutrition; for example it is favoured by illumination (which causes a surplus of carbohydrates). On the other hand, a deficiency of nutrients in the soil, especially shortage of phosphate and nitrogen, often has a stimulating effect (MITCHELL and ROSENDAHL 1937, BJÖRKMAN 1942, 1943).

Mycorrhizas frequently occur on trees, but also at times on herbaceous plants. The roots attacked by fungi change their form and swell up (Fig. 105). Hyphae which penetrate into the cortex form haustoria in the living cell, thus indicating a mutual metabolism; but the fungal hyphae which are only adjacent must also make a certain exchange of materials with the roots. The advantages appear to lie overwhelmingly on the side of the fungi, a view put forward by STAHL (1900). The hyphae are mostly found in the position which would otherwise be occupied by the root hairs. It has been mentioned that the fungi render phosphoric acid available from apatite (ROSENDAHL 1942). According to MÖLLER (1947) the fungi on the other hand are not adapted to supply nitrogen. The increase of root respiration, often two- or fourfold, by mycorrhiza formation is important in weathering and mobilisation of nutrient cations in the soil (investigations on *Pinus echinata*; ROUTIEN and DAWSON 1943).

(f) *The Importance of Growth Substances*

The heterotrophic properties of bacteria and fungi appear not only in respect to preformed organic nutrients, but often also in respect to the requirement for specific growth substances supplied from outside. These relationships are like the vitamin requirements of animals and man.

Bacterial cells contain proteins, nucleoproteins, carbohydrates and lipids (lecithin, cephalin, etc.), which are partly coupled with nucleoproteins. Their protoplasm thus seems in the main to be built up similarly to that of higher organisms. The requirements of bacteria for specific nutrients suggest the gaps in their biochemical equipment. To these may be added also the vitamin requirements.

Some bacteria require either *biotin* or *desthiobiotin* (p. 235), whilst others can convert the latter into the former.

Pneumococci are the only bacteria which need a supply of choline (p. 234). In one species the formation of mucilage from polysaccharides is stimulated by a *polynucleotide*, which can also be supplied from outside and incorporated into the protoplasm

R

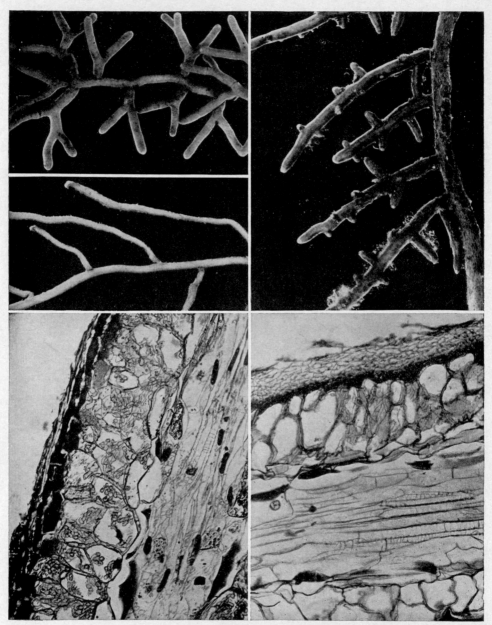

Fig. 105. 1. Typical forked Mycorrhiza in pine (above). The lower picture shows roots without Mycorrhiza ($\times 10$). 2. Typical monopodially branched Mycorrhiza in spruce ($\times 10$). 3. Longitudinal section through endotrophic Mycorrhiza in pine. A large intercellular network is visible, but also fungal hyphae in the interior of the cells. There is little or no outer mantle of hyphae ($\times 300$). 4. Longitudinal section through the Mycorrhiza of spruce (cf. 2). Well developed hyphae mantles and rather unimportant intercellular network ($\times 300$) (after BJÖRKMAN).

(AVERY *et al.* 1944). This therefore is a rare case of inheritance of acquired characteristics.

Yeast cells require the addition of *nicotinic acid* or *nicotinamide* (p. 236), of which
the latter is the more active. It is contained in cozymase.

Acetic acid bacteria require *pantothenic acid* (p. 234). This compound contains
β-alanine, and it has been found that β-alanine can partly replace pantothenic acid
in yeast and diphtheria bacilli.

Purines and *pyrimidine bases* act as growth substances in many bacteria and fungi.
The thiamine heterotrophism of fungi has been investigated in detail (FRIES 1938,
SCHOPFER 1943).

These relationships are of course very important for the occurrence of heterotrophic organisms in nature. Fungi which supplement each other with respect to
growth substances thus tend to live in association. The substrate specificity usually
observed in fungi may also be connected with the availability of growth substances.
Something similar may apply to the nodule bacteria and mycorrhizal fungi. It is also
due to such relationships that algae and flagellates are stimulated in soil extracts
(PRINGSHEIM 1936). The view put forward by NIKLEWSKI that higher plants also can
be stimulated in a similar way is more doubtful.

The rate of growth depends, of course, not only on vitamins and growth substances
but also on a sufficiency of nutrients. Where parasitism is concerned a suitable constitution of the cell walls of the presumptive host plants may be of importance. It has
been found that a connection exists between the nutritional state of plants and their
receptivity towards parasites (SCHAFFNIT and VOLK 1930, WINTER 1940). Here it may
be mentioned that a plant's own secretions can do it harm. *Chlorella*-cells, according
to PRAT and FOUG (1940) secrete a compound which inhibits their own growth.

Seeds of higher plants show a rich mosaic of seedling inhibitions. The seeds of
Vaccaria pyramidata (Caryophyllaceae) contain an inhibitor of germination which is
removed only by adsorption in the soil (BORRIS 1936). Tomato seeds behave similarly.
Mutual inhibitions occur in germinating seeds (FRÖSCHEL and FUNKE 1939, RUGE
1939) and may occur also in roots (LOEHWING 1937, VARMA 1939).

The questions touched on here are of course of outstanding importance in parasitism. Many fungi attack only single species. Morphology, annual periodicity, etc.,
may play a part. Many observations have been made on the pronounced substrate
specificity towards organic nutrients. *Aspergillus niger* and *Penicillium glaucum*, for
example, absorb *d*-tartaric acid much more readily than *l*-tartaric acid. In other cases
a gradual adaptation of the fungus to the substrate ensues, as a result of which the
end-product of the metabolism may also be altered (RAISTRICK *et al.* 1931). *Aspergillus*,
for example, forms the enzyme tannase only if the substrate contains tannins or tannic
acid (KNUDSON 1913; other examples on p. 152). Metabolism is thus characterised
by a certain degree of variability, which includes a potential adaptability to the milieu.
Such an adaptability is of course not entirely lacking in any living being. In micro-
organisms it forms a counterpart, so to speak, to the specialisation of tissues in higher
plants.

Brief mention should be made at this point of lethal mutations which can be elicited
e.g. by X-ray radiation. FRIES (1946) prepared a number of such mutants of *Ophio-
stoma multiannulatum*, which e.g. had lost the ability to synthesise nucleotides or their
components such as hypoxanthine. The materials then had to be supplied from outside.

A more or less pronounced specialisation e.g. for carbohydrates has been observed in the culture of excised root tips. BURSTRÖM (1941) found e.g. that wheat roots prefer glucose to fructose. Fructose can only be used after conversion to glucose. The utilisation of different sugars is usually species-specific.

3 PARASITES

The term 'symbiosis' was first introduced by DE BARY; the lichens are the classical example. Similar symbioses although not so firmly united morphologically occur in bacteria and soil algae.

The boundary between symbiosis and parasitism is, as emphasised above, not definite. It often seems, for example, that the Leguminosae are parasitic on the nodule bacteria. In more virulent parasitism, however, one partner is seriously damaged and may even die. Plant pathology affords numerous examples of fungal diseases, gall formations, etc., in which the aggressive parasite attacks higher plants, mostly through secreted toxins, and exhausts them for its own development.

Examples of parasitism among higher plants are less numerous. Some species however are specially equipped to draw organic nutrients, and sometimes transpiration water, from other plants.

Examples of root parasites are given by *Orobanche* and *Lathraea*. *Orobanche* attacks the roots of clover among others, and *Lathraea* chiefly the roots of hazel. The roots of the parasite form special sucking organs, haustoria, which penetrate the host roots, so that the xylem and phloem of the parasite are attached to the corresponding tissue of the host. This parasitism is associated with a restricted spontaneous nutrition of the parasite. Of its leaves only scales without chlorophyll remain, and the inflorescences dominate the structure. The adaptation to the parasitic type of life is carried so far in *Orobanche*, for example, that the seeds germinate only in contact with the roots of the host plant.

Cuscuta europaea is a stem parasite, which sends its haustoria into the stem of heather, flax, stinging nettles, willow, etc. The corresponding tissues of parasite and host are again joined together. The parasite is supplied not only with sugars and amino acids, but also with salts and water. In *Cuscuta* which is practically leafless and without chlorophyll one also finds a thoroughgoing adaptation to the life of a parasite. The germinating plant has completely stunted cotyledons, and the stem is spun out into a long thin thread, which moves forward because the hinder part delivers nutrient to the tip. The tip of the thread circles round until it finds a host plant, round which the thread at once twines. On the inner side appear wart-like excrescences, out of which the haustoria grow at the point of contact. The haustoria spread themselves like hyphae in the host body and make connection with its conductive tissues.

In all true parasites the vegetative parts are greatly reduced. The most extreme are certain tropical parasites, e.g. the Rafflesiaceae. From outside, only the flowers are to be seen; the body forms hyphae-like strands in the stem of the host plant. The flowers can attain a diameter of a metre, e.g. in *Rafflesia arnoldi* which is native to Sumatra and parasitic on a *Cissus* species.

A unique mode of life is developed by those phanerogams which are parasitic on fungi. To these belong the orchids *Neottia*, *Corallorhiza* and *Epipogium* which live in the shade of woods, as well as *Monotropa* (Pyrolaceae). Their roots are wholly specialised as mycorrhiza so that the fungus supplies everything that it obtains from the ground by means of its saprophytic life. These plants are sometimes termed 'humus plants'.

The fungus host of *Neottia* has been investigated by WOLFF (1926). It belongs to the genus *Orcheomyces* and is said to be able to assimilate atmospheric nitrogen. As the mycorrhiza is endotrophic in the orchids, but ectotrophic in *Monotropa*, although both fulfil the same functions, it seems to follow that there is no considerable difference of nutritional physiology between the two types. Their parasitism lies on the border of symbiosis. There has been found for example in *Neottia* the glucoside, tannin, much in demand by the fungus. The fungus even secretes an enzyme, tannase, which cleaves the glucoside.

In the phanerogam parasites roots have practically no absorption functions of their own. It is known, however, that the roots are able to metabolise both sugars and organic compounds, and thus to a certain extent to lead a saprophytic life. This is also a precondition for the culture of isolated roots, which must be supplied with growth substances as well as sugar and salts. In spite of this ability of roots to adapt themselves, only one case of true saprophytism of a higher plant is quoted in the literature: this is *Wullschaegelia aphylla*, which has no chlorophyll and on which no mycorrhiza has been found.

Apart from the *holoparasites* already discussed there is a number of *semi-parasites* which have not wholly adopted the easy life of parasites, but are able to contribute to their food supply by their own chlorophyll-bearing shoot system.

A well-known semi-parasite is mistletoe, *Viscum album*, which is parasitic on tree branches, in which it sinks its peg-like haustoria. These haustoria are connected however, only to the xylem, and are thus restricted to taking water and salts. Mistletoe develops green, photosynthetically active leaves. It has been found by experiment that the parasite still thrives after the phloem of the host plant has been interrupted by ringing.

A whole series of green herbaceous plants, which on superficial consideration one would not regard as semi-parasites, reveal themselves on further investigation as root parasites. To these belong some of the Scrophulariaceae, *Euphrasia*, *Rhinanthus*, *Pedicularis*, *Melampyrum*, the Santalacea *Thesium* and others. Even in these plants the parasitism appears to be restricted to taking up water and salts.

4 INSECTIVOROUS PLANTS (CARNIVORES)

This group of heterotrophic and semi-heterotrophic plants includes a fairly large number of species (about 400) which belong to a few families, viz. the Droseraceae, Lentibulariaceae, Sarraceniaceae, Nepenthaceae and Cephalotaceae. They are distinguished by the fact that although they have chlorophyll and are thus autotrophic, they obtain organic food from various small animals, chiefly insects, which they catch by special arrangements, kill and digest. They should get enough carbohydrates through the activity of their green leaves, but on the other hand the uptake of salts, and especially of nitrogen, is apparently inadequate because of the weak development of the root systems. It may be mentioned that *Drosera* leaves also absorb salts. This epidermis thus forms to a certain extent a substitute for the reduced absorbing area of the roots (OUDMAN 1936). Many insect-eating plants live in moor or swamp soils, which are poor in salts and soluble N-compounds.

The leaves of *Drosera* are beset with numerous secretory hairs, which in the middle of the surface are short, but at the edge attain greater length (Fig. 106). The glands secrete a viscous glistening slime which attracts insects. The animals are held by the slime, whereupon the hairs round the edge are bent inwards like tentacles. At the same time the leaf surface curls up to form a spoon, in the bowl of which the insect body is incarcerated. Proteases are secreted by the glands and start digestion. The amino acids and salts liberated are absorbed by the leaf epidermis. The process usually lasts several

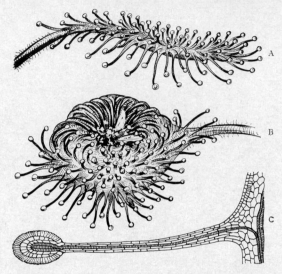

Fig. 106. *Drosera rotundifolia*. A. Leaf with outstretched tentacles; B. from above, with part of the tentacles curved in; C. section through a secretory hair ($\times$ 60) (after STRASBURGER).

days. After the end of the digestive process the leaf surface and secretory stalks again stretch themselves out. The processes of attraction and secretion are accompanied by characteristic cyclical changes in the protoplasm (cf. p. 55).

In *Pinguicula* the tentacles are missing and the edge of the leaf is folded round the insect. The upper side is provided with small secretory hairs, which exude the protease-bearing secretion.

The water plant *Utricularia* has developed another system, viz. small bladder-like traps which hang on the submerged, deeply divided leaves. The opening of the trap is surrounded with hairs and has a trap-door, which opens inwards (Fig. 107). The specially constructed wall of the closed bladder absorbs water, and thus causes a partial vacuum. When a minute aquatic animal touches the valve or its fork-like hairs, the door suddenly opens and the water rushing in takes the animal with it. In this way it is imprisoned in the trap. The whole process of capture occurs very quickly. According to LLOYD (1933), who took ciné photos of the happenings, it takes less than one-sixteenth of a second. The bladder wall seems not to secrete any enzyme, but the animal after its death is attacked by bacteria and digested. The digestive products are absorbed by the bladder wall, which is provided with glands. The water absorption is so rapid that the bladder is ready within a quarter of an hour for a new capture, until it is filled with victims.

The leaves of *Dionaea muscipula* (Fig. 108) and *Aldrovanda vesiculosa* are really fly-traps. The middle rib of the leaf works like a hinge. If an insect touches the tapered hairs of the upper side, the two halves clap together round the trap. Strong peripheral hairs prevent the prey from slipping out.

In *Sarracenia* and a number of tropical carnivores, *Nepenthes*, *Cephalotus* and *Darlingtonia*, the leaves or parts of them are shaped as pitcher-like traps. In *Nepenthes* the pitchers hang at the tip of the climbing, extended midrib (Fig. 109). They are lined internally with an epidermal layer, which on contact with an animal body secretes proteolytic enzymes. The lower part of the pitcher is filled with liquid, down into which slide the insects enticed by the sugary secretion of the smooth epidermal layer. A waxy layer on the upper part of the pitcher further prevents the captured insects from escaping. In *Sarracenia* (Fig. 110) the liquid seems to contain a narcotic or a substance which lowers the surface tension and stupefies the victim. The inner walls of the pitcher actively absorb nitrogen compounds (urea, asparagine, peptone, etc.) and salts (HEPBURN *et al.* 1920).

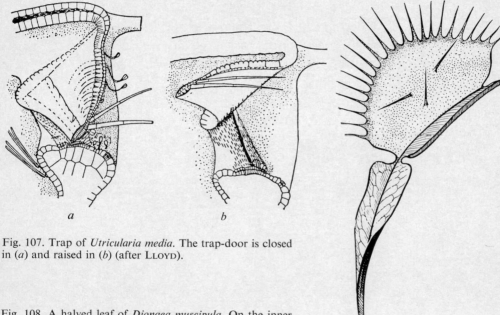

a   *b*

Fig. 107. Trap of *Utricularia media*. The trap-door is closed in (*a*) and raised in (*b*) (after LLOYD).

Fig. 108. A halved leaf of *Dionaea muscipula*. On the inner side glands and isolated tactile hairs. The hairs at the edge are slightly curved inwards.

Fig. 108

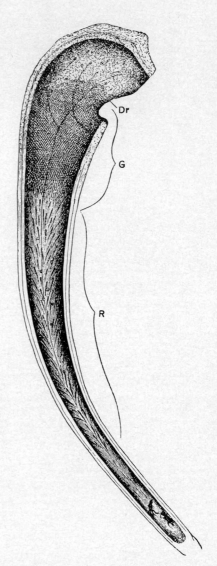

Fig. 109. The pitcher of *Nepenthes rafflesiana* (after GOEBEL).

Fig. 110. Halved leaf of *Sarracenia psittacina*. Dr—glandular zone; G—slippery surface; R—zone with stiff hairs ($\times ca$. 20) (after GOEBEL).

Chapter 6

UPTAKE AND TRANSPORT OF MINERAL NUTRIENTS. SAP FLOW

A. Mechanism of Salt Uptake

1 GENERAL

The supply of plants of inorganic salts from soil and water includes the elements potassium, calcium, magnesium, iron, manganese, phosphorus and sulphur. These are the main elements (*macroelements*) which are taken up in larger amounts and utilised to build up living substance. To these are added the trace elements (*microelements*) which must be accessible in very small amounts in order to ensure the correct and effective functioning of the organism. The term 'mineral nutrition' is not exact, since carbon occurs in large quantities in minerals rich in carbon, without however competing to any extent with the uptake of CO_2 from the air and water. Nitrogen, on the other hand, seldom occurs in minerals, but is taken up by plants in the same way as other nutrient salts. The upper layers of the soil, because of their ability to adsorb, operate a closed cycle of mineral nutrients and nitrogen, which circulates between living plants and the decomposing humus layer of the soil. As far as aquatic plants are concerned, a similar cycle occurs in the water, which after the decay of the dead plant parts holds liberated salts ready for renewed uptake.

One speaks in general of nutrient salts and salt uptake, but it is easy to see that in general ions are absorbed and not electroneutral molecules. The neutral salts, in which most nutrients are present, are composed of strong bases and acids, which are almost completely dissociated at the high dilution in which they normally occur. It is therefore better to speak of 'nutrient cations' and 'nutrient anions' and of 'ion uptake'. If for example a plant is in a solution of K_2SO_4, there is usually a much stronger uptake of the K^+ cation than of the SO_4^{--} anion. From KNO_3, on the other hand, the NO_3^- anions are preferentially absorbed, and still more so if the uptake is from a solution of $Ca(NO_3)_2$.

Among the *essential cations* are included K^+, Ca^{++}, Mg^{++}, Fe^{+++} and Mn^{++}, and among the *essential anions* $H_2PO_4^-$ and SO_4^{--}. Nitrogen is taken up either as the anion NO_3^- or as the cation NH_4^+. At higher pH values nitrogen can also be taken up as the molecule NH_4OH.

Chlorine, though not essential, may be specially mentioned, because it is generally stored in large quantities. The most important trace elements are Cu, B, Zn and Mo, but the list also includes many other elements whose effects are being gradually revealed. Manganese takes up an intermediate position between a macro- and a microelement.

The uptake of weak electrolytes is dominated by permeability phenomena. For $Ca(HCO_3)_2$, which almost always occurs in natural water, the uptake is assumed to be as the bicarbonate molecule. The possible collaboration of a bicarbonate uptake in the cation absorption of the roots has not been clarified. Boric acid, which is weakly dissociated, may enter partly as a neutral molecule; and the same applies at lower pH values for most of the organic acids which occur here and there in the soil. Experiments with salts of a number of weak acids, e.g. malonic, acetic, monoiodoacetic, hydrocyanic and hydrofluoric acids, have shown that their effect on metabolism is in inverse ratio to the degree of dissociation, i.e. the undissociated molecules are absorbed much more quickly than the acid anions (see e.g. LUNDEGÅRDH 1949).

A complete nutrient solution should contain in appropriate mixture all those cations and anions which the plant needs, e.g. $KCl + KH_2PO_4 + Ca(NO_3)_2 + MgSO_4 +$ Fe citrate $+ MnCl_2 + CuSO_4 + ZnSO_4 + H_3BO_3$ and possibly other trace elements. The ratio between the individual salts may vary according to the species of plant and the total concentration should amount to about 0.2%. From such a solution the ions are found by experiment to be taken up independently of the original salt combinations of the ions. In the long run there is an approximate equivalence between the amounts of cations and anions taken up (cf. MCCALLA and WOODFORD 1938). Over shortage periods and with lack of balance between the individual salts, more of the one type of ion may be taken up than of the other. Shifts in the pH value of the medium, of course, result. By liberation of bicarbonate ions an unbalanced uptake of anions can to a certain extent be balanced, and similarly, in a one-sided uptake of cations, H-ions may pass out into the medium.

During the developmental cycle the nutrient ions are usually taken up with different intensities. The uptake of phosphorus predominates e.g. during the young stages. Young plants of rice and oats absorb nitrogen preponderantly as NH_4^+, whereas in the older plants NO_3^- is preferred, and so on. The presence of an easily absorbable non-essential ion, e.g. Cl^-, can often exercise an advantageous compensatory effect, as excessive shifts of pH in the medium reduce growth.

The approximate balance between anions and cations taken up can be attained in various ways. This may be seen from the innumerable recommendations for appropriate nutrient solutions. SHIVE and others have found that optimal growth is attained in a number of different salt combinations. This is connected with the fact that the plants possess only a limited power of selection. The choice is naturally influenced to a certain extent by the specific requirements of the tissue; but beyond this plants have only a limited ability to reject unneeded or even harmful ions. Dispensable ions however can, as already mentioned, have a certain importance for the ionic balance and for the maintenance of the internal pH value.

Ideas of the *mechanism of salt uptake* were for a long time dominated by ideas and results on permeability for non-electrolytes (cf. Chap. 1). OSTERHOUT, for example, put forward the hypothesis that cations were absorbed as the neutral ionic combination MOH and anions as the ion pair HA, in which of course the uptake would be equivalent to that of non-electrolytes. This hypothesis is, however, contradicted by the results of experiments on uptake at various hydrogen-ion concentrations. The requirements for a combination HA are, for example, favoured by falling pH, but in spite of this the uptake of the anions of neutral salts is relatively insensitive towards changes in pH. The increased uptake of metallic cations with rising pH, on the other hand, follows from the principles governing membrane equilibria (p. 47) which are based on the balance of ions, not of ionic pairs.

The active researches of the last decade have shown convincingly that ionic uptake obeys rules quite different from those governing the uptake of non-electrolytes. Whereas the entry of non-electrolytes is regulated by diffusion and the phenomena of solution or dispersion, ionic uptake is dependent to a considerable extent on electro-chemical processes. Metabolic activities, upon which depend the high internal osmotic pressures so important to plants, also take a greater part in salt uptake than in the absorption of non-electrolytes. Active processes, i.e. coupling with exergonic reactions, must play a part especially in all processes of accumulation in which the cell sap shows a higher concentration of a material than the surrounding medium, i.e. where $c_i > c_e$, where the suffix i = internal and e = external.

Organic materials, e.g. sugar and asparagine, are also accumulated in cell sap and it has been possible in certain cases to show a connection with aerobic respiration. The collaboration of respiration in the accumulation of inorganic and organic salts in the cell sap has been studied in particular detail. An important difference between the accumulation of organic substances and of salt ions, however, is that in the former case the materials themselves participate as intermediates in metabolism. Sugar molecules are e.g. involved in phosphorylation processes and so can probably acquire osmotic energy of accumulation. In a similar way amino acids, amides, etc., are collected from the equilibria in the protoplasm, in which they take part. For the inorganic salts corresponding relationships occur only for individual ions, e.g. NH_4^+, NO_3^-, SO_4^{--} and $H_2PO_4^-$, which participate in the known metabolic processes (see Chap. 5) in which, however, they lose the character of free ions. But it appears very doubtful whether the accumulation of ammonium ions, nitrate ions and phosphate ions in the cell sap—although it is actually observed and in certain cases is very strong—can be explained solely by their participation in reversible metabolic equilibria. Such a possibility appears to exist only for phosphate ions (cf. LUNDEGÅRDH 1958).

Investigations have actually shown that the living cytoplasm exercises a strong attraction on all inorganic ions, which can be described as an adsorption regulated by ion exchange. This ability to adsorb is closely related to that of inorganic and organic colloids or 'ion exchangers', but in the cell it also assists active accumulation in the cell sap.

2 ION EXCHANGE AND ION ADSORPTION IN THE CYTOPLASM

In Chapter 1, Section E, it was explained that the older interpretation, according to which the surface of the cytoplasm was a simple lipoid film, gave an incomplete and partly erroneous picture of the composition of the cytoplasmic membrane. It was mentioned above that the permeability for non-electrolytes showed great differences between different forms of tissue and cell types and that changes with ageing had also been observed. The later idea of a porous lipoid-protein-film (e.g. BOOIJ 1940) also forms an inadequate theoretical basis for the interpretation of the processes which are active in ion uptake.

The electrochemical properties of the cytoplasmic surfaces (p. 47) show that the cytoplasmic membrane contains large molecules with partly acid and partly basic dissociation forming a mosaic. The first step in ion uptake may on this account be comprehended as an ion exchange with the 'carriers' $R^+ \cdot OH^-$ and $H^+ \cdot R^-$, a view which was developed by LUNDEGÅRDH (1938-41) and others and still forms the prevailing basis of ideas on ion uptake. The carriers are conceived as large organic ions.

It must further be assumed that the dissociation of the surface layer, composed of several substances, is restricted (cf. LUNDEGÅRDH 1940, 1941) leaving plenty of room for the uptake of non-electrolytes, that is for the activity of the surface layer as a lipo-protein-filter. The high electrical resistance of the protoplasmic surface (according to COLE 1940, 1,000-10,000 ohms per cm², according to OSTERHOUT even higher) likewise indicates that the scattered sites for the passage of ions form only a relatively small fraction of the surface layer.

If e.g. a desalted root is placed in a diluted salt solution, ion exchange in the surface layer starts almost immediately. This is demonstrated by oscillographic recording of the changes in the electrochemical surface potential which are connected with the exchange (LUNDEGÅRDH 1941). This primary ion exchange was considered also by ROBERTSON and TURNER (1945) as the first 'non-metabolic phase' of ion uptake. These workers utilised as experimental material thin discs of storage tissues, e.g. of potatoes, beetroots and artichokes.

Where the active groups of the membrane, i.e. the 'ion carriers', are already charged with salt ions, these are competitively exchanged according to the law of mass action. Specific effects also come in both on account of anion hydration and probably also the molecular configuration of the carrier ions. Such specificities have actually been observed.

The ions taken up into the surface layer by exchange find their way into the cyto-plasm by continuous exchange with new carriers. It can be imagined that as a result of thermal rotation the carrier ions pass the salt ion taken up to the next carrier inwards, and so on in continuous chain formation, until an equilibrium between the external medium and the internal protoplasm is attained (cf. Figs. 111 and 112). The

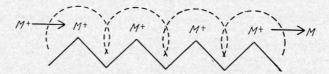

Fig. 111. Diagram of rapid ion transport along an adsorption surface.

whole process of charging the cytoplasm naturally takes somewhat more time than the very rapid exchange on the surface. The exact charging time can be measured only with difficulty, as in such experiments multicellular organs such as cereal roots with a radius of about 0·25 mm usually have to be used. Thus diffusion through cell walls, etc., comes into play. The experiments carried out by different methods have shown that in wheat roots the total ion exchange is completed in about fifteen minutes.

For this *non-metabolic ion exchange* no noteworthy transfers of energy are necessary. The process is therefore reversible and is directed according to the strengths of the ions (activities) on the two sides of the protoplasmic surface. The existence of a revers-ible cation exchange was found in living roots of cereal seedlings and pea plants (LUNDEGÅRDH et al. 1932, LUNDEGÅRDH 1945). It was further shown that a consider-able exchange took place even when oxygen is completely excluded, which emphasises the purely physico-chemical nature of the process. The non-metabolic character of exchange-absorption follows from the observation that it has a very low temperature coefficient.

As a further illustration of the competitive character of ion exchange the following experiment may be mentioned: wheat roots charged with salts liberate 77 μ mole K+

in distilled water, and in a solution of 0·001 mole of $KHCO_3$ or KCl only 37-46 μmole K^+. The potassium ions present in the external medium thus restrict the exchange between K^+ in the root and H^+ in the water. But conversely if the hydrogen-ion concentration in the medium is increased, e.g. by saturation with CO_2, the amount of potassium exchanged increases above 77 μmole. It can be said in summary that living plant tissues behave with respect to cation absorption like the 'ion exchangers' of technology. Similar relationships are shown also by different types of colloid such as soil colloids.

The total absorption capability of the cytoplasm, i.e. its 'exchange capacity', is considerable. From experiments with living and homogenised wheat

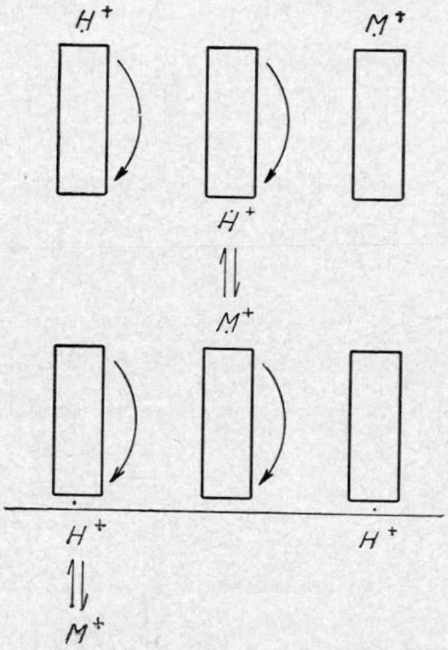

Fig. 112. Diagram of the absorption of ions by carrier molecules and the transmission through rotation of the carriers and repeated exchange.

roots it has been calculated that the cytoplasm can absorb salt ions up to twelve times the volume concentration of the medium (LUNDEGÅRDH 1958).

Whereas there was already convincing experimental evidence of a powerful ability to exchange cations, a non-metabolic adsorption of anions was found only recently (LUNDEGÅRDH 1959). Because of the predominantly acid dissociation of the cytoplasmic surface, the penetration of cations through the surface layer of the protoplasm is favoured by the membrane equilibrium. It has been possible to show, for example, that the electro-negatively charged surface of certain bacteria makes anion uptake more difficult (McCALLA 1940, RANDLES and BIRKELAND 1944). The protoplasmic membrane of *Amoeba* and *Rhizoclonium* permits the entry of cations, but is almost impermeable for anions (CORSON 1943). The protoplasm of *Chara* has also been found permeable to cations (MEYER and BERNFELD 1943). Model membranes, permeable either for cations or for anions, have been made from layers of collodion impregnated with phospholipoids or other dissociatable large molecules (WEATHERBY 1943, CARR and SOLLNER 1944).

Although the cytoplasmic surface of many plant cells electrochemically facilitates the passage of cations, nevertheless it has been found experimentally that in the long run just as many anions as cations are taken up. The results of researches on the dissociation of the surface layer, e.g. on the external walls of the root epidermis, have clearly led to the conclusion that the surface layer has an amphoteric character and that in addition to the carriers H^+R^- the carriers $R^+ \cdot OH^-$ also exist. Entry-ports for anions are therefore present and it depends on the *adsorption capacity* of the whole cytoplasmic mass how high the non-metabolic adsorption of anions may rise. Recent investigations (LUNDEGÅRDH 1958) have actually shown that, calculated per volume of tissue, the adsorption capacity for the anions Cl^- and $H_2PO_4^-$ is about the same as for the cation K^+. In addition a slow liberation of anions, similar to that of cations, has also been observed when salt-laden tissues are brought into distilled water.

A slow exchange of phosphate ions has similarly been observed (OVERSTREET and JACOBSEN 1946).

For electrochemical reasons a negative surface charge of course favours the excretion of anions, whereas on the other hand it has the effect of a protective wall against loss of cations (cf. MAZIA 1940). The tendency of the surface of organs to release large organic anions e.g. nucleic acids, may possibly be connected with the negative charge. The generally well limited excretion of inorganic anions, on the other hand, may be connected with the restricted number of the negative carriers $R^+ \cdot OH^-$ in the cell surface.

In addition to what was said in Chapter 1 about membrane charges it may be emphasised again here that the surface charge of cells is not an absolute property, but that it lies higher or lower according to the ion concentration in the medium and that it also varies according to the age of the cells. It is also to be expected that the surface potentials of cells in the inside of a tissue are different from (probably lower than) those at the boundary layer between the tissue and the medium. From the distribution of the surface potentials along the longitudinal direction of a root it seems to follow that the young still-growing roots are more 'ion active' than older cells. In spite of this the root cells lying several centimetres behind the zone of growth take up salts with almost equal energy (LUNDEGÅRDH 1949). The importance of the electrochemical properties of the surface layer for the intensity and the direction of the salt uptake should therefore not be exaggerated.

Along with the rapid initial salt adsorption by the tissues due to progressive ion exchange there is naturally also some salt uptake by simple diffusion. Ideas about the effectiveness of the diffusion permeability for salts are very variable, and there are also difficulties in the experimental treatment of this question.

Early permeability experiments in general gave very low values for the rate of uptake of salts, and the defenders of the 'lipoid theory' (p. 41) pointed to the small fat-solubility of most neutral salts (cf. also KROGH 1946). HOAGLAND and BROYER (1942) found no 'passive' uptake of salts in roots, even at high external concentrations. On the other hand HOPE (1953) and EPSTEIN (1955) believe that diffusion processes play a part, but the experimental foundation of their conclusions is not convincing. In investigating diffusion a method must of course be chosen which does not interfere with adsorption processes, and that is no easy task. Diffusion and ion-exchange both show low Q_{10}-values and in this way differ from the active processes which have 'chemical' Q_{10}-values.

An experimental separation between salt diffusion and salt adsorption has been shown in later researches (LUNDEGÅRDH 1958) to be possible because the salt adsorption is stopped almost completely by respiratory poisons e.g. cyanide (cf. below). LUNDEGÅRDH and BURSTRÖM (1935) were able to discover in roots which had been treated with cyanide a very weak uptake of Cl^- and a somewhat greater uptake of NO_3^-. The values for chlorine amounted to less than 1%, and for NO_3^- to 5%-16% of the normal uptake. These experiments lasted six hours. Later experiments with shorter time intervals generally showed no measurable uptake from KCl solutions to which 0·002 mole KCN was added. In only a few cases was a somewhat larger uptake observed, which can rise to 50% of the normal in sixty minutes; the uptake generally amounts to 2·5%-6% of the normal. A calculation of the diffusion quotient for KCl gives values between $0·004 \times 10^{-6}$ and $0·04 \times 10^{-6}$ per cm^2 per second, which amounts to only 1/50-1/5 of the rate of diffusion of CO_2 in water.

From these experiments it must be concluded that *pure diffusion of salts has a subordinate importance for the transport of salts from the medium into the tissue.* The varying values of the diffusion factor just mentioned are due apparently to the fact that the inactivation of the carrier (adsorption) function of the protoplasm caused by cyanide can be, according to the circumstances, more or less complete. The minimum values mentioned are therefore probably the most reliable.

Before we go into the peculiar fact that the ability of the protoplasm to adsorb or exchange ions is dependent on the progress of normal respiration, the presence of *specific carriers* may be considered.

The exchange reactions in protoplasm may be summarised in the following equations:

$$R^+OH^- + M^+A^- \rightleftharpoons R^+A^- + M^+OH^-$$
$$H^+R^- + M^+A^- \rightleftharpoons M^+R^- + H^+A^-$$
(81)

R^+ and R^- here symbolise the two categories of 'ion carriers'. Each category of course includes actually a number of uni- or multi-valent organic ions, which have in common only the fact that because of their size they cannot penetrate the two surface layers (Chapter 1) at all, or can do so only with great difficulty (about the slow exudation of nucleic acid see p. 48). From the definition it follows that many carrier ions, because of a special surface configuration or other physical properties, preferentially attract particular salt ions. Such specific ion adsorptions have often been observed, especially with cations. K^+ and Rb^+ e.g. are adsorbed in a similar way, although their ionic radii as well as their degree of hydration are different (BURSTRÖM 1937; cf. also EPSTEIN 1955), whilst there are large differences e.g. for K^+ and Na^+. A number of workers assume that cations, e.g. Na, K, Ca and Mg, are combined with different 'substrates' (SPIEGELMANN and REINER 1942, SCOTT 1944).

There are also specific differences of ion adsorption between different species of plants. The adsorption ratio K^+/Li^+, for example, rises to 24 in wheat roots, whereas for pea roots it amounts to only 1·2-1·5. Pea roots absorb only 1·0-3·0 times more potassium than sodium, whereas the ratio K^+/Na^+ for wheat roots amounts to 5·6-24·0, etc. (cf. also COLLANDER 1941, DAWSON and REINER 1942, SPIEGELMANN 1942, ARISZ 1946).

There are also specific differences in the adsorption linkage of anions. It has been found, for example, that chloride ions are held by tissues more strongly than phosphate ions. A specially strong attachment to the protoplasmic structure is shown, as would be expected, by certain heavy metal ions e.g. Cu^{++}. Here the charge, hydration etc., are of course concerned, but the presence of specific linkages follows e.g. from the fact that Co^{++} is held much more weakly than Cu^{++}. Experiments with heavy metal ions are made more difficult by the fact that many of them even in extreme dilution are retained as trace elements and that in somewhat higher concentrations they denature the proteins. Successful experiments on carrier functions of protoplasm can in any case be carried out only with salt ions which are actually involved in the uptake mechanism and accumulated in the cell sap, because they alone have the ability to form reversible adsorption linkages with the carrier ions. Only the reversibly linked ions are therefore of interest for the phenomenon of continuous salt uptake.

The exchangeable specific ion linkages constitute the first fundamental stage of nutrient salt uptake; their exchange capacity is dependent on the individual dissociations of the protoplasmic colloids, i.e. on the concentrations of the carrier categories R^+ and R^- at the time. The ratio between the salt concentration of the medium and the initial absorption of the tissue follows an adsorption curve. The amounts of salt adsorbed in fifteen minutes, i.e. before salt accumulation in the cell sap has begun, corresponds to a carrier concentration of the fully respiring protoplasm of about 0·1 M (LUNDEGÅRDH 1958). This value is at least 100 times higher than the R^--concentration of the external protoplasmic surface calculated from potential measurements (LUNDEGÅRDH 1940). From the almost equally strong initial adsorption of K^+ and of Cl^- or $H_2PO_4^-$ from KCl or KH_2PO_4 the conclusion can also be drawn that the carrier categories R^+ and R^- are present in the main mass of the protoplasm in approximately equal concentrations, although in the external surface layer R^- greatly predominates.

This fact, that in protoplasm itself the carrier categories R^+ and R^- show approximately the same capacity, arouses great interest in the usually low position of the isoelectric point (according to BOGEN 1953, HOPE and ROBERTSON 1953: the IEP= pH 3-4). The *Donnan equilibrium* which is determined by the presence of free carrier ions R^+ and R^- thus reflects only a part of the adsorption capacity, i.e. in the first place that of the cation adsorption (R^-).

Through the predominantly acid character, i.e. the stronger acid dissociation, of the protoplasm in the absence of metallic cations the basic dissociation (R^+) is partly suppressed. The predominance of the H^+R^- groups now causes an electronegative Donnan potential, as has been shown for the protoplasmic membrane (cf. p. 49). In the presence of a neutral salt $M^+ \cdot A^-$, however, so many M^+ ions are exchanged against H^+ ions of the group $H^+ \cdot R^-$ that the Donnan potential and the H-ion concentration in the cytoplasm decrease very rapidly. In this way the basic dissociation (that is $R^+ \cdot OH^-$) rises and more anions are exchanged. The measurements of the boundary surface potential on roots have shown that with a salt concentration of 0·01-0·1 M the free R^+ and R^- hold roughly a balance towards each other and thus about equal quantities of M^+ and A^- of the salt are adsorbed, somewhat as in the adsorption of a salt on wood charcoal. This theoretical explanation corresponds to the actual observations on the initial salt absorption. The exchange capacity for anions (that is groups $R \cdot OH$) can thus be calculated only from direct observation of anion adsorption.

The experimentally ascertained fact that free diffusion plays a subordinate part in the initial salt absorption and that this on the contrary is governed chiefly by adsorption and ion exchange, may be expressed by the term 'exchange capacity of the protoplasm'. By others (HOPE 1953, HYLMÖ 1953, BRIGGS and ROBERTSON 1957) the expression 'apparent free space' has been proposed for the non-metabolic salt absorption. Here one calculates the percentage share of the adsorbed salts in the cell or tissue volume, which, however, leads to erroneous ideas about the means by which the salts penetrate into the cells.

Investigations on wheat roots about 17 mm long show that the total dry matter amounts to about 6% of the fresh weight, i.e. of the volume of the living cell. Of this, approximately 1% is homogenisable protoplasm (mitochondria, microsomes, etc.) and approximately 3% cell walls. The remaining 2% or thereabouts are osmotically effective substances of the cell sap. The adsorption capacity of the cell walls, which consist chiefly of cellulose, is relatively small. One can therefore conclude from this that, from a salt solution surrounding the roots, at the most an amount corresponding to about 5% of the tissue volume can pass directly into the cell walls. The experiments on initial salt absorption, however, show that in the first fifteen minutes a quantity of solution is absorbed which corresponds to 60%-100% of the total volume. From this it is clear that the only really 'free space', that is the cell walls, in the above case harbours at most 1/12 of the actual amount of salt taken up.

The importance of the cell walls as paths of communication should not be under-estimated, but they certainly take part only to a subordinate extent in the initial salt absorption. The vacuole should also in all probability be excluded. It is found (see below) that the phase of salt accumulation, i.e. the raising of the osmotic value of the cell sap, comes into operation only after the initial absorption is over. It follows from this that by far the largest amount of the initially absorbed salt is located in the proto-plasm. The protoplasm of wheat roots amounts to about 1% of the fresh weight. This means that the absorption capacity of the protoplasm amounts to about a twelvefold volume concentration; which could be explained only by assuming a considerable adsorption and exchange capacity, as has been shown above.

According to the scheme of adsorption of cations and anions in the protoplasm given above, the former hasten ahead and prepare the way for the latter by alteration of the ionic balace. In all these exchange linkages, as explained above, the general rules concerning ionic radii, charge and hydration are effective as well as specific carrier properties, and can often simulate specific compounds. Of general physio-logical importance is the high exchangeability of the potassium ion in comparison with that of the sodium ion, which is connected with the smaller hydration of the former (cf. PEECH and BRADFIELD 1940). The high competitive ability of the calcium ion as compared with that of potassium is due to its higher charge. The high exchange-ability of the H-ion is well known. Among the anions similar relations are also valid. The adsorption of anions decreases in the following order:

$$OH > PO_4 > SO_4 > Cl > NO_3 \qquad (KUBLI\ 1947).$$

As to the true nature of the carrier ions, no detailed investigations are available. One can, however, guess that the cation carriers (R^-) include a number of high mole-cular organic phosphoric acid compounds, e.g. nucleic acids, phosphatides, etc. In bacteria cation adsorption on nucleotides lying on the surface has been found. But the amphoteric proteins also possess weak acid dissociation. In the category of anion carriers (R^+) one should certainly reckon the basic groups of proteins and phospha-tides; which also agrees with their weaker dissociation as compared with the R^- groups.

To the groups of compounds mentioned here, hopefully regarded as ion carriers, a number of others should of course be added. It is known that haem enzymes, for example, are partly anion-fixing. The total haem enzymes (cytochromes + peroxidase) of wheat roots amount, however, at most to 10% of the calculated concentration of the anion carriers.

Investigations on particulate fractions of wheat roots have shown that the cyto-chromes permeate almost the whole of the cytoplasmic structure, and not only the mitochondrial fraction, which is usually quoted as the seat of the respiration enzymes and of ion adsorption. Considering the close relationships between salt absorption and cytochrome activity one could draw from it the conclusion that the organised cytoplasm absorbs salt ions as a whole.

The possibility of a definite distinction between anion carriers and cation carriers is due to the fact that the former are inactivated by cyanide much more than the latter (LUNDEGÅRDH 1958). Cyanide inhibits the activity of cytochrome oxidase and,

S

consequently, also oxidative phosphorylation to a considerable extent (cf. p. 181). A positive phosphorylation, in conformity with the equilibrium $ADP + PO_4 \rightleftharpoons ATP$, is undoubtedly needed for the maintenance of protoplasmic structure. Even in great dilution (1-10 μmole) 2,4-dinitrophenol operates even more strongly than cyanide and causes a very rapid discharge of the previously adsorbed salts. Cyanide exercises a considerably weaker effect on cation adsorption and the opinion may be expressed that cations are adsorbed more on the hyaloplasm, which is continued into the surface layer, whereas the anions are bound more to the mitochondria and microsomes.

3 PASSIVE ION UPTAKE INTO THE PROTOPLASM

As ion exchange broadly speaking follows the law of mass action and the Donnan principle (cf. LUNDEGÅRDH 1941), after adsorption has been completed a shifting equilibrium is established. In the growing or mature cell the protoplasm forms a thin layer between the medium and the cell sap, that is between two aqueous phases. In the initial non-metabolic salt adsorption, the protoplasmic lining is charged with salt ions, and the process ends with an adsorption equilibrium between external solution and protoplasm. A similar equilibrium is then developed between the protoplasm and the cell sap, and at equilibrium the vacuole comes to about the same concentration as the medium.

There can, of course, be no true salt accumulation in the vacuole by means of adsorption and Donnan equilibrium alone; for this energy-supplying processes are necessary. There is a sharp barrier between initial salt adsorption and progressive active salt accumulation in the cell sap. We have described the initial adsorption as non-metabolic because it leads to a condition of equilibrium extraordinarily quickly and almost independently of temperature. Active accumulation, on the other hand, has a high temperature coefficient and continues for a long time with the co-operation of respiration.

The initial salt adsorption can, however, also become progressive either by new adsorption points constantly being formed through growth or, e.g. in roots, by the adsorbed salts being removed in the rising sap stream.

A diminution of the internal cation concentration can take place by crystal formation or precipitations, e.g. of calcium oxalate, or oxides or peroxides of Fe and Mn. The NH_4-ion is worked up into amino acids and amides, and so disappears from the ionic balance, releasing new adsorption points for cations. A growing protoplasm automatically creates new positive and negative adsorption points, and it can be imagined that a growing plasmodium, for example, covers its requirements for ions in this way. Plant acids formed in metabolism dissolve metallic cations from their adsorption linkages and thus make these free for new importations. Even the CO_2 production in respiration forms a 'suction pump' for metallic cations, as has been demonstrated e.g. by OSTERHOUT in model experiments.

Anions are drawn into the chemical machinery in still greater amount than the cations (with exception of NH_4^+) and thus maintain a continuous diffusion gradient. The nitrate ion partly disappears in protein formation, as also SO_4^{--}. Synthesis of the phosphate ion into organic compounds, however, does not diminish the negative charge, since organic phosphoric acid compounds tend to be at least as strongly dissociated as inorganic phosphoric acid.

Finally, it has long been known that increased transpiration brings with it increased salt supply to the aerial organs (see Section C). Some workers (e.g. HYLMÖ 1953) believe that the salt ions circulating or adsorbed in the cell walls and protoplasmic lining are removed and carried along with the stream of water passing through. The adsorption equilibrium of the 'initial absorption' may thus be continually shifted so that fresh amounts of salt stream in from the medium. The extent of these purely physical aspects of sap flow, whose existence no one has doubted, is however still but little known (see below).

4 ACTIVE SALT UPTAKE AND ANION RESPIRATION

(a) *General Characteristics*

That salt accumulation in the roots depends on aerobic respiration was first shown by LUNDEGÅRDH ad BURSTRÖM (1933). STEWARD (1933) showed the necessity of oxygen access for salt uptake in thin discs of storage organs. Whereas STEWARD, HOAGLAND and their collaborators (HOAGLAND and BROYER 1936, 1942, STEWARD and PRESTON 1941) restricted themselves to proving that respiration is a general requirement for salt accumulation, LUNDEGÅRDH and BURSTRÖM (1933, 1935) and LUNDEGÅRDH (1935, 1937, 1940, 1945, 1950, 1954, 1955, 1958) were able to show that the relationships between respiration and salt uptake are quantitative and that the amount of salt ions taken up depends on the intensity of that part of respiration which is inhibited by cyanide. The ground respiration almost resistant to cyanide (see p. 167) does not exercise any distinct influence on salt uptake.

From the investigations of LUNDEGÅRDH and BURSTRÖM it also appeared that it was especially the anions of the salt which showed this quantitative relation with the cyanide-inhibitable respiration. This fraction of the aerobic respiration was therefore termed *anion respiration*. In the literature the term *salt respiration* is also used. The results of LUNDEGÅRDH and collaborators were confirmed by a number of other workers (VAN EIJK 1939, ROBERTSON 1941-8, VIETS 1944, PEPKOWITZ and SHIVE 1944, MACHLIS 1944, WOODFORD and GREGORY 1948 *et al.*).

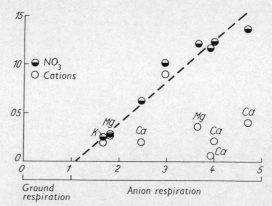

Fig. 113. Relations between ion uptake and respiration (measured as CO_2 release). Experiments with dilute solutions of K-, Ca- or Mg-nitrate. The nitrate ions are taken up in approximately quantitative ratio to a fraction of the respiration (i.e. anion respiration), whereas the cation uptake takes place less regularly (after LUNDEGÅRDH and BURSTRÖM 1933).

Later LUNDEGÅRDH (1951, 1952, 1954) was able to show by spectrophotometric observations that the biochemical basis of anion respiration is the activity of the cytochrome system. The oxidation-reduction state of the cytochrome system is very

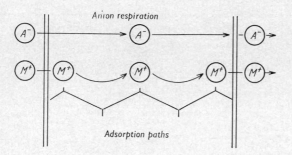

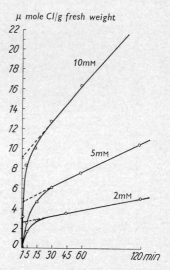

Fig. 114. Diagrammatic representation of the mechanism of active salt accumulation. The anions of the salt during anion respiration are actively forwarded through the protoplasm into the cell sap. The cations are passively transported along the adsorption paths (of the cation carriers).

Fig. 115. Time course of the uptake of chloride anions in wheat roots. Effect of salt concentration on the speed of uptake. The initial salt absorption in the cytoplasm takes place in the first 15-20 minutes; the almost constant continuous accumulation of salt in the cell sap starts after about 30 minutes (after LUNDEGÅRDH 1958).

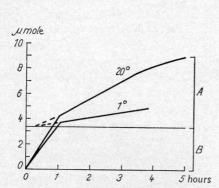

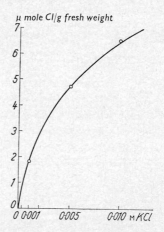

Fig. 116. Absorption of phosphate from 0·005 M KH$_2$PO$_4$ at two different temperatures. The values are expressed in μ moles per hour and per 1 g. of fresh weight. B. Initial absorption: this is almost independent of temperature. A. Accumulation phase: this is strongly dependent on temperature (after LUNDEGÅRDH 1958).

Fig. 117. Dependence of the initial chloride absorption on salt concentration. This process shows little dependence on temperature.

closely connected with the presence or absence of salts (see Fig. 118). It is shown e.g. that on washing out the salts from roots the cytochromes are more strongly reduced, and that on addition of salt the cytochromes are oxidised at the same rate as the active accumulation takes place.

The course with time of the progressive salt uptake in a washed ('desalted') tissue that is transferred into an aerated solution of chloride or phosphate is shown in Figs. 115 and 116. The steep rise during the first minutes corresponds to the initial salt absorption, which ends after about 15 minutes. The initial absorption is almost independent of temperature and with rising concentration follows a slightly convex curve (Fig. 117) which resembles an adsorption curve. In the period 15-30 minutes the curve of the progressive salt uptake changes over to an almost straight line, rising obliquely, which corresponds to the progressive salt accumulation now beginning.

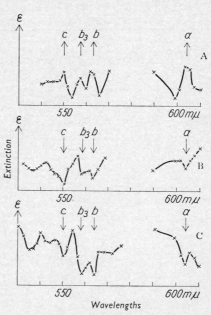

Fig. 118. Difference spectra of a 17 mm thick bundle of wheat roots, which show the regulating effect of salts on the oxidation-reduction state of the cyto-chrome system. A. Roots that have grown a consider-able time in distilled water (i.e. de-salted): the cytochromes a, b, b_3 and c show the reduced bands in the red and the green. B and C. Effect of 0·07 M KCl during 30-40 minutes respectively: the reduced bands disappear, which in the difference spectrum gives negative peaks at the appropriate wavelengths (after LUNDEGÅRDH 1958).

The salt accumulation continues in most experimental materials for at least 3-5 hours at an almost constant rate and leads to osmotic accumulation of salt in the vacuoles. In wheat roots a 3-5-fold accumulation as compared with the medium occurs in 4-5 hours from an 0·005-0·010 M solution of KCl, which corresponds to an osmotic value of 1·2-1·5 atm (LUNDEGÅRDH 1958). From very dilute solutions (0·0005 M), as has been shown in experiments with electric recording of the salt uptake, the accumu-lation over longer periods of time can take place at an almost constant rate (LUNDE-GÅRDH 1949). Gradually, however, it ceases, that is when a definite excess has been reached.

The rate of salt accumulation increases with the external concentration (Fig. 115), but to a much less extent at low temperature (3°C) than at higher temperature (21°). This is because the mechanism of salt accumulation works through the initially absorbed salt and not by getting the salt directly from the medium. The initial absorp-tion thus forms an effective buffer equipment against a fall of temperature. For this reason with lower salt concentration in the medium the salt uptake at 3°C is almost as intensive as at 21°C.

(b) *Hypotheses on the Mechanism of Active Salt Accumulation*

From the foregoing sketch of the time course of salt uptake it follows that during the initial adsorption, lasting in thin tissues about 15 minutes, no accumulation occurs in the cell sap. During this initial phase only the cytoplasm is charged with ions. During the initial period absorption is non-metabolic, but has a metabolic background

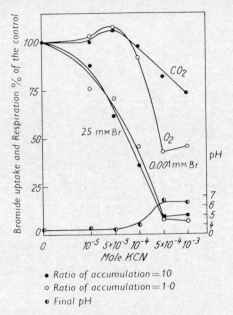

• Ratio of accumulation = 10
○ Ratio of accumulation = 1·0
⊙ Final pH

Fig. 119. Effect of cyanide on the absorption of bromide from 1 and 25 mM K Br and on the respiration (O_2 absorption and CO_2 liberation). The values are expressed in percentages of the control without CN (after MACHLIS 1944).

because the anion barriers function properly only with uninhibited aerobic respiration. The close connection with the cytochrome system is seen from the fact that at the beginning of the initial adsorption the cyanide-inhibitable respiration suddenly enlarges (cf. below). The following diagram illustrates the processes determining salt accumulation.

$$
\begin{array}{c|cc|c}
\text{I.} & & & \text{II.} \\
 & a & b & \\
M^+A^- + & R^+ + R^- \xrightarrow{\ } R^+A^- + M^+R^- \xrightarrow{\ } R^+ + R^- & & + M^+A \\
\text{Medium} & \text{Cytoplasm} & & \text{Cell sap}
\end{array}
$$

In this scheme *a* indicates the initial adsorption and *b* the accumulation. In the first phase (*a*) the carriers R^+ and R^- are charged with the salt ions M^+ and A^-. In the latter (*b*) the carriers are discharged and become available again for adsorption .I signifies the external surface and II the tonoplast.

For this process, represented in the form of a diagram in Fig. 120, to work as a salt pump, it is necessary that energy should be available at a or b or both. A supply of energy at a is improbable because the initial adsorption, as mentioned above, is in itself not metabolic. Thus b remains. Energy is needed here in order to break at least one of the ion linkages, e.g. R^+A^-, and to transport A^- through the tonoplast against the concentration gradient of cell sap→medium. The accumulated anion (or the acid H^+A^-) will then spontaneously liberate metallic cations from the carrier combinations M^+R^-. A similar result would of course follow if the cations M^+ were to be actively accumulated. The alkalinity thus caused in the cell sap would then liberate acid anions from the carrier linkage R^+A^-. Such adjustments during unilateral accumulation of anions or cations have been observed experimentally (see above). The important principle here is that it suffices for a mechanism of salt accumulation if only one category of ions of an electrolyte is actively transported.

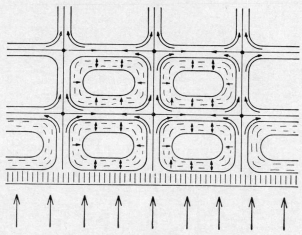

Fig. 120. Diagram of salt uptake in a tissue. The uptake from the medium is indicated by the lower arrows. The salts move by diffusion and 'sliding adsorption' (*cf.* Fig. 111) into the cell wall reticulum and pass, by exchange at the large carrier ions of the protoplasmic membrane and of the cytoplasm, into the protoplasmic structure (mitochondria etc.). At the boundary between cytoplasm and cell sap (that is the tonoplast) the salts are actively accumulated in the latter. The double-headed arrows indicate that all exchange processes are reversible; in external deficiency salts are thus again excreted and moreover the freely circulating salts (e.g. in the cell wall reticulum) can be transported with the transpiration water. The role of the plasmodesmata in the intercellular transport is still unknown.

Different hypotheses have been put forward to explain the process at b in the above scheme. Of these hypotheses two have been much discussed in the literature.

The advocates of the first hypothesis predicate that the carriers are oxidatively broken down at b and are again synthesised at a. Such a cycle could be driven by respiration. It has been suggested later that there is an indirect effect of respiration, viz. through oxidative phosphorylation.

As a support for the hypothesis of a collaboration of high-energy phosphate formation in active salt uptake the observation is usually put forward that the salt accumulation is inhibited by 2,4-dinitrophenol (DNP) in spite of the continuation of cyanide-inhibitable oxygen respiration.

DNP is known to be an inhibitor of phosphorylation. On the other hand it has been pointed out (LUNDEGÅRDH 1952, 1958) that poisoning with DNP causes severe general disturbances in cell operation. For example, cytochrome b is partly side-tracked, so that aerobic respiration must be maintained through an injured or at least greatly disturbed cytochrome system. The whole protoplasmic structure suffers severely under the effect of DNP as is seen from the loss of its carrier properties. The salts already accumulated flow back extensively into the medium. Through the disturbance of the carrier properties of the cytoplasm the initial salt adsorption fails. Since this represents the starting point of the actual accumulation, the latter process fails too.

One can therefore say that the maintenance of oxidative phosphorylation is certainly a necessary precondition for an active salt accumulation to take place, but that it has so far by no means been shown that a positive $\sim$ph metabolism is the direct driving force of the accumulation process. In the current lively discussion about the possible mechanisms of accumulation there is no rational explanation of how it might be possible for a cell to accumulate salts when the inhibitor (i.e. DNP) opens the door for a massive exosmosis of salt. The explanation of the absence of accumulation in DNP poisoning might thus well be that the accumulation process continues, but that the accumulated salts leak out just as quickly again.

The second hypothesis, which is the basis of the theory of anion respiration (LUNDE-GÅRDH 1945, 1950, 1954, 1955, 1958), sees in the active salt accumulation a result of the electrochemical properties of the cytochrome system.

Here (LUNDEGÅRDH 1945) the fact is used as a starting-point that the cytochromes are not freely mobile but are organised in fixed unions in which the electrons move in a definite direction. The electron stream is maintained by the Fe atoms of the individual cytochromes changing their valency continually, thus:

$$\underset{e}{\overset{e}{\rightleftharpoons}}Fe\underset{e}{\overset{e}{\rightleftharpoons}}Fe\underset{e}{\overset{e}{\rightleftharpoons}}\text{and so on} \qquad (82)$$

In the sphere of molecular dimensions a valency change means a strong change in electrical charge, and it can be imagined that freely mobile cytochrome molecules compensate the change in charge by intermittent attraction and repulsion of a salt anion found in the environment according to the scheme

$$Fe^{++}+anion\underset{+e}{\overset{-e}{\rightleftharpoons}}Fe^{+++}\cdot anion \qquad (83)$$

in which changes of charge, which might block a transfer of electrons, are eliminated.

It has now actually been found that *in vitro* the oxidation of reduced cytochrome c is accelerated by the presence of free salt anions (BOERI and TOSI 1954). The oxidation of added reduced cytochrome c by a suspension of mitochondria is also accelerated by salt ions (LUNDEGÅRDH 1953, BUTLER 1953). In this case it is probably the acceleration both of the electron transfer cytochrome $a_3 \rightarrow O_2$, and of the oxidation of cytochrome c by cytochrome oxidase, that is concerned.

We have learnt in Chapter 5 that the cytochrome system of living plant cells is, so to speak, built into the living structure. In fact, the cytochromes a_3, a and b are so strongly attached to the structure that it is almost impossible to bring them into solution as free molecules, whereas cytochrome c may be isolated easily. Enzyme-kinetic observations further suggest that the bound cytochromes are most probably present in close multimolecular unions, which are built together to an elementary structural unit, a 'multi-enzyme'. It is generally believed that the cytochrome system occupies the surface of the mitochondria, but other particles and the tonoplast also may equally well be provided with bound cytochromes. The sub-microscopic arrangement of the individual enzymes is still unknown. In analogy with the ideas about the construction of chloroplasts (p. 33), chromosomes, muscle fibres, etc., it may be imagined that the individual enzyme unions are arranged on each other in discs or layers, in such a way that the electron stream flowing from the dehydrogenases to the cytochrome oxidase passes through the structural complex in a definite direction, as is shown diagrammatically in Fig. 121. The whole enzyme complex consequently

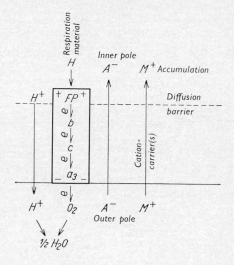

Fig. 121. Diagram of the electrochemical effect of the cytochrome system on salt uptake. Electrons pass through the system from the positive pole (at flavoprotein) to the negative pole (at cytochrome oxidase). In the current circuit thereby produced outside the system anions are forwarded from a_3 to b-FP electrophoretically, whilst the H^+ions, formed in equivalent quantity at the positive pole, take the opposite direction.

operates like an electric battery, with the positive pole at cytochrome b–flavoprotein, where the electrons enter into the system, and the negative pole at cytochrome oxidase, where the electrons leave it, to activate the oxygen in the environment.

According to the principles of electrochemistry it is necessary, in order to bring a battery into operation, that the internal electron stream should be closed by an external circuit. This external circuit in the cytochrome system flows through the electrolyte ions of the environment. The intensity of the aerobic respiration is regulated by the velocity of the internal electron stream. It consequently rises and falls with the electrolyte concentration of the environment, as has been experimentally shown.

In the external circuit of the cytochrome battery anions are transported electrophoretically in the direction from cytochrome oxidase to cytochrome b-flavoproteins, and cations in the reverse direction. Since no anions are produced in the terminal oxidation of the respiration cycle, the electrophoretic anion stream must be maintained wholly by the salt ions from the environment of the cytochrome system. On the other hand cations, that is H^+, are produced at the dehydrogenase end of the cytochrome system, i.e. in electron transfer to cytochrome b, so that the hydrogen taken over from the dehydrogenases is split up into protons and electrons. The electrons follow the path through the enzymes, whilst the protons are caught by the external electrophoretic circuit. Since the quantity of protons exactly corresponds to the quantity of electrons and of anions transported, the electrophoretic cation stream is restricted mostly to the H^+ ions, which at the site of the cytochrome oxidase form water with the excited oxygen atoms. Thus it is explicable that *anion respiration in the main transports only salt anions*.

It was originally considered that the cytochrome system was built into the cell surface in such a way that the salts would be accumulated in the ground mass of the cytoplasm in order to pass thence by diffusion or exchange into the cell sap. With the discovery that the cytochrome system is attached to mitochondria and the other structures scattered about in the cytoplasm as a whole, this assumption must be somewhat modified. It has actually been possible to find a definite salt uptake associated with increase of respiration both in isolated mitochondria and in intact protoplasm. If the structures are charged with salts, these pass via the tonoplasts into the vacuole, where the actual accumulation takes place. Thus there arises the following steady state:

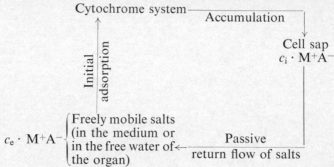

However the transfer from the cytoplasm into the cell sap may occur, it is sure that with external deficiency of salt (this applies especially to root tissues) or with weakened cytochrome respiration, previously accumulated salts come out of the vacuole again. In doing this they must of course again pass through the cytoplasm, in order to reach the freely circulating water of the cell walls. One can therefore assume that the intracellular aqueous solution usually shows a higher concentration than the medium (cf. sap flow below). Normally accumulation exceeds passive exosmosis.

The wide distribution of the cytochrome system, especially in metabolically active tissues, suggests that the idea developed here about anion or salt respiration corresponds to a very common phenomenon. Similar ideas have been expressed about electrolyte movements in animal tissues, e.g. the hydrochloric acid secretion of the mucus membrane of the stomach (CRANE et al. 1948). Meanwhile there are other enzyme systems than the cytochrome system that operate with valency change, and these also would of course be suitable for ion transport, provided that they were built into the structure of the protoplasm. Such cases are, however, so far unknown. Cytochromes do not operate exclusively with O_2 as the end acceptor, and the activating effect of salt ions has actually been observed also under anaerobic conditions (see below).

The best way to determine in a suitable material, e.g. in cut-off ends of cereal roots, thin discs of potatoes, carrots, artichokes, etc., the quantitative relation between ion uptake and anion respiration ($Q \text{ an}/O_2$), is progressive inhibition by cyanide (see Table 12). Determinations of the time course of ion uptake and respiration are also instructive. After the initial period is ended, these run strictly parallel for a considerable time.

ROBERTSON et al. (1948) point out that if the electrochemical scheme of anion respiration (cf. Fig. 121) is correct, for every oxygen molecule consumed in respiration a maximum 4 anions are transported and accumulated. This follows from the summary equation of cytochrome respiration,

$$4H^+ + 4e + O_2 \rightarrow 2H_2O \tag{84}$$

Table 12

Quantitative Ratio between the Chloride Uptake (in μmole Cl per 1 g fresh weight per hour) from 0·005 mole KCl with Stepwise Inhibition by KCN. Material: 0·5 mm thin, washed (de-salted) discs from potato tissue. Temperature: 20°C. Duration of experiment: 2 hours (after LUNDEGÅRDH 1958)

	Control without inhibitor	Added concentrations of KCN				
		$+10\mu M$	$+30\mu M$	$+100\mu M$	$+300\mu M$	$+1000\mu M$
Chloride taken up	2·59	2·11	1·34	0·95	0·51	0·00
Oxygen consumed	2·59	2·30	1·76	1·53	1·24	0·90
Anion respiration*	1·69	1·40	0·86	0·63	0·34	0·00
$Q\frac{Cl}{O_2}$	1·53	1·51	1·56	1·51	1·50	—

*Calculated as the difference between total respiration and respiration in $1000\mu M$ KCN (= ground respiration with Cl-uptake = 0).

In a number of experiments with fairly high salt concentrations ROBERTSON obtained values of Q an/O_2 which approached 4, but never exceeded this value. These experiments are however not decisive, since initial adsorption and continuing accumulation were not experimentally separated. Strong initial adsorption can with a short period of experiment actually give considerably higher values than 4 (according to LUNDE-GÅRDH 1958 up to about 25). Some workers, e.g. SUTCLIFFE and HACKETT (1957) and many zoologists, see in this high Q an/O_2 value evidence against the correctness of the electrochemical interpretation given above. This conclusion is, however, premature. Excessive values of salt uptake arise only in the rapidly occurring initial absorption. In later experiments higher values than 4 have not been observed for the steady accumulation process even when the intensity of respiration was reduced by a big drop in temperature (to $+1°C$) and salt concentrations up to 0·22 M were used.

The experimental investigations of active salt accumulation in plant cells thus support the theory of anion respiration. The low temperature coefficient (Q_{10}) of the initial adsorption speaks against a collaboration of ~ph formation in the initial stage, as ~ph formation has a high, biochemical temperature coefficient.

A fact important for the correct understanding of salt uptake is the competitive character of the process. Even the initial adsorption is, in its way, competitive, since the ions present in the medium surrounding the cell are adsorbed in accordance with the principles of mass action and the Donnan equilibrium besides specific properties. In the anion accumulation occurring electrophoretically in accordance with the theory, the mutual concentration relationships (activities), etc., naturally make themselves felt. Anions of higher activity are accumulated in larger amounts than anions more sparsely present. Such luxury accumulation, e.g. of phosphate or nitrate, has often been observed. Already at an early period (LUNDEGÅRDH and BURSTRÖM 1933) it was also found that with an equal external concentration the anions were accumulated in conformity with the electrophoretic speed of migration:

	NO_3^-	Cl^-	SO_4^{--}
Degree of accumulation with uniform respiration	3	1·5	1

The anion respiration is thus in itself unspecific, but the specific properties of the ions can produce characteristic differences in accumulation.

According to the diagram in Fig. 121 it is predominantly anions that are actively accumulated, but as these are immediately combined at the positive pole of the system with metallic cations (from the carrier M^+R^-) the specific properties of the cations are not without effect on the intensity and the course of the salt accumulation. Easily mobile cations favour anion accumulation and less mobile cations retard it, as shown in the following series (LUNDEGÅRDH 1937):

> *Intensity of nitrate uptake per unit of respiration*
> $Na > K > Mg > Ca > NH_4 > Sr > Ba$
>
> *Intensity of chloride uptake per unit of respiration*
> $K > Mg > Ca > NH_4 > Sr > Ba.$

As according to experience almost all cells of a tissue show anion respiration (cf. below), all the ions circulating in the cell wall reticulum must also compete with each other in the uptake. The anions present in the free water of the cytoplasm, which circulate in the immediate vicinity of the cytochrome units, are also of course carried along by the electrophoretic current. A piece of tissue, that is isolated or taken directly from a nutrient solution, for this reason shows anion respiration even when it is surrounded by distilled water.

This endogenous respiration, however, decreases greatly when the tissue is washed for a considerable time with distilled water, i.e. is desalted (cf. Table 13). That, in addition to the salts previously accumulated and now circulating in the tissue, the acids produced in metabolism itself also participate in anion respiration is seen from the fact that the endogenous respiration decreases still further with a decrease in pH, which simultaneously reduces the content of malic acid (Table 13). Only after

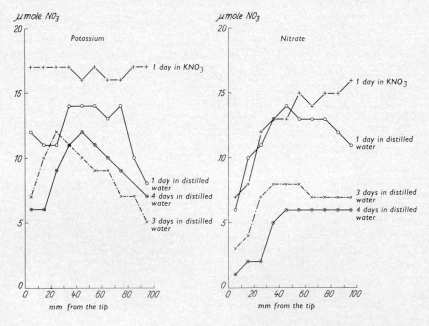

Fig. 122. The accumulation of potassium and nitrate in wheat roots kept for 24 hours in a KNO_3 solution. The K-content after the salt uptake is uniformly high in the whole root (values in μ mole per 10 mg of dry weight) whilst the nitrate content decreases towards the tip. After transfer of the roots into distilled water both cations and anions were released again, partly also through the bleeding stream. On this account the content sinks also in the middle zone (30-80 mm) although more slowly than in the tip zone (0-20 mm) (after LUNDEGÅRDH 1945).

desalting has been accomplished is it possible for salts coming from outside to compete successfully with the ions of the tissue itself. In this way the ratio Q an/O_2 increases (where 'an' means anions coming from the outside, not those already circulating in the tissue). Since a de-salted tissue also produces a certain amount of organic acids, the maximum value Q an/O_2=4 can only be approximated when fairly concentrated salt solutions are supplied at low temperatures (see LUNDEGÅRDH 1949c, 1958).

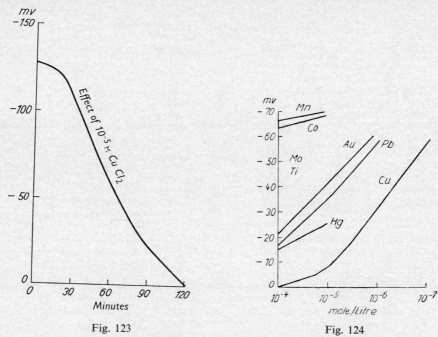

Fig. 123

Fig. 124

Fig. 123. Decrease in the surface potential of wheat roots by uptake of Cu ions.

Fig. 124. Effect of heavy metals (as chlorides or nitrates) on the surface potential of roots. For Cu, Hg, Pb and Au the potential decreases with increasing concentration, which gives the degree of toxicity. The normal potential amounts to about −60 millivolts. Copper must therefore be supplied as a trace element in concentrations of 0·1 μM or less. Mn, Co and Mo, which also occur as trace elements, even at 100 μM do not damage the normal charge of the cell surface.

Table 13

Effect of de-salting and removal of Organic Acids on the Cyanide-inhibitable Endogenous Respiration in Distilled Water

Results of experiments with wheat roots

	Medium and time of the pre-treatment					
	5mM $KHCO_3$ pH 9·5	Distilled water pH 5-6				0·3mM HCl pH 3·5
	1 day	1 day	2 days	4 days	5 days	1 day
Cyanide-inhibitable respiration relative per 1 g	131	100	56	36	27	11
Malic acid in the tissue (mM)	236			156		75

One may therefore assume that anion respiration represents a universal mechanism for pumping salts and organic acids into the vacuole. Since the oxygen concentration at the surface of a cell or of an organism is greater than in the interior, one can of course imagine that the electrolytic ions are transported along the falling oxygen gradient. This assumption is, however, not really necessary, since the orientation of the axis of the cytochrome units (cf. Fig. 121) determines the site of the accumulation. The above results suggest that in the mitochondria the axis of the cytochrome units stands vertically to the surface. Many controversies in this very topical field of research are caused by insufficient consideration of the complicated nature of the problems.

In summary it may be said that by means of this hypothesis of the mechanism of anion respiration an abundance of observed facts can be viewed from a common standpoint by reference to basic physical-chemical laws. An important biochemical advance is the detection of close relationships between the organised haem enzyme systems and transport or accumulation of salts and of organic acids. It is in the nature of cytochrome respiration that anions are actively transported in the first instance. But under special circumstances, e.g. in over-saturation of tissues with salt, metallic cations might also be transported by the same mechanism, though to other sites than the anions: for example, they could be secreted into the medium. An uptake of salt cations independent of anion respiration has been shown experimentally. Cations are much less affected than anions by an inhibition of cytochrome respiration, and the Q_{10} values for cation uptake are lower than those for anion uptake (ULRICH 1942, WANNER 1944, 1948). It has also often been observed that anions are taken up quite independently of the salt cations associated with them, for example NO_3^- independently of Ca^{++}. It has finally been shown that the anion carriers are affected more than the cation carriers by a disturbance of the $\sim$ ph metabolism. In active salt uptake the cations and anions enter the cytoplasmic structure separately by exchange. The anions are then actively moved on by the accumulation mechanism, whilst the cations, because of the Donnan potential thus arising at the site of the accumulation, passively follow.

Notwithstanding the separate mechanisms, however, salt anions and salt cations on the whole follow each other. Large deviations from equivalence occur only in the following circumstances: (1) if acids are produced or degraded in metabolism; (2) if anions taken up (e.g. NO_3^-) are consumed in metabolism; or (3) if the oppositely charged ions are transported at different speeds (temperature relations also have an influence here; see above).

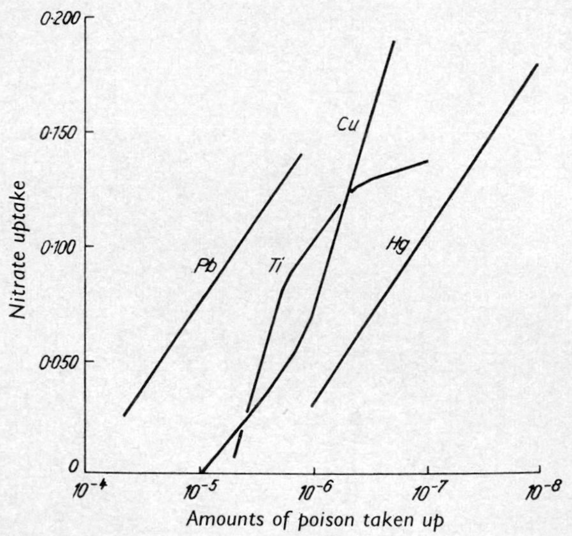

Fig. 125. Effect of heavy metal ions on the active uptake of nitrate in wheat roots. The abscissa gives values in milligram atoms per 100g dry substance.

Apart from the examples given above of adjustments of unequal ion uptakes, the following examples may also be mentioned. From potassium bentonite virtually free of anions only K^+ is absorbed and a corresponding amount of organic acids is produced in the roots to maintain internal balance (OVERSTREET et al. 1942). Several workers have shown that with an unbalanced nitrate supply many more organic acids are formed in the plant than with ammonium. In the former case the NO_3^- ions carry cations, e.g. K^+, in with them. After the proteinisation of NO_3^- the excess potassium ions are saturated by acid production. In the latter case, after proteinisation of NH_4^+ an internal excess of anions arises, which leads to the oxidative disappearance of a corresponding amount of organic acids (cf. p. 200).

By periodic accumulation and elimination of organic acids of course not only cations but also anions can be taken into the cell sap without the collaboration of anion respiration. With further production of organic acids, more cations are taken up. On disappearance of the acids the excess salt cations draw further anions in. Periodic variations of CO_2 production could act in a similar way. There is, however, no experimental evidence for such a mechanism being generally active in salt accumulation.

5 RANGE OF ACTIVE SALT UPTAKE

In conformity with the ideas developed above about the electrochemical activity of the organised cytochrome system, the accumulation of salts and organic acids in the cell sap governed by it is a widely distributed phenomenon. Few plant cells and tissues dispense with an active cytochrome system (cf. Chap. 5, YAKUSHIJI 1953, MARCH and GODDARD 1939, MATSKOV and FARFEL 1940, HARTREE 1956, LUNDEGÅRDH 1958). Some workers (STEWARD and PRESTON 1941, GOLDACRE 1952) believe that active salt uptake occurs only in connection with protein synthesis, that is only in growing organs. It was hinted above on p. 259 that the growth of the protoplasm automatically increases the number of carrier ions. The salt uptake thereby caused, is, however, restricted to the initial absorption. True accumulation in cell sap, that is accumulation against the concentration gradient between cell fluid and the external solution, occurs only in vacuoles, and this active accumulation persists a long time after the termination of the growing period.

Salt accumulation has been observed in mature algal cells (KROGH 1946) and in the cortex of roots at a considerable distance from the growing tip. This question has been investigated in special detail in wheat roots (LUNDEGÅRDH 1949, 1950). The unbranched roots of 2-3 weeks old seedlings were divided into three zones, viz. 0-20, 20-40 and 40-60 mm from the tip respectively. It was found that in all zones the salt uptake and the anion respiration proceeded with about the same speed. A spectrophotometric analysis of the haem enzymes in addition showed about the same content of cytochrome in all zones.

Active salt uptake thus proceeds independently of the state of growth of the cells, if only the necessary enzyme mechanism is in operation. The accumulating cells require supplies of glucose and oxygen. On account of the intensive autoxidation of the cytochrome oxidase the process is virtually independent of limited reductions of the oxygen pressure; a noteworthy inhibition was observed in wheat roots only on reduction of the oxygen to 1/2-1/5 normal pressure. This fact is of course of importance for salt uptake from the soil, where the supply of oxygen is at times restricted. On the other hand it has been found that oxygen diffuses very quickly through the tissue. Even the inner parts of rather thick tissues can on this account still accumulate salt, but it is conceivable that a lower oxygen pressure in the inside facilitates secretion from the parenchyma round the vessels (see below).

Active salt uptake disappears only with complete exclusion of oxygen. Under the influence of cyanide, carbon monoxide, azide, etc., the cytochrome oxidase is blocked, and the total respiration sinks by a half or more. In the remaining ground respiration, cytochrome b is still active (LUNDEGÅRDH 1955, 1958), but the active salt uptake is blocked. The same applies to the inhibition of cytochrome b, e.g. by fluoride, when cytochromes a_3 and c remain functional (LUNDEGÅRDH 1952). The electrochemical mechanism of salt accumulation, i.e. anion respiration, thus requires the undisturbed activity of the whole cytochrome system.

6 SALT TRANSPORT IN TISSUES

Fundamental for our comprehension of salt transport in tissues is the fact that the mechanism of accumulation of the cell works centripetally i.e. takes up salts at the surface and accumulates them in the vacuole.

It has been shown experimentally (LUNDEGÅRDH 1950) that, against the active centripetal salt stream, there is a passive centrifugal stream, i.e. a slow outward diffusion of salts, etc., from the vacuole. There thus arises the steady state described on p. 268. The temporary accumulation of salt in the vacuoles is thus due on the one hand to the activity of the salt pump, i.e. the cytochrome respiration, and on the other to the more or less complete impermeability of the tonoplast barriers. In wheat roots an equilibrium was attained experimentally at about 1·5 atm osmotic pressure of the salts. The salt barrier here is not especially effective, which is connected with the function of the roots in the conduction of sap (cf. Fig. 126). In other cases the tonoplast is more successful in preventing escape of the accumulated salts, e.g. in older living cells, in over-wintering storage organs, etc.

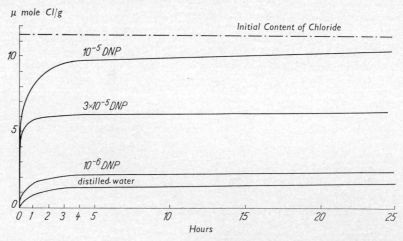

Fig. 126. Passive release (leaking out) of previously-accumulated chloride (in experiments with potato tissues). The most rapid leakage takes place in the first few minutes (negative adsorption curve) and the period between 4 and 24 hours is unimportant. By addition of increasing concentrations of dinitrophenol (DNP) the leakage is strongly accelerated, which is related to the decrease in the carrier properties (adsorption ability) of the cytoplasm.

Filling the vacuoles of the inner cells of a tissue would, however, not be possible if the salts did not also circulate freely in the cell walls and in the free water of the cytoplasm. The concentration of this circulating salt solution is as a rule higher than that of the external medium, e.g. higher in roots than in the soil water, which follows at once from the balance between the rising and falling branches of the internal salt cycle (p. 267). Thus in roots the greatest rise in concentration takes place between the external medium and the epidermal cells, whilst the cortex cells are fed by the already partly enriched free solution phase of the cell walls, and so on. In other organs the sap stream of the xylem takes over the role of medium. In this case the first increase of concentration has already taken place.

The distribution of the salts in a tissue may thus to a certain extent reflect the simultaneous intensity of the cytochrome respiration. Some salt transport probably takes place also in the plasmodesmata, but the main free circulation is undoubtedly in the young unlignified cell walls, which in this way operate under a certain salt pressure. Here short transport paths, that is from cell to cell, are referred to, not the long-distance transport, for which the capacity of the cell walls is much too restricted (cf. below). SCOTT and PRIESTLEY (1928), STRUGGER (1938, 1943) et al. emphasise strongly the transport in the cell walls, already suspected by SACHS (1887), BOKORNY (1890) et al., which of course conducts to the extent that the transpiration water flows through, carrying the salts present with it. But STRUGGER also admits the collaboration of an active component.

The sap stream rising from the roots is normally, as far as K^+, NO_3^- and $H_2PO_4^-$ are concerned, considerably more concentrated than the external medium. The work of concentration is in the last resort of course governed by the anion respiration of the cortex. The parenchyma directly bordering on the vessels is especially active and probably also the young endodermis with its cells rich in protoplasm. It is merely a matter of wording if with HOAGLAND and BROYER (1942), ARISZ et al. one speaks of an active secretion in the vessels. According to this idea the lower parts of the root vessels would function somewhat like large vacuoles, in which the salts are accumulated by the activity of the surrounding cytoplasm. In any case the concentration increase of the xylem sap reflects the anion respiration of the living root cells.

The metabolic origin of the bleeding- and sap-stream is indicated also by the surprising specificity of the salt content, which suggests a regulated choice of salt ions. In halophytes, whose roots are bathed in a strong salt solution, the sap stream is usually very low in Na^+ and Cl^-. These ions are, so to speak, filtered off during the passage through the protoplasm. The phenomenon would be quite incomprehensible if the salts were simply sucked up with the transpiration stream through the cell walls. The cytoplasm by means of its specific ion carriers can undoubtedly block certain salt ions and thereby oppose the passage of the appreciable accumulation in the free wall phase. This lack of salt uptake which is actually very marked in many halophytes, e.g. mangrove trees (p. 307), supplies striking evidence against the assumption of a considerable direct long-distance transport through the cell walls. The wide mesh of the submicroscopic structure of the cellulose walls could not cause such a sieve effect.

7 OTHER MECHANISMS OF SALT UPTAKE

From the hypothetical mechanisms of active salt uptake sketched above we have picked out anion respiration (cytochrome respiration) as the one best studied. The

T

simple carrier hypothesis maintained by some workers, i.e. a circulation of carriers between the cell surface and the tonoplasts, is actually only a bare description of the facts. That ion carriers are present in the cytoplasm and that they play an important part in the whole process, is in no way disputed. It may be that some workers are satisfied with the mere idea of a continuous cycle of carriers, as in a transport belt, but the real problem still remains, viz. by what mechanism the transport belt is turned and how the observed quantitative relations between cytochrome respiration and accumulated salt ions are to be explained.

Phosphorylation processes have been mentioned in connection with the uptake of special ions. Recent investigations (LUNDEGÅRDH 1958), however, show that $H_2PO_4^-$ is itself transported by means of the general anion respiration, even though at higher concentrations the phosphorylation mechanism may help. The mechanism might also be connected with the transport of glucose, which operates also under anaerobic conditions (LUNDEGÅRDH and BURSTRÖM 1944). BRAUNER and HASMAN (1940), however, mention that the 'permeability' for glucose rises when oxygen is lacking. It should be noted that phosphoric acid in the cell sap is present usually in the organic form (LITYNSKI 1935). Possibly at low pH values phosphoric acid is also taken up as the molecule (HONERT 1937).

At low pH the dissociation of the organic acids produced in the cytoplasm is also depressed, and because of the higher speed of transport of the molecules they can then be easily exosmosed. At the normal pH of cytoplasm containing salt cations (mostly at pH 5-6) all acids are dissociated and thus protected against exudation. They are then conversely accumulated in the vacuole by means of the anion respiration.

As far as potassium is concerned, photosynthesis seems to favour accumulation. On darkening, the same potassium migrates back into the soil, according to LUTTKUS and BÖTTICHER (1939). The cations of salts seem generally to be the more easily mobile in the sense that they readily exchange (p. 254). OVERSTREET and JACOBSON (1946) by means of radioactive isotopes demonstrated an exchange of phosphate ions, which however proceeded more sluggishly than with Rb^+.

In summary it can be stated that the complicated and much-branched biochemical machinery of the cell naturally provides a number of possibilities of taking up salt ions independent of the general mechanism of anion respiration. Since the majority of biochemical processes depend in the last resort on energy produced by the cytochrome respiration, there may well be connections between respiration and ion uptake quite independent of the anion respiration hypothesis (also between respiration and active transport of asparagine, etc.; cf. ARISZ 1942, 1946). Of these more indirect effects of cytochrome respiration, the maintenance of the ion carriers in the cytoplasm is undoubtedly the most important. It spontaneously evokes a strong salt adsorption, which in cells filled with protoplasm causes a concentration to more than ten times. This spontaneous carrier adsorption is not governed by any quantitative relations with cytochrome respiration, as has been clearly demonstrated by experiments at different temperatures (LUNDEGÅRDH 1958).

It may be suspected that many of the data in the literature on variation or absence of a relation between respiration and salt uptake are due quite simply to the fact that the spontaneous initial adsorption on carriers has been confused with true accumulation. For cells filled with protoplasm, e.g. in the primary meristem, the spontaneous carrier adsorption is strongly dominant. But even cells with normally filled vacuoles can of course show considerable spontaneous ion exchange, without this leading to appreciable accumulation, since the steady state admits of no further increase. Animal cells, which have no vacuoles, likewise belong to the category of those that absorb salts almost wholly spontaneously. From all this it is seen how important it is in investigations of salt uptake to choose suitable research material prepared with adequate forethought.

B. Root Pressure and Bleeding

1 THE LOCATION OF ACTIVE SALT UPTAKE

The root system is the mineral salt pump of the plant. Even water-plants take up the necessary salts to a great extent through their roots. This applies also to those algae that are provided with rhizoids, e.g. *Chara* (VOUK and BENZINGER 1929).

A limited salt uptake, however, appears to occur in the leaves of water-plants; and photosynthesis may possibly be the driving force. According to ARENS (1933) and LAUS-BERG (1935), bicarbonates are adsorbed by the under side of the leaves and their cations secreted as saturated carbonates by the upper side (cf. p. 130). This phenomenon, in the opinion of some workers, may have a counterpart in land plants, but many are sceptical about the assertion that the salts are secreted again at the upper surface of the leaves (ENGEL 1939). Certain observations connected with leaf analysis methods (see Chap. 7) show that at least young leaves can take up salts. These capabilities, however, have no great importance in the life of land-plants.

Active salt uptake through the roots is not restricted to the still-growing root hairs, that is to the few millimetres of the elongation zone. MACHLIS (1944) describes active salt uptake in pieces of root which were excised several centimetres from the tip. Wheat roots adsorb salts along the whole of their length from the growth zone (about 4 mm from the tip of the root cap) to about 100 mm back. The root hairs, however, multiply the adsorption area by several hundred per cent, so increasing uptake from the soil. Active accumulation of the absorbed salts occurs at least to a distance of 100 mm from the tip (see p. 273); about transport in the root see also POPESEN 1926, WIERSUM 1946). The salts stored in somewhat older root zones are also used up under starvation conditions.

2 BLEEDING

The well-known phenomenon of bleeding from the cut surface of decapitated root systems is an active process, in which water and salts leak out under considerable positive pressure (see below) through the opened vessels. The exact study of this phenomenon begins most suitably with an analysis of the sap exudation of individual roots.

The conditions of transport in wheat roots have been studied in especial detail (LUNDEGÅRDH 1950). Both the salt exudation of individual zones and the direction of the salt streams in the cortex were investigated experimentally.

When an unbranched wheat root 100 mm long is divided into two halves, the sum of the exudation of the pieces is equal to the exudation of the intact root. The exudation was measured by inserting the upper and lower ends of the pieces into capillary tubes.

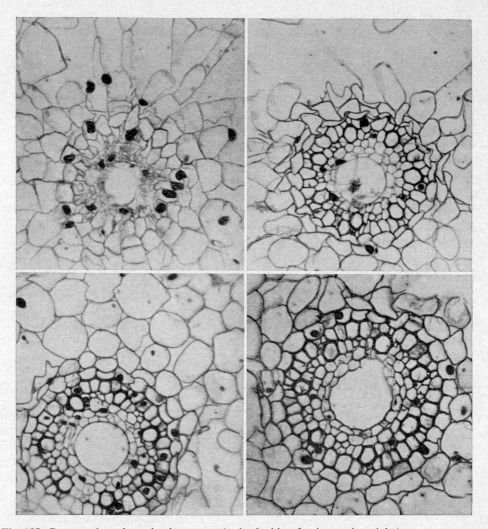

Fig. 127. Cross-sections through wheat roots (stained with safranin–gentian violet).

(1) 2·5 mm from the tip. In still undifferentiated vascular bundles, numerous large cell nuclei; the central lacuna is already present.

(2) 22·5 mm from the tip. Differentiation of the vascular strand beginning but the endodermis is still parenchymatous.

(3) 37·5 mm from the tip. The tracheids are lignified; endodermal thickening is commencing.

(4) 52·5 mm from the tip. Completed vessels and clear U-thickening of the endodermis cells (also nuclei). Passage cells opposite the tracheae (× 500).

Both the volume of the exuded sap and its salt content were determined. The lower 40 mm of a 100 mm long root bleeds somewhat more than the remaining 60 mm.

The bleeding sap is secreted from the vascular epithelium into the xylem vessels. The sap movement in the vessels is non-polar, i.e. the liquid flows out of both ends of an excised piece of root. The discovery is interesting that in spite of its axially elongated cells no considerable longitudinal sap movement takes place in the cortex. The sap movement through the cortex proceeds, therefore, at right angles to the longitudinal axis of the root. This result was found from measurements in roots with ringed cortex.

A restricted longitudinal conduction of materials in the cortex takes place only in the tip zone and is there devoted exclusively to the nutrition of the meristem.

Water and salts are exuded simultaneously, but the ratio of exuded water to exuded salt can vary. Starving roots, with a low salt concentration in the tissues, exude a strongly diluted solution. This is explained by general osmotic principles (see Chap. 1). From these it also follows that, after the metabolic disappearance of osmotically active materials (e.g. of NO_3^- in 'nitrate assimilation'), 'extra water' is excreted. In conformity with this it is found that the growing zone at the tip exudes a more dilute solution, since here the synthetic activity is greater than in the mature zones.

Contrary to the ideas of JAMES and BAKER (1933), the root vessels are thus the principal conducting elements for the bleeding stream. In spite of the slow lignification of the endodermal walls this impervious ring does not hinder lateral exudation from the cortex, probably as a result of the existence of passage cells (Fig. 127). In older portions of root the cortex is often disorganised and ruptured by side roots breaking through it. In these older parts only the long-distance transport takes place through the central cylinder.

(a) *The Sap Stream from the Roots*

Characteristic differences in the ratio of exuded water to exuded salt have been observed under the influence of respiratory poisons. Poisoning with potassium cyanide, that is inhibition of cytochrome oxidase respiration, increases the secretion of water into the root vessels, but conversely lowers the secretion of salt. The ratios exceed those in starved roots and indicate that with cyanide the active salt transport, i.e. anion respiration, is hampered, whereas glycolysis, i.e. consumption of osmotic substance (sugar, etc.) still continues.

Addition of fluoride, on the contrary, very strongly increases the salt exudation of the cortex; this is connected with the fact that fluoride, like 2,4-dinitrophenol (DNP), disorganises protoplasmic structure and starts a large escape of salts from the vacuoles (Fig. 126). With this poison, as with DNP, a lot of salt even escapes through the epidermis. In accordance with osmotic principles, this exudate is more concentrated than in normal bleeding.

It is characteristic of the normal bleeding of cereal roots that only salts (especially nitrates and phosphates of K and Ca) and not organic materials are secreted from the vascular epithelium. In this case there is not a high general permeability of the protoplasmic boundary surfaces, but a selective permeability. Since this includes electrolytes which otherwise penetrate only with difficulty, it is due probably more to ion exchange than to pure diffusion. Of great theoretical importance is the fact that the salt secretion into the root vessels has low temperature coefficients ($Q_{10} = 1 \cdot 3\text{-}1 \cdot 5$, as compared with $2 \cdot 2\text{-}2 \cdot 4$ for anion respiration) and is independent both of aerobic respiration and of glycolysis.

Bleeding thus persists for a time both under anaerobic conditions (inhibition of oxygen respiration) and in fluoride poisoning (inhibition of glycolysis). These facts thus directly contradict the hypothesis sometimes put forward that the salt secretion in the vessels might be equivalent to active salt accumulation in vacuoles. Internal salt exudation can on the contrary be classed with increased passive leakage of salts from vacuoles into the free phase of cell walls, etc. On the other hand, for the persistence of exudation the continuous activity of anion respiration is of course necessary. For this reason also the salt content of the bleeding stream sinks slowly if salts are removed from the external medium, or—which is also equivalent to starvation—the anion respiration is inhibited by cyanide, etc.

In the intact plant, of course, the rising sap stream does not appear externally. It is reabsorbed wholly or partly on its way through the stem and leaves. Many plants, however, in damp air exude drops of water through hydathodes. This *guttation* is a visible manifestation of the excess hydrostatic pressure of the active sap stream. The guttation fluid, however, loses part of its salt content during its passage through the plant, and, conversely, may be charged on the way with organic substances, as is seen by comparing analyses of the bleeding sap and of the guttation fluid. With the smallest amount of transpiration guttation fails, since the actively transported water then evaporates from the leaves.

With increased transpiration the rate of the stream of course increases. The hydrostatic pressure which otherwise is usually high (according to WHITE 1938, up to 6 atm in tomatoes) at the same time falls and changes to weak negative values, which can be measured by inserting manometers into the trunks of trees (LUNDEGÅRDH 1954).

The concentration of the bleeding sap normally exceeds that of the nutrient solution. If the roots of young wheat plants dip into a solution of 0.01 M $Ca(NO_3)_2$ (corresponding to a 0.16% nutrient solution), the bleeding sap collected from it maintains about 0.02 M With a 0.0005 M solution the bleeding sap shows about 0.015 M, which corresponds to a 30-fold increase in concentration. Osmotic work is, therefore, being done.

When the concentration of the bleeding sap at varying osmotic values of the medium is investigated, a remarkable constancy is found; the osmotic value of the medium in itself has little effect. From this follows the peculiar fact that at low external concentration the sap becomes hypertonic and at high external concentrations hypotonic. In a medium of $Ca(NO_3)_2$ the concentration of the bleeding sap remained at about the same value (see above) even when the external concentration increased to 0.100 M (LUNDEGÅRDH 1943, 1945).

The salt exudation thus operates sometimes against and sometimes with the concentration gradient, that is to say, independently. On the other hand, as is shown below, there is a clear relationship between the osmotic value of the medium and the *speed* of the bleeding stream. The relative constancy of the concentration of the bleeding sap is especially pronounced with calcium nitrate in the medium. With potassium nitrate it is easier to increase the osmotic value by 50%-100%, but even then there is no proportionality at all between the external and the internal pressure.

From the above it follows that the intensity of the anion respiration has indirectly an important influence on bleeding. With comparable osmotic pressures a potassium nitrate medium induces a more concentrated sap than a medium with calcium nitrate or glucose. With an osmotic pressure of the medium of about 0.9 atm, the bleeding sap reaches about 0.025 M with KNO_3, but 0.015-0.020 M with $Ca(NO_3)_2$ and only 0.007-0.009 M with glucose. From a KNO_3-solution both ions are taken up easily, but from $Ca(NO_3)_2$ mostly the NO_3^-. The salt exudation in the bleeding sap thus depends to a certain extent on the supply of suitable ions. The impoverishing effect of glucose is due to its accelerating effect on nitrate assimilation, whereby NO_3^- ions are removed from the exudate.

The main solutes of the bleeding sap of wheat roots are the easily transportable ions K^+ and NO_3^-, together with smaller amounts of Ca^{++}, $H_2PO_4^-$, Cl^-, etc., depending on their availability in the tissues. Complete equivalence ordinarily exists between the metallic cations and the acid anions; and the CO_2 content of the sap remains low. The influence of anion respiration is evident because, when it is inhibited by cyanide, etc., the secretion of acid anions is first restricted and that of metallic cations persists longer; the latter are then compensated by HCO_3^-. The collaboration of active processes in bleeding which persists for a considerable time also is clear from the temperature coefficient being about 2 (SPEIDEL 1939).

What has been said above also shows that the respiration inhibitable by cyanide assists the non-metabolic salt secretion from the cells surrounding the vessels, not only by continuous absorption from the medium, but indirectly also by maintaining the adsorption surfaces (carrier capacity) and the transport within and between cells. The gradual decrease of bleeding from roots which have been treated with HCN or NaN_3 or kept anaerobically, shows that the bleeding is not stopped instantly by these influences and that the gradual decrease is due to the active processes being switched off.

In the light of what was said on p. 265 about the adsorption capacity of the cytoplasm, the limited salt exudation from roots poisoned with cyanide, etc., may be referred partly to the inactivation of the carrier R^+. Ions are then excreted not only from the cells surrounding the vessels but also from the epidermis. Normally, however, the loss of salt through the epidermis is considerably less than the exudation into the vessels. The entire root system thus operates rather as in an experiment by OSTERHOUT (1947); he allowed one end of a *Nitella* cell to take up sugar; and fluid came out of the other end.

The radially polar function of the roots means that the epidermis takes up salts whilst the cells round the vessels secrete them. In this, as expounded above, osmotic forces are active, which we identified with the anion respiration. These forces, however, are restricted to the charging of the vacuoles of the individual cells with salts and thereby also the transport of salts from the surface to the inside. The secretion in itself is not an active phenomenon; to all appearances it is identical with the passive return flow of salts from the vacuoles of the individual cells into the cell walls.

Fig. 128. Course with time of the bleeding from an intact root, from the excised tip zone (0-30 mm) and from the basal zone. The bleeding from the last was measured separately at the two ends. The bleeding with water as a medium is shown by the dotted lines, and the bleeding after addition of 1 mM KCN by the solid lines. Stimulation of the bleeding of the tip zone and slow decrease of the bleeding of the basal zone are shown (after LUNDEGÅRDH 1950).

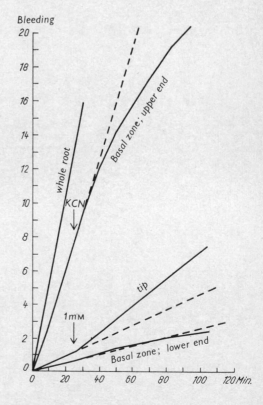

A number of observations, among others the measured electrochemical potential, suggest that the external plasma membrane of the epidermal cells forms a very efficient barrier against passive penetration of salts. The corresponding internal surfaces between the cells round the vessels and the vascular fluid is much more penetrable by salts. There thus arises the radially polar leakage of the salts accumulated by anion respiration into the central vessels.

(b) *The Relations between Bleeding and the Chemical and Osmotic Properties of the Medium surrounding the Root*

The concentration of the bleeding sap is influenced to a remarkably small extent by the osmotic properties of the medium. On the other hand the rate of the bleeding stream shows a marked relation to the osmotic situation.

In a number of bleeding experiments with wheat roots (LUNDEGÅRDH 1945) the results could be expressed by the following equation:

$$Bl = K(\sqrt{P_i} - \sqrt{P_o}) \tag{85}$$

in which Bl = the rate of bleeding, P_o = the osmotic pressure of the medium and P_i = the bleeding pressure. The equation is strongly reminiscent of the well-known theorem of TORRICELLI, which states that the rate at which a fluid flows out of an opening in the bottom of a vessel is proportional to the square root of the hydraulic pressure.

The *bleeding pressure* is defined as the driving force of the sap flow, in other words as the hydrostatic counter-pressure at which bleeding stops. This pressure can of course be measured directly, by connecting a manometer to a cut stem or root. Such measurements were carried out by the earlier plant physiologists with mercury manometers. The sap pressure of bleeding trees, e.g. birches, can be measured at boreholes.

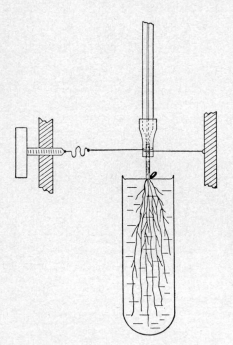

For laboratory experiments it is more convenient to measure the bleeding pressure by osmotic methods. According to the definition the bleeding, i.e. the active transport of water from the medium into the vessel, continues only as long as P_i is greater than P_o. When $P_o = P_i$, the bleeding ceases and P_i is then identical with the known osmotic pressure of the medium. A suitable arrangement of the experiment is illustrated in Fig. 129.

By this method one can also easily observe the changes of P with changes in the composition of the medium. One then finds e.g. that in an external medium of KNO_3-solution the bleeding pressure gradually rises. The bleeding pressures determined by the method

Fig. 129. Arrangement for measuring the bleeding of seedlings. The capillary tube has a diameter of 0·4-0·5 mm. The movement of the water meniscus is read off with a horizontal microscope.

sketched in Fig. 129 are of the same order of magnitude as those measured directly, and in well-nourished wheat roots they attain values of several atmospheres. In starved and salt-deficient roots the values can sink to 0·7 atm, but increase again rapidly after uptake of nutrient salts from the medium.

From the explanation given above for the bleeding phenomenon it follows that the exuded salts derive from the passive flow from the cell vacuoles. If the apertures of the vessels are stopped up, the concentration of the xylem sap can gradually increase to the same value as in the vacuoles, i.e. the equilibrium pressure of the bleeding approaches the turgor pressure of the living root cells. Not only salts are secreted from an elastic-ally stretched cell, but with them also water in an amount which corresponds to the pressure drop consequent on the salt exudation. The assumption of SABININ (1925) and other research workers on bleeding, that the bleeding pressure may simply be identical with the osmotic pressure of the expressed sap, is unsatisfactory, whilst, as mentioned above, bleeding can indeed take place even when the sap is hypotonic as compared with the medium. The explanation of this phenomenon lies in the fact that for osmotic reasons water, as well as salts, is excreted, and this under the full turgor pressure.

Thus 'extra water', as well as the salt solution, is secreted. This extra water is identical with the so-called 'non-osmotic water transport' (a very unsatisfactory term; cf. p. 60 *et seq.*) i.e. in this case water is moved actively against the osmotic pressure gradient. This phenomenon, however, has nothing mysterious about it; it lies wholly in the sphere of normal osmotic phenomena. The extra water in this case is simply pressed out of an elastically extensible cell, when it experiences a fall of internal osmotic pressure; the extra water thus comes out under the full turgor pressure of the secreting cells. The fundamental osmotic principles of secretion are represented diagrammatically in Fig. 130.

The proportion of extra water in the total bleeding sap of course depends on the intensity of the respiration and of the synthetic processes, i.e. on all metabolic processes in which osmotically effective molecules are consumed, e.g. sugar, NO_3 (in protein formation), etc. In conformity with this more extra water is secreted by the growing tip zone than by the mature part of the root and the bleeding sap is consequently more diluted there. The secretion of water increases considerably under the influence of

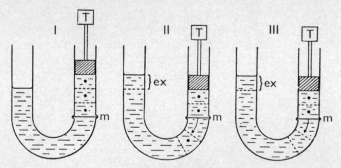

Fig. 130. Diagrammatic representation of the relations between turgor pressure and sap exudation.
I. m semi-permeable wall (≡ cell wall + cytoplasm), T piston (≡ turgor pressure). Black dots represent osmotically effective particles. Shading represents water.
II. On exudation of an osmotic particle $1/n$ of the cell water is simultaneously exuded under the pressure T.
III. In metabolic disappearance of an osmotic particle (cf. the text) $1/n$ of the cell water is likewise secreted, now as 'extra water'.

cyanide, which is probably due to the fact that because of the Pasteur effect more glucose is now consumed (cf. Fig. 130). Conversely, the secretion of extra water decreases under the influence of fluoride, which is a glycolysis poison.

In summary, the following may be said about bleeding.

Salts and water are secreted into the vessels under a hydrostatic pressure corresponding to the turgor pressure of the extensible cells of the inner root tissue. The secretion of salts is theoretically identical with the passive (non-metabolic) loss of salts accumulated in the vacuoles in the direction of the concentration-gradient, cell sap > free water in the cytoplasm and cell walls. The radial direction of the sap flow is determined by a higher permeability to salt of the cytoplasmic boundary surfaces between root parenchyma and vessels as compared with that of the epidermis.

The dependence of the central salt secretion on anion respiration is indirect, because the intensity of the passive salt flow is determined by the level of accumulation in the vacuoles.

The central water secretion is of dual nature and includes (1) water lost with exuded salt ions on osmotic grounds; and (2) extra water. The amounts of water combined with the salt ions are non-metabolically secreted like the former. The extra water, on the other hand, is secreted only in connection with metabolic processes. Since the extra water usually represents a considerable or even predominant part of the total volume of the bleeding sap, it is here that the usually observed dependence of bleeding on temperature changes is to be sought. The amount of the salts secreted was mostly disregarded in earlier work. It should, however, be remembered that extra water is secreted also under anaerobic conditions, in cyanide poisoning, etc., among other reasons because sugar is consumed.

The observed quantitative relationship between bleeding intensity and the opposed osmotic pressure in the medium (equation (85), p. 282) is easily understood when one knows that the bleeding pressure is identical with the turgor pressure of the bleeding tissue. The internal secretion of water thus follows the general physical rules. It is likewise clear from the above considerations that the relation between the bleeding intensity and the value of the turgor pressure, that is $P_i - P_o$, is valid only for the water flow out and not for the amounts of salt secreted.

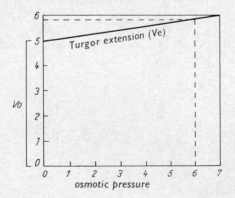

Fig. 131. Diagram of the relations between osmotic pressure, turgor extension and volume of the cell. V_o = the volume of the plasmolysed cell; V_e = the supplementary volume of the cell stretched by the osmotic pressure. Only this volume is available for water exudation. The diagram in Fig. 130 applies for an unlimited elasticity of the cell wall.

C. Sap Flow in Plants

The osmotic principles state that in the living body every dissolved molecule or every ion is accompanied by an amount of water in inverse ratio to the osmotic pressure prevailing at that point (= turgor pressure).

The salt ions absorbed on the surface of the root thus carry with them corresponding amounts of water from the medium, which become less, the higher the pressure in the epidermal cells rises. The molecules newly formed in metabolism, e.g. CO_2, draw corresponding amounts of water from the surroundings into the plant, and so on. Inside the plant it is generally either solutions or 'extra water' that are extensively transported.

These general osmotic relations necessarily decide the sap movements in the plant, as has been clearly demonstrated among others by MÜNCH (1930). MÜNCH, however, goes rather too far in wishing to establish a theory of sap movement exclusively on osmotic principles. The *active* transport processes sketched in the preceding section promote sap movements, but other, still obscure, factors are also concerned. We will devote this section to a review of sap movements and their possible causes.

1 THE DIRECTION OF THE SAP STREAMS

We can distinguish an active rising sap stream, which begins in the roots and flows through the whole vascular system, carrying with it absorbed mineral salts, from a descending sap stream coming from the leaves and bearing the products of photosynthesis.

These main streams show variants, since the photosynthetic products of the leaves also pass upwards to the floral regions or to the tips of the shoots; and rising streams of organic solutions go from the endosperm of the seeds, and from the cotyledons, bulbs, root nodules, rhizomes, etc., to the growing green organs. Furthermore, during the active spring period of trees organic materials together with salt solutions are carried upwards in the tracheal elements of the stem. In stems with secondary thickening sap streams are conducted into the cambium. In root tips the active flow of salt solutions is divided near the growing point into a main rising stream flowing to the aerial parts and a much weaker descending stream divided off for the growing point.

The tissues that conduct sap are the vascular bundles. The special functions of the xylem and phloem have been frequently discussed (e.g. CRAFTS 1935). In general, the conclusion has been reached that the xylem carries the rising stream of mineral salts and water, a transport which is ordinarily hastened considerably by transpiration (Chap. 8), whilst the phloem is reserved for the transport of organic materials. This interpretation finds support in spectroscopic investigations on the conduction of lithium (BODENBERG 1929) and experiments with radioactive isotopes (COMAR and NELLER 1947, RABIDEAU and BURR 1945). GUSTAVSON (1939) assumes a restricted upward conduction of mineral salts through the phloem. It needs to be remembered, however, that phosphoric acid, for example, is also transported in organic form.

MASKELL and MASON (1929 and later) by their extensive investigations on cotton plants, were strengthened in their conviction that nitrogen goes in inorganic form through the stem xylem into the leaves, from which it flows down again in organic form through the phloem. It can thus be stored temporarily in woody stems both in the bark and in the wood. The idea has, however, been put forward that the phloem also transports salts. To collect sap from xylem and phloem separately involves almost unsuperable technical difficulties; one is restricted to total analyses of bleeding sap or guttation fluid. Most investigations on sap movements refer to trees, from which the sap can be obtained in various ways, both from the wood and from the bark, without endangering the life.

When coniferous trees are cut down they show no, or only very weak, bleeding from the stump and there is no springtime flow of sap from boreholes. It is known that the root growth of coniferous trees begins later in the spring than that of deciduous trees. In the latter new root tips are encountered very early (cf. MÜNCH 1930, p. 181). Of our northern trees, however, only the birch shows considerable sap pressure in spring.

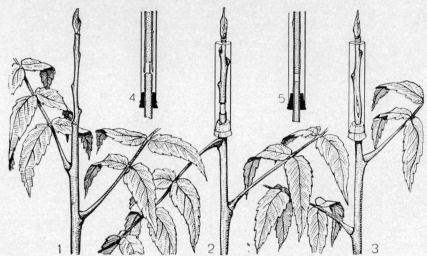

Fig. 132. Experiment on ringing. 1. Controls, in which the tips of the shoots were defoliated; 2. Ringing of the shoot (removal of the phloem); 3. Xylem removed, but phloem intact (the enclosing tubes are filled with water); 4. Ringing with abscission of both xylem and phloem; 5. Longitudinal section of 3 (after CURTIS 1935).

From boreholes in mature birch trees one can collect about two litres of sap per day, and pressures of 3-4 atm are developed (see Fig. 133). The bleeding pressure, however, sinks gradually as the time of leaf formation approaches. The sap contains 30-40 mM of invert sugar and about 8-10 mM of soluble N-compounds, principally amino acids. The ratio of glucose : fructose often rises, e.g. in *Carpinus betulus* (LÖHR 1953), considerably above unity. The nitrate content on the average is very low, and characteristically there is a rise in the content of mineral materials, particularly calcium, as the season advances (see Table 14). This, however, is partly due to the decrease of active water transport. The sap of the sugar-maple (*Acer saccharum* and other North American species) contains 2%-8% of sugar.

Table 14

Analyses of the Bleeding Sap of the Birch Tree (mM)

Date	K	Ca	Mg	Mn	PO_4	NO_3	Invert sugar	Amino acids
12 April	1·90	1·85	0·85	0·05	0·27			
13 April	2·05	2·35	0·85	0·06	0·28			
19 April	2·35	1·75	0·90	0·05	0·30			
20 April	2·15	1·70	0·90	0·04	0·53			
23 April	3·40	2·90	1·20	0·10	0·67	0·02	36·7	8·2
25 April	4·30	3·40	1·20	0·08	0·77			
27 April	4·20	4·40	0·90	0·15	0·66			
1 May	3·50	6·00	3·50	0·16	0·70			
4 May	4·10	8·50	3·50	0·19	0·65			

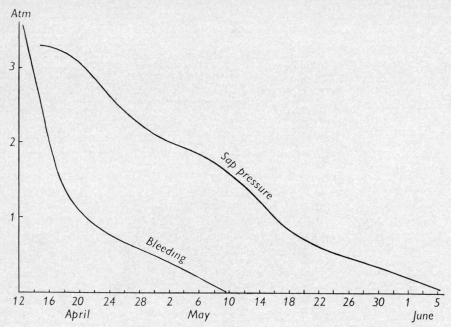

Fig. 133. Sap pressure and relative amounts of bleeding of the sap of a birch tree flowing from a borehole.

The wood parenchyma is ordinarily well developed. Its cells are full of reserves, chiefly carbohydrates, but they contain little protein. The wood parenchyma is arranged in thin strands, which give an enormous internal area, according to MÜNCH (1930) several hectares per cubic metre of wood. It is thought that the reserve materials, when they are mobilised in spring, pass out into the vessels and are carried along by the rising xylem stream. It has in fact been shown that carbohydrates are not always obstructed in their movement by ringing the bark (Fig. 132).

Normally the medullary rays running in a radial direction are discharged into the phloem of the bark, and the transport upwards is then restricted to this tissue. As far as the birch tree is concerned, however, there is no doubt that in spring carbohydrates, etc., flow in considerable amount in the xylem. The actively rising stream is thus produced by the joint effect of root pressure and exudation from parenchyma layers rich in nutrient. The tracheal sap of apple trees contains an abundant selection of amino acids and amides, which are formed in the roots from the inorganic nitrogen compounds taken up (BOLLARD 1956).

It is often objected against ringing experiments that the xylem is easily blocked by the phloem exudate and the sap stream through the wood thus hindered. The dual flow in the wood, i.e. a rising salt-bearing stream in the inner wood layers and a descending stream of organic materials in the young wood, which has been asserted by a number of workers (BIRCH-HIRSCHFELD 1919, DIXON 1924, MACDOUGAL 1926, ARNDT 1929), appears to be very doubtful. Even though the vessels are fairly well shut off from each other in a lateral direction, it is difficult to admit the possibility of two streams flowing simultaneously but in opposite directions in the dead tissue.

A temporary translocation of carbohydrates by means of the upward xylem stream often occurs in spring, especially in trees which show considerable bleeding. This can be regarded as a shunt to the phloem stream caused by the increased demands on transport just at this period, which decrease again after the unfolding of the leaves. At the period of rapid transpiration in the summer the soluble organic materials have already been washed out of the wood.

The possibility of a strongly differentiated transport, i.e. the existence of streams flowing simultaneously in different directions or with different speeds, seems considerably more likely in the phloem, since its conducting elements are formed of living cells. One is becoming more inclined to ascribe to the phloem—whose chief function is the long-distance transport of organic materials—fairly specialised functions. Transport over shorter distances is usually reserved to the parenchyma, which may be adapted to the function by the presence of long cellular elements (conductive parenchyma).

In the conductive parenchyma the living protoplasm must always play a part, possibly even in the form of plasmodesmata. MÜNCH (1930) especially ascribed great importance to the latter and considered them as living bridges, which unite the cells into a symplast. Tissues consisting of dead cells MÜNCH named apoplasts. He calculated that each plasmodesma in the leaf parenchyma can transport by diffusion $2 \cdot 1$ to $3 \cdot 7 \times 10^{-8}$ mg of material per 24 hours, and thought that, because of the great number of plasmodesmata, this would suffice for the evacuation of assimilates from the photosynthetic cells. Probably sliding rapid transport also collaborates here (cf. p. 254). As adjacent parenchymatous cells can show large chemical differences, this suggests that on the other hand normally no mass streaming of protoplasm takes place through the plasmodesmata.

The sap streams have various functions in the life of the plant. The rising xylem stream supplies the shoot meristems with nutrient salts, while the leaves convert some of them into organic compounds, which are distributed by the phloem streams to the growing tissues and storage organs. Metabolism of inorganic nitrogen takes place even in the roots. J. VON SACHS spoke of 'organ-forming materials'. We now know that these materials in addition to carbohydrates and amino acids also include hormones which, however, can often be transported in the xylem as well. All this tells against the assumption of undifferentiated mass flows. It is known, for example, that the fruits of certain trees draw their materials from all parts of the plant.

On account of the synthetic activity of the growing tissues, osmotically active material continuously disappears; which involves the liberation of 'extra water' according to the scheme in Fig. 130. This water ordinarily finds its way back to the conducting tissue and to the transpiration stream. Conversely, water passes from the rising transpiration stream and its active components (cf. root pressure) to the newly formed osmotic substances in the leaves (sugars, etc.). Thus there arises an internal water circulation, which is, indeed, quantitatively restricted, but which can serve as the original cause of certain mass flows (see below).

MÜNCH (1930) has calculated that transpiration and root pressure together pump 1,500-2,100 m³ of water annually through one hectare of beechwood. The internal water circulation would take only 128 m³ of this, or 2 litres per tree per 24 hours. The water circulation caused by the synthetic activity of the cambium would approximately correspond to the water content of the sapwood.

2 THE DRIVING FORCES OF SAP FLOW

The real driving force of the active flow of sap up the xylem in herbs and certain trees is the salt exudation governed by the cyanide-inhibitable respiration in the lower parts of the vessels. Due to the high hydrostatic pressures thereby attainable, the necessary nutrient salts may, even when transpiration is stopped, be raised to considerable heights.

In many trees, however, root pressure is insufficient, and one must conclude that, for the supply of salts to the growing leaves and shoots, they depend on transpiration, which even in the presence of active salt uptake in the roots represents a fruitful supplementary means of salt transport. Even in herbaceous plants transpiration helps the roots to an efficient elution of the salts exuded into the vessels. In young wheat plants transpiration under normal growth conditions increases to about 6 times the amount of the active bleeding stream.

The attempts made by earlier workers (URSPRUNG, MÜNCH et al.) to explain root pressure and the consequent active transport of water and salts through the xylem by differences in osmotic pressure between the cortex, endodermis and central root parenchyma, or by a pressure gradient diminishing from the shoots towards the roots, failed to explain the continuous persistence of the phenomenon. It is obvious that when water is short, that is when the cells are in danger of losing their turgor, those that show the highest osmotic value will remain turgid longest.

On the other hand, it is by no means the case that, when the water supply increases, the bulk of the water flows towards those cell groups which show the highest osmotic pressure. The amount of water taken up by a cell depends entirely on its degree of stretching when turgid, and this can rise to high values, in the meristem for example, even in cells with low osmotic pressures. Most of the water then flows towards these cells. According to equation (6) (p. 61):

$$Sp = O_v - Tg$$

where Sp = suction pressure, O_v = osmotic value and Tg = turgor pressure, it follows that a cell group with a low osmotic value can draw to itself a flow of water just as much as one with a high osmotic value.

The different osmotic pressures in different tissues have little importance for the normal sap flow, but on the other hand a high pressure offers a certain guarantee against wilting during water shortage. The opinion defended by many workers (e.g. URSPRUNG, ILJIN) that a pressure gradient decreasing from above downwards must be present, is, however, not valid (see also Chap. 8). Even when two tissues show different suction pressures, it is still true that the turgor extension is quantitatively decisive. A high suction pressure, which arises in a cell not elastically extensible, is saturated by a quite inconsiderable amount of water, whilst strongly elastic cells can take up considerable amounts of water even with a low suction pressure.

The idea, put forward by URSPRUNG and then taken up by a great number of plant physiologists, that differences of suction pressure are the cause of fluid movements, rests moreover on the unfounded assumption that the differences are maintained continuously. This would only be possible on the assumption that metabolic processes were assisting; and we thus come back again to the previously discussed facts and views on active sap transport. The best evidence against the suction force hypothesis of URSPRUNG is given by the fact that the roots fully develop their root pressure and active salt transport only when fully turgid, i.e. when there is no suction force.

The 'mass flow' theory propounded by MÜNCH (1930) is based on the principle advocated by PFEFFER, that in an interconnected osmotic system solution moves from a point with higher osmotic value to a point with lower. According to the scheme in

Fig. 134 the water is thus taken up at A and pressed out at B. In this way there is a flow within the system from A to B and outside the system a return flow in the direction from B to A. MÜNCH conceived a flow under pressure from the assimilating leaves, where osmotically active substances arise, towards the meristems where the substances disappear again. This 'active' pressure flow produces a passive suction flow, which passes *inter alia* from the roots to the leaves (Fig. 135).

Whilst MÜNCH's theory is built on a theoretical basis which is in itself unobjectionable, great difficulties arise in its application to actual circumstances. It has already been found that root pressure is something quite different from a simple osmotic suction flow. Against the existence of a mass flow in the phloem there may be brought

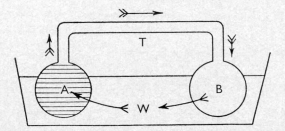

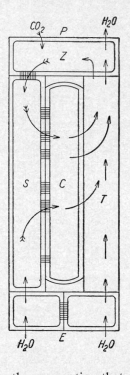

Fig. 134. Diagram of osmotic pressure flow. A cells with high and B cells with low osmotic values, connected by the tube T and immersed in a water bath W. Doubly-feathered arrows show the direction of the pressure flow, and singly-feathered arrows the flow of water in the medium (after MÜNCH 1930).

Fig. 135. Diagram of the mass flow theory according to MÜNCH. T xylem vessel, P leaf parenchyma, S sieve tubes, C cambium, Z sugar and E endodermis. Simple arrows show the direction of flow of the water, singly-feathered arrows the movement of CO_2, and doubly-feathered arrows the movement of sugar (after MÜNCH, from CURTIS 1935).

forward observations which can be interpreted only on the assumption that different dissolved substances can move simultaneously in different directions. The flow under pressure postulated by MÜNCH must be a mass flow, which transports passively all the dissolved substances present in one and the same direction. Even the fundamental assumption of MÜNCH's theory—that the 'delivering' organs must have a higher osmotic value that the 'receiving' organs—fails in many cases. The osmotic value at the point of reception, e.g. in the meristem, is often actually higher than at the point of supply, e.g. in leaves or storage tissues. For example, CRAFTS (1935) points out that, according to freezing-point measurements on sprouting bulbs, the meristem had an osmotic value of 12·9 atm but the storage tissue only 7·0 atm. It is also generally known that many storage organs, e.g. potatoes, wilt even with turgescent shoots. The evacuation of leaves before leaf-fall also means a movement of dissolved substances in a direction contrary to the concentration gradients. According to PHILLIS and MASON, the concentration of cane sugar (which they consider to be the transport form of sugar in the cotton plant), is higher in the receiving leaf veins than in the producing mesophyll. In other plants, e.g. bananas (BELVAL 1930) or *Helianthus* (BRUNS 1925) where hexoses are also said to be transported, exactly opposite gradients have been observed.

Thus it can scarcely be denied that the participation of active processes, similar to anion respiration, must be affirmed for the transport of organic substances also. ARISZ has found a connection between the transport of asparagine and aerobic respiration; and active accumulation of glucose has also been found. Everything therefore suggests that the meristems actively direct the flow of 'body-building materials' to themselves, once the growth hormones, partly acquired in other ways, have initiated cell increase.

Active transport of organic materials takes place even in the parenchyma. The sugar produced in the leaf mesophyll is thus probably accumulated actively by the companion cells of the sieve tubes. These are usually considered as storage organs (CZAPEK 1897, PHILLIS and MASON). SCHUMACHER (1933) found that fluorescein accumulated especially strongly in the companion cells. The possible role of the plasmodesmata in sugar transport is still unknown; but there are observations which indicate a relatively rapid passage of sugar molecules through the external protoplasmic surface, whilst according to WEEVERS (1931) the tonoplasts may be less permeable. Data about low permeability to sugar may therefore, according to WEEVERS, be due to investigators of plasmolysis having generally worked with cells with thin protoplasmic linings (cf. also WENT 1946). According to this interpretation sugar moves from cell to cell through the protoplasts, avoiding the vacuoles. The speed of transport would therefore be directly dependent on the thickness of the protoplasmic linings.

That sugar penetrates the external surface layer with relative ease may be seen from the fact that small amounts always escape from the surface of roots, and in the guttation fluid (LUNDEGÅRDH 1943, p. 32). This penetration of sugar is of course not necessarily a simple diffusion through a partially permeable membrane, but may be, like ion uptake, an active equilibration regulated by biochemical processes.

A pre-condition for active sugar transport against the diffusion gradient is a shift of the steady state in favour of one side of the membrane. It may be mentioned here that according to DIJKSTRA (1937) the removal of assimilates from leaves is strongly inhibited by shortage of oxygen (cf. the findings of ARISZ above). Ideas on the osmotic relationships of the cell have developed considerably with time and become more distinct. The relative impermeability of the protoplasm towards a number of dissolved substances (salts, sugars, amino acids, etc.) was formerly considered an obvious requirement for the maintenance of an osmotic pressure difference. MÜNCH (1930) even regarded a 'practically impermeable protoplasmic membrane' as a necessity if a pressure flow were to take place.

Recent plant-physiological discoveries, however, have shown the external protoplasmic membrane to be fairly permeable for a large number of organic compounds which contribute to the osmotic pressure, and the latter is increasingly regarded as a steady state between active accumulation processes and passive leakage outwards. Specific metabolism processes associated with anatomical and physiological differentiation are becoming more and more conspicuous in connection with translocation and movements of sap.

The sap flow in phloem proceeds on the average more slowly than that in the xylem. This is connected with the different demands which are placed on the two systems, and is reflected in the dimensions of the conducting elements. In the stolons of

U

potatoes the tissues show the following percentage distribution (according to CRAFTS 1931-3):

	% of the total cross-section	(of which)
total phloem	18·5	(phloem walls 6·0)
sieve tubes	5·7	(sieve pores 0·1)
xylem	39·3	
cortex	36·5	(medulla 5·5)
	100·0	

The xylem thus occupies more than twice the cross-sectional area of the phloem. In woody plants the predominance is still greater, but there not all xylem elements conduct water. CRAFTS (1939) is of the opinion that on account of the abundance of water in the phloem walls (more than 50%) these also function as conducting elements. The greatest problem concerning flow in the sieve tubes is set by the sieve plates, about whose function there is not yet agreement.

In comparison with the total cross-section of herbaceous plants, the conducting elements mostly take a very modest place. About 50 mm from the tip of a wheat root the cross-section of the vessels plus central hollow space amounts to only 2·5% of the total area, of which the cortex occupies 83%.

MÜNCH (1930) collected large amounts of sap from partly detached strips of oak bark, and came to the conclusion that the phloem forms a connected system along its whole length. He believes that the sap in the sieve tubes has great mobility, but is often restricted by partial coagulation. Such a stoppage of the vessels can be caused even by cutting off opposite leaves (WENT and CARTER 1945). Even mechanical disturbances, e.g. bending by the wind, may also influence the phloem and the speed of sap conduction. The callus plugs easily formed at the sieve plates may have the function of preventing losses of sap after damage or functional disturbances. The sap usually contains much sugar and organic N-compounds. KRAUS found in cucumber sap 8·8% dry matter with 6%-9% sugars, 5·4% protein and much phosphate. In trees the sap contains mostly sugars, predominantly glucose, but in Quercus predominantly sucrose.

Later investigations and discussions on the function of the phloem (HUBER 1937, 1938, CRAFTS, 1938, 1939, ESAU 1939, 1954) have not led to any unified theory. SCHUMACHER (1930) showed that, if the sieve tubes are blocked by eosin, the transport of carbohydrate ceases. From this it definitely seems to follow that transport is through the lumen, and not, as CRAFTS formerly thought (see above), through the walls. Even if the pores of the sieve plates are in certain cases, e.g. in Cucurbita (CRAFTS 1932), probably narrower than had been supposed, they are nevertheless penetrated by proto-plasm, and one cannot therefore doubt the continuity of the system postulated by MÜNCH.

Support for the hypothesis of a free passage through the sieve tubes is given by investigations on the movement of viruses. Virus diseases are not found in gymno-sperms; but in angiosperms viruses accompany the carbohydrates. Differences in speed of transport of the carbohydrates, e.g. slower in tobacco and faster in sugar beet, occur also in movement of the virus. The transport of virus ceases with incisions into the phloem. This does not happen with auxin, which is conducted in the xylem

(WENT and CARTER 1945). The auxin, because of its low pK value (4·5-5·0), occurs preponderantly as anion and can therefore be transported also by the anion respiration (cf. Chap. 10).

Attempts have been made by various methods to measure the speed of transport in the phloem. Strikingly high values were observed, but the amounts transported mostly remain small. Speeds of 18 to 88 cm per hour have been measured, values which, according to MASON and MASKELL (1934), are about 40,000 times greater than could be caused by diffusion. It is therefore self-evident that the sieve tubes have available a special transport mechanism.

Several workers have thought of protoplasmic streaming as the agent of translocation. Others have objected that, whilst the protoplasm seldom streams more quickly than 0·3 mm per minute, the phloem flow shows values up to 10 mm per minute (CRAFTS 1939; according to ZIMMERMAN 1958 about 10 mm per minute in *Fraxinus*, according to SCHUMACHER 5·6, and according to SMALL 1939 only 0·13-1·0 in cucumber sieve tubes). It should be noted, however, that only the movement of microsomes, etc., has been measured; it is possible that the hyaloplasm flows more quickly. The differences found between protoplasmic streaming and sap flow, however, are considerable.

The often-observed division of protoplasmic streaming into strands with different directions of flow has also been applied to the differential transport of various substances, which has in fact been proved (SCARTH 1927). Direct investigations on the possible connection between protoplasmic streaming and translocation, however, yield no convincing evidence (see e.g. KOK 1931, 1933 on transport of lithium in leaves of *Vallisneria* and tentacles of *Drosera*). It is also worth noting that protoplasmic streaming occurs only in mature vacuolated cells, and not in primary meristem cells, where an active metabolism takes place. On the other hand the streaming in root hairs is certainly of importance for the metabolic relations between the nucleus and the growing tip (cf. p. 66).

VAN DEN HONERT (1932) directed attention by some model experiments to the extraordinarily rapid transport which can take place in the boundary layer between two immiscible fluids. In this the surface tension forces make themselves felt. VAN DEN HONERT found an acceleration to 68,000 times the speed of diffusion, i.e. somewhat more than was observed in the sieve tubes. It appears, however, dubious whether such coherent surface films occur actually in the sieve tubes. One might rather think of a surface flow along the protoplasmic surface layer, a hypothesis which may be combined with the idea of STRUGGER (1938) of conduction in the cell walls. One imagines the cell wall as a system of micro-capillaries with a diameter of 0·1-0·5 mμ (RUSKA 1940, on cotton fibres) in which, as long as the wall is young, solutions can flow fairly easily in the longitudinal direction. The lignified walls of the xylem, on the other hand, conduct water only with difficulty (LUNDEGÅRDH 1954). The high water content is in itself no evidence for high conductivity of the walls.

Some attention must be given to the attempts to explain the observed rapid sliding of molecules and ions over surfaces to which they are attached by weak bonds. The physicist LANGMUIR (1939) observed such rapid transport along monomolecular layers. MANGHAM (1917) imagined a conduction of sugar molecules through a medium which adsorbs sugar, with the molecules jumping from one adsorption position to the next as in a bicycle chain. On the other hand it can be contended that adsorption, according to all experience, has a retarding effect (KIDD 1917, CURTIS 1935). This applies primarily, however, to firmly adsorbed ions, e.g. heavy metal ions in the soil, protoplasm or inorganic colloids (LUNDEGÅRDH 1932, BURSTRÖM 1934). But in a loose exchangeable adsorption, as with the strongly hydrated light alkali ions, such a lateral movement along the adsorption points is quite conceivable (cf. Fig. 111, p. 254).

Ion exchange is also accelerated by thermal rotation of the carrier molecules, as was clearly described e.g. by LANGMUIR (1939) for monomolecular layers. Such rapid transports, to all appearances, play an important part in cation exchange between the medium and the root tissue; and here the fibrous molecules of proteins may well function as carriers. Even the active anion uptake is also connected with polar exchange processes.

Supporting the existence of a mass flow in the sieve tubes is the above-mentioned fact, that molecules of very different sizes, e.g. sugar and virus, are transported at equal speeds (cf. CRAFTS 1939, KÖHLER 1942); a pressure flow driven by active processes is here conceivable. Active transport of sugar molecules has been demonstrated in leaf tissue. A certain amount of water necessarily flows with the sugar molecules, and the pressure wave thus arising can press sap through the phloem. CURTIS (1935) is of the opinion that the osmotic pressure gradients for this would have to be 0·2 atm per cm (cf. MASON and PHILLIS 1941); this he finds unlikely. This objection is hypothetical, as we know nothing definite about the pressure gradients. Moreover, neither CURTIS nor MÜNCH takes into account the high pressures which an exuded sap can develop (cf. p. 283). Those active processes which bring about sugar absorption in the meristem, for example, may also affect the gradients.

A theoretical difficulty for the theory of mass flow is the fate of the water which flows continuously into the meristems and which must be removed somewhere or other. It might be imagined that the water accompanies the respiratory CO_2, which does indeed make its way to the surface of the organs. The role of CO_2 in the osmotically caused flow of water through the plant has up to now been completely neglected.

The modified pressure- and suction-flow hypothesis put forward here should of course not conceal the problem of translocation in different directions. To a certain extent xylem and phloem certainly work together. The stream of water rising in the xylem can carry with it organic compounds which are synthesised in the roots, whilst other organic compounds, e.g. sugars, flow downwards at the same time in the phloem. It is also reported that in the leaf stalk nitrogen compounds and carbohydrates migrate in opposite directions (FISCHER 1936; in many cases inorganic and organic nitrogen were not clearly distinguished). Opposite flows could also proceed in the internal and external phloem (ROUSCHAL 1941). The phloem would then behave like a telephone cable, which of course would be conceivable only for a living tissue and not e.g. for the wood.

MASON and PHILLIS (1941) have objected against the older mass-flow hypothesis of MÜNCH, etc., that experience shows oxygen to be necessary, which suggests the collaboration of active processes. This objection, however, does not affect the train of reasoning developed above, in which an active impulse plays a decisive role. The active osmotic process in the xylem, in which inorganic salts are the main thing carried, is anion respiration. Organic compounds, which get into the xylem, can, however, be carried along passively. The active processes in the phloem flow are, above all, those which are connected with production, uptake, absorption or consumption of organic materials. The phloem flow can of course also carry inorganic salts along with it passively (cf. GUSTAFSON 1939).

STOUT and HOAGLAND (1939), in their investigations with radioactive isotopes, found that salts are conducted mainly in the transpiration stream and thence move secondarily into the cambium and bark. When the xylem is removed, however, the phloem can transport small amounts of salts. For phosphoric acid also the xylem is the normal transport route, and in accordance with this one finds that radioactive phosphorus is transported through a killed section of the stem (RABIDEAU and BURR 1945). On the other hand ^{14}C which is incorporated in organic compounds cannot traverse such a zone; for this therefore the phloem is necessary.

During the transport of assimilates downwards from the leaves organically bound phosphoric acid naturally accompanies the other organic compounds. It is also believed that the downward transport of inorganic salts before yellowing in autumn is also provided for by the phloem (cf. PHILLIS and MASON 1941). Dual directions of flow in the xylem are, as shown above, difficult to imagine. The return flow of salts in autumn can be quite considerable. After having been well fertilised, leaves of radishes exude large amounts of potassium and also phosphate (according to EPERJESSY 1941, up to 120 mg per 100 g of leaves).

3 BLEEDING AND GUTTATION

We have described the rising active (i.e. independent of transpiration) sap stream as a flow under pressure driven by anion respiration. In conformity with this the bleeding phenomenon is strongly dependent on the aeration of the soil and on the supply of carbohydrates to the roots.

The importance of aeration has been dealt with by ARNON and HOAGLAND (1940) and others. These workers mention that with tomatoes the same yields were obtained from soil-, sand- or water-cultures, provided that adequate aeration was supplied. The diurnal periodicity of the bleeding was related in many cases to the diurnal rise and fall in photosynthesis (HUBER et al. 1937). According to TOPCUOGLU (1940) sieve tube bleeding shows a minimum about midday and is quicker in the afternoon. For similar reasons the adsorption of mineral substances diminishes after ringing of the stem, as a result of the arrest of the downward flow of carbohydrates (MASON and PHILLIS 1945). The decrease in mineral salt uptake during heavy fruit formation and its increase after the removal of the fruits can also be related to the improved carbohydrate supply to the roots in the later period (EATON and JOHAM 1944).

Active transport, as emphasised above, is not restricted only to individual organs, e.g. roots. Phloem bleeding can also be observed in isolated twigs or fruits (TAMMES 1933, JAMES and BAKER 1933). This suggests a certain activity in the whole length of the phloem system. Here one may refer also to the numerous lateral contacts with living parenchyma, even when the phloem is partly screened off by sclerenchymatous sheaths or plates. A capacity for polar transport is, however, characteristic of almost every cell.

The sap streams flowing through the conducting tissues represent typical long-distance transport, but diversions pass out from each leaf and each twig attachment. These branchings always end in parenchymatous tissue, into which the sap stream is led by a combination of pressure from the supplying organs and suction from the receiving organs. The surplus 'extra water' of the rising sap stream usually disappears in the transpiration of the leaves. Transpiration also assists further concentration of the sap, which explains why the salt content of strongly transpiring leaves is usually high (see Chap. 8). Under these conditions no positive hydrostatic pressure develops in the xylem, but rather a weak negative pressure is caused by the transpiration suction.

The positive hydrostatic pressure in the xylem of birch trees in spring (cf. Fig. 133) falls to zero at the time of bud break and in summer changes to a negative pressure of -200 mm of mercury (LUNDEGÅRDH 1954, p. 91). In *Tilia europea*, which at no time shows any noteworthy pressure in the xylem sap, tensions to -80 mm of mercury have been measured in summer. *Quercus robur* behaves similarly.

In some trees and in many herbs the active xylem stream usually leaks through the hydathodes or in other ways if transpiration is restricted; this is the guttation phenomenon. Guttation occurs in almost all plants (FREY-WYSSLING 1941), although with different intensities. It can be caused in certain plants, which normally show no guttation, by warming the soil above the air temperature (GÄUMANN 1938). The explanation of this is to be sought in an increase in the rate of anion respiration ($Q_{10} = 2$-$2 \cdot 5$). A sudden big fall in temperature (e.g. $15°$) evokes a cold shock which has been observed under similar conditions in leaves and which temporarily stops guttation.

The connection of guttation with the active salt transport in the root may be seen from the fact that it does not occur if nutrients are deficient, but on supply of easily mobile ions, such as NO_3, H_2PO_4 or K, it again increases (RALEIGH 1946). Ions not easily mobile, such as Ca and Mg, have small effect.

The composition of the guttation fluid can deviate considerably from that of the bleeding sap (SCHMIDT 1930), which may usually be connected with the fact that during the passage of the sap through the plant salts can be given up to neighbouring tissue and conversely organic materials can be secreted into it (cf. LUNDEGÅRDH 1945). For the supply of salts by the roots the medium is only indirectly responsible, i.e. as ultimate supplier. The active accumulation in the vacuoles and the internal exudation are the processes directly concerned; this is why the sap stream of well-nourished wheat roots carries the easily transportable ions K^+ and NO_3^- for a considerable time, even when only distilled water is present externally.

ANDERSEN (1929) analysed the tracheal sap of birch trees and compared the values with those of soil extracts. In May he obtained the following values (in milligrams per kilogram of sap or extract):

Table 15

	Ca	Mg	K	Fe	SO$_4$	PO$_4$
In the soil extract	18·0	7·2	140·9	1·8	37·2	1·0
In the tracheal sap	84·7	23·5	59·6	2·1	31·8	25·2

Thus certain ions are more strongly accumulated than others, although the ratios found are different from those in wheat, where K and NO_3 dominate. Other plants also differ from wheat (cf. for example SABININ 1925). Individual differences have similarly been observed in the comparison of the tracheal sap with the guttation fluid. CURTIS (1935) found approximately the same ratios in both, whereas in the guttation fluid of maize WILSON (1923) found many organic substances, chiefly organic acids, but also sugars and enzymes.

In other cereal plants also the guttation fluid, unlike the bleeding sap, contains organic materials. From barley plants six days old a guttation fluid was collected which contained $0.7\%_0$ of dry substance. Salts amounted to only $0.16\%_0$, whereas $0.54\%_0$ was organic substances, of which $0.14\%_0$ was sucrose and $0.01\%_0$ reducing sugars. The low salts content of the guttation fluid is striking. In two series of experiments the bleeding sap contained 14-21 millimoles per litre of KNO_3, whereas the guttation fluid showed only 0.3 millimole per litre of this substance.

This removal of salts from the rising sap stream is of course due to absorption by the tissues passed through, and provides clear evidence for the important function of the rising sap stream as the supplier of salts to the aerial parts. As the ion content in the leaves is considerably higher than that in the rising sap (e.g. 174 millimoles per litre of K and 23 millimoles per litre of NO_3), a very active absorption of salts by the leaves must be assumed. In conformity with what has been said above, this increases still further the pressure stream coming from the roots.

The organic substances entering the rising sap during its passage through the leaves originate from the leaf mesophyll. The mesophyll cells of young leaves are arranged to absorb salts and conversely to give up assimilates. The results found seem to indicate that the assimilates do not migrate only through plasmodesmata, but at least partly also through the cell walls. On this account, when transpiration is arrested, some assimilates are caught up by the guttation stream before reaching the phloem. When transpiration is fast, secretion at the surface of the leaves is prevented by the presence of the cuticle.

The alternative explanation, that the assimilates may be actively secreted into the rising stream, is difficult to defend. On the basis of the 'valve mechanism' postulated by PHILLIS, MASON, CURTIS et al., the assimilates are actively sucked into the companion cells of the phloem. They therefore almost completely escape being drawn off by the transpiration stream, which indeed takes other paths than the guttation stream. From this point of view it is to be expected that the leaf excretions observed in certain halophytes and xerophytes should contain little organic material but on the other hand much NaCl, lime, etc. These of course originate from salts in the rising sap stream which were not consumed on the way.

D. The Metabolism of Phosphorus and Sulphur

Phosphoric acid is usually taken up as the mobile univalent ion $H_2PO_4^-$, but the phosphate ion, unlike the nitrate ion, undergoes no reduction. The phosphorus maintains its oxidation form and is incorporated as the phosphoric acid group into phosphatides, phospholipids, phosphoproteins, nucleotides, etc., which play a leading part in metabolism.

The fairly strong dissociation of phosphoric acid is usually increased in organic combination. Along with the carboxyl group, phosphoric acid groups must play an important part in the formation and maintenance of the acidoid properties of the amphoteric protoplasm, and electronegative surface potentials, etc. In addition phosphoric acid has the extraordinarily important property of being able by oxidative or photosynthetic phosphorylation to change the steric linkage of O and P in such a way that the molecular energy is increased.

The general and special importance of high-energy phosphates has been described in detail in Chapter 4. By means of these 'packets of energy' reaction barriers which would otherwise be difficult to overcome are surmounted, and a number of endergonic syntheses are made possible which would not happen without them. A leading role in this regulated transfer of energy between cytochrome respiration and synthesis is played by the adenosine phosphates (ADP and ATP), and also by metaphosphates and pyrophosphates as intermediate products.

Part of the phosphoric acid absorbed in the roots is worked up *in situ* to organic P-compounds necessary for its own growth. Quantitatively, however, this activity is subordinate to that of N-metabolism, possibly because the amounts of phosphoric acid necessary for energy transfer are fairly small due to the cyclic character of the processes. Actually, rather large amounts of inorganic phosphate are usually absorbed, and a fair proportion appears to be metabolised directly. In six hours 14%-27% of the nitrate taken up by wheat roots disappeared as organic compounds; the remainder was transported upwards with the xylem sap. In the same time 24%-31% of the inorganic phosphate taken up was fixed in organic compounds, and the remainder found in the sap. The actual amount of nitrogen metabolised was ten times greater than the amount of phosphate. The elaboration of nitrate is closely connected with glucose metabolism (cf. p. 226), whereas phosphate fixation is more independent (cf. LUNDEGÅRDH 1945, p. 67).

The absorbed inorganic phosphate, as already stated, is passed as such into the xylem. The phosphate may often be similarly transported between leaves and fruits in the inorganic form. One finds, e.g. in grass seeds, an almost complete equivalence between the amounts of K and PO_4; which suggests transport as monopotassium phosphate. The ease with which even large excesses of phosphoric acid are stored in the green organs of grasses (LUNDEGÅRDH 1932, 1941) similarly suggests a strong accumulation in the cell sap. It is known that the inorganic phosphates contribute effectively to the buffering of the cell sap against changes in pH.

Phosphoric acid is an important component of many enzymes, e.g. pyridine nucleotide -enzymes and carboxylase. The coenzyme effective in the last, thiamine pyrophosphate is also very important as a plant hormone. It has been shown (LUNDEGÅRDH 1943) that added thiamine stimulates the germination of certain seeds only if phosphoric acid is supplied simultaneously. As general mineral nutrients, meta- and pyrophosphates appear to have the same effects as orthophosphate, according to WEISSFLOG and MENGDEHL (1933).

The metabolism of *sulphur* shows great similarity to that of nitrogen, in that the sulphur atom as such enters directly into organic linkages. In addition, however, sulphur, like phosphorus, can also enter as an acid radical, viz. as sulphate, e.g. chondroitin sulphates, about whose occurrence in plants, however, little is known.

WOOD and BARRIEN (1939) regarded the following as probable metabolic sulphur compounds: inorganic sulphate, 'conjugated' or ethereal sulphates like phenol sulphonic acids, sulphur-containing proteins, the two sulphur-containing amino acids cystëine and methionine, and glutathione. Of these, according to certain data (MOTHES and SPECHT) the steric sulphates may form a kind of sulphur reserve in plants, which however is an assumption not yet confirmed. Cyclic S—S-compounds play an important part as regulators of the redox state of many enzymes (cf. Chap. 4; GILBERT 1951, PIRSON 1955).

The main source of sulphur for higher plants is the sulphate ion, of which, as with nitrate and phosphate, a certain part is metabolised in the root itself (KYLIN and

HYLMÖ 1957). How the incorporation of the sulphur into the S-containing proteins takes place is not quite clear. It appears, however, that the first step must be the reduction of SO_4 to SH. The reaction series $SO_4 \rightarrow S + 2O_2$ needs about 118 kg-cal. This reaction is well known also for sulphate-reducing bacteria, in which the necessary energy is obtained by oxidation of carbohydrates.

Cystëine is, according to WOOD and BARRIEN, the sulphur-containing component of proteins, but not its oxidation product cystine, which is easily formed *in vitro*. According to the investigations of LAMPEN *et al.* (1947) certain strains of *Escherichia coli* show differences in their sulphur metabolism. Some strains lack the ability to reduce SO_4 to SO_3, whereas in others the step from SO_3 to S is deficient. A blocking of the production of trioses for the formation of cystëine from reduced sulphur can also occur.

The investigations of WOOD and BARRIEN show that there is a definite relationship between protein nitrogen and protein sulphur. The contents of sulphur-free amino acids and of cystëine therefore run parallel. Only in acute sulphur deficiency does addition of sulphate lead to an increase in the content of organic sulphur. Increased formation of cystëine, on the other hand, follows increased supply of ammonia; so ammonia may be the limiting factor which regulates the metabolism of sulphur.

In the hydrolytic or oxidative catabolism of the sulphur-containing amino acids, the sulphur finds its way back to the sulphate stage. One can easily imagine, as with ammonia, a steady state maintained by exergonic processes between sulphate and proteins. If the sulphate supply has sunk so far that an actual deficiency arises, amino acid formation can indeed continue for a period; but it finally ceases and a pile-up of carbohydrates and nitrate nitrogen occurs in the tissues (NIGHTINGALE *et al.* 1932). Because of the active sulphate cycle by way of soil micro-organisms and adsorption on the soil colloids, however, an actual sulphate deficiency can seldom occur in nature. It should also be stated that the uptake of nitrogen and sulphur is modified by phosphate deficiency (STREBEYKO 1938).

E. Ionic Antagonism

Investigations of LOEB (1906), OSTERHOUT (1906, 1908) and HANSTEEN-CRANNER (1910) showed that pure solutions of NaCl or KCl injured or even killed algae and young wheat plants, whereas the same solutions with small additions of $CaCl_2$ were readily tolerated.

This phenomenon indicates the importance of maintaining a certain quantitative balance between different cations, to preserve the normal functions of the protoplasm. In many later investigations (literature survey in LUNDEGÅRDH 1932, 1945, 1957, PIRSCHLE 1930, 1932, BARBIER 1936, EISELBERG 1937 *et al.*) attention was directed more to those aspects of ionic antagonism which relate to salt absorption. These effects are termed *competitive*.

Antagonistic or competitive effects exist between most ions (see also BURSTRÖM 1934), e.g. between K^+ and Ca^{++} or Mg^{++} and Na^+; between Ca^{++} and K^+, Na^+, Mg^{++} and Mn^{++}; between Mn^{++} on the one hand and K^+ and Ca^{++} on the other; between NH_4^+ and Ca^{++}; between Ca^{++} and H^+; etc. That the antagonism between Ca and K has occupied the foreground of interest is due to the key position of these ions in the metabolism both of plants and animals. For the correct functioning of cells fairly large amounts are usually necessary, especially of potassium (about the importance of calcium see also NIGHTINGALE 1931, KERSTING-MUNSTER 1938). In the animal organism, the antagonism between Ca and Na is most important.

Ionic antagonism has until now been studied in detail mainly in cations. Antagonism, however, occurs also between anions. Among these, however, it is in general less pronounced, which may be connected with the active uptake mechanism. Anions, however, also undergo an initial absorption before they are taken up into the mechanism of anion respiration (cf. p. 263), and in this primary stage competitive exchange, of course, occurs, similar to that affecting cations (Fig. 139, p. 303).

The known cases of anion antagonism, however, are restricted to ions which poison metabolism, i.e. the antagonism affects especially chemical combination in the protoplasm. Such antagonisms have been found, e.g. with SO_4^{--} and SeO_4^{--} (HURD-KARRER 1938: Fig. 136), NO_3^- and ClO_3^- (ÅBERG 1947); phosphate and arsenate (Fig. 137); etc. The investigations made by ÅBERG on the antagonism between nitrate and chlorate are of special interest in this connection.

It follows from the examples given that antagonism between cations usually operates in both directions; the calcium ion influences the effects of the potassium ion, and conversely the potassium ion influences the effects of the calcium ion. As a manifestation of an ionic antagonism, the earlier workers took the overall state of the organism, ordinarily the growth. The ionic effects were thought of as colloidal effects. Usually they were thought to be localised at the cell surface or organ surface. Only after the uptake and spread of ions inside the plant body had been investigated in greater detail, was it recognised that antagonistic phenomena occur also internally influencing, for example, the speed of transport of the ions between different organs. Later cell-physiological investigations finally revealed the fact that ionic antagonism was felt not only in the surface of individual cells but also in the protoplasm.

Antagonistic phenomena occur also between anions and cations. These, however, belong to a special category, since here ionic charge and chemical competition play a more subordinate part. These phenomena are developed in connection with metabolism and are suitably described as *pseudo-antagonisms*. We will restrict ourselves in this section to ionic antagonism itself.

A pre-condition of true ionic antagonism is the amphoteric dissociation of the protoplasm and the reversible linkage of ions depending on it, above all of small inorganic

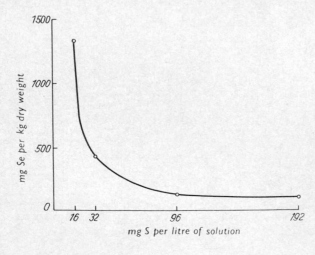

Fig. 136. Antagonism between sulphate and selenate anions. The abscissa gives the sulphur content of the nutrient solution and the ordinate gives the amounts of selenium taken up (Se-content of the solution is constant).

ions, of which the positive ions are most important in the surface layer. Furthermore, cation adsorption is less dependent on respiration than anion adsorption is (LUNDE-GÅRDH 1958).

As ion exchange is regulated by the charge and the hydration of the ions (cf. Chap. 1, E 6) the antagonism, considered physico-chemically, is an expression of the principle of mass action. The ionic activity, however, in these processes is influenced to a high degree by the specific power of combination. Calcium ions, for example, are

Fig. 137. Anion antagonism between phosphate and arsenate. The toxic effect of the arsenate is completely eliminated by a 20-fold supply of phosphate. 1. Control 2. Arsenate 250 mg per kg of soil. 3. Same amount of arsenate $+5$ g per kg of phosphate. 4. 5 g per kg of phosphate only (after L. FREDRIKSSON).

usually fixed more firmly than potassium ions in the protoplasmic membrane (cf. MAZIA 1940) or in the surface layer between protoplasm and cell wall. This fact explains why even small concentrations of calcium influence the effect of potassium ions. The stronger fixation of the Ca-ion is also reflected in the slowness with which the surface potential of the roots is changed, if a calcium salt is exchanged for a potassium salt, instead of the reverse (Fig. 138).

The especially strong fixation of the heavy metal ions such as Cu, Pb and Hg makes the antagonistic protective effect of lighter ions more difficult, even when these are supplied in high concentrations. Such antagonism probably affects the uptake of many trace elements. It should however be remembered that no element, even when it is supplied in great excess, can completely exclude the uptake of another element. For example, the weakly adsorbable rubidium is taken up although it occurs in the soil only in very low concentrations. One can therefore state that the protoplasmic surface always shows the same assortment of cations as the medium, although the quantitative relations of the individual elements may be very different.

The exchange of ions in the cell surface is only the first phase of ion uptake. Naturally it always has an important effect on the mass relations of the elements finally taken up, but further modifications occur during the successive adsorptions on the ion-carriers in the inner protoplasm. Anion respiration also contributes to this sieve effect, especially as it accelerates the transport of mobile ions. The strong retention of heavy and more adsorbable ions manifests itself in protoplasm and whole tissues just as in soil colloids.

Ionic effects on the swelling of the protoplasm of plant and animal cells, investigated by several workers, show clearly that ionic antagonism occurs throughout the protoplasm. The 'cap plasmolysis' described by HÖFLER may e.g. be connected with the strong hydration due to unbalanced alkali ions, for example K^+. On addition of calcium ions the swelling is reversed. The antagonism of $Ca^{++} \rightleftarrows H^+$ can explain certain observations on root-hair growth (LUNDEGÅRDH 1946). In this purely chemical processes interfere, because calcium pectate, whose formation is inhibited by H^+, is necessary for wall formation (cf. Chap. 2). The boundary between the purely chemical effects of cations, e.g. on the solubility of organic salts, and their more colloid-chemical effects is, as already emphasised, indefinite.

Changing the hydration of the protoplasmic colloids also affects their dissociation, and ionic antagonism is thus reflected in the surface potentials. For example, treating wheat roots with dilute potassium salt solutions induces a considerable reduction in potential. On addition of calcium salts the potential again rises. Continuous recording of the surface potential of the roots shows that there are also alterations in the internal plasma (cf. Fig. 138). Whilst the ion exchange $Ca \rightleftarrows K$ at the surface and the effect of calcium on the cell wall are complete in a few seconds, it takes about 1-3 minutes before the calcium ion evokes a change in dissociation of the surface. This can be explained only by the calcium ions first penetrating into the ground mass of the protoplasm before their chemical effect, the increase in dissociation, can take place, as a result of which the surface potential rises.

The increases in the surface potential of roots which are observed on addition of small amounts of Mn^{++} and of H_3BO_3 are probably similar to those with calcium. The chemical effects of ionic antagonism are also clear in the universal increase of respiration which follows treatment with Ca ions in place of K ions (LUNDEGÅRDH 1937, VIETS 1944). It may be that changes in respiration are evoked by the exchange of

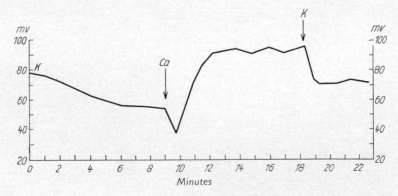

Fig. 138. Change in the negative root potential after exchange of K^+ or Ca^{++}. K^+ causes a slow (about 6 minute) decrease in the potential, but Ca^{++} a somewhat faster (3-4 minute) increase. The very rapid decrease of the potential during the first seconds following the change of solution illustrates the ion exchange in the cytoplasmic surface. The slower changes illustrate the reactions of the whole protoplasm.

Ca, Mg or Mn ions, which are effective in the enzyme systems as coenzymes or activators, against ineffective alkali cations. Such effects are also observed in nitrate assimilation.

Though the biological effects of cation antagonism may depend on the competitive intervention of the ions in the chemistry of the protoplasm, the phenomenon is nevertheless in the main one of ion exchange in the protoplasm as a whole. The functions of protoplasm are to a large extent dependent on the supply of a number of cations which are termed either *essential elements* or *trace elements*. A balanced nutrient solution should thus contain a selection of these elements in such ratios that phenomena of ionic antagonism are avoided.

The absorbing surface of the root is of course, as far as ion exchange and ionic balance are concerned, directly dependent on the composition of the medium. In the inner layers of root tissues even the specific speed of migration has an effect. For example, potassium ions move more quickly than calcium ions which go faster than manganous or ferric ions, and so on; and thus a different ionic balance is maintained inside the root from that at the surface. As a result of this the concentration of certain ions, e.g. K^+ and NO_3^-, increases relatively strongly in the rising sap stream. Other quantitative differences are also found in the distribution among the remaining plant organs of the salts transported over a distance.

It may therefore be said that the ionic balance in the surface layer influences the total uptake of salts, but that the further distribution of these can be compared with a selective filtration. The easily mobile ions consequently press forward and the less mobile lag increasingly behind. The importance of the long-distance transport unobstructed by diffusion barriers in the conducting tissue must lie not least in the fact that it limits selective ion filtration to organs in which the sap flows through parenchyma. As an example of the differences in the selection of ions which occur in the roots and the green parts of oat plants, a number of analyses are given in Table 16.

In the series reproduced in Table 16 the concentrations of calcium, magnesium and manganese were thus the same throughout; only the concentration of potassium was varied within wide limits. It was found that the uptake of potassium increased strongly with the concentration, but that this, in conformity with the mobility of the element

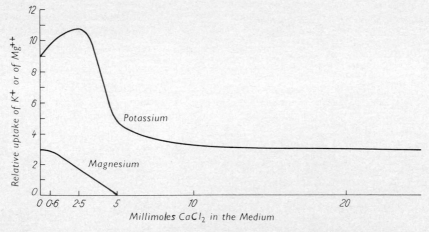

Fig. 139. Ionic antagonism between calcium and potassium or magnesium. The experiments were carried out with seedlings of wheat. In the Ca-K series the basal solution was 0·01 M KCl. To the basal solutions increasing amounts of $CaCl_2$ were added (after LUNDEGÅRDH 1932).

Table 16

The Cation Content in Milligram Atom %* in Shoots and Roots of Oat Plants, which were cultivated with increasing supplies of Potassium Nitrate in complete Nutrient Solution. Analyses at the time of flowering.

Nutrient solution + (g KNO₃ per litre)	K		Ca		Mg		Mn		K × Ca	
	R**	S***	R	S	R	S	R	S	R	S
0·00	27	58	8·4	13·7	4·7	19·3	1·00	1·63	230	800
0·05	45	57	7·1	12·3	10·6	15·8	0·90	1·26	320	700
0·20	41	83	9·2	13·8	9·0	21·9	0·48	1·07	380	1070
0·50	33	100	12·6	9·8	8·4	21·6	0·32	0·75	420	980
1·50	22	104	29·7	8·9	13·3	23·4	0·29	0·45	650	920
3·00	16	164	37·8	5·1	13·7	27·1	0·46	0·43	600	820
6·00	14	227	36·2	4·0	12·1	22·7	0·32	0·46	510	910

* This means milligram atoms per 100 g dry weight.
** = root.
*** = haulm + leaves.

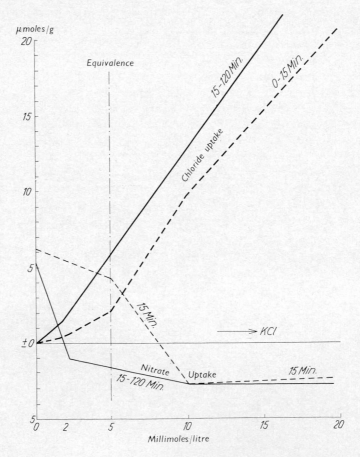

Fig. 140. Ionic antagonism between nitrate and chloride in salt uptake of wheat roots. The basal solution is 0·005 M KNO₃ with supplementary additions of KCl. There is a depression of the uptake of Cl about the point of equivalance. There is a depression of nitrate uptake increasing with Cl-concentration and finally release of the native nitrate of the cells.

as an ion, became evident only in the green parts. This concentration of potassium in the shoots antagonised their calcium content, which finally sank to one-third of the original.

The converse result, surprising at first sight, that the calcium content of the roots rises continuously when the KNO_3-content of the medium is increased, is explained by the fact that NO_3-ions usually move faster than K ions and consequently carry other cations with them also. The transport-increasing properties of the nitrate ions have often been observed (cf. BURSTRÖM 1937).

In an antagonistic exchange between two cations M_1^+ and M_2^+ it has been observed that the product $M_1^+ \cdot M_2^+$ usually assumes an approximately constant value, even when the ratio between the components changes markedly. HOAGLAND (1923, 1928), LOEHWING et al. noted the tendency to a constant value of the product of $K \cdot Ca$. The phenomenon was studied in the greatest detail by BURSTRÖM (1934). In the Table the mean variation of the ionic product $K \cdot Ca$ in the shoot is only about $\pm 5\%$ about the average value of 890, although the absolute contents of K and Ca vary by as much as 400%.

This tendency for the antagonism $K \rightleftarrows Ca$ to maintain an approximately constant ionic product in the organs suggests a very simple law in the initial adsorption, viz. the following:

$$[K] \cdot [Ca] = \text{constant}$$

If the concentration of one ion is doubled, the concentration of the other ion is halved, and so on. Hence it may be supposed that potassium and calcium are bound with about the same intensity to the carrier ion R^-, since a sudden change in the antagonism occurs at about the same concentration of both (cf. below). Whether this regularity is valid for adsorption on inorganic colloids is not known with certainty; but certain observations suggest that it is (cf. BURSTRÖM 1934). If two antagonistic ions are adsorbed with unequal intensity, the equation must take a different form, as then an adsorption exponent (a) has to be introduced (cf. also LUNDEGÅRDH 1941).

We have assumed that an adsorption equilibrium at the cation carriers determines the occurrence of the constant ionic product $K \cdot Ca$. From this it follows that K and Ca are adsorbed competitively on the same carrier. In adsorption on different carriers the phenomenon of true antagonism disappears. One can also conclude from this that, wherever ionic antagonism has been observed, identical cation carriers are present. It has been mentioned that only with sodium is antagonism not found, and this may be due to the presence of specific sodium carriers.

Since the total content of potassium and calcium in a tissue by no means remains adsorbed exclusively on the cation carriers of the protoplasm, but is largely lodged in the cell sap, one must conclude from the actual observations that the initial adsorption in the protoplasm determines the movement into the cell sap. We have shown in section A that, as far as the active transfer of salt anions is concerned, the initial adsorption, in this case on the carriers R^+, largely determines the intensity of accumulation. The theory of anion respiration further states that the actively accumulated anions release the cations from their adsorption bonds (to the carriers R^-), so that, in the main, neutral salts are stored in the cell sap. With equal exchangeability, K and Ca must therefore be accumulated in about the same proportions in the cell sap as they are originally adsorbed in the protoplasm; from which the observed total balance between K and Ca follows.

BURSTRÖM (1934) observed in his studies on ionic antagonism that the concentration ratio of the competing cations in the medium markedly influences the ionic product within the organ. He found a characterstic break near the point of equivalence. The ionic product remained almost constant with $[K] < [Ca]$, but with $[K] \geqslant [Ca]$ it changed to a different value, which again remained almost constant as long as K showed an excess over Ca.

We find such an inversion in Table 16 for the ionic product $K \cdot Ca$ in the roots. Between the concentration values 0·20 and 1·50 g/l KNO_3 in the medium, i.e. when the ratio K/Ca changes from $\leqslant 1$ to > 1, the product $K \cdot Ca$ in the root suddenly increases from about 300 to about 600. For the theoretical explanation of the inversion in the value of the ionic product occurring at the equivalence point we restrict ourselves here to the following observations. Under steady conditions the absolute concentration of the cation carriers of the total protoplasm of an organ remains almost constant. The antagonistic cations react with this constant amount of carrier R^- competitively. A sudden change in the ionic product, e.g. in the neighbourhood of the 'equivalence point', appears to be explicable only by the number of cation carriers changing e.g. by an inversion of the dissociation of H^+R^-.

Ionic antagonism influences to a high degree the rate of uptake of the individual ions. Whilst in single salt solutions, e.g. KCl, the uptake follows a more or less convex curve rising with the concentration, this changes into an S-shaped curve if the concentration of an antagonistic ion rises simultaneously (cf. Fig. 139). If nutrient ions are concerned, an optimum curve of growth results (cf. Chap. 7). In the multilateral combination of different cations in a complete nutrient solution the antagonistic phenomena of course become very complicated. One can also easily observe in natural substrates the effects of the antagonism between K and Ca and between K and Mn. These antagonisms have considerable ecological and agricultural importance, and they occur both in higher plants and e.g. in unicellular algae (*Chlorella*; PIRSON 1937).

The more detailed study of antagonism has, as already mentioned, led to a correct understanding of its nature. It is undoubtedly based on the fact that the cations, and also to a large extent the anions, of the neutral salts are exchangeably combined in the general protoplasm. Antagonism is certainly not a mere surface phenomenon. From this it follows that the salt uptake, whose introductory phase is also the initial adsorption, depends to a high degree on the general state of the protoplasm. This in its turn is determined by biochemical processes, such as the disturbances in the ionic balance mentioned at the beginning, which occur in the absence of an essential ion. Active potassium uptake by a wheat root ceases if it remains for long in a pure KCl solution. The K uptake recommences, however, after a small amount of calcium ions are added. Calcium is thus an indispensable 'lubricant' of the protoplasmic machinery. One can consequently say that a minimum of ionic balance has the effect of maintaining normal protoplasmic functions, including the formation of ionic carriers.

Only with somewhat greater additions of calcium does actual ion antagonism of $K \rightleftarrows Ca$ begin. This boundary between biochemical ionic effects and ionic antagonism is to be seen from the shape of the curve in Fig. 139. The boundary may of course lie higher or lower according to the type of plant. OLSEN (1942) observed, e.g. in *Sinapis*, *Dianthus* and *Hordeum*, antagonism between K and Ca only at fairly equal concentrations. With *Tussilago farfara* on the other hand the antagonism $Ca \rightarrow K$ first occurred only with fairly high K-concentrations. Only by carefully arranged experiments can one distinguish to what extent deviations from the general plan of antagonism are due to biochemical ionic effects or to deviations of concentration connected with the speed of migration of the ions.

The importance of the ionic balance for the maintenance of certain properties of the protoplasmic membrane is shown by shifts in the balance being reflected in the permeability for non-electrolytes e.g. sugars. It is usually thought that such alterations are connected with hydration, and so with the permeability of pores as influenced by the adsorption of salts and ions.

F. The Distribution of Mineral Substances in the Plant. Pseudo-antagonism

The distribution of mineral substances is due to the following factors: (1) ion uptake by the roots, (2) conduction of sap, (3) specific absorption capacity of the organs.

Transpiration shows no pronounced specific influence, but it undoubtedly contributes to the long-distance transport of salts, since the passive transpiration stream elutes the salts that the roots actively accumulate (cf. also HUBER 1941-2, BROYER and HOAGLAND 1943, LUNDEGÅRDH 1954, 1958). The greater salt content of sun leaves as compared with shade leaves may thus possibly be due to their stronger transpiration.

The roots modify at the start the relations between the mineral substances taken up. In addition to ionic antagonism, some ions, e.g. Na, are blocked by the specificity of the ion carriers making itself felt. These ions are, so to speak, filtered off. In the first place ions without intrinsic biological function are to some extent rejected for various reasons, such as strong hydration, and are only weakly adsorbed. WALTER and STEINER (1936) were surprised by the virtual absence of NaCl in the sap stream of certain halophytes, e.g. mangrove. This phenomenon may be due to the fact that Na and Cl stay outside because of their weak exchangeability; but it is difficult to avoid the assumption of actual blocking. The small combining power of sodium is illustrated by the fact that BURSTRÖM (1934) was not able to evoke an antagonistic effect of Ca on Na.

There is furthermore a clear parallelism between the speed of migration in colloidal media and the distribution of ions in the plant. This problem was investigated in cereals by LUNDEGÅRDH (1932) and BURSTRÖM (1934, 1937). During the sprouting of Sambucus shoots RIPPEL (1923, 1926) found potassium more mobile than calcium and magnesium. Similar results have been communicated also by other workers (e.g. JAMES 1930, 1940).

In cereal plants potassium is distributed in such a way that the largest amount is stored in the haulm. Calcium accumulates chiefly in the roots and leaves. The same is true, although to a lesser degree, of magnesium. The smallest percentage amount is accumulated in the seeds. There is a slight excess of magnesium over calcium and potassium.

The distribution of potassium reflects the great mobility of the potassium ion. The percentage content of this element in the younger developmental stages is about the same in the haulm and in the leaves; calcium on the other hand is stored much more strongly in the leaves. These relations may be connected with the sap flow: the salts are first carried into the leaves, to be later transferred back from these partly into the fruits and, at later developmental stages, again into the roots. Non-mobile ions, i.e.

x

calcium and to a still higher degree manganese and iron, lag behind. The partially irreversible absorption of the bi- or multi-valent ions, as sparingly soluble oxidation products or salts, also contributes to the fixing of these ions during transport, e.g. in the leaves.

Leaves usually get an excess of metallic cations, since the rising sap stream contains nitrates, of which the anion is consumed in protein formation. Of the remaining anions, phosphate, like potassium, is distributed in about the same concentration between haulm and leaves. A strong concentration of phosphate, however, takes place in the fruits, which is made possible by the easy mobility of $H_2PO_4^-$ associated with K^+. In the fruits organic phosphate compounds are synthesised.

A similar distribution of the mineral substances to that described here for cereals is found also in many other plants. In sugar beet, for example, enormous amounts of potassium are accumulated in the leaves, whereas the K-content of the roots remains low even in maturity. On the other hand the calcium content of the roots is here comparatively high—usually about half the potassium content. In the leaves on the other hand there is about 3-5 times as much K as Ca. The leaves also show on ageing a strong shift towards an excess of calcium. It should be noted that with an unbalanced supply of nutrients considerable shifts in all these distributions can arise.

The pseudo-antagonism mentioned in the foregoing section (p. 300) can have various causes. The simplest are the mutual effects which go back to transport relationships, e.g. the favourable or inhibiting influence of the NO_3 and SO_4 ions on the cation transport. An apparent antagonism of NO_3 towards heavy metals, e.g. Mn^{++}, arises through the fact that nitrate favours growth and consequently extends the transport route for other ions. (Fig. 142 and LUNDEGÅRDH 1931-2). This is by far the most outstanding cause of the occurrence of manganese deficiency symptoms in nitrate fertilisation. Another form of the same 'metabolic antagonism' is shown when the presence of certain ions introduces processes which hinder the uptake of other nutrients. A potassium uptake beyond the optimum can thus inhibit the uptake of both calcium and phosphate. Increased supply of nitrogen can also restrict phosphate uptake. The reason may here be the same as with heavy metals—that the phosphate uptake cannot keep pace with the increased growth. These relations may lead to a delayed flowering or may take part in certain anatomical changes.

Pseudo-antagonism can also occur as a result of changes in the composition of the soil. The restrictive effect of liming on manganese uptake is probably due not only to a regular ion antagonism $Ca \rightleftarrows Mn$, but probably even more to the fact that the lime increases the pH of the soil and thereby lowers the solubility of the manganese compounds (Fig. 141). BURSTRÖM (1937) has elucidated the often complicated results of liming in field experiments. The increased lime content mobilises the phosphoric acid of the soil chemically. On the other hand the increase of the pH lowers the solubility of the iron and manganese compounds. A higher calcium content of the plant tissues lowers the mobility of the Fe, Mn and Cu ions, whereby their concentration in the leaves is diminished. Finally, in certain conditions the ionic antagonism $Ca \rightleftarrows K$ makes its influence felt.

Among other pseudo-antagonistic effects may be mentioned the fact that increased supply of phosphate lowers calcium uptake (LUNDEGÅRDH 1945, p. 75). This effect can be annulled by supply of nitrate, which increases the mobility of the Ca ion. Nitrogen nutrition seems, according to WOOD and WOMERSLEY (1946), to improve the mobility of heavy ions, e.g. iron and copper.

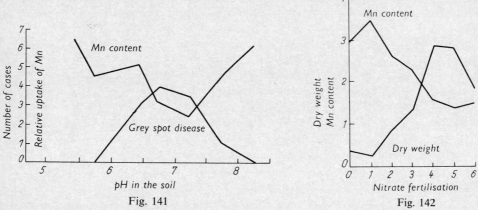

Fig. 141

Fig. 142

Fig. 141. The dependence of manganese uptake and grey spot disease on the hydrogen-ion concentration of the soil (after LUNDEGÅRDH 1932).

Fig. 142. Pseudo-antagonism between nitrate and manganese. With increasing uptake of nitrate and the resultant increased growth, the uptake of manganese becomes deficient (after LUNDEGÅRDH 1932).

G. The Biochemical Effects of the Elements

The non-metallic elements carbon, hydrogen, oxygen, nitrogen, phosphorus and sulphur are built into the components of protoplasm and the cell structure. No sharp dividing line can be drawn, however, from the metallic elements, although the effects of the latter usually depend on their occurrence as ions. Magnesium, for example, is partly a component of the chlorophyll molecule, partly a coenzyme or an enzyme activator, and partly participates as a free ion in the general ionic balance.

Potassium operates almost exclusively as a free ion, and because of its high ionic mobility exercises a dominating influence as a regulator of the ionic balance, including the pH. In addition, as already mentioned, the potassium ion influences the physical properties of the protoplasm, and, finally, certain biochemical effects of potassium have been found. Potassium is stated to take part in the phosphorylation processes, which regulate the equilibria between hexoses, sucrose and starch (JAMES 1930, PULVER and VERZÁR 1940, SIDERIS and YOUNG 1945). In this way the transport of the carbohydrates from the leaves into the storage organs may be influenced (PHILLIS and MASON 1939, BARBIER 1945). According to CORI (1946) the potassium ion activates the formation of phosphopyruvic acid from pyruvic acid + ATP. PIRSON (1955) has collected various data on the biochemical effects of potassium deficiency.

Many attempts have been made to replace potassium with *sodium* or *rubidium* (RICHARDS 1944). Actually rubidium is seldom absent from plant tissues (BERTRAND 1946), but the mere presence of a trace element of course does not indicate its biological indispensability. It is possible that Na or Rb can replace the general ionic properties of potassium. On the other hand, the purely chemical or enzyme-chemical effects are certainly more strongly specific. It has been shown that potassium ions cannot be replaced by caesium ions in the growth of *Chlorella*, but rubidium can, to a small extent, take over the role of potassium (PIRSON 1939, 1955). Rubidium appears to be similar to potassium biologically as well as chemically. According to KELLNER (1955) the alga *Ankistrodesmus* can be genetically adapted to rubidium. Concerning effects in barley see RICHARDS and BERNER (1954).

The considerably stronger hydration of Na^+ as compared with K^+ may, when there is an exchange, cause great alterations in the water balance (state of swelling) of the protoplasm. Such drastic changes can certainly influence protein formation among other things (cf. Chap. 5). The halophytes on the other hand are always adapted to a relatively high Na-content. The effect of sodium salts on succulence has been studied by many workers. It can be realised that the Na-ions are fairly loosely adsorbed on the protoplasm from the fact that salt-rich halophytes give off common salt from the roots, if they are transferred into distilled water (REPP 1939).

Certain effects on the cell nucleus may be ascribed to potassium. Potassium favours, according to SCHMALFUSS (1936), the formation of bast fibres in flax and, according to ARLAND (1936), may lower transpiration and thus improve the water balance. These data, have, however, been doubted by other workers, e.g. SNOW (1936).

Magnesium is known above all as an indispensable component of chlorophyll. An exchange of magnesium with other metal atoms may be carried out chemically (HANSON 1939), but the photosynthetic properties of the chlorophyll are then lost. In a similar way the enzyme effect of peroxidase ceases if the iron in the porphyrin group is exchanged for manganese (THEORELL 1945). Only in exceptional cases, e.g. in a species of *Chlorella* (SAIZEWA 1929), has a direct ratio between Mg-addition and the amount of chlorophyll been observed. Magnesium also seems important for the state of solubility of nucleates, e.g. in the surface of certain bacteria (HENRY and STACEY 1943). The importance of magnesium as an enzyme activator has been covered in Chapter 4.

Northern soils in general contain sufficient magnesium and deficiency of this nutrient occurs very rarely, but magnesium-deficiency diseases are known in other countries (SMIT and MULDER 1942). Shifts in the general ionic balance can have an effect here (VAN ITALLIE 1937). Over-dosage of magnesium may be harmful to fungi. Strangely enough, this poisoning can be annulled by concentrations of mercuric chloride, which would be harmful if given alone (RIPPEL and LOHRMANN 1940). Similar antagonistic effects have been described for Al and Cu (LIEBIG *et al*. 1942).

Some plants are well known for their high resistance to high magnesium contents. To these belongs *Ruppia maritima*, which tolerates Mg better than Na (McKAY1935). The tolerance in this case, however, is connected with the simultaneous presence of sulphate. *Ruppia* can consequently be considered as a magnesium plant, and the plants growing on serpentine soils also belong to this category (KRETSCHMER 1930).

The importance of *calcium* for the hydration and permeability of protoplasm and its effect as a specific growth factor (cf. also BURSTRÖM 1954, PIRSON 1955) have often been mentioned above. The importance of calcium for buffering protoplasm, e.g. by the formation of basic adsorption compounds, and for the consistency of the pectins, has also been described.

A large part of the calcium in the cells is found in the ionic form. Ca^{++} like K^+ undoubtedly takes an important part in the general acid-base balance of the cell. The low solubility of certain calcium salts is also of importance, because by this means oxalic acid, for example, is detoxified. It has been observed that plants that are poor in oxalic acid contain many free Ca-ions in the cell sap, whereas these disappear with a high oxalic acid content (PIERCE and APPLEMAN 1943).

An excess of lime in the soil may cause metabolic disturbances in many plants, which may lead to yellowing, *chlorosis*. In this the citric acid content of the cell sap tends to increase greatly, at times up to 10% of the dry weight (ILJIN 1938, HÖFLER

1942). *Lime plants* on the other hand (see Chap. 7 and LUNDEGÅRDH 1957), which colonise lime-rich soils, produce malic acid to neutralise the cations (ILJIN 1936, 1938, C. OLSEN 1941). Oxalic acid and citric acid also of course tend to fix bases; but they appear to be produced in large amounts only in those plants which are unable to prevent an excessive uptake of lime, and one then speaks of *citric acid disease* or *calciosis*. The nitrogen balance is also altered, as is made evident by the increase in the content of soluble N-compounds in the cell sap.

The biochemical importance of *iron* appears to be connected with its ability to change its valency. Cu and Mo also belong to this group, as appears from the description of enzyme effects (Chap. 4). The collaboration of Mn in redox processes is not so well known as that of Fe (about Cu and Mn see also ERKAMA 1947). The collaboration of manganese in arginase catalysis (Chap. 4) and in transamination is well known. It has correspondingly been observed that with a deficiency of manganese the protein content falls (FRIEDRICHSEN 1944). Excessive supplies of Mn cause poisoning (OLSEN 1936), which appears to be partly eliminated by oxidation with peroxidase (KENTEN and MANN 1957). GERRETSEN (1937) states that manganese deficiency can decrease photosynthesis by 50%. The chlorosis and cell necrosis caused may however also be due to a need for manganese in essential oxidation processes. PIRSON and BERGMANN (1955) have described the co-operation of manganese in the photosynthesis of *Chlorella*.

It seems from certain chloroplast analyses that iron occupies a central position not only in oxidoreduction processes (LIEBICH 1941, BENNET 1945). A distinction is made between the iron combined in the stroma and that in the grana. The former was termed by BENNET 'residual iron' and the latter 'active iron'. The former does not seem able to change over to the latter. A part of the iron taken up by the plant is probably fixed as hydroxide, a fact that explains the often widely varying results of analyses. The same probably applies in still greater measure for manganese. Leguminosae are said generally to contain relatively little manganese, whereas grasses take up a lot of this element (McHARGUE 1945; about the effect of the ratio of Fe/Mn on growth see TWYMAN 1946).

The reciprocal roles of iron and manganese in nitrate reduction have not yet been clarified (FRIEDRICHSEN 1944, BURSTRÖM 1945; cf. p. 225). Hypotheses about the antagonistic redox effects of Fe and Mn have not led to any final conclusion (SOMERS and SHIVE 1942, McHARGUE 1945). The same applies to the different statements about the antagonism between iron and other heavy metals (cf. for example PIRSON 1955). In the soil also, according to MANN and QUASTEL (1946), redox relationships regulate the availability of the manganese. In general the Mn^{++} and Mn^{+++} represent the 'active manganese' (SHERMAN and McHARGUE 1942), and the Mn^{+++} is easily reduced. Manganese oxides, which are oxidised only with difficulty, can be formed by special bacteria which have their pH optimum at 6.5-7.8 and by locking up the manganese help to cause grey spot disease (GERRETSEN 1937; cf. Fig. 141, p. 309).

Of the actual *trace elements* Cu, Zn, Mn, Co, and Ni are readily exchangeable, although here the high exchange capability of the hydrogen ion always stands in the way (PALLMAN *et al.* 1940; review of trace elements in LUNDBLAD 1945, STILES 1946, BRENCHLEY 1947, LUNDEGÅRDH 1957). The uptake of the trace elements, however, follows the same general laws as that of the macroelements. One can estimate their fixation in the surface layer of the protoplasm from the falling surface potential (Fig. 123, p. 271).

Manganese adsorption in the tissues of carrots, according to STILES and SKELDING

(1940), follows the adsorption equation $I = CE^k$, where $I =$ the internal concentration in the adsorbing body, $E =$ the concentration of the solution and C and k are constants. The amounts of Cu, Zn, H_3BO_3, etc., usually taken up are so small that one can scarcely ascribe to them any importance in the general ionic balance of the cell. The enzymatic importance of the elements named has been described above (cf. also PETERSON and WALTON 1943, BEZSONOV and LEROUX 1945). SOMMER (1945) has prepared some specifically active copper proteins. Among the metabolic changes that occur in copper deficiency may be mentioned the accumulation of organic N-compounds at the expense of the carbohydrate reserves (GILBERT et al. 1946). Ribonuclease may be inhibited by Cu and Zn (ZITTLE 1946), an example of the general chelating effect of metal ions, which one eliminates in enzyme preparations by the addition of cystëine, EDTA, etc.

With *copper* also the valency change (between Cu^+ and Cu^{++}) may play some part. In this way certain antagonistic effects between copper and iron could perhaps be explained, e.g. in the soil (SOMMER 1945). It should be noted, however, that the actual redox potentials of the two elements are not very suitable for a direct antagonistic effect. Like other bi- or multi-valent cations, copper assists chain linkage of organic molecules, which probably explains the observed increase in the viscosity of the proto-plasm under the influence of small amounts of copper (ANGERER 1942). We have often referred above to the toxicity resulting from excessive adsorption, by which the proto-plasmic structure is irreversibly deranged. While for many plants copper is an import-ant trace element (the yellow tip disease of cereals, for example, is a symptom of Cu-deficiency), the question of its essentiality is often debated (MULDER 1938, HOFFMANN 1939, PIPER 1942). Considering the general distribution of important copper-containing enzymes, e.g. ascorbic oxidase, one can however scarcely doubt the essentiality of this trace element. REINERT (1955) showed e.g. the importance of copper-containing enzymes (phenol oxidases) for the culture of coniferous tissues *in vitro*.

There is still much uncertainty about *zinc*. Investigation of the trace elements is usually made difficult by the fact that in most plants they are stored by the seeds, and on this account plants must be cultivated for several successive generations in trace-element-free solutions, before the symptoms of deficiency appear. Glass must of course be avoided, but instead of expensive platinum or quartz vessels one can use paraffin wax or plastic.

In testing for trace elements the simplest criteria are growth effects, etc. The effective amounts can be analytically determined only with difficulty, and spectral analysis gives the best results (cf. H. LUNDEGÅRDH 1936, P. H. LUNDEGÅRDH 1947; a literature survey on flame spectroscopy is given by MAVRODINEAU 1956). Devoting attention to growth symptoms alone is unfortunately often misleading, as different elements often evoke very similar biological effects. Biochemical analysis, i.e. the discovery of any metalloenzymes, is of course in the last resort decisive. Important achievements of this sort have been reported recently. To judge from these biochemical results a consider-able part of the elements of the periodic system appears to be active in the living organism.

Zinc has been ascribed a function in protein synthesis and carbohydrate meta-bolism (LOHMANN 1939, HOAGLAND 1945), and also in the redox equilibrium of proto-plasm. Such uncertain speculations, however, exist for most trace elements. According to SKOOG (1940) zinc may take part in the formation of auxin. Considerable biochemical importance is ascribed to the zinc content of carbonic anhydrase (KEILIN and MANN

1944; cf. Chap. 4). Of biological interest is the statement that certain plants accumulate zinc and in this way indirectly assist zinc uptake by other plants (CAMP 1945).
An excess of zinc in the soil is disadvantageous (STAKER and CUNNINGS 1941).

Zinc is an indispensable nutrient for *Aspergillus niger* (ROBERG 1931) and *Rhizopus
nigricans* (FOSTER and WAKSMAN 1939). As the usual methods of soil analysis have been
shown to be inadequate for zinc, the method of leaf-analysis is to be preferred
(HIBBARD 1943), a conclusion which applies also to other trace elements.

Little is known about the biochemical importance of *nickel* and *cobalt*. Vitamin B_{12},
important for animals, is apparently less significant for plants, which nevertheless
act as collectors of cobalt. Cobalt's striking lack of toxicity as compared with nickel
has been discussed above. This result is of interest since it has been shown that most
plants accumulate nickel much the more strongly (MITCHELL 1945). Seaweeds contain
relatively large amounts of cobalt, which does not occur in them in vitamin B_{12} but
in other organic combination (SCOTT and ERICSON 1955).

Molybdenum was early shown to be indispensable for *Azotobacter* and *Aspergillus*
(STEINBERG 1936; cf. MULDER 1940). ARNON *et al.* (1955) found molybdenum necessary for *Scenedesmus*. There are also positive results for higher plants (ARNON 1938,
HOAGLAND 1945, ROBINSON and EDGINGTON 1945, WARINGTON 1946). The discovery
of a biochemical function of molybdenum in nitrate assimilation places it among
the indispensable trace elements.

Vanadium (GERICKE 1940) has been shown to be necessary for the growth of
Scenedesmus obliquus (ARNON and WESSEL 1953). The importance of *gallium*
(HUTCHINSON 1945) and of the *rare earths* (ROBINSON and EDGINGTON 1945) which
are accumulated in the leaves of the hickory tree, is not yet known.

Geologists have attempted to determine the occurrence of metals in the subsoil
by spectral analysis of the leaves of trees. The method may, of course, sometimes be
successful, but it should be borne in mind that uptake through the roots, conduction,
and accumulation in the leaves involve so many factors which are difficult to control
that the results can be used for the stated purpose only with the greatest care.

Among metals that are not essential but always present, in addition to sodium,
aluminium may be mentioned. Certain groups of plants accumulate aluminium
preferentially, e.g. *Hydrangea, Thea, Mitchella, Symplocos, Alsophila* and *Lycopodium*.
(YOSHII and JIMBO 1932, HUTCHINSON 1945).

Aluminium is probably never completely absent and thus it forms a parallel to
silicon, which is considered an essential element by some workers (WAGNER 1940).
Only Pteridophyteae appear to require aluminium as a nutrient. Considerable amounts
in the soil however cause damage, especially at low pH values. The relatively small
accumulation of aluminium seems to be due less to the sparing solubility of Al^{+++}
and $Al(OH)^{++}$ than to their low speed of migration in biological media. The basic
ion $Al(OH)^{++}$ appears to predominate in the soil solution. The low speed of transport
of aluminium is revealed by the strong concentration gradient from the roots to the
leaves. As a result, aluminium becomes a pronounced root poison (SCHARRER and
SCHROPP 1936).

Of the alkaline earths *barium* is usually poisonous (GERICKE 1940), although a
harmless accumulation has sometimes been found (ROBINSON and EDGINGTON 1945).
Strontium also damages protoplasm in pure solutions, even though it resembles
calcium and is always taken up in small amounts because of its universal presence in
the soil.

We have already spoken of the biochemical functions of the non-metallic elements. The non-essential *chloride ion* is always taken up to a certain extent, especially by halophytes. The general importance of chloride in the ionic balance of the cell, e.g. as a substitute for nutrient anions or organic acids, has been emphasised above. Since the chloride ion enters the accumulation mechanism, it naturally affects the intensity of respiration. It is also said that the chloride ion influences growth and transpiration (EATON 1942), relationships which may be connected with the water balance. About *fluorine* see ROBINSON and EDGINGTON (1946). There are great differences between species in the absorption of *iodide* (JOHNSON and BUTLER 1957); which shows that the specific properties of carriers are notable with anions also.

The succulence evoked by NaCl is due more to the anion than the cation, as is shown by the fact that all chlorides induce succulence (V. EIJK 1939). The collaboration of sodium is shown by NaCl causing succulence in higher salt concentrations, whereas other cations do not have this effect. In this connection it may be mentioned that substitution by sodium in soil colloids evokes a swollen, mucilaginous consistency. Among the anions only Cl^- has this effect and neither NO_3^- nor SO_4^{--}, the former of which is usually stored in large amounts in the cell sap. Toxicity due to excessive accumulation can occur both with Cl^- and with SO_4^{--}, whereas nitrate and phosphate ions apparently can be accumulated in large amounts without causing side-effects.

Among the anionic trace elements selenium, arsenic and boron may be specially mentioned.

Selenium, which is closely related to sulphur, has attracted attention particularly in the USA, where it occurs patchily in such amounts that its accumulation in plants can cause cattle diseases (WILLIAMS *et al.* 1940, TRELEASE *et al.* 1944). Selenium, like other trace elements such as zinc, is taken up more by some plants than by others. Selenium-accumulators include *Astragalus pectinatus* and *A. bisulcatus*, and also *Agropyron smithii* (TRELEASE *et al.* 1942, OLSON *et al.* 1942). The content can vary between 0 and 70 mg per kg of dry weight. Here again leaf analysis is the best method for analysis. The physiological effects of selenium are mostly unknown, but one can suspect that in the anabolism of proteins selenium partially replaces sulphur (cf. p. 300). A stimulating effect on deer has been reported for low Se-concentrations (2 mg per kg of soil) (BOBKO *et al.* 1945). SeO_3^{--} is said to be more harmful than SeO_4^{--}, corresponding with the strong toxicity of the sulphite ion as compared with sulphate ion. A similar connection between state of oxidation and toxicity has also been observed for arsenic.

Electro-negative elements, just as the positive, can exchange with chemically related nutrient elements, so causing changes in metabolism in a regular ionic antagonism (cf. p. 300). The toxicity of arsenic may thus be due to an exchange with phosphorus; which implies an antagonism between these elements. Similarly the toxicity of chlorate may be due to exchange with nitrate. Poisoning occurs when the chlorate is reduced to chlorite or hypochlorite (ÅBERG 1947).

The most important of the non-metallic trace elements is undoubtedly *boron* (BRENCHLEY and WARINGTON 1927, SHIVE 1945), which is without exception taken up as *boric acid*. According to LOHNIS (1937) tourmaline can serve as a source of boron, which can also be fixed in the soil (PARKS and SHAW 1941). The indispensability of boron for normal development has been clearly shown for a number of plants. The boron content of plants appears to lie on the average 100%-200% higher than in animals (BERTRAND 1938). The biochemical function of boron is not fully understood.

Boric acid increases the acidity of the protoplasmic surface, thus favouring cation exchange (cf. also REHM 1937). Complex linkages also occur between boric acid and organic molecules, and this reduces the speed of transport of boron (EATON 1944). It has been found that the increase of acidity caused by boric acid is due to the formation of boromannitic acid. For the relationships between boron and pyridoxin see Chapter 4 (p. 209) and WINFIELD (1945).

Of especial interest are the numerous statements of a direct relation between boron and calcium absorption (WARINGTON 1934, SWANBACK 1939, COOK and MILLAR 1940, MARSH and SHIVE 1941) or the effect of Ca-ions in the cell. Boron may thereby influence calcium pectate formation (WINFIELD 1945), and thus growth. Root growth is inhibited by a deficiency either of boron or of calcium (REHM 1937).

The ratio Ca/B in the nutrient solution is important (DRAKE et al. 1941). A ratio of Ca/B = 1340 : 1 is normal for tobacco, but with a mere increase to 1500 : 1 boron deficiency arises. Other biochemical effects of boron are described by TAUBÖCK (1942). He found that boron combines with flavanols, which provides a sensitive microchemical reaction. On this account boron deficiency is stated to occur easily in plants that are rich in flavanol, whereas those that do not form flavanol, as well as fungi and animals, manage with minute amounts of boron. KUHN et al. (1942) say that in certain Algae the boric acid acts as an inorganic female sex hormone. Even a concentration of 10^{-10} M enables the female gametes of *Chlamydomonas* to fuse. The boric acid acts by inactivating an inhibitor, viz. quercetin methyl ether, which is a flavone derivative.

The external symptoms of boron deficiency are specific only in a few cases, e.g. in the heart rot of beet (BRANDENBURG 1939). Usually boron deficiency shows itself in a degeneration of the apical meristems, and so in a general inhibition of development. The importance of boron was first discovered in the Leguminosae (WARINGTON), but *Helianthus* can also serve as an indicator plant (COLWELL 1943).

The study of the trace elements has led to better nutrient solutions for plant culture and also to more correct fertilisation. Now a number of trace elements, e.g. Cu, Zn, B, Al, Sn, Ni, Co and Ti, are usually included in every nutrient solution ('A-Z' solution of HOAGLAND and SNYDER 1933). The plants, however, usually grow just as well without trace elements, since they are contributed by the seeds. Both in experiments and in agriculture the additions are usually limited to manganese, copper and boron. As far as *manganese* is concerned, this element is almost always present in the soil, but can from time to time be difficult for the plant to take up because of an unsuitable redox potential, unsuitable pH value, or certain relationships with bacteria. Supplying manganese fertiliser usually proves inadequate in these cases, since the added manganese becomes fixed. Indirect methods are then needed, such as fertilisation with 'physiologically acid' ammonium sulphate, of which the anion remains in the soil. Liming or 'physiologically alkaline' artificial fertilisers, e.g. $NaNO_3$ and $Ca(NO_3)_2$, should be avoided.

Certain natural inorganic fertilisers, e.g. Chile nitrate, contain a number of trace elements as 'impurities'. The requirements of individual plants however are fairly diverse. Micro-organisms in particular afford examples of special adaptations. Elements that are indispensable in considerable concentration for higher plants can occur in lower plants as trace elements. According to STEGMANN (1940) for example, *Chlorella* requires calcium in a concentration of only 0.1γ per 100 ml of nutrient solution.

Chapter 7

THE RELATIONS BETWEEN NUTRIENT UPTAKE AND GROWTH

A. Plants and the Soil

Although a description of the world's soils belongs to the sphere of soil science, an account of nutrient uptake cannot altogether neglect the general physical and chemical properties of the soil, since these are closely connected with the functions of the roots.

Physically the soil is the anchorage of land plants, and chemically it represents the supplier of nutrients. The permeability of the soil for gases is of great importance, since it regulates the oxygen supply, which is necessary, among other things, for active ion uptake. The removal of the CO_2 formed is also important, as certain biochemical processes would be hindered by accumulation of this gas. The requirements of plants for aeration of the soil, however, vary greatly (CHODAT and ANAUD 1936), which brings marsh plants into a special category (METSÄVAINIO 1931, TADROS 1940). The ground water level determines the depth to which air has free access, and thus determines the topographical distribution of plants with deeply penetrating aerobic roots (GOODWIN et al. 1932, COSTER 1932).

The competition for soil oxygen is of course especially strong in the tropics (COSTER 1933). In Swedish arable soils down to a depth of 30 cm the oxygen content is little lower than in the atmosphere, whilst the CO_2 content is about ten times higher. The variations caused by rain, temperature, etc., are naturally considerable (LUNDE-GÅRDH 1924, 1957, GELTZER 1939). Contents above 1% of CO_2, which can be described as the upper limit for normal life, are however uncommon. The main uptake of water from moist layers of soil is by roots which do not penetrate very deeply. It is now known that the capillary rise of water in the soil is much less important than had been thought earlier (BOUYOUCOS 1947).

An idea of the capacity of the root system was given by the calculations of PAVLY-CHENKOS (1937) on the total length of the roots of a cereal plant. He concluded that oat, wheat and rye plants show a total root length of 90 km, with a maximal root depth of 1·6 m. Competition with other individuals considerably restricts the branching of roots e.g. in thick sowing to about one-quarter, and in competition with *Sinapis arvensis* still more.

The chemical properties of the soil are to a large extent dependent on its developmental history. It suffices to mention here that the geological substratum always exercises a certain influence, but that plants partly create their own medium by exchanges with the soil (GRAF ZU LEININGEN-WESTERBURG 1931, GRANLUND and WENNERHOLM 1934, LYON and BUCKMAN 1943).

The *humus* which is so characteristic of the soil arises by the decay of earlier plant generations with the aid of micro-organisms. Because of this the most abundant plants indirectly determine the path of breakdown. The general nutrient capacity (salt content, etc.) of the soil layer is also involved. Birch trees, for example, give a mild humus, alders one rich in nitrogen, and so on (AARNIO 1934, PLICE 1934). On the other hand, as plants take up nutrient salts directly from mineral particles, the rock basis also has its effect. A substratum low in bases gives an acid humus, from which rain water easily washes out the most valuable constituents (proteins and lignoproteins), and normal decay is made still more difficult (GAARDER and ALVSAKER 1938). A substratum rich in bases favours the development of a neutral humus with a high adsorption capacity.

Humus low in bases is characteristic of the podsol soils which cover large areas of the wood and heath regions of Scandinavia, and here the humus layer covers the mineral soil as a continuous layer. The upper layer of the mineral soil forms a thin bleached zone of pale earth, whilst the lower layers contain reddish precipitates. The podsol humus is distinguished by its high content of cellulose and hemicellulose and low content of proteins (WAKSMAN and HUTCHINGS 1935, WAKSMAN 1938). As a consequence of the deficiency in bases, lignin and protein disperse and are precipitated only in the lower layers. Here iron, aluminium and silica are also precipitated, in the order given (AALTONEN 1939; see also MATTSON 1931, WEIS 1932, MATTSON and GUSTAFSSON 1934).

In soils rich in bases, whose typical representatives are the humus soils of the steppe regions, e.g. the Russian black soil, humus materials are fixed by precipitation in the upper layers. Readily soluble salts are also retained by adsorption, and the sharp boundary with the mineral soil characteristic of podsols is not found. Rainfall influences the development of the different soil types to a considerable extent because the nutrient salts are more easily washed out of the soils of humid climatic zones than from steppe- and desert-soils.

In addition to the humus materials the soil also contains *inorganic colloids*, which are formed by weathering of the mineral particles or brought in by water as clay. Generally speaking, these colloids resemble the protoplasmic colloids in their dissociation and fixation of ions by exchange. The physico-chemical properties of clay, including its crystallinity (expanding and non-expanding lattices) and ion exchange, have been described extensively in the literature (e.g. WIEGNER 1931, CERNESCU 1931, KELLEY et al. 1931, OHLE 1935, HAUSER 1941, GRIM 1942 et al.). The soil colloids are usually more markedly crystalline than the protoplasmic colloids but do not attain the same high adsorptive power for salts.

The decaying plant residues retain still strongly acid compounds, e.g. nucleic acids (WRENSHALL and DYER 1941) or carboxylic acids, which may compete with the acidoid carriers in the protoplasmic surface. The acidoid nature of the clay particles is determined very largely by silicic acid, while the sesquioxides (of Al, Fe, etc.) react as bases (MATTSON 1931). Ferric hydroxide overlays the soil particles with a basic film, so that phosphate ions, for example, can be exchanged. These can be again driven out by silicic acid, a fact that explains the usually advantageous effect of soluble silicic acid on the nutrient state of the soil (KELLEY and MIDGLEY 1943). In general the rules for weak electrolytes apply also for the dissociation of the soil colloids.

Schematically one can envisage the surface of the soil colloids as an amphoteric double layer, in which the inner surface consists of dissociated large molecules and the outer surface consists of the adsorbed anions and cations of the medium. The effective pH-value of the colloids is determined by the degree of ion exchange. With an adequate supply of neutral salts having K, Na, Ca and Mg as cations, the pH-value rises. With a deficiency of salts H-ions predominate at the outer surface of the double layer, and the acidoidity of the colloids elicits a negative surface potential. Since the dissociation and dispersion of the colloids depend to a large extent on surface charge, the concentration and type of circulating salts, and solid bases, such as lime, determine the development of the soil.

Amphoteric substances show a minimum of dispersion, solubility and dissociation at the isoelectric point, where they are therefore most stable. In 'isoelectric weathering' (MATTSON et al. 1932, 1935, 1937, 1939, 1940) many salts become free and discharge the colloids so that a neutral 'saturated' humus arises. This possesses good exchange properties, especially for cations, but also to a certain extent for anions.

At pH-values above the isoelectric point the colloid complex of the soil reacts anionically and is dispersed in the form of large anions, which are washed away into the subsoil. This leads to the type of soil poor in humus which is known as laterite and occurs in the tropics. At lower pH-values the negative surface charge of the colloid particles decreases. In this way hydrolysis starts and part of the basoid humus materials is eluted and later precipitated in the subsoil or escapes with the soil water. The residual humus layer then becomes cationic as compared with the soil water, which causes poor base exchange.

Although the fixation of salt ions on the soil colloids is of the exchangeable adsorptive type, specific fixations can be observed here, as in the protoplasm. Potassium is especially strongly adsorbed, so that the exchange capacity for other cations is diminished; sodium, calcium and magnesium are more loosely bound (JOFFE and LEVINE 1938). These relationships may possibly be due to secondary reactions between cations and humus (BROADFOOT and TYNER 1939). According to WILSON (1929), potassium is adsorbed more strongly than calcium from equimolecular solutions. But the Donnan equilibrium must be kept in mind, because it causes displacements between mono-, di- and polyvalent ions, when the concentrations vary (cf. p. 49). According to ZADMARD (1939), the ion exchange favours alkalis when the soil is rich in potassium and alkaline earth ions when the humus contains calcium.

With normal water-content the soil particles are surrounded by a thin layer of capillary water, and the colloids are swollen. The *aqueous phase* remains in adsorption equilibrium with the particles, but the equilibrium of course shifts with the water content. The soil colloids thus act as stores of available nutrient ions. In drought the stores are filled, and during strong rainfall, when large amounts of 'gravitational water' disappear into the ground water, salts are eluted, but because of the enormous internal surface of the colloids the elution is greatly retarded. The soil colloids are thus essential for the more superficially rooting plants to exist, and in any case for a continuous cover of vegetation. Although cation adsorption is most obvious in soils, anions, e.g. phosphate and nitrate ions, are also adsorbed on clay particles or humus colloids (COLEMAN 1942, JENNY 1946).

The root hairs cling closely to the soil particles and are, so to speak, interwoven with them, which suggests a 'contact exchange' between soil colloids and the living root surface (JENNY and OVERSTREET 1938). A direct exchange of ions could, however, take place only if the distance between particles and protoplasm were very short, probably of the order of an ion diameter. Between the soil colloids and the protoplasm of the epidermal cells of the roots there is actually a cell wall of the thickness of $0{\cdot}1$-$1{\cdot}0$ μ, i.e. corresponding to as much as 1,000 ion diameters (Fig. 143).

Exchange must therefore in any case be by way of the colloids of the cell wall; but it is more likely that most of the uptake is through the water circulating freely in it.

The difference between the uptake from the soil and from a nutrient solution is probably due, not to a different kind of ion exchange, but to the colloids offering the nutrients in a concentration higher than that of the surrounding soil solution because of their adsorption. The anions exchanged by the roots must, however, be replaced from surfaces further away (cf. ALBRECHT 1942, PETERSBURGSKII 1944), which pre-supposes an ion transport which would meet greater resistance in the soil than in a free solution.

Experimental results in fact show that even bivalent ions are fairly immobile in the soil (for calcium see WILSON 1930; for Ca, Mn, etc., see LUNDEGÅRDH 1932). The diffusion of iron and manganese, according to WINTERS (1940), takes place slowly in colloid gels, but increases with fall of pH. Due to the abundance of cation carriers R^- and the considerable acidoidity of the root surface, the exchange equilibrium is displaced strongly in favour of the root (LUNDEGÅRDH 1942); ion uptake from the soil is, however, a more complicated process than uptake from a solution.

Movements of ions in the soil are made easier by the fact that the capillary and even the hygroscopic water seem to be fairly mobile (LEAMER 1942; cf., however, BOUYOU-COS 1947). Among the anions, phosphate uptake does not seem to depend much on an adsorption on clay particles (DEAN and RUBINS 1945). As is known, the soil colloids act as a buffer against changes in pH, and this indirectly regulates the availability of certain ions, e.g. Fe and Mn (GILE and FENSTAL 1943).

Ion uptake from the soil is regulated by a number of special factors such as aeration, water content, colloid content and pH, which are most easily con-

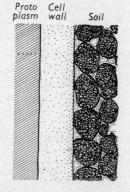

Fig. 143. Contact surface between root and soil. The cell wall prevents direct contact between the cytoplasm and the soil particles. This aqueous phase, which prevents a direct ion exchange, is about 1μ thick.

trolled experimentally in water cultures. A more detailed account of these relationships, however, comes within the sphere of experimental ecology.

Even the CO_2 liberated in root respiration affects the local pH-value and the solution of ions adsorbed in the soil. The corrosion of a marble surface by roots was observed long ago. This effect is increased by the natural acidity of the root surface. Nucleic and other acids, in addition to CO_2, are functionally secreted by the root surface, but simple carboxylic acids, e.g. acetic, are secreted scarcely at all. An increase in absorption from the soil may also be caused by mycorrhiza (ROUTIEN and DAWSON 1943) and the bacteria of the rhizosphere.

B. The Dependence of Growth on the External and Internal Supply of Nutrients

In this chapter 'growth' is an expression for the development of all meristematic tissues and is roughly what farmers, gardeners and others understand by growth. This overall development of course requires a continuous supply of all the essential nutrients; and the interactions among these form, broadly speaking, the theme of this chapter. Going into greater detail brings one first to the relations between vegetative and reproductive growth, and then to the special meristematic mechanisms in which hormones play a part. The latter problems are treated in greater detail in Chapter 9.

1 CARBON DIOXIDE AS A GROWTH FACTOR

As the carbohydrates directly or indirectly form the main mass of plant substance, the dominating growth factor must always be the intensity of photosynthesis. This is shown, for example, by the fact that mean growth roughly follows the temperature curve of photosynthesis. The general dependence of growth on light and concentration of CO_2 is also due to the effect of these factors on photosynthesis. The relation naturally varies in individual cases, since respiration continues in the dark periods and the translocation of assimilates also has a limiting effect at times.

The most important general regulator for the CO_2-factor is the availability of other nutrients, that is the balance between atmospheric nutrition and soil nutrition. An illustration of this is given by experiments with sugar beet, grown with two different CO_2 concentrations (0·03 and 0·042% of CO_2 in the air) and two different salt supplies, but under identical light conditions. The ratio of growth increase to CO_2 enrichment amounted for the unfertilised plants to:

0·68 for roots and 0·34 for leaves.

For the plants with mineral fertilisation the ratio amounted to:

1·98 for roots and 0·89 for leaves.

This experiment gives an example of the biological relativity law, showing the limiting effect of the growth factor which occurs in the minimum.

That the CO_2-concentration of the air is a growth factor whose variation, like the variation of any essential nutrient, influences the end-result, is not surprising. It was however, once thought, and is still sometimes maintained, that plants always absorb as much CO_2 as they need and that the CO_2 in the air is a residue unused by plants. Today, however, we know that the CO_2-content of the air represents the balance between photosynthesis and biological CO_2 production, that the position of the equilibrium is shifted considerably according to the intensity of these processes, and that increasing the CO_2-concentration above the normal ('CO_2 fertilisation') usually leads to an increase in growth.

The balance between carbohydrate nutrition and salt nutrition (especially the supply of N) changes with the transition from the vegetative stage to seed-formation. The vegetative organs may themselves show different requirements. Thus REID (1929) mentions that the intensity of photosynthesis is especially reflected in the growth of roots and stem, but that no direct effect on leaf growth can be observed; the leaves are more dependent on nitrogen nutrition. GREGORY (1926) also has drawn attention to this effect of nitrogen. Since chlorophyll formation shows a strong relation with N supply, the connection between nitrogen nutrition and photosynthesis is evident. Experience with growth substances shows that these usually migrate in ways different from the carbohydrates, for which reason in considering any effect of a nutrient on the growth of an organ the hormones must also be taken into account.

2 SALT SUPPLY AND GROWTH

The extraordinary importance of nutrient salts for the practical cultivation of plants has for many years directed attention to the relations between the quantity of nutrient added and the amount of plant substance produced. LIEBIG's Law of the Minimum was the first attempt to represent the connection by a curve. Later MITSCHERLICH (1920, 1928) attempted to express mathematically the fact that the effect of an increase of one factor occurring at a minimum is shown by a convex curve which finally runs asymptotically. A graphic representation is usually considered enough; but MITSCHERLICH systematised the process by applying the mathematical statement 'of organic growth' to actual experimental results. MITSCHERLICH's basic equation is the following:

$$y = A(1 - e^{-cx}) \qquad (86)$$

Here A is the maximum growth when all factors have their optimal effect, e is the base of natural logarithms, c is a constant, x is the variable nutrition factor and y is the actual growth. BAULE later improved the formula to include the interaction between nutrient factors.

The Mitscherlich formula and similar mathematical attempts are of course schematisations and have found little application in pure plant physiology. The method introduced by MITSCHERLICH, of calculating the fertiliser requirements of a soil from a number of pot experiments with graduated doses of artificial fertilisers, is now used much less than formerly because of its inconvenience. This indeed is also connected with the complexity of biological associations, which makes each individual result the consequence of a whole series of interacting factors. Simple mathematical formulae do not cover these complex processes. The danger of mathematical formulations is that they give an appearance of simple regularity to what are in fact the results of complicated interaction of several factors. Among other attempts to express the relationships between nutrition and growth mathematically one by MASKELL (1929) may be mentioned (see also GOODALL et al. 1955).

It is, of course, true that growth, like mono- or multi-molecular chemical reactions, tends to show logarithmic relations. All attempts at formulae, which seek to express a relation between nutrient content or concentration of the medium and growth or yield, suffer, however, from the common defect that they ignore an important intermediate stage, viz. uptake and translocation within the plant itself. It is obvious that only those nutrients and those quantities of them which are taken up into the plant can have any importance at all for development. Absorption of nutrients through the roots, however, shows such deviations from simple diffusion and adsorption processes, that it is impossible to equate the external concentration of a nutrient with its effective internal concentration. All this has been discussed above, and as an example we need only recall the effects of ionic antagonisms, of which those between K and Ca are the most striking.

If the potassium concentration in the soil rises but the other nutrients remain constant, a corresponding increase in the uptake of potassium is found. The rising internal concentration of potassium influences growth positively; there is, however, no simple ratio between the two magnitudes, but the growth response diminishes progressively, and thus a still higher internal K-concentration results. The dependence of growth on the potassium concentration thus follows a convex 'logarithmic' curve (Fig. 144). A similar increase in the absolute and relative content is found also for phosphate and nitrate, although the convexity of the curve depends on how far the minimum region of the particular factor extends.

An increase of the internal K-concentration now finally causes an antagonistic decrease in the Ca-uptake, even when the external Ca-concentration remains constant. Apart from a short initial phase (cf. also Fig. 139 and Chap. 6), the Ca-curve becomes a mirror image of the K-curve (Figs. 144 and 145).

The uptake of Mg and Mn is also affected antagonistically in a similar way to that of potassium. These antagonistic effects increase the convexity of the growth curve. Apart from strict ion-antagonism pseudo-antagonism also becomes apparent in the relation between nutrient concentration and growth. An increased nitrate uptake inhibits manganese uptake, for example, and finally an internal manganese deficiency and inhibition of growth result. An abundant phosphate uptake, on the other hand, appears to have little influence on the uptake of other nutrients. The examples given here show convincingly the danger of neglecting the process of uptake. Only analysis of the plant makes it possible to determine the nutrient quantities that are actually effective.

3 INTERNAL NUTRIENT CONCENTRATION AND GROWTH. THE PRINCIPLES OF TISSUE ANALYSIS (LEAF ANALYSIS)

From the plant-physiological point of view the amount of nutrients taken into the plant is naturally of primary interest. Only when a nutrient is taken up without complications due to ionic antagonism, etc., can one expect that the concentration in the plant would vary more or less proportionately to its available concentration in the soil. As, however, it cannot be known beforehand whether e.g. antagonism is playing a part, one must *a priori* regard with scepticism the so-called 'soil mapping', since this draws conclusions about the availability of a nutrient for the plant merely from soil analyses. Even if from an average of several hundred analyses one finds a positive relation between potassium in the soil and the yield, the application of this result to the individual case depends on the amplitude of the variations. This is usually large, since complications in absorption of the type mentioned above often occur. Soil analyses also usually suffer from experimental errors, above all in the processes used for the extraction.

Since the results obtained by plant analysis include possible sampling errors, in recent years the advantages of this method for judging the fertiliser requirements of the soil have been critically re-examined.

A postulated regular relation between internal nutrient concentration and growth is fundamental for the methods of plant analysis. Literature surveys may be found in LUNDEGÅRDH 1945, 1957 and GOODALL and GREGORY 1947. Among the works on plant (or leaf) analysis there may be mentioned HERSCHLER (1933), MITCHELL (1937), CHAPMAN et al. (1940, 1943), MOSER (1940), BOYNTON et al. (1941), LINDNER and HARLEY (1942), SCARSETH (1943), ULRICH (1943), PLICE (1944), THOMAS and MACK (1944, 1945), TYNER and WEBB (1946) and GOODALL et al. (1955). A detailed study of the distribution of nutrients in plants (Chap. 6 F, p. 307) shows that the leaves maintain the most nearly constant and, on the average, highest nutrient level; which is

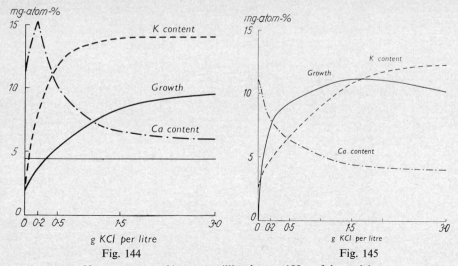

Fig. 144   Fig. 145

Note.—mg-atom-% *means* millimoles per 100 g of dry weight.

Fig. 144. The effect of potassium supply on the uptake of calcium and on the growth of oats, in pot experiments using quartz sand which was moistened with nutrient solutions of increasing KCl-content, while the other nutrients, including Ca, were constant. The ordinate shows the potassium content in the crop. The calcium values on the average amount to one-tenth of the amounts supplied. The line at 4·4 milligram-atom-per cent gives the critical calcium content (after LUNDEGÅRDH 1932).

Fig. 145. Pot experiments with oats with varying potassium supply. Items as in Fig. 144. In this series of experiments the calcium uptake was somewhat depressed. The calcium content therefore approaches the critical value of 4·4-milligram-atom-per cent (after LUNDEGÅRDH 1932).

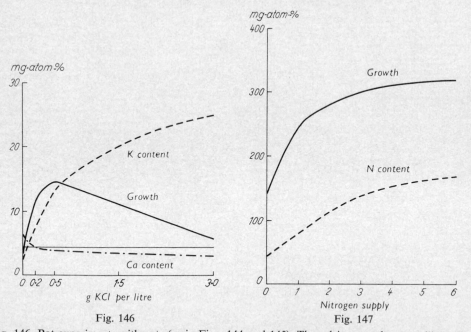

Fig. 146   Fig. 147

Fig. 146. Pot experiments with oats (as in Figs. 144 and 145). The calcium uptake was still further reduced, as colloidal silicic acid was added. The Ca-content therefore sinks finally below the critical value of 4·4 milligram-atom-per cent, which leads to a decrease in growth (after LUNDEGÅRDH 1932).

Fig. 147. The relations between internal nitrogen content (KJELDAHL-N) and growth of oats (after LUNDEGÅRDH 1932).

Y

connected with their function as food laboratories of the plant. In the leaves of trees the level of the mineral substances also seems to vary little during the growing period (DELEANO 1911 with *Salix fragilis*). Leaf analyses can therefore be used with some success also for forest trees (TAMM 1954).

The idea of leaves as transitory storage organs for the nutrient salts rising from the roots is experimentally well founded and is also confirmed by the fact that during the grand period of growth the nutrient salt level of the leaves reaches an optimum, to fall again in autumn before yellowing. The concentration of the mineral nutrients (tn- cluding nitrogen) in the leaf renders them generally available for the leaf metabolism and for secondary supply to the meristems. JACOB and ALTEN (1942) showed this for the K-content of the leaves, and several other workers for the N-content (LUNDE- GÅRDH 1945, p. 37). The photosynthetic activity of the leaves (according to JACOB and ALTEN 1941) follows an optimum progress curve (cf. also SPANING 1941).

The rate of photosynthesis in the mature leaf, according to SANDE-BAKHUYSEN (1937), remains almost constant for a considerable time. He calculates that 0·8 mg of photosynthetic products (carbohydrates + N-compounds) are produced per square centimetre of leaf per day. During the first weeks 0·42 mg of this amount go to the stalk and 0·38 mg are used for the growth of the leaf itself. After the leaves are fully grown, which takes about three weeks, the ears (flower spikes) also take over part of the amounts not retained by the leaves. After the maturation of the stalk and leaves, which takes about 5-6 weeks, the whole production goes to the ears.

During the vegetative development of the cereal plant the relation between internal nutrient concentration and growth can be followed by total analyses of leaves and straw. In this it is found, for example, that the growth is in a regular ratio to the potassium concentration as long as the other factors remain at a maximum, i.e. do not have a limiting effect. Even with potassium values below about 3 mg-atom-% the growth curve rises steeply and then bends over asymptotically but even at 10 mg-atom-% shows some rise. Even at 15 mg-atom-% no limit, i.e. no optimum, was observed (Fig. 144). On the other hand, on account of ion antagonism the internal Ca-concentration may be depressed to such an extent that Ca becomes a limiting factor (Fig. 145). This critical point occurs in oats at about 4-5 mg-atom-% of Ca. The optimum curve that is at times observed with a constantly rising supply of potas- sium (Fig. 146) is thus compounded from a rising K-curve and a falling Ca-curve. While the critical point, that is the concentration below which varia- tions in the potassium level con- siderably influence the growth, lies at about 50 mg-atom-%, for cal- cium it amounts to only about 4-5 mg-atom-% and for phosphorus about 8-10 mg-atom-% (Fig. 148; see LUNDEGÅRDH 1945, 1951).

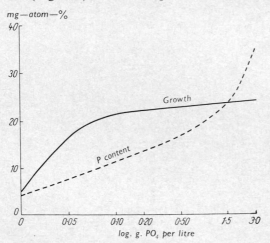

Fig. 148. Relationships between phos- phate uptake and growth in oats. Optimal growth is reached with an internal PO_4-content of about 10 mg- atom-%. Further phosphate uptake has no effect (after LUNDEGÅRDH 1932).

The internal nitrogen content influences growth in the same way as the potassium content, although the critical minimum lies still higher—at about 200 mg-atom-% of N (i.e. Kjeldahl nitrogen; see Fig. 147). Direct ion-antagonistic effects were not observed with phosphate and nitrate; with nitrogen on the other hand various pseudo-antagonistic effects arise, which are connected with the great increase in volume and are only partly offset by the simultaneous improvement in the ion transport.

Inhibiting effects (that is, supra-optimal effects) of N or P have not been observed. P-contents of 30-40 mg-atom-%, that is about five times the upper minimum limit, and N-contents of 400 mg-atom-% are apparently tolerated without side-effects, provided that the remaining nutrients are not limiting. If optimum curves occur, they can usually be connected with antagonistic effects, through which the content of any essential nutrient comes to lie below the upper minimum limit. The same applies for the changes in development which occur with an unbalanced N-surplus.

Complicated effects can arise because N-supply, for example, does not favour all organisms equally (LOO 1936). It is known that root development usually varies inversely with the N-supply, and hence in N-deficiency the roots are much elongated, a phenomenon that is termed *nitrogen etiolation* (Fig. 149). The growth of the aerial parts can of course be indirectly restricted by this.

The dependence of growth on the concentration of nutrients in the leaves is itself a mass action, i.e. the rate of growth is a function of the actual concentration of the active components; but the relationship is in reality more complicated. Increased concentration in the leaves follows transitory accumulation and is thus a manifestation of the general 'growth potential' of the plant. The relation between growth and nutrient concentration at the point of consumption can, however, vary. No fixed relation is observed, e.g. in the ears and at seed-formation (LUNDEGÅRDH 1932, BURSTRÖM 1937). This may be explained by saying that the nutrients which come from the leaves flow

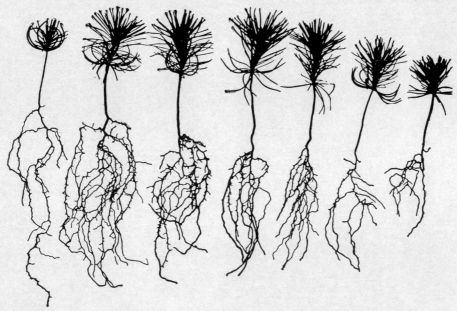

Fig. 149. Silhouettes of pine seedlings raised with increasing supplies of nitrogen. From left to right: 0, 88·2, 425·9, 838·9, 1239·0, 2077·9 and 2490·8 mg of N as NH_4NO_3 per litre of nutrient solution (after MITCHELL 1939).

directly into the production mechanism. Thus a reaction of the zero order is involved. It is therefore not the concentration, but the rate of nutrient supply that determines the production. The 'logarithmic' average relation between the yield and the nutrient level in the leaves would thus have to be determined in the first place for the translocation processes from the leaves to the meristems.

The interaction between the various mineral nutrients reminds one in general of similar relationships among the external factors of photosynthesis (see Chap. 3 G, p. 122), and thus follows the biological relativity law. Detailed investigation shows that in mature plants it is particularly the leaves that reflect the supply of nutrient from the soil. The leaves prepare the nutriment for the fruits, for other active meristems and for the active root system (about the importance of the leaves for root formation in cuttings see OVERBEEK et al. 1946). In cereal plants the leaves are supported by the sheaths (LJUBIMENKO et al. 1930, BOONSTRA 1937; for the contrary GABRIELSEN 1942).

The fundamental importance of the leaves is clear from the way in which the plant seeks to protect itself against losses of active leaf surface. Thus, for example, green fruits take over a considerable part of the photosynthetic functions if conduction from the leaves is restricted (KURSANOV 1934, FELDBACH 1938). In sugar beet, if the number of leaves is reduced to 2-4 neither sugar production nor growth is notably reduced, since the remaining leaves intensify their function (KOKIN 1930). This fact is already illustrated by the positive relation between fertilisation and yield.

BAULE (1930) in his modification of MITSCHERLICH's equation has taken into consideration the interaction of the nutrient factors x, x_1, x_2, etc., by introducing the corresponding constants c, c_1, c_2, etc. The equation would then be as follows:

$$y = E\,(1 - e^{-cx}) \cdot (1 - e^{-c_1 x_1}) \cdot (1 - e^{-c_2 x_2}) \cdot \text{etc.} \tag{87}$$

where E represents the maximum growth at optimal effect of all factors.

Some pot experiments using quartz sand with nutrient solutions illustrate the effect of varying supplies of N, P and K. The percentage increase of yield with increase of a given factor, the others being maintained constant, is shown in Table 17.

Table 17

Increase in Yield with Increase of a Single Nutrient Factor in the Leaves. Pot Experiments with Oats

Varying factor	Increase in yield in % with					
	low N	high N	low P	high P	low K	high K
N (nitrate)	.	.	10	54	14	42
P	−25	6	.	.	−20	4
K	7	33	4	32	.	.

Leaf analysis reveals why an increase in the P-supply in Table 17 has a negative effect at low N and K contents: it is because the calcium content is reduced by a pseudo-antagonism. The negative effect is eliminated if at the same time a high dosage of nitrate is given, since NO_3 increases the speed of transport of Ca. The P, on the other hand, favours the transport of K which usually migrates as KH_2PO_4.

The interaction among the nutrient factors is of enormous ecological and practical importance. In fertilising arable fields and garden beds the principle of the harmonious collaboration of the different nutrient factors must always be the guide. The full effect of fertilisation with phosphate is attained only after the minimum limits of nitrogen, potassium, etc., have been exceeded. Information about the fertiliser requirements is given most reliably by leaf analyses, if the samples are taken at the correct time, viz. at the time of flowering (LUNDEGÅRDH 1945). The analytical results should be evaluated by comparison with the experimentally determined upper minimum values of the decisive factors K, P, Ca and N. A 'levelling off value' (in mg-atom-%) of a factor which is in the minimum region then indicates that there is a deficiency which should be removed by appropriate fertilisation.

By summarising graphically leaf analyses from a great number of field experiments, in which e.g. the effect of potassium fertilisation was tested, a system of curves could be drawn showing the probable increase in yield due to a 'normal fertilisation' (e.g. 100-150 kg of 40% potash salts per hectare). In this the yield increases in inverse ratio to the K-levelling off value found. If the system of curves also reproduces the effect of P one finds correspondingly that the effect of K increases in direct ratio with the levelling off value found for phosphorus. In a similar way the ratios between the N- and P-levelling off values and the effect of corresponding nitrogen- and phosphate-fertilisation are determined.

Leaf analysis was tested at an early date with woody plants (vine, conifers, apple trees, lemon trees, rubber trees, etc.) (cf. LAGATU and MAUME 1930, LUNDEGÅRDH 1954). Among herbaceous plants wheat, meadow grasses, potatoes, clover, ground-nuts, etc., have been investigated. The guiding principle of leaf analysis is the selection of that organ of the plant which most reliably shows the internal nutrient level.

As a variant of leaf analysis the injection of nutrients e.g. into the leaves has been investigated (HILL and ROACH 1940, ALMEIDA 1941, ATKINSON et al. 1944, LAL 1945).

4 HYDROGEN-ION CONCENTRATION AS A GROWTH FACTOR

By their strong exchange capability hydrogen ions exert a very considerable influence on ion exchange at the cell surface. Active ion uptake is influenced rather less, since anion respiration and the absorption of ions take place inside the cells in the ground mass of the protoplasm. But variations in H-ion concentration of the medium have, via the Donnan equilibrium, a certain regulating influence on salt uptake.

At a certain pH-value, for wheat roots about 3, the protoplasmic membrane is discharged. At still lower values the boundary surface potential changes over to the positive, and then the protoplasm is overwhelmed by inflowing anions. ARNON et al. (1942) found that the nutrient uptake of many plants ceased at pH = 3. The unfavourable effects of a rising H-ion concentration are accentuated by the simultaneous disappearance of important cations, e.g. Ca, from the cell surface. Calcium is certainly necessary for the maintenance of a normal structure, rigidity, dissociation and permeability of the protoplasm. The danger zone mentioned is, however, specific for the species. Roots of certain species are discharged even at pH = 4; others, such as tomatoes and flax, only at 2·5 or even 2·0. These specific differences are certainly of great ecological importance. There are also examples of micro-organisms which are extremely resistant to acid conditions.

The effect of high pH-values is ecologically less important, since acid soils are much commoner than alkaline. According to the principle of the membrane equilibrium, at high pH-values, which in certain soils can reach 10-11, the absorption of metallic cations is strongly favoured. Through the compensatory over-production of organic acids thereby caused, this may involve certain drawbacks. Even at pH $=9$ ARNON et al. (1942) found an almost normal salt uptake, except for restriction of phosphoric acid. The respiration intensity also is remarkably little influenced by the external pH-value (cf. LUNDEGÅRDH and BURSTRÖM 1944).

The above-mentioned effects on the availability of many nutrients in the soil are related to the physiological effects of pH. Apart from the dependence of phosphates and carbonates on the pH-value, discussed above, it may be mentioned that Fe and Al precipitate phosphoric acid even at pH <5.5, calcium at pH 6·5 and magnesium at pH >7.5 (BEAR and TOTH 1942). The availability of manganese is also very dependent on the pH-value.

The actual hydrogen-ion concentration of the soil is influenced by many factors. The effect of neutral salts (through ion exchange), of rainfall, of the subsoil and of aeration, and especially CO_2-concentration (PANKAKOSKI 1934, WHITNEY and GARDNER 1943) have already been mentioned. These relationships also determine an annual periodicity in the pH value of the soil, which according to GAUGER and ZIEGENSPECK (1930) shows a maximum in winter and a minimum in May.

The methods of determining the pH of the soil often leave something to be desired. A determination of pH at a low moisture content shows as a rule lower values than a determination with a plentiful supply of water (CHAPMAN and CURTIS 1940, HAAS 1941). The soil particles are surrounded with swarms of H- or OH-ions, which are exchangeable with neutral salt ions (WIEGNER and PALLMANN 1930). In pH determinations one thus determines the H-ion concentration in the solution with which the charged soil colloids are in equilibrium, and not the value at the surface of the particle. This value is ordinarily lower (compare also what was said in Chapter 1 about the protoplasmic surface; and about 'pH$_s$' see p. 208). The pH of the solution changes with the inward or outward exchange of salt ions, that is with the salt concentration. This is, however, not quite the same as the well-known 'salt error' (TERÄSVUORI 1930). As the roots are mostly in contact with the ions found in the soil solution, the most customary pH-determinations usually give a fairly good interpretation of the decisive H-ion concentration; but it is important that the soil sample should be extracted with little water.

The ingenious buffering mechanisms of plant roots eliminate the effect of fairly large fluctuations in the pH of the soil. In addition, plants influence the pH-value of nutrient solutions and even to some extent that of the soil, which has been emphasised by KOZLOWSKA (1933), PRIANISJNIKOV (1934), RÜHL (1936), KIVINEN (1938) et al.

The initially high expectations of an absolutely dominant influence of pH on the welfare of plants have been shown to be exaggerated, since it has been seen that all ions of the medium collaborate and that the H-ion effects can be modified by other cations. PIRSCHLE (1931) came to the conclusion that there is no absolute or definite pH-optimum for a species, since the form of the pH curve changes according to the overall nutrient conditions. ARNON et al. (1942) in conformity with this found that variations between pH 4 and 8 often evoked no clear differences in growth, provided that other nutrient ions were present in sufficient concentration. The pH of the expressed sap in these experiments kept remarkably constant.

Cation uptake also tends to proceed fairly independently of the pH value. In experiments with young wheat plants approximately constant amounts of K, Ca, Mg and

Na were absorbed in the pH range of 4·5-8·4, with an indication of an optimum at about pH = 6·5. Sensitivity to pH may be greater where heavy metal ions are concerned, although here specific differences have been observed, e.g. a greater sensitivity of Cu than of Mn (Burström and Boratynski 1936).

The data on ecological pH limits should therefore not be generalised uncritically (cf. also Pallmann and Haffter 1933, Emmett and Ashby 1934). Cell-physio-logically, internal pH changes are of outstanding importance, since almost all enzymatic processes show pH-optimum curves (p. 144). It is stated that the mechanism of movement of the stomata is strongly influenced by fluctuations in pH (Small and Maxwell 1938). An example of the regulating effect on enzymatic processes is given by the discovery mentioned by Quednow (1930), that organic compounds, e.g. glucose, are utilised best at pH 4·5-4·7. The strong buffering capacity of the plant cell against fluctuations in pH may be interpreted in general as a protection against derangement of the enzymatic processes. In this connection the micro-organisms, because of their high specific surface, are naturally much worse off, which may well contribute to their well-known sensitivity to pH; but even in these organisms, e.g. in yeast, effective buffering mechanisms are active.

Attempts have often been made to explain the physiological effect of pH by the position of the isoelectric point of the protoplasmic colloids. There may, however, be no sharp isoelectric point in the protoplasm, but only a broad isoelectric region (Fig. 150) in which pH variations have no effect on the dissociation. Sharper reactions towards pH changes are, however, to be expected with individual biologically important substances. For example, the pK-value of auxin lies between 4·5 and 5·0; the dissociation of auxin is therefore influenced by pH variations between about 3·5 and 6, and one may expect an optimum growth curve, since the auxin effect depends, among other things, on the degree of dissociation of the molecule (cf. Chap. 9). Much depends, of course, on the buffering effect of adsorbed metallic cations, which move the pH-optimum (Lundegårdh 1942).

The buffering effect of the metallic cations is of course often specific; which may be due not only to a different exchangeability but also to the effect on chemical processes. This applies e.g. for calcium. The antagonistic effect of Ca against H-ions was observed by Brenner (1920), Prianisjnikov (1923) and Lundegårdh (1924). In the root-hairs of wheat the growth rate falls quickly if in the absence of metallic cations the pH-value of the medium goes below 6. An addition of KCl remains without effect,

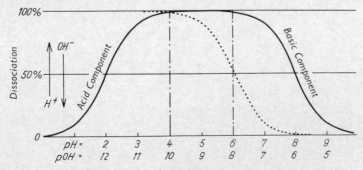

Fig. 150. Diagram of the dissociation on a cytoplasmic surface. The acid components have a pH of 1-2 and the basic components of apparently at least 8. There is a broad isoelectric zone between pH 4 and 6. With weaker basic dissociation (dotted curve) the isoelectric zone becomes narrower.

but $CaCl_2$ has a strongly protective effect and lowers the pH-optimum by at least a unit (LUNDEGÅRDH 1946).

One can of course in this case speak rather of a 'minus-calcium' effect. Even in organisms for which Ca is not an actual nutrient, this effect can play a part e.g. in the fungus *Gibberella* (LUNDEGÅRDH 1924). In the alga *Chlorella*, according to PIRSON (1937), calcium can be dispensed with at pH values greater than 4·5, but not in more acid media, in which Ca detoxifies the H-ions. The 'minus-calcium' effect can also explain many cases of lime deficiency and aversion to lime (see LUNDEGÅRDH 1957). PEARSALL in 1922 was already of the opinion that in many acid soils it is not the H-ion concentration but the lack of Ca ions that keeps out many plants.

The biological balance between NH_4- and NO_3-ions which is regulated by the pH has been studied by several workers. For example, with an acid reaction maize takes up little NH_4 but with an alkaline reaction it is flooded by ammonia (MEVIUS and ENGEL 1929). The variation in the ratio of NH_4 to NO_3 determined by the pH can also follow curves with many peaks (DASTUR 1925, 1953, LOO 1931).

Among the metabolic shifts connected with changes in internal pH it may finally be mentioned that according to WOOD (1933) the proteases are active at pH values between 3·5 and 9, whereas at pH $<5·5$ amino acids are accumulated. At pH $>5·5$, on the other hand, deamination takes place, with an optimum at pH 8-9, so that ammonia and amides are accumulated. These data apply to *Atriplex nummularia*, whose leaves show a normal pH value of 6·5; on continued wilting the value rises to 7·8. WOOD found both in leaves and roots a complicated chemical buffer system, in which a number of acids collaborate, e.g. between pH 3·0 and 5·3 oxalate, between pH 3·0 and 6·0 malate, between pH 5·2 and 8 phosphate and between pH 6 and 7 bicarbonate.

Chapter 8

THE WATER BALANCE

A. The Components of the Water Balance

The function of water as a medium and as a component of metabolism makes it of surpassing physiological and ecological importance.

Since plants, unlike animals, do not use water to remove waste products of metabolism, their water requirement is to a large extent limited to the water drawn osmotically into the cell. The limited water cycle shown by submerged hydrophytes is a consequence of the osmotically regulated transport of materials. Those nutrient ions and oxygen molecules which are absorbed through rhizoids, roots, leaves, etc., are for osmotic reasons (p. 283) always accompanied by certain amounts of water, which are excreted at different places together with expired CO_2 or exuded ions and molecules.

In hydrophytes the water balance offers no ecological problem, since the availability of water exceeds the consumption. Only in land plants does the unavoidable transpiration enter as a decisive factor into the balance. These plants are dependent on an appropriate supply of water from the soil, and so the conditions arise for an ecological plant-geographical differentiation. Like temperature, the availability of water is a dominant ecological factor determining the distribution of plants on the earth's surface. Along with light, water also contributes to the vertical zoning within plant communities.

If for the present we ignore ecologically specialised types of plant, the components of the water balance are: (1) *water uptake* from the soil, (2) *water transport* through the vascular system, and (3) *transpiration*.

The water uptake, as far as delivery is concerned, is dependent on the availability of the water found in the soil and on the retaining pressure. On the absorption side there is the active and passive water uptake of the roots and the suction pressure developed. The rate of movement through the plant is determined, not only by transpiration and the resultant hydrostatic suction force, but also by the number and dimensions of the vascular bundles and the possible conduction in the parenchyma. The transpiration depends on the size of the surface, and the distribution and peculiarities of the stomata in the aerial parts, especially the leaves. The stomata are conspicuous in this respect, but the anatomy of the leaf is equally important. The osmotic relationships, the osmotic values and the turgor extension of the organs and the existence of possible water containers, which even out fluctuations in the water balance, are also properties affecting the water cycle.

B. Water Uptake from the Soil

1 THE ABILITY OF THE SOIL TO SUPPLY WATER

The availability of soil water is determined by the rainfall and the *water capacity*, i.e.

the ability of the soil to retain water between the periods of precipitation and thereby to level out fluctuations in the water supply. That fraction of the rainfall which simply flows straight through the soil is termed *drainage* or *gravitational water,* and the fraction which is absorbed by soil particles is known as *capillary* or *hygroscopic (imbibitional) water.*

The water capacity is determined to a large extent by the ability of the soil colloids to swell, i.e. on their hydration, and their capillary suction force. The limitation of surface evaporation is very important in maintaining the supply of water in the soil. This is achieved agriculturally by breaking up the top layer of the soil. Deep ploughing in spring tends in the opposite direction, since it breaks the capillary connections with the subsoil and the water table. The same end is attained in nature through the 'förna' and also by the formation of a continuous plant cover. Mosses and förna, according to STÅLFELT (1937), reduce evaporation to a half, whereas covering the soil with a growth of *Polygonum hydropiper* increases its loss of water 5-7 times. This increase of course reflects the effect of transpiration.

The denser or looser texture of the soil surface also regulates the rate of drainage of rain. Even from level fields, according to SHREVE (1934), 5%-39% of the rain is lost. The amounts of water remaining in the soil can be determined in various ways. It has been suggested that the electrical resistance or the thermal conductivity should be measured (BOUYOUCOS and MICK 1940, CUNNINGS and CHANDLER 1940). The 'internal surface' of the soil can be measured by its capacity for adsorbing water vapour or other gases. The amount of heat generated on moistening a dry soil has also been suggested as a measure of the hygroscopicity.

Plants are unable to secure for themselves the whole of the soil water. The amounts finally remaining are held back with a force which exceeds the maximal suction power of the roots. The 'wilting point', as emphasised by SACHS in 1887, has different values for different plants and soils. According to GRADMANN (1932), wilting tends to start at 1% water content in sandy soils and at 8%-12% in humus soils. In the latter water is very immobile, and the soil colloids develop high swelling pressures.

The 'soil suction pressures' can be measured in various ways, e.g. by burying in the soil a porous flask with a vertical tube and a solution with a known osmotic pressure. If the solution rises in the tube, the soil suction pressure is lower than the osmotic pressure of the solution; but if it falls, the soil has the stronger suction. It has also been suggested that a soil sample should be enclosed in a glass bell-jar, hung with filter-paper strips impregnated with sugar solution. The strips are weighted, and by varying the concentration of the sugar solutions the osmotic pressure can be found at which water vapour is neither taken up from the soil nor yielded to it. This value is then assumed to be the same as the soil suction pressure (STOCKER 1930, GRADMANN 1934; a critique is given by ROUSCHAL 1938, HERTEL 1939).

In order that the roots may take up soil water, they must develop osmostic pressures which exceed the soil suction pressure. Since the root suction pressure is developed only if the turgor pressure falls below the osmotic pressure, roots are partially wilted by high suction pressures in the soil; but this does not usually appreciably diminish their viability.

The depth of the roots also determines the intensity of the water uptake. Steppe plants with deep roots can thus have an active transpiration even with relatively low osmotic pressures (VASILJEV 1930, BIRAUD 1938). The type and extent of the branching of the roots are also important; grass roots are excellently developed, and in addition grow very quickly (up to 5-6 cm per day), whilst e.g. pine roots grow much more slowly (PAVLYCHENKO 1937, DITTMER 1937). A rye plant is provided with several million roots of various sizes and with a total length of many kilometres, and the total daily growth in length is calculated as 4-5 km, to which billions of root hairs may be added. It is, therefore, not surprising that the plants can recover considerable amounts of water daily even from an apparently dry soil.

For the root growth of mesophytic plants, as also for active salt uptake, the supply of oxygen and the removal of CO_2, or in other words suitable *aeration*, are quite as important as soil moisture, and this requires a certain looseness and adequate drainage. According to CANNON (1925), the roots usually require 8%-10% of oxygen in the soil atmosphere, although weak growth occurs even at 0·5%-2%. BOYNTON and COMPTON (1944) obtained with apple-tree roots the following results:

0·1%-3% O_2—the roots survive but do not grow.
5%-10% O_2—roots grow but active water-transport is weak.
10%-12% O_2—water-transport is normal.
over 12% O_2—new roots form.

The *soil temperature* also strongly influences water uptake. ROUSCHAL (1935), NITSCHE (1937) *et al.* found that a fall from $+20°C$ to $+5°C$ reduced water absorption by *Calluna*, *Alnus*, *Phaseolus*, etc., as much as 50%-80%. A temperature drop may also diminish the transpiration, although to a lesser extent. The suction force of the roots, of course, increases with the relative water deficit of the upper parts of the plant. The decrease in mobility of the water on fall of temperature may be due partly to the viscosity, which doubles with a temperature drop from $+25°$ to $0°$, and partly to an increase in the viscosity of the protoplasm, which, over this temperature range, increases by 4-5 times.

2 ABSORPTION MECHANISMS

Water is absorbed by the whole length of the non-lignified roots, but the enlargement of its surface may favour the root-hair zone (SIERP and BREWIG 1935). Close contact of the hairs with the soil particles facilitates utilisation of the imbibitional and capillary water. At optimal moisture conditions, however, a good water supply appears to be secured even without root hairs; and the same applies for nutrient salt uptake. At high salt concentrations the absorption by the cells without root hairs (atrichoblasts) suffices, but at low concentrations the enlargement of the surface of the cells with root hairs (trichoblasts) increases efficiency. The capillary water appears to be surprisingly easily mobile, at least in a lateral direction (KRAMER 1944, 1945). As a rule, the life span of the root hairs is short, but certain species, e.g. orange trees (HAYWARD 1942), appear to be able to produce secondary root hairs from the hypodermal cells.

The older parts of roots behave as water suppliers only when there is a strong transpiration suction, and with an adequate supply from the medium. Active water uptake is relatively limited in amount, but may play a certain part in xerophytes with adaptations restricting transpiration. As explained above, the active process can bring into play strong suction forces, which are regulated, not by the static osmotic relations, but by the respiratory metabolism. These active processes may explain the fact sometimes observed (SIMONIS 1936, REPP 1939) that plants survive even when the soil suction forces temporarily exceed the osmotic value of the root tissue.

Water can also be passed as vapour from a point with high vapour pressure to one with lower, e.g. from the soil into the roots, if these show a lower vapour pressure. Such a movement of water, however, appears to play a subordinate part, although an uptake of water vapour occurs in tropical tree epiphytes whose roots do not reach the ground (RENNER 1932). Unicellular algae living epiphytically, e.g. *Pleurococcus vulgaris*, also thrive and multiply in an atmospheric humidity of only 62%. Here hygroscopic phenomena and imbibition probably also take part.

In normal cells of the roots of higher plants the swelling pressure of the protoplasm cannot exceed the osmotic value of the cell sap, since there is an equilibrium between the two. No hygroscopic water uptake seems to take place, and uptake is due to a combination of suction pressure according to the equation $Sp = O_v - Tg$ (p. 62) and active water transport (i.e. translocation governed by metabolism). A limited water uptake appears to take place in the aerial parts (leaves, etc.) during rain and mist or, in general, at high atmospheric humidity, e.g. in conifers and Ericaceae (MICHAELIS 1934). During the night green parts may take up a considerable amount of water (KESSLER 1932), and also in dew (LEICK 1932, ZATTLER 1932).

Of the two components of the rising water stream, the active rise and the transpiration, the former can at times predominate. In other cases the active water transport, measured as bleeding, may cease when the available water in the soil has fallen only to about one-half, whereas the transpiration suction still continues for some time.

3 ACTIVE WATER TRANSPORT

Although the bleeding of decapitated stems may not fully reproduce the active components of the rising sap stream in intact plants, it does give an approximate idea of it. The very great differences in the degree of bleeding in different species, to which there are no corresponding converse differences in the intensity of transpiration, give an indication of the subordinate importance of the active processes in water transport as a whole. Bleeding occurs also in ferns and has been observed even in water-plants, where the transport function of the active sap stream is quite clear.

A well-known example of strong bleeding is given by the sugar maple, which yields 5-6 litres per day or 25-75 litres of sap through the growing period. It is, however, surpassed by the birch, which can yield 675 litres of sap per growing period. Even herbs usually bleed so strongly that the total yield exceeds the volume of the plant by several times. Bleeding usually has a daily periodicity, with a minimum in the night and a maximum by day.

The general physico-chemical requirements for active transport of solutions were set forth by BROYER (1947) and others. As far as trees are concerned, SACHS early distinguished between bleeding resulting from root pressure and local exudation from the trunk. One can assume that in spring, when osmotically active substances, e.g. sugars, are mobilised in the wood parenchyma and passed into the vessels, a corresponding osmotic stream of water will also be activated (cf. EATON 1943, BURSTRÖM and KROGH 1947). In summer there is no appreciable active movement in isolated pieces of stem of birch, lime, hazel and willow (LUNDEGÅRDH 1954). A small and very slow upward movement of water may indeed be measured, but it is unimportant compared with root pressure.

While it cannot be doubted that sap rises actively in all higher plants, it is surprising that only a few trees bleed when decapitated. The total amount of the actively rising sap through a spring period is in any case not very important; this becomes clear from the fact that in wheat even about a sixth of the normal transpiration is sufficient to remove the actively rising water. In trees the trunk forms a large water reservoir and it may be surmised that this affords an explanation for the differences mentioned in the amount of external bleeding. This surmise is supported by observations on the seasonal variations in water content (Table 18):

Table 18
Water Content of Tree Trunks at Different Seasons (after LUNDEGÅRDH 1954)

Season	Water content (% of dry weight)		
	Lime	Birch	Oak
Summer	115	98	77
Winter	162	96	89

From the table it is seen that the wood of the birch, which bleeds, is unable to store water above its summer values, whereas the woods of the non-bleeding oak and lime store considerable amounts of water in winter. This reserve can probably take up at least part of the active water, so that bleeding is excluded. GIBBS (1939) also found the water-content at its maximum at the time of the bursting of the buds.

4 OSMOTIC RELATIONSHIPS

The normal osmotic value of the water-absorbing root cells is a decisive factor ecologically. Plants whose root cells are plasmolysed for considerable periods of time do not remain alive. In some specialised steppe or desert plants the dilemma is solved by the roots dying off in the dry periods and then being renewed when water returns (cf. STOCKER 1930, 1933). In others some roots penetrate down to the soil-water level and provide for water uptake (WEAVER *et al.* 1934).

The connection between the osmotic values of plants (the roots unfortunately have seldom been investigated) and the water factor of their location has been discussed by many workers. On the whole it is found that there is a parallel variation, in that xerophytes show higher pressures than mesophytes (ILJIN 1929, BRAUN-BLANQUET 1931, WOOD 1934) and the osmotic values also reflect in detail the relative dryness of the location (YOSHII and JIMBO 1931, MALLERY 1935, SIMONIS 1936). The early data obtained by the plasmolytic method with occasional very high pressures are unreliable, according to WALTER (1935). VOLK (1937), however, found by the cryoscopic method values up to 80-102 atm in some xerophytes (*Aster linosyris, Potentilla arenaria, Carex humilis*).

A direct relation also exists between the osmotic values of plants and the concentration of the soil solution (KNODEL 1939); the former are ordinarily the higher by about 5-6 atm. All this can of course be referred to the physiological fact that the active mechanism of the roots accumulates available salts and that the intensity of this process is in a positive relation to the external concentration (p. 263). Properties specific to the species also contribute to developing really high pressures, since the cells obviously possess a regulating mechanism which prevents excessive pressures (cf. LUNDEGÅRDH 1958).

Exceptionally it happens that the average osmotic value of a plant is less than that of the soil (BEHR-NEGENDANK 1939 on *Salicornia herbacea*). In this case obviously active water-transport by the roots must play a decisive part (cf. Chap. 6 B), but it is to be presumed that the osmotic value of the roots is higher than that of the aerial parts.

In seaweeds, whose thallus is surrounded by an aqueous medium, one finds, as expected, higher pressures than in the sea water (according to KYLIN 1938, 31-55 atm as against 23 atm). These seaweeds also often have high imbibitional pressures in the cell walls, which are not fully swollen in sea water. In fresh water the walls swell so strongly that the cell content is compressed. The seaweeds of the surf zone usually show higher values, which according to BIEBL (1937) is connected with their periodic drying out.

Apparent exceptions to the rule of a direct connection between the water relationships of the location and the osmotic values are supplied by those plants which raise soil water poor in salts by means of deeply penetrating roots. Plants equipped with large water storage tissues are also less sensitive towards dry periods, which they survive without water uptake.

These examples underline the great importance of a regulated water balance. Plants appear to develop high cell sap pressures only when it becomes necessary to take up water against high soil suction pressures. This adaptability in regulating the water balance is also encountered in the seasonal variations of the osmotic pressures. Many plants show higher pressures in winter (THREN 1934, SIMONIS 1936). Frost damage in winter is usually due to the greater difficulty of water uptake from frozen ground or to restricted water conduction in the frozen xylem (cf. SCHMIDT 1936, TAGAWA 1937).

The power of adaptation to increased soil suction pressure is, as mentioned, determined to a large extent genetically. Chemical properties are also concerned, e.g. the ability of halophytes to endure high NaCl-concentrations. The osmotic range can naturally vary and with it the ability to withstand strong variations in the water factor. The overall water balance is of course the decisive thing. It may happen, for example, that a variety of sugar beet which is little resistant to drought has higher osmotic values than a more drought-resistant variety, if the latter is equipped with more quickly reacting stomata and a less sensitive photosynthetic system (STOCKER *et al.* 1944).

A wide osmotic amplitude seems to be especially characteristic of alpine plants (YOSHII and JIMBO 1931). An increase in the osmotic values of the roots is connected either with increased salt uptake (see above) or with accumulation of sugars, organic acids, etc. Some degree of self-regulation follows heavy water loss in dry soil, since the elastic cells are thereby diminished in volume and in this way increase their osmotic pressure (STEINER 1939).

5 THE RESISTANCE TO TRANSPORT IN THE PLANT

Part of the water taken up from the soil moves in the cell walls (STRUGGER 1938), but the main part of the transpiration stream must go through the interior of the cell including the protoplasmic lining. The permeability of the protoplasm, whose water content is not very high (for wheat protoplasm about 30% was found; LUNDEGÅRDH 1958), therefore acts to a certain extent as a regulator. Investigations on the flow at constant suction pressure (LUNDEGÅRDH 1945, 1947) have shown that the presence of salts has a relatively small effect, although a slight increase in permeability by calcium and a decrease by potassium were observed (about the influence of salt see also LUNDE-GÅRDH 1911). KRAMER (1939), RICHARDS *et al.* (1940) and others also mention a regulating influence by the protoplasm of the cortical cells. Water penetration may be restricted to some extent by a low pH-value, but this has so far not been confirmed.

Further re-examination is also necessary for the scattered data about salt effects on the speed of water transport and transpiration. For example, WIENKE (1940) stated that potassium salts accelerate the transpiration stream; but an analysis of the cause of this has not yet been given. Here many individual effects are in competition. With long-continued salt effects the differentiation of tissues may also be involved, and in addition one must remember that the active water transport, which is strongly influenced by salts, always participates as a component of the transpiration stream to a small extent. The active stream amounts to 15%-20% of the maximal transpiration of young wheat plants. A favourable effect of potassium ions may thus, at least partly, be connected wth the easy mobility of the potassium salts.

If suction is applied to a decapitated root system surrounded by an aqueous solution, the amounts of water passing through show that the stream encounters very little resistance. The resistance of the epidermis and cortex to penetration is thus very small. The water drawn through these tissues passes directly into the open vessels, and, in herbaceous plants, partly also into the intercellular spaces, which can function as reserve conducting channels.

SIERP and BREWIG (1935) observed that increased demands on transpiration water increase water transport. This was observed also in wheat plants (Fig. 151). SIERP and BREWIG state that the phenomenon is due to bringing in the older parts of the roots. It can be imagined that the water passes through breaks in the surface into the intercellular spaces and thence into the vessels. HAYWARD (1942) states that with strong transpiration suction, water can pass even through suberised root surfaces. Water penetrates also through dead roots (KRAMER 1933).

In trees the water flows both through the youngest vessels and through the tracheids (see section C). In cut twigs it flows preferentially through the wide vessels which in the living tree tend to be partly filled with air. Experiments with hydrostatic suction on cut pieces give no conclusive insight into the mechanism of water transport in the intact tree trunk. Similarly, the rapid rise of coloured solutions in the wide vessels of excised twigs does not show that these represent the main conductive pathways of the normal transpiration stream. In an excised twig the vessels come into direct contact with the water, which then rises rapidly because of the capillary effect. Any air present escapes into the intercellular spaces. When the twig is inverted, i.e. placed with the excised tip in water and with the base reaching up into the air, the capillary rise in the large vessels proceeds very much faster, since the air bubbles can now come directly out of the cut surface. The height of the capillary rise in the vessels often amounts to 1-2 m.

Water under pressure flows much more quickly through a piece of oak wood (which has large vessels, cf. below) than the transpiration stream flows in the intact tree. If the large vessels are plugged up by precipitated calcium oxalate, the rate of flow falls to about one-seventh, which thus corresponds to the flow through the wide and medium-wide tracheids. This flow, however, suffices completely for the normal water balance of the tree.

On the basis of a great number of measurements on the tissue elements of the wood of lime, birch and oak the following average values for the lumen and the wall thickness were obtained:

Table 19

Anatomical Dimensions of Vessels and Tracheids measured on Cross-sections of Trunks (after LUNDEGÅRDH 1954)

A. Vessels

Species of tree	Number per mm²	Cross-section in μ (and average)	Area in μ²	Percentage of the total cross-section of the trunk
Tilia europaea	197	20—90 (40)	1,070	20
Betula alba	175	10—70 (40)	890	15
Quercus robur	10	20—220 (95)	7,100	7

B. Tracheids (average of 50-160 cells)

Species of tree	Dimensions in μ	Wall-thickness in μ	Average area in μ²		Percentage of the trunk	
			lumen	wall	lumen	wall
Tilia						
early wood*	23·8 × 14·7	1·2	350	48	88	12
late wood†	12·8 × 8·4	1·5	108	34	76	24
Betula	11·7 × 7·2	2·1	84	44	66	34
Quercus I	6·5 × 4·0	2·9	26	39	40	60
Quercus II	10·3 × 6·1	2·7	63	52	55	45
Quercus III	14·1 × 6·8	2·5	96	59	62	38

*80% | of the total area.
†20% |

C. Area of the conducting elements in the wood

Species of tree	Percentages of the trunk		
	Vessels	Tracheids	
		Lumen	Walls
Tilia	20	69	11
Betula	15	56	29
Quercus	7	45	48

These anatomical measurements, in conjunction with experimental observations of the movements of water and air in the trunks of trees, confirm a conclusion drawn from the absence of vessels in certain groups of trees. They suggest that the main stream of the transpiration water flows through the tracheids, whilst the wide vessels, which unlike the tracheids are partly filled with air, serve as reserve conducting elements and combined water- and air-containers.

Most of the water in the wood remains imbibed in the cell walls, but a part is always enclosed in the lumina of the tracheids and probably also in the youngest vessels. The majority of the large vessels and the wider tracheids also contain air. The medium-wide and narrower tracheids, on the other hand, are completely filled with water and, together with the wood parenchyma, form a coherent water path from the roots to the leaves. Anatomical measurements on the wood of lime, birch and oak (given above) show that the majority of the tracheids are fairly narrow capillaries.

For understanding the water transport in woody stems it is vitally important to know how much of the water normally present is actually mobile enough to serve as a transport medium for the transpiration flow.

It may be expected, in the first place, that the movement of water will meet with considerable resistance in the lignified walls of the woody cells, and that the rate of movement in the lumina of vessels and tracheids will be largely determined by their capillary dimensions. These questions were clarified in a comprehensive research on lime trees, birches and oaks in which centrifugation was used to determine the degree of mobility of the water (LUNDEGÅRDH 1954). Pieces from freshly felled tree-trunks 10 cm long were subjected to a centrifugal force of $1,400 \times g$ in the longitudinal direction. The water driven out at the upper end was measured at intervals of 20 minutes. The total water content was determined at the end of the experiment by long drying at 105°C. As Fig. 152 shows, even after long-continued (200 minutes) centrifuging only about 15%-20% of the total water content of a fresh piece of stem was expelled. The remaining 80%-85% corresponds to the 'relatively immobile water' whose speed of transport is quite inadequate to supply the water of transpiration or to act as a protection against wilting in dry periods.

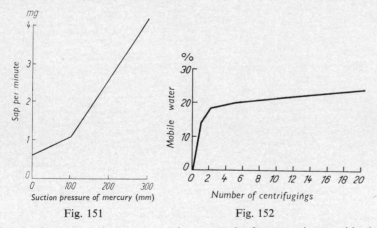

Fig. 151   Fig. 152

Fig. 151. Relation between suction pressure and water uptake, from experiments with wheat seedlings (after LUNDEGÅRDH 1945).

Fig. 152. The removal of the easily-mobile water by centrifuging from a piece of birch 10 cm long. Each centrifuging lasted 20 minutes at 1400 g. The mobile water is expressed as a percentage of the total water in the intact trunk (after LUNDEGÅRDH 1954).

The relatively immobile water corresponds to the imbibitional water of the cell walls and partly also to the water in the narrowest tracheids. It is retained during wilting. Only complete desiccation of the wood changes the capillary structure of the walls in such a way that the water now becomes somewhat more mobile (Fig. 154) The mobility of the water in the wood is subject to seasonal variations and is greater

Z

in winter than in summer. This may be due to the larger tracheids, in which the water resistance remains low, also being filled with water during the winter.

It seems, then, that the rapidly mobile water (Fig. 152) comes mostly from the medium-sized tracheids. The largest tracheids, like most vessels, contain much air. Tracheids with middle-sized lumina and the narrowest tracheids certainly have continuous filaments of water.

According to Poiseuille's law the resistance to transport in capillaries varies inversely with the fourth power of the diameter. The relative resistance to transport of the tracheids actually present, according to their relative sizes, is given in Table 20.

Table 20

Calculated relative Resistance to Transport in Tracheids (after LUNDEGÅRDH 1954)

		Diameter in μ					
	4	8	12	16	20	30	40
Relative resistance to transport	1000	63	13	4	1·6	0·3	0
Percentages of the dimensions { Tilia	17	20	22	20	21	0	0
Betula	21	30	6	0	0	0	0
Quercus	40	16	7	0	0	0	0

N.B. The two largest sizes correspond to the dimensions of vessels.

One can assert *a priori* that the narrowest tracheids, which show a resistance to transport about 10,000 times higher than that of the vessels, transport very little water. The oak has a very large number of these very narrow tracheids. The easily mobile water is for the greater part to be looked for in the tracheids with dimensions above

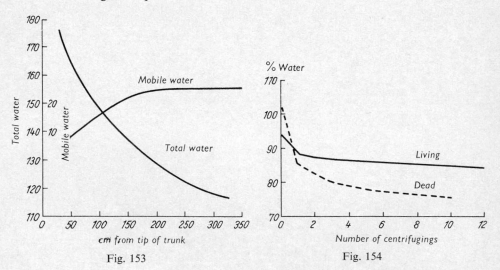

Fig. 153   Fig. 154

Fig. 153. The amount of 'total water' (expressed as a percentage of the dry weight) and 'mobile water' (as a percentage of the total water) at different levels of a birch trunk.

Fig. 154. Differences in the water-retaining power in living wood and in wood that has been killed by desiccation, then re-wetted. More water is removed from the latter by centrifuging (after LUNDE-GÅRDH 1954).

about 10 μ, which in *Tilia* forms 72%, in *Betula* 18% and in *Quercus* 11% of all tracheids. This order agrees with the relative volumes of the easily-mobile water, which follows the order *Tilia* > *Betula* > *Quercus*. Since in the tracheids of 8-12 μ diameter the resistance to transport is 100-600 times greater than in the vessels, it is evident that even a few young, water-filled vessels would suffice to transport the same amount of water as the whole of the medium-sized tracheids.

We thus come to the conclusion that the rising transpiration stream in the xylem of trees follows the wide and medium tracheids and vessels, provided that they are not blocked by air bubbles. The dimensions of the wide and medium tracheids satisfy high requirements for water conduction, but it is mostly assumed that the water flows preferentially in the younger annual rings (GIBBS 1935, 1939, MÜLLER 1949), and this would probably imply that the young vessels also help.

The youngest annual rings of the tree trunk contain, in *Tilia* and *Betula*, 20%-30% more water than the older (in *Quercus* this is not the case). The water is, however, anchored in the cell walls which are highly swollen. The younger parts of the wood do not contain more readily mobile water than the older. This result supports the idea that the older middle-sized tracheids also help in the conduction of water. The wider tracheids and the vessels on the other hand are mostly filled with air. That the medium tracheids actually help the passage of the transpiration water is shown by the comparison in Table 21 between the speeds of transport calculated according to Poiseuille's law and the amount of the easily mobile water determined experimentally.

Table 21
(after LUNDEGÅRDH 1954)

	Species of tree		
	Tilia	*Betula*	*Quercus*
Calculated relative speeds of transport—			
in the large vessels	0·4	0·3	1·0
in the tracheids	8·5	3·0	1·0
Experimentally-determined easily-mobile water			
(ratio)	13·8	8·8	1·0

C. The Transport of Water

It follows from what has been said in the previous section, that the rate of movement of the transpiration stream is determined by the cross-sectional area of the conducting elements and therefore varies with anatomical characteristics. The rate is, of course, regulated in the last resort by the suction pressure in the leaves. FARMER (1918) investigated the transport rate per unit of cross-sectional area in 60 woody plants and found high speeds in *Quercus robur* and *Fagus sylvatica*, medium speeds in *Pyrus malus* and *Euonymus europaeus* and low in *Taxus baccata* and *Prunus laurocerasus*. Direct measurements carried out by COSTER (1931) indicated speeds of 50-80 cm per minute in herbs and undershrubs, 100 cm per minute in tomatoes and bushes, 100-200 cm per minute in trees and a maximal 250 cm per minute in lianes.

HUBER (1932) and HUBER and SCHMIDT (1936, 1937) used a thermo-electric method to measure the speed of flow in intact trunks of trees. A thermocouple was inserted into the trunk and connected with a galvanometer; then a part of the trunk below the thermocouple was locally heated. The warmed water in the vessels flows upwards and the speed is calculated from the time interval between heating and the movement of the galvanometer (see also BAUMGARTNER 1934). For the same purpose one can also use radioactive isotopes, which are injected at a certain distance from a Geiger-Müller tube inserted into the trunk. LUNDEGÅRDH (1954) inserted two parallel silver electrodes and injected a salt solution at a known distance. Here the change in the conductivity between the electrodes served as the indicator. The method can also be used to determine the electrolyte concentration of the sap.

In forest trees HUBER found similar speeds of transport to COSTER, i.e. up to 75 cm per minute. Ring-porous trees (*Quercus*, *Robinia*, *Fraxinus* and *Castanea*) show high speeds (30-75 cm per minute), whilst the diffuse-porous (*Populus*, *Juglans*, *Tilia*, *Acer*, *Carpinus* and *Fagus*) attain only 1·7-10 cm per minute. HUBER suggested as an ecological result of these differences that the ring-porous trees could spread into dry regions whereas the diffuse-porous were dependent on a moister climate. GILBERT (1940) considers the former as the more highly developed. Their water transport system may, however, be adapted to shorter growing periods (HANDLEY 1936).

Measurements by LUNDEGÅRDH (1954) on young oaks showed considerably lower speeds than those mentioned above, that is 1 cm per minute at most. Even in excised twigs with transpiring leaves the rate of rise of dye solutions in the vessels was not more than about 2 cm per minute. These values agree well with measurements of the uptake of transpiration water into young, cut trees (see below and Table 23, p. 346). It was found that a water stream which flows with a speed of about 1 cm per minute requires only about 25% of the total cross-sectional area for the conduction, which agrees well with the anatomical results above. Values of a similar order of magnitude for the speed of the transpiration stream seem to apply also for moss; ZACHERL (1956) here found a speed of about 2-3 cm per minute.

An investigation of the resistance to conduction in various tissues (KÖCKEMANN 1932) confirmed the relatively high permeability in the longitudinal direction of the wood (WARNE 1942). The resistance to conduction in the leaf veins is also small as compared with the relatively high resistance to the passage from the vessels into the mesophyll (MER 1940). There is also an apparent block in the transpiration stream at the point of attachment of the leaf, i.e. in the abscission layer. This may be due to a local constriction of the vessels passing through it (ROUSCHAL 1941). Local zones of resistance are found also in the intercalary growth zone of the grass leaf and at the transition between root and shoot, where the vascular bundles are anatomically rearranged. According to KRAMER (1945) the resistance to transpiration in the parenchyma may often be so high that wilting can occur even with an adequate water supply. This does not apply to the root parenchyma.

Of great interest is STÅLFELT's discovery (1954) about the effect of a water deficit on the fluidity of the protoplasm. He mentions that a mere deficit of 5% greatly increases the viscosity of the protoplasm. This finding throws light on the sensitivity of shade plants towards small water losses which is often great, and may perhaps also be used to explain observed transpiration changes which are not connected with movements of the stomata. Changes in the consistency of the protoplasm may possibly influence also its permeability to water (cf. also ORDIN and KRAMER 1956). It is known that the specific transpiration intensity changes with the age of the leaves (HOLZL 1955).

With strongly depressed transpiration, the rising sap stream is driven actively into the stem xylem. That the hydrostatic forces at work are sufficient to raise the water to quite considerable heights follows from the recent investigations on bleeding pressures. It may on the other hand be doubted whether the active sap stream plays a practical part in sap movements except in early spring. The considerable capillary conduction in the lignified walls of the conducting elements asserted by SACHS (1887) has not been confirmed by later investigations (LUNDEGÅRDH 1954), which show the very small mobility of water in the wall.

This relative immobility is specially apparent in the walls of the younger parts of the trunk. In dead wood the water in the wall is 2-5 times more mobile, which however is still always insufficient. KRAMER (1941) has observed that in a decapitated plant the bleeding ceases even with a water-content of the soil which is above the normal wilting point of the intact plant. This is not surprising, since water can be sucked passively even through a plasmolysed root, and since bleeding and transpiration are separate physiological processes. Transpiration causes a suction pressure which adds the necessary extra amount of water to that from bleeding. As the root pressure always adds on to the suction force in the leaves, one can of course also say that the root pressure is a factor favouring transpiration, which was also observed by RUFELT (1956) in wheat plants.

That in summer there is usually a negative suction pressure in the xylem of trees can be demonstrated in various ways. One can e.g. cut off a twig under a coloured liquid or under mercury. The liquid then penetrates into the opened vessels as a result of the negative pressure (SACHS 1887, KRAMER 1939). LUNDEGÅRDH (1954) connected closed mercury manometers to water-filled bore-holes in the trunks of *Tilia*, *Betula* and *Quercus*. Negative pressures then appeared in all trees, and in *Betula* attained a level of −260 mm of mercury. Water supplied was sucked in through the bore-holes.

The problem of a continuous suction flow through a tube system, whose height exceeds that of a water barometer, i.e. about 10 m, has long aroused the attention of plant physiologists. SACHS (1887) was of the opinion that capillary forces must be responsible. He thought of the vessels as the paths of transport, that is of cross-sections of 0·06-0·70 mm. The capillary rise in these is modest, at most 1-2 m, and SACHS thus found himself obliged to look for still finer capillaries, and ended with the micro-capillaries of the cellulose cell walls. We have seen above that these micro-capillaries in fact show a very high resistance, so that the water contained in them is practically immobile and in any case is not available for normal transpiration.

From the physical point of view indeed a coherent water column can attain a con-siderably greater height than 10 m without breaking, provided that no air is dissolved in it. The cohesion of the water is assisted also by the adhesion of the capillary walls. DIXON, RENNER, URSPRUNG and other defenders of the so-called *cohesion theory* maintained that the cohesion of the water was able to support negative pressures of 150-350 atm. If the water in the vessels has such a high cohesion, it should be able to support without difficulty negative pressures of 3-10 atm, which suffice to raise water to the crown of even the highest trees (*Sequoia gigantea* has a maximum height of 130 m). But there is the critical difficulty that tree-trunks always contain considerable amounts of air.

The living wood of lime, birch and oak normally contains about as much air as water. This air is under atmospheric pressure, and is not at the negative suction pressure of the water-columns. It is, however, hard to believe that none of it would be dissolved in the rising transpiration water. There is also dissolved CO_2 from the respiration of living cells in the trunk.

Ideas about the magnitude of the suction pressure proceeding from the leaves are greatly exaggerated. Carefully measured pressures in the water columns of tree-trunks (LUNDEGÅRDH 1954) have never given values higher than about $-1/3$ atm. There is therefore no experimental basis for assuming that water is sucked in a coherent column from the roots up to the leaves. On the other hand, on the basis of experimental observation it cannot be doubted that continuously flowing water filaments do exist in the living tree. The apparent dilemma can be resolved only if one assumes a continuous moistening system which brings water at any height laterally into the conducting channels, so that a vacuum is not formed at any point.

GODLEWSKI, a pupil of SACHS, asserted that the wood parenchyma cells are involved; they certainly possess the osmotic forces necessary to raise water to great heights. GODLEWSKI imagined a kind of osmotic pump, and assumed that the wood parenchyma cells suffered periodic variations of osmotic pressure. This hypothesis is unsupported by any actual observations, and it would be difficult to understand mechanically how such variations in pressure would work. The idea that the rows of living cells distributed in the wood fulfil some function in the water transport system is, however, undoubtedly right, and one can only wonder that it should have been completely overlooked by later workers.

The presence of turgid living cells, whose walls are in places in direct contact with the wood elements, means that an equilibrium exists between the osmotically maintained water of the former and the water in the vessel walls. The living tree trunk is actually encircled by a closed layer of moist cells, i.e. the cambium and its living derivatives. To this is added also the wood parenchyma. There is an equilibrium between the living cells and the tracheid water-absorbing vessel walls such that at atmospheric pressure the living cells associated with the sap stream are fully distended, i.e. they develop a suction pressure of nil. When there is a suction pressure in the sap stream of, say, $1/3$ atm, the cells are so far relaxed that they show a suction pressure of the same magnitude.

An equilibrium (actually 'steady state') of course exists also between the suction pressure of the living cells and the imbibition pressure of the vascular and tracheidal walls, which therefore lose water when there is a negative pressure in the vessels. This equilibrium extends also to those wood elements which are not in direct contact with living cells. The fact that the younger wood elements are to a certain extent preferred as channels of conduction is explained by their proximity to the cambium ring.

Thanks to the buffering action of the living elements just described, with an adequate water supply saturation of the conducting tissues is secured at every level in the trunk. This prevents the formation of a vacuum or the appearance of air bubbles, as follows also from the transpiration suction pressures actually measured, which are very moderate. The considerable amount of air contained in the large vessels and partly in the large tracheids, especially in older parts of the wood, thus cannot destroy the continuous water filaments in the conducting tracheids and young vessels. A critical situation arises only with insufficient water supply and in this respect a study of the wilting of trees is very instructive.

Young trees were sawn through near to the ground and the trunk left in a vertical position near the stump. The transpiration of the foliage continued until wilting began. The trunk was then divided into parts, in which the easily mobile and the total water were determined by the methods previously mentioned. The results are reproduced in Table 22, from which it follows that a surprisingly small amount of the total water in the trunk is available for transpiration. In *Tilia* and *Betula* even the 'easily mobile water' is only partly consumed. It is equally striking that the younger parts of the wood near the tip retain more water than the older parts at the base. This fact is due to the stronger water absorption by the cell walls of the younger wood mentioned above.

Table 22

The Water Relationships in Wilting Trees about 4 m high. The Values are expressed as percentages of the Dry Weight (after LUNDEGÅRDH 1954)

	Species of tree		
	Tilia	*Betula*	*Quercus*
Water in the intact trunk	121%	106%	77%
Water in the stem of the wilting tree	109%	93%	68%
Available water	12%	13%	9%
Easily mobile water, total	24%	22%	9%

Distribution of the water content (birch tree)

	Metres from the tip		
	0·6	1·9	3·2
Water on wilting	90%	81%	71%

All the known facts suggest that the cause of wilting is a gradual filling of the water-conducting elements with air. This results from rising suction pressure, from the abundant supply of air in the trunk, or as a result of the breaking of the water filaments. The 'JAMIN chains' which arise are shown by experience to reduce very greatly the ability of the conducting tissues to transport water. Air of course penetrates most easily into the open vessels, already acting mainly as air canals. The tracheids make possible a fairly free passage of water in the longitudinal direction by means of their oblique end walls furnished with pores. The longitudinal walls, also provided with pores, allow some movement transversely.

The pores let air through only with difficulty and so form an effective protection against its entry. The wider tracheids in particular are nevertheless, at least in places, gradually filled with air bubbles and thus eliminated as water transporters. The values in Table 22 refer to the situation at the beginning of wilting. Even when wilting is complete there remains at least 60% of water in the trunk.

The filling of the tracheids with air is probably mostly irreparable, since the air, once it is brought in under strong suction pressure, cannot readily be driven out again through the pores, especially as corresponding positive pressures are seldom developed.

SACHS (1887) observed that wood once dried offers a greater resistance to conduction of water than normally moist wood. On the other hand, it is likely that the air in the wider vessels is easily driven out again, e.g. by root pressure. The vessels can therefore be considered as water reservoirs, which are filled when water is abundant but otherwise function partly as ventilation canals.

The refilling of the vessels and of the wide tracheids with water becomes evident if the stump of a felled tree is at once covered with water; water is then sucked in and conversely air comes out. The explanation is to be sought in the fact that in the intact tree, on account of the negative pressure due to transpiration, the water columns are under negative suction and capillary pressures, which are relaxed by decapitation. The air in the living wood, on the other hand, is in equilibrium with the surrounding atmosphere through the lenticels, etc. If the stump is left exposed, an amount of air corresponding to the imbibitional and capillary filling of the conductive elements can flow out without difficulty.

Table 23
Calculation of the Capillary Forces in Wood (after LUNDEGÅRDH 1954)

Species of tree	Observed suction pressure	Capillary suction	
		Calculated level	Calculated pressure
Lime	−80 mm Hg	150 cm water	−114 mm Hg
Birch	−260 mm Hg	300 cm water	−230 mm Hg
Oak	—	750 cm water	−530 mm Hg

The capillary forces calculated from the average tracheid dimensions as measured are reproduced in Table 23. It follows from the Table that not inconsiderable capillary forces are developed in the wood. The parallelism between the observed suction pressures and the calculated capillary suction pressures suggests that in the living wood capillary forces play a not unimportant part. As mentioned above, it is unlikely that the capillary tracheids admit air under the moderate transpiration suction pressure. The capillaries are only slightly compressed elastically. On release of the pressure they suck in a corresponding amount of water.

The elasticity of the wood elements is also shown by the fact that a piece of wood shrinks on drying by 9%-14%. The filling of the elastically compressed tissue elements with water can also be studied in excised pieces of trunk. In 24 hours they imbibe 5%-6% of water, part of which is turgidity water. The sudden release of the elastic tension on cutting a branch under water or mercury causes the previously-mentioned penetration into the vessels. A certain elasticity of the lumina of the conducting elements is also assumed by BROUWER (1954).

The root pressure which sets in with full force during damp still nights or in rain, for example, when transpiration sinks almost to zero, can be considered as a 'water-filling mechanism' of the vessels, in those herbs and trees which develop sufficient root activity. Similarly the water content of tree trunks (cf. Table 18) increases in winter, although air still remains in them.

The driving force of the transpiration stream is the evaporation of water from the leaf surfaces. On account of the evaporation the turgor of the epidermis and mesophyll cells sinks, and there arises an osmotic suction force according to the equation

$Sp = O_v - Tg$. Water thus flows from the conducting tissue, giving rise to the mano-metrically measurable suction pressure. From the moderate level of this pressure it follows that the turgidity of the leaves normally sinks only a little.

The turgor of mesophyte leaves can sink until 25% of their water is lost without causing wilting (cf. MAXIMOV 1929 [*Helianthus*], HÄRDTL 1930), whilst with shade plants this limit can be reached even with a loss of 2%-3% of water. The osmotic values of deciduous trees lies at a medium height of 12-20 atm (e.g. birch, oak, walnut, etc.) and so can develop high suction pressures in critical periods; but, as we have seen, this may introduce a danger of irreparable damage to some of the tracheids. Desiccation of the tips of trees is, of course, not uncommon, and unfortunately cannot be cured.

Sun leaves of tree-like prairie plants have osmotic values which lie 2-5 atm higher than those of the shade leaves (MARSH 1941). Shade plants can however also, according to PISEK and CARTELLIERI (1932), show pressures of 9-13 atm, with daily variations of 2 atm. In this connection reference has been made to the reduction of transpiration by a reduced vapour pressure. The permeability for water may also be lowered on account of the partial reduction of swelling connected with the high osmotic value (BOON-LONG 1941). In the preliminary stages of wilting these factors have a self-regulating effect on the transpiration, since in wilting the osmotic values rise auto-matically.

The controversy about the relations between osmotic value and water transport in trees has already been referred to. It has been shown that the transpiration suction is determined, not by the osmotic value as such, but only by the suction pressure due to loss of water, whereas the full value of the osmotic pressure represents a kind of insurance against catastrophe. We have seen above that the necessary suction pres-sures when water supply is good are actually very variable. A kind of gradation of the suction pressures from below upwards is thus quite superfluous and in fact has been shown to be undesirable. DIXON and ATKINS (1915-16) for the press sap of *Populus alba* describe a weak rise: root 13·2, trunk cortex 14·6, young leaves 16·0, mature leaves 17·9 atm. Such a gradation can, however, be explained just as well secondarily by the deposition of salt from the sap stream. Salts are in general readily accumulated at the end points of transport paths.

The connection between salt transport and transpiration was discussed in Chapter 6. Salts may be carried passively from the soil; but the active processes increase their availability, since they are brought to a higher concentration level. Similar interpreta-tions were put forward by BROYER and HOAGLAND (1943). The increased concentra-tion of the rising sap due to active processes has been shown experimentally (LUNDE-GÅRDH 1945, 1950). It is obvious that transpiration hastens the removal of salts actively exuded into the lower parts of the vessels and thus indirectly assists the continuation of the active uptake. Improved aeration of the roots with air-saturated water and the simultaneous removal of the CO_2 formed, also have a favourable effect and benefit the leaves too.

HYLMÖ (1953) and others have returned to the case for assuming a fairly extensive passive movement of salts in the transpiration stream. The advocates of this idea believe that the soil solution is drawn through the protoplasm and the cell walls, without acquiring any considerable addition from the salts actively accumulated in the cell vacuoles. This neglects, however, the exudation from the vacuoles which has actually been shown, and also the consideration that, between salts in the cell sap and salts in the protoplasm and cell walls, there is a dual equilibrium, thanks to which salts from the vacuoles are passed into the vessels as required. Passive translocation of salts does, of course, occur in the transpiration water, particularly through older parts of the root; ideas of its efficiency however, are often exaggerated.

The initial salt absorption in the protoplasm brings the salts to a concentration 10-12 times higher than that of the external medium (p. 263), but this absorption is by its very nature an adsorption and exchange phenomenon and cannot by itself increase the salt concentration of the transpiration water. The assertions of WRIGHT (1939) and BÖTTIGER and BEHLING (1939), that P, K and NO_3 are taken up by means of vital processes, whereas Ca usually accompanies the transpiration stream direct, are also doubtful. They overlook the great differences in the speed of transport, which we have discussed above. Calcium is much less mobile in the tissues than potassium is. Calcium that has once entered the leaves does not readily migrate back down the phloem, as potassium does. All the complications caused by the different speeds of migration must be taken into account before reliable conclusions can be drawn about the nature of the transport.

D. Transpiration

1 THE GENERAL IMPORTANCE OF TRANSPIRATION

Transpiration has relatively little effect on the general energy balance of the plant. The energy required for evaporation is taken mainly from the surroundings, and the fall in temperature of transpiring leaves is usually unimportant (see below). On the other hand, the work done in maintaining the water balance, or the force raising the sap stream, is supplied by transpiration.

Even though the transpiration stream, as has been mentioned in the preceding paragraphs, can scarcely by itself supply all the salts required, it still has an important function for their supply to the upper parts e.g. of trees. In such plants the active sap stream is far too weak to bring the salts accumulated in the roots up to the growing shoots. When this important function is fulfilled, any further increase in transpiration is usually an 'unavoidable evil'. Measures to restrict transpiration are therefore one of the most important ecological adaptations.

Thus it must be considered established that many herbaceous plants are adequately supplied with salts by the active salt stream itself, whereas among trees root pressure suffices to fulfil this function only in 'bleeding' ones. In 'non-bleeding' trees, which form the great majority, the active stream undoubtedly rises some way up the trunk, but is cancelled out merely by the transpiration of the bark, buds, etc., alone. To its function of passing water through, the transpiration stream adds a passive transport of salts. In general, there is a certain, but usually not very pronounced, correlation between the intensity of transpiration and the salt content of the leaves.

The transpiration balance may indirectly also have morphological results. It is e.g. considered that the differentiation between shade and sun leaves is determined more by differences in transpiration than in illumination (BÖTTIGER and BEHLING 1939; cf. LUNDEGÅRDH 1957, Chap. 2). Varying soil humidity may also determine leaf sizes and the frequency of the stomata (NIEMANN 1932). According to CLEMENTS (1937), soya beans in times of drought become richer in hemicellulose and N-compounds, with the result that more turgescence water is retained (cf. also KOKETSU 1932). The water content of the leaves, according to WOODS, PETRIE *et al.*, regulates the balance between amino acids and proteins (cf. Chap. 5). It is clear that in these and many other cases the induction of morphological and biochemical changes in development is not directly dependent on transpiration, but that changes in the degree of hydration of the growing cells may be the decisive factor. The causal connections are, however, very involved and often not known completely. Effective adaptations for the regulation of the water balance are often brought about not by water as such, but by another factor varying accidentally with it, e.g. salt supply or light.

The purely physical side of transpiration, which is not dealt with further here, has been discussed e.g. by SEYBOLD (1930, 1931). One can say with KORIBA (1937) that the two physical components of transpiration are convection and evaporation.

Table 24 presents some experiments on the uptake of transpiration water through the base of felled saplings. During the felling water was continuously poured over the surfaces, and immediately afterwards the trees were placed with the sawn-off ends in large flasks with distilled water.

Table 24

Water Absorption through the Base of the Trunks of Young Trees, over a Period of Observation of 1—2 Days. The trees bore 300-400 leaves and were erected on location in the open. After the end of the experiment the 'easily-mobile water' of the trunks was determined (cf. p. 339) (After LUNDEGÅRDH 1954)

	Unit	Species of tree		
		Tilia	Betula	Quercus
Water absorption:	g per hour			
maximum		90	350	80
minimum		12	90	26
Calculated speed of flow in the trunk:	cm per hour			
maximum		90	250	100
minimum		12	64	33
Cross-sectional area of the trunk	cm²	13·7	16·0	21·0
Calculated conducting area	cm²	1·0	1·4	0·8

The results in Table 24 show that the rising transpiration stream is covered by the easily mobile water, which represents only a few per cent of the total water in the trunk. Only in the birch does the mobile water seem to lag behind; but here one should also take into account the share of the actively moved water. It is surprising that the birch, which transpires faster than the lime and the oak, also shows the highest suction pressure in the trunk.

In a trunk of 10 cm² cross-sectional area transpiration rates of 100-450 g per hour would correspond to a speed of flow of only 10-45 cm per hour, if the whole cross-sectional area conducted. This of course is not the case, since firstly the non-conducting walls occupy at least half the cross-section of the trunk, and in the oak considerably more; and secondly only a fraction of the vascular elements conduct water quickly enough. The volume of the easily mobile water amounts in the lime to about 15%, in the birch to about 18% and in the oak to about 8% of the total water, which occupies about half the total volume of the trunk. The easily mobile water thus amounts to only 7·5%, 9% and 4% respectively of the volume. From this it can be concluded that the vascular elements available for the transpiration water occupy at most only 4%-9% of the cross-sectional area of the trunk. The calculated speed of transport must therefore on the average be multiplied by 11-25. This gives the calculated speeds which are shown on Table 24. Thus in the birch, the calculated speed of flow amounts to a maximum of about 4 cm per minute, and the minimum about 1 cm. In the lime and the oak the speeds were considerably slower. The speeds of flow calculated in Table 24 agree well with the direct electrometrical determinations (p. 342). How the speeds of flow quoted in the literature, some of which are very much higher, may be explained remains to be investigated.

2 THE MEASUREMENT OF TRANSPIRATION

The classical method is to weigh a potted plant whole, while the pot is protected against evaporation by wrapping it in tin foil or something similar. Transpiration weighings can be carried out easily with automatic recording (BRAUNER 1931). Investigations have been carried out gravimetrically on the connection between transpiration and the salt content of the substrate (halophytes and psammophytes; see BICKENBACH 1932), the soil humidity (MARTIN 1940) or the air humidity (MARTIN 1943).

The difference between the actual water content and the degree of humidity of air saturated at the same temperature is termed the *saturation deficit*. This determines the speed of evaporation from a free water surface. Transpiration which, on physical grounds alone, should rise in direct proportion to the saturation deficit, actually usually follows a convex curve (GÄUMANN and JAAG 1936). This is due to the decrease of turgidity which is connected with rising transpiration and decreasing turgor pressure, as a result of which evaporation decreases.

Instead of determining the water given up in transpiration one can measure the water taken up in the same time by the roots or the lower cut surface. F. DARWIN constructed the *potometer*, which has long been used. In its simplest form this instrument consists of a water-filled flask provided with a horizontal measuring tube into which is inserted the lower end of a transpiring twig, the insertion being made air-tight. The water uptake is read off from the movement of the meniscus in the measuring tube. This instrument can also easily be made self-recording (BRAUNER and KÖCKEMANN 1931).

The potometer measures the second component of the water balance concerned in transpiration. When the water balance is constant, transpiration and water uptake remain equal, but fluctuations commonly occur (TAKENOUCHI 1929), sometimes rhythmical, e.g. the secondary oscillations of a normal day-periodicity. Diurnal periodicity is induced by the higher temperature obtaining during the day and the consequent higher saturation deficit, and by the light-induced movements of the stomata (MONTERMOSO and DAVIS 1942). Autonomous daily variations may also occur.

It is of great ecological and physiological interest to investigate the differences in transpiration between different leaves of the same plant or between upper and lower sides of a leaf. Formerly the semi-quantitative *cobalt test* was utilised for this purpose.

This method is based on the change in colour from blue to pink when anhydrous cobaltous chloride takes up moisture and passes over into the hydrated form. A strip of filter paper is impregnated with cobaltous chloride solution and allowed to dry in a desiccator and is then pressed under a protective glass slide against the surface of the leaf. The time of the colour change gives an approximate measure of the relative intensity of transpiration (SOLOMON 1945).

Distinctly more reliable values of the total (i.e. cuticular plus stomatal) transpiration are obtained by enclosing a leaf in a container with air of a known degree of humidity. From the increase in the moisture content the transpiration can be determined. The measurements are carried out most conveniently with circulating air. GLOVER (1941) utilises the principle of the hygrometer, i.e. the comparison of a dry and a wet bulb thermometer, but instead of the ordinary thermometer he uses thermoelements made of constantan-copper. The water-content of the air can also be measured spectrophotometrically from the infra-red absorption of the water vapour.

The enclosing of leaves or twigs in a vessel is of course inconvenient and often also unecological. Among experimental ecologists the rapid weighing of freshly cut leaves is preferred. This method, according to PFLEIDERER (1933), reproduces the natural transpiration satisfactorily as long as the measurements are taken in the first 2-4 minutes. After this time the stomata begin to close. The longer periods of observation used earlier (e.g. STOCKER 1924) give values that are too low e.g. for halophytes (SCHRATZ 1937). The method cannot be used for determining the transpiration in Orchideae, since their stomata close immediately the leaves are cut off (WALLACH 1938).

If the transpiration is carried out under conditions which prevent the closing of the stomata it is found that the intensity is dependent not only on the size of the surface but also on the form of the leaf. This is connected with the *marginal effect* already discussed, which leads to narrow, long leaves transpiring more per unit of area than round leaves (MAASS 1935). It is also found that the *cuticular transpiration*, which proceeds with closed stomata, is strongly influenced by the protective arrangements which enhance the resistance to dryness (KAMP 1930, PISEK and BERGER 1938; cf. Chap. 2 C). An effective protection against strong winds is also afforded by the partial drying-out of the external epidermal wall (MICHAELIS 1934). The vapour pressure reduction caused by high osmotic pressure also affords some protection.

3 STOMATAL TRANSPIRATION

For the study of stomatal transpiration and the mechanism of movement of the stomata one can utilise either comparative measurements of transpiration on leaves with open and closed stomata (about the corona-hygrometer recommended for this purpose see ANDERSON and HERTZ 1955, VIRGIN 1956), or one can investigate the degree of opening indirectly.

Among the indirect means the *infiltration method* introduced by MOLISCH, NEGER *et al.* is the best known. It is based on the penetration of liquids with low surface tension (e.g. alcohol, ether, acetone, benzene, etc.) through the open stomata. The size of the dark spots which are formed by the penetration of the liquids into the intercellular spaces is estimated. The infiltration-liquid is dropped on to the leaf surface, or the leaf is dipped into it (STÅLFELT). One can also allow the leaf to float

on the liquid (CHODAT 1940). Infiltration can also be carried out with water; the air
is then first evacuated. One can of course also apply a weak positive pressure. All these
methods suffer from the drawback that they are only qualitative and moreover
uncertain.

The direct measurement under the microscope of the state of opening of the stomata
is of course to be preferred, but such measurements must be carried out quickly in
order to avoid secondary movements. BUSCALIONI and POLACCI took collodium
impressions of the stomata, which were then studied microscopically. LLOYD removed
the epidermis quickly and placed it in alcohol. These methods have, however, been
severely criticised by others (SCHORN 1930, HARTSUIJKER 1935, NADEL 1938). Better
results are apparently given by studies of leaves which are enclosed in paraffin oil
(STÅLFELT 1932). With this method good agreement between the degree of opening
of the stomata and transpiration has been found.

A very sensitive indirect method of measuring stomata is the *porometer method*
introduced by F. DARWIN (see also ASHBY 1931, GREGORY and ARMSTRONG 1936).
A small glass dome is placed on the surface of the leaf and, if a slight vacuum is induced
in this, the speed of the air stream going through the stomata gives a relative measure
for the degree of opening. The porometer method has been theoretically discussed by
PENMAN (1942); but this method has also been criticised. NIUS (1931) for example has
noted that the amount of air passing through is determined more by the width of the
intercellular spaces in the mesophyll than by the width of the stomata. When critically
evaluated, however, the porometer method can yield valuable results, e.g. on the
usually very different ventilation of the upper and lower sides of a leaf. An old method
of demonstrating this difference is to cover one side with petroleum jelly and to measure
the resultant fall in the transpiration. This method may, however, not be very
reliable.

That the movements of the stomata are to a high degree dependent on the water
balance scarcely needs to be mentioned, but it may be recalled that in certain types
of leaf, e.g. in grasses, the movements of the stomata are less important than they are
in other types. The relatively high osmotic values of the grasses afford protection,
since the lowering of the vapour pressure prevents excessive evaporation (KERL 1929).
A unified interpretation of the regulating effect of the stomata has not yet been reached.
In spite of much work, the sensitivity of the stomata towards external factors is still
incompletely understood (see also Chap. 10, F 4).

Although the stomata usually open on illumination, viz. with blue light (PYRKOSCH
1936, SEYBOLD and EGLE 1937, VIRGIN 1956), the water-balance is still the dominating
regulatory factor (STÅLFELT 1929, 1955, PISEK and CARTELLIERI 1931). Thus the stomata close even in strong light if the water deficit of the guard cells rises. With strong
wilting, because of the abnormal tensions in the epidermis, a renewed opening can
occur (ILJIN 1932). On the other hand neither temperature fluctuations (KERL 1929)
nor variations in salt nutrition (DESAI 1937) have any notable influence, although a
certain minimum temperature seems to be necessary to keep the mechanism in operation (with alpine roses about 0°C, and with spruces considerably higher; MICHAELIS
1934).

The extent of the lowering of the water-balance needed to start closure is typical of
the species. SEYBOLD (1937) introduced the term *transpiration resistance* to express the
relation between the vapour-pressure difference between air-and-leaf and the transpiration per unit area. According to FÜSSER (1933) and BREWIG (1933) the amplitude

of the transpiration resistance, which is determined essentially by the movements of the stomata, is greater in the xerophytes than in the hygrophytes. The sensitivity of the stomata towards an increase of the water deficit is closely connected with the resistance towards water losses. *Carex physodes* thus endures complete drying out, and millet survives great loss of water, but beans only a small one. The resistance may also vary in different organs (TUMANOV 1930). In *Helianthus* transpiration begins to decrease when two-thirds of the available soil moisture has been used, and at the same time the stomata begin to close (MARTIN 1940). In many xerophytes absence of any need to close their stomata may be due to their possession of an excellent, deeply-penetrating root system. VASILJEV (1930, 1931) states that the desert plant *Smirnovia turkestana* renews the whole water store of the leaves in 7-8 minutes, which amounts to more than 5 ml per g of fresh weight per hour.

According to PISEK and CARTELLIERI (1939), some trees begin to restrict transpiration with a water deficit of only a few per cent, and it is not surprising that the stomata of *Corylus*, *Fagus* and *Picea* are completely closed with a water loss of 16%-24%. According to what has been stated above, the easily mobile water in the trunk must at this stage have been used up. The less mobile water moves thirty times more slowly (LUNDEGÅRDH 1954) and thus at most can support merely the cuticular transpiration for a time. The stomata of *Betula* are said to operate still more sluggishly. Deciduous trees during the growing period consume very large amounts of water, which however decrease greatly when wilting begins (cf. Table 24, maximum and minimum values). From the maximum and minimum values given in Table 24 it follows that when wilting has started, that is with closed stomata, transpiration has sunk to a third or a ninth. Cuticular transpiration must therefore be relatively strong in birch, lime and oak, and the cuticle confers only a rather limited protection against drought.

The influence of *wind* on transpiration has been investigated by many workers (STÅLFELT 1932, FILZER 1933, MARTIN and CLEMENTS 1935, GÄUMANN and JAAG 1939 *et al.*). It is remarkable that the maximal transpiration is reached even at relatively low wind speeds. The harmful effect of strong wind appears often to be due to purely mechanical factors which damage the protoplasm.

According to STÅLFELT (1932) transpiration is extraordinarily sensitive towards weak air movements. An increase of about 160% was observed with wind speeds of only 0·5 m per second; higher speeds did not increase the effect. WRENGER (1935) gives the upper limit for *Helianthus* as 4 m per second. These results seem to show that from the point of view of the water-balance wind has no great effect. On the other hand desert plants show numerous adaptations limiting the evaporation due to air movements. There are for example the 'still air vestibules' of the stomata, and there are leaves which form larger calm spaces by rolling up or folding, and so on. The structure of the intercellular spaces must also play a large part in the restriction of internal evaporation.

Holoparasites are in a class of their own with respect to their water economy (HÄRTEL 1937). Even though the birch can restrict its transpiration by movements of the stomata, mistletoe parasitic upon it does not engage in such protective arrangements. The parasite consumes much more water per unit of leaf area than the birch itself; only in winter is there some restriction. It is not known whether the mistletoe can also tap the less mobile water through its haustoria. The semi-parasite *Orthanta lutea* also may show very high transpiration rates.

E. Survey of the Anatomical-morphological and Ecological Adaptations Protecting the Water-balance

1 ANATOMICAL-MORPHOLOGICAL ADAPTATIONS

The surpassing importance of the water-balance for the life of land plants is reflected in the adaptations of their structure. These are dealt with more in detail in ecological accounts (NEGER 1913, MAXIMOV 1926, WARMING-GRAEBNER 1933, SCHIMPER-FABER 1935, WEAVER-CLEMENTS 1938, LUNDEGÅRDH 1957 et al.). Here we give only a short summary.

(a) Cell-physiological Adaptations

These consist chiefly in greatly increasing the *drought resistance of the protoplasm*. This occurs particularly in those plants which survive complete drying-out, some-times even in a desiccator. Examples are lichens and certain mosses as well as some desert plants. Long drying-out usually, however, causes injury, such as the inhibition of assimilation in lichens (ELLÉE 1939). Drought-resistance is a widely distributed property of plant protoplasm, as follows from the fact that spores and seeds in general dry out without losing their viability. The marked sensitivity of many other cells, e.g. those of the leaf mesophyll, towards loss of water may be connected with the dependence of metabolism on an appropriate hydration of the protoplasm. Drought-resistance appears on the whole to be closely connected with the degree of hydration of the protoplasm. In this there is a certain analogy with the resistance to cold.

A general cell-physiological protection against a diminished water-balance, i.e. against an excessive water deficit, is yielded also by the increase in the osmotic value of the cell sap. Examples of this have been given above. Increases in osmotic pressure can be evoked by increased salt uptake or by changes in enzymatic activity, e.g. by the increase in the activity of the hydrolytic enzymes which accompanies diminished hydration. Those morphological changes which occur in plants cultivated in air of varying moisture content may also be due to effects on enzyme activity. Besides the examples quoted above there may also be mentioned some of the experiments carried out by NIGHTINGALE and MITCHELL (1934) with tomatoes. At 35% air humidity the leaves become thick and light green, growth proceeds slowly and many carbohydrates and insoluble N-compounds are accumulated. At 95% air humidity the plants grow rapidly, the leaves become thin and dark green, and few carbohydrates and proteins are accumulated.

According to AMOS and WOOD (1939), in *Lolium perenne* (rye-grass) the total carbohydrate content is not changed by reduction of the water-content of the leaves; the contents of sucrose and fructosan increase, but hemicellulose and starch decrease. WALTER (1947) has attempted to make the ability of plants to tolerate variations in the water balance more comprehensible by introducing the term *hydrature* ('water state') and giving special attention to changes in the vapour pressure. The term 'hydrature', however, hardly signifies anything more than the expression 'degree of hydration'. For the correct functioning of protoplasm a certain degree of hydration is necessary, and cells and organs strive to maintain this degree of hydration through the cell-physiological adaptations which have been described.

(b) *Factors favourable to Water Uptake*

The positive side of the water-balance is favoured especially by enlargement and deep penetration of the root system, of which examples have been given by describing steppe- and desert-plants, which send roots down to the soil water level. They may be spoken of as 'soil water plants'. Grasses are usually without any pronounced protection against transpiration (MES *et al.* 1935), instead of which they possess a widely branched root system.

With a good supply of water plants can of course manage without any restriction of transpiration. This seems to be the case e.g. with the arctic flora of northern Sweden (STOCKER 1931). Here the water-balance is highly favourable, and the stomata remain wide open to the advantage of photosynthesis. In this way the short summer is fully utilised. A very favourable water-balance is possessed also by plants in tropical rain forests, although the tops of the trees, because of the radiation of the sun, are usually exposed to a climate of an aridity which resembles that of the dry steppes.

The halophytes of the seashore also can to a large extent dispense with the closing of stomata, and do in fact transpire very actively. Their fleshy leaves appear to be xeromorphic; but this can be considered as a side effect of over-saturation with salt.

Among the adaptations favouring water uptake may also be counted the hygro-scopicity of 'mist plants', water-absorbing hairs and the swelling tissue of certain epiphytes.

(c) *Restriction of Water Loss*

Most xerophytic adaptations come under this heading. High osmotic values, because of the reduced vapour-pressure, operate against strong evaporation through the physi-ology of the cell. The protective effect increases, of course, with the dehydration (cf. 'incipient drying') and concentration of the cell sap. This tolerable drying out is considered by many workers (LIVINGSTON, LOFTFIELD, MAXIMOV *et al.*) to be more important than the closing of the stomata. As is well known, the stomata restrict transpiration only when fairly strongly narrowed. The protective effect of partly dried cell walls of course extends to all mesophyll tissues adjacent to intercellular spaces. It can therefore be conjectured that with a normal water balance there is a certain suction pressure of the mesophyll cells, which holds the walls in a partly dried state. In tree-trunks, as explained above, there is a similar balance between transpiration suction pressure and the partly dried walls and narrowed vascular capillaries. On account of the internal resistance to conduction in the leaf, however, the suction pressures may considerably exceed those in the trunk. According to other workers the importance of 'incipient drying', is often exaggerated, but theoretically its participa-tion in regulating transpiration cannot be denied.

More important, however, than the cell-physiological adaptations restricting the loss of water from the leaves are the morphological adaptations. These include

2A

thickened epidermal walls, cutinisation, wax coverings and screening of the stomata. Local protection of the stomata against wind can cause, according to RENNER (1913), a reduction in transpiration up to 30%-80%. Restricting the number of stomata seems to be less important, and in many xerophytes the stomata are fairly close together. Among morphological means of protection may further be mentioned hairs, which also protect against radiation. A reduction of total leaf area also restricts transpiration, of course, and in extreme cases results in the stem taking over photosynthesis. It has been calculated that a spherical cactus shows only one-thousandth of the transpiration of an *Aristolochia* of equal weight. In the desert succulents the stem functions also as a water container and so enables the dry periods to be surmounted. Leaves and roots can also form water containers (for the literature about succulents see EVANS 1932).

2 THE WATER-BALANCE AND THE HABITAT

The foregoing account has shown that recent physiological and ecological research has attained a more comprehensive understanding of xerophytism than the older morphological and biological approach in which external features were over-emphasised.

The term 'xerophytism' should be reserved for those plants which show a limited water balance and tolerate high water deficits. Many plants such as moor plants (Ericaceae etc.), which have a xeromorphic appearance and high cell-sap pressures (10-19 atm, according to FIRBAS 1931), behave physiologically as meso- or hygrophytes, i.e. they contain considerable amounts of water. So also do halophytes, conifers and many other evergreen plants. Only a detailed investigation of its water-balance and drought resistance can give information about a plant's degree of xerophytism. The general water-balance of the habitat should be investigated also. With water it is usually the degree of variation that matters, because as a rule it is the isolated periods of extreme drought that are the eliminating factor.

STOCKER (1924) distinguishes glycophytes and halophytes. The distinction is not a sharp one, however, since a considerable amount of salt in the soil or water has a double effect: partly chemical (NaCl) and partly osmotic, but these do not always coincide. Many investigators believe that the inhibited growth of halophytes is determined ordinarily by the osmotic pressure in the soil and not by the chemical effect of the salt. There is always, of course, a relation between water uptake and the osmotic pressure of the substrate (TAGAWA 1934), although transpiration is not directly affected. According to EATON (1942), with opposing osmotic pressures over 1 atm corresponding growth-inhibitions occur. Since in a very dilute solution growth is depressed by lack of nutrients, gradual increase of the concentration gives an optimum curve with a peak usually below 1 atm. The data about changes of metabolism due to high external pressures are contradictory, but usually protein formation seems to decrease more rapidly than carbohydrate production (HAYWARD and LONG 1941, UPHOF 1941).

Most halophytes grow also in substrates which contain neither NaCl nor considerable amounts of other salts. They are thus distinguished from the glycophytes especially by the fact that in general they show great adaptability to high osmotic pressures in the soil provided that enough water is supplied. This is also the way in which they differ from xerophytes. The degree of adaptation is reflected in zoning on the seashore

(LUNDEGÅRDH 1919, GESSNER 1930, STEINER 1934, SCHRATZ 1936). The elimination of a pressure difference usually depends on an increase of the internal osmotic value by a corresponding uptake of chloride. The mangrove in this way eliminates about two-thirds of the total pressure difference, which in the upper zones rich in salt can rise to 62 atm (WALTER and STEINER 1939). SCHIMPER believed that the halophytes, on account of osmotic pressure differences, suffered from 'physiological drought'. This idea was later dropped when it was found that the external pressure is counterbalanced by a corresponding rise of the internal pressure, and that the halophytes can transpire considerably more strongly than the xerophytes (STOCKER 1924).

The relations between halophytes and sodium chloride have already been discussed. As well as many which can thrive even without salt (the facultative halophytes), there are some obligate halophytes which seem to have become chemically specialised to NaCl. To these belongs *Salicornia herbacea*, which seems to grow best in 2% NaCl; and in this case the sodium chloride cannot be replaced by other salts. Contrary to statements that *Salicornia* may absorb only a little NaCl (KELLER 1925), there are others which report over 9% of NaCl in the tissues (SCHRATZ 1936). *Suaeda maritima* also appears to belong to the obligate halophytes. According to the investigations of HÖFLER *et al.* (1939), its protoplasm is considerably more resistant to plasmolysis by solutions of pure alkali salts (cf. cap plasmolysis, p. 54) than that of mesophytes.

That the water factor dominates growth in those climatic regions which fluctuate between dry (arid) and wet (humid) periods, e.g. in the steppe regions of Asia, Africa and the Americas, follows from the observations of WALTER (1939) that the productivity varies with the amount of precipitation. In the South African grass velds every hundred mm of rainfall increases the yield by about 1,000 kg per hectare. Similar results are available for irrigation experiments in Scandinavia and central Europe, although the relation between rainfall and yield is not so strictly linear, but follows more nearly a parabolic curve (HALLGREN 1947).

The leaf-fall of trees and shrubs, and the perennation of perennial herbs by rhizomes, roots, bulbs, nodules, etc., can be conceived as a protection against loss of water just as much as against cold. The water uptake from a frozen soil of course encounters great difficulties. The trunks of deciduous trees have a protection against transpiration in the form of an air-filled layer of bark, but in spite of this they may lose more water than the evergreen conifers. The osmotic adaptation to cold is at the same time a protection against excessive transpiration. One-sided insolation on sunny but cold winter days is harmful especially if it is also windy. It is well known that wind contributes to the shaping of the crowns of trees.

The temperature increase connected with the sun's radiation has, especially in high latitudes, a strong effect in increasing transpiration. It decides the snow covering in winter and often also the geographical-topographical distribution of plants (SÖRENSEN 1941). As an example of micro-climatic differences it may be mentioned that, according to LEICK and PROPP, soil and air temperatures can show differences of 36-40°C. HUBER (1937) is of the opinion that soil temperatures can rise to 60-75°C without endangering the vegetation; but this seems decidedly doubtful.

High *leaf temperatures* have been observed in the *maquis* plants of the Mediterranean coast; according to ROUSCHAL (1938) many of these plants tolerate leaf temperatures of 45-55°C for a considerable time. MICHAELIS (1934) found that spruce needles in the sun were 9-12°C warmer than the surrounding air. Even light reflected from the snow can cause an increase of 1°C. Conversely the leaf temperature can sink

0·2-2·1°C below the air temperature on account of radiation at night. Increase in the temperature of insolated leaves was also observed by FRITSCHE (1933), DÖRR (1941) *et al.*

Wind of course has a cooling effect (ALSAC 1942), partly due to evaporation of water but chiefly to the transfer of heat by convection (HARDER 1935). According to HERZOG (1938), the cooling effect of wind may be especially valuable in deserts, where even weak movements of the air save the succulents from the danger of overheating. Cooling by transpiration is also of considerable importance for thin leaves. It has been observed for example, that leaf edges show lower temperatures than midribs (SEYBOLD 1929). CURTIS (1936) maintains that the change of vapour pressure caused by raising the leaf temperature 5°C above that of the surroundings corresponds to a lowering of the relative humidity of the air by 30%-38%. CURTIS (1938), however, denies any considerable participation by transpiration in the fall of temperature due to wind. He calculates that with irradiation equivalent to 0·7 cal/cm² per minute the rise of temperature could only be eliminated by a transpiration of 7·3 cc/dm² per hour. Such high rates of transpiration are rarely attained. The temperature effect of the sun's radiation naturally varies considerably with its spectral composition, and especially with the intensity of the infra-red rays. The moisture content of the atmosphere plays a considerable part, as water strongly absorbs infra-red radiation.

Apart from the temperature of the leaf itself, transpiration is also greatly affected by the air temperature, since at constant absolute humidity the deficit in vapour pressure increases with the temperature. The diurnal curve of transpiration is on this account essentially determined by the daily drift of the temperature.

Chapter 9

GROWTH

A. Dormancy

Variations in vitality, i.e. in metabolic rate, are characteristic of all cells, tissues and organisms. Vitality can, however, express itself in different ways. Even in 'resting' cells which are fully developed, the protoplasm may respire vigorously. On the other hand fully grown cells can still take part, for example, in turgor movements. Rapidly growing or dividing cells, however, always have an active metabolism, whereas typical dormant states are characterised by cessation of cell multiplication and growth and by a sluggish metabolism.

The dormant state of seeds and spores is often, but not necessarily, connected with a low water-content of the cells. It can be imagined that with the disappearance of free water and a decrease in hydration, dormancy signifies a separation of the enzymes from their substrates. Enzymes can be blocked in various ways. There are, for example, dormant states which are caused by deficient oxygen supply or an accumulation of CO_2 (KIDD 1941, KISSER and POSSNIG 1932, STILES and LEACH 1933). The presence of so-called germination-inhibitors (see below) may also induce dormancy. This, like CO_2 accumulation, appears to be largely a matter of narcosis, i.e. certain respiratory enzymes are blocked.

There seems to be a general rule that the ability of the protoplasm to resist harmful external influences such as heat, frost and chemicals is in inverse ratio to the water-content of the protoplasm. The same apparently applies to the longevity of seeds. As respiration, i.e. the consumption of reserves, decreases with the water-content, drying out must extend the survival time. Wheat grains can retain their ability to germinate for ten years or longer, whereas rye is apparently less robust. Seeds of Leguminosae are usually distinguished for their long viability, as are also the seeds of Nelumbiaceae, Malvaceae and Labiatae (50-100 years); OHGA (1926) found *Nelumbium* seeds which were capable of germinating even when they were 250 years old.

Dry seeds and spores can endure temperatures down to $-250°C$ (in liquid hydrogen) or heating for hours at $100°C$, without losing their ability to germinate. The theory of 'panspermia' i.e. of the transport of bacterial spores through outer space, is based on their resistance to cold which has been experimentally verified. The length of life may also be extraordinarily great in the deep-frozen condition, since chemical reactions cease almost completely. Seeds of red clover survive preservation for years in absolute alcohol, and the same applies to spores of *Phycomyces*. Pollen grains of the tea bush and of *Camellia* can be preserved unharmed for months in a desiccator.

It is a peculiar fact that the survival of seeds and spores during dormancy is not necessarily associated with a continuous, even if slow, respiration. Seeds and spores can be preserved for months without oxygen or in an absolute vacuum, without losing their ability to germinate. The reduced speed of reaction may also be the reason why dry seeds endure high doses of X-rays and why seeds can be treated with mercury preparations.

The dehydration of the protoplasm is such a characteristic condition of dormancy in seeds and spores that one easily overlooks the early chemical stages of the inhibition of germination, which usually set in before the drying out. Biochemical inhibitory mechanisms are, however, very often involved. Without these the seeds would readily begin their new life, even on the mother plant. The chemical nature of these 'blasto-kolines' (KÖCKEMANN 1936) is still uncertain (cf. AUDUS 1953). They cause e.g. fresh seeds of various fleshy fruits (apples, pears, plums, cherries and tomatoes) to germinate only after having been kept for several months at low temperature. The inhibitors are usually to be found in definite parts of the seed, e.g. in the seed coat or in the nucellus. Removal of these parts hastens germination; but the inhibitors can also disappear by adsorption on the soil colloids. They are slowly broken down during storage, a phenomenon that is described as after-ripening.

Biochemical factors also determine the dormancy of suppressed adventitious buds, which are distinguished from seeds by not enduring complete drying-out. These buds, as well as the terminal buds of the shoots, thus have some, even though it is greatly reduced, metabolic activity. In spite of a considerable amount of hydration in parts, their respiration is much reduced also. It has been found that the protoplasm of winter buds, as also of the cambium in winter, is probably in a gel condition (PRIESTLEY 1930, BÜNNING 1939), which is only another way of saying that the reactive groups are chemically blocked (for inhibitors and total growth see FRÖSCHEL 1956).

It is well known that auxins act as inhibitors of buds and that the inhibition is reversed by high concentrations of adenine (SKOOG and TSUI 1951). In seeds imperme-ability of the seed coat to oxygen may play a part. Oxygen concentration in general is a factor controlling the lifting of dormancy and the rate of growth (KIM 1955, RANSON and PARIJA 1954).

Auxins apparently regulate the correlative inhibition of the side buds by the ter-minal meristems. It is thought that the latter produce a surplus of auxin which inhibits development, as in the growth of roots (see Chap. 10). It has been found experimentally that supplying auxin artificially also hinders the opening of the lateral buds if the shoot tip is removed (THIMANN and SKOOG 1934, MÜLLER 1935). In the intact plant, however, other inhibitors may also take part. There is no doubt that these correlations are not due to competition for nutrients, but are determined hormonally (BEHRE 1929).

Those inhibitors which prevent or delay the opening of buds are translocated for considerable distances in the vascular bundles. Removal of these shoot sections can thus terminate the dormancy (SNOW 1932). We do not yet know how the hypothetical inhibitors act. It might of course be a case of competitive exchange of the type de-scribed on pp. 151-2. Of two similar materials one might be an auxin, while in the other the active group, able to set in motion the enzyme process specific for growth, was missing. It can be imagined that the auxins are accompanied by inhibitors or are partly converted into these, and that these inhibitors survive after the auxin has been consumed in the process of growth. An 'inhibition wave' can thus be transmitted to the basal shoots.

The dormancy of potatoes, according to HEMBERG (1947), is determined by special inhibitors found in the peripheral parts. The auxin content remains low (cf. also GUTHRIE 1939, MICHENER 1942). More about inhibitors and 'anti-auxins' is given in Chap. 10.

B. The Germination of seeds and spores

1 SWELLING

Physiologically, germination means the cessation of dormancy, that is the removal of the factors causing it. As loss of water and decreased hydration are general factors causing dormancy, germination is usually introduced by water uptake and swelling. The first water taken up is water of imbibition, which explains the high pressures and evolution of heat developed. Towards the end of the swelling osmotic forces are also mobilised, e.g. by the hydrolysis of starch, or of proteins to amino acids and amides. It is not surprising that germination is inhibited by high external osmotic pressures. According to the results of several workers, isotonic solutions of various salts all exercise about the same effect on germination. These effects are ecologically significant in the germination of halophyte seeds (POMA 1922, MONTFORT 1927).

The speed of swelling is a function of the temperature ($Q_{10} = 1 \cdot 6 - 2 \cdot 0$), but the total water uptake remains about the same at different temperatures (BROWN and WORLEY 1912, SHULL 1920), though it varies with different species. Seeds of Leguminosae e.g. absorb large amounts of water (peas 186%), whereas cereal grains take up 40%-60% and the seeds of *Pinus austriaca* only 36% of water (NOBBE 1876).

The uptake of water is usually checked by the low permeability of the seed coat, or by other arrangements which can be considered as adaptations increasing the seed's length of life and preventing premature germination. The latter is especially important for seeds that fall on damp soil or are carried away by water. According to NOBBE, the seeds of *Robinia* can lie in water for more than thirty years and then germinate. Inhibitors that are difficult to destroy may of course be concerned in this. If one wishes to have a rapid germination of seeds like those of *Lathyrus*, it is advisable to make cuts through the seed coat which otherwise is penetrated by water only with difficulty. The seeds of *Polygonum* and *Spergula* are also well known for the slowness of their swelling. Sometimes a treatment with concentrated sulphuric acid or with boiling water can hasten water uptake; and, if the seeds are resistant to wetting, pre-treatment with alcohol or other substances that lower surface tension may help (VERSCHAFFELT 1912, CROCKER 1916).

As water is taken up the intensity of respiration increases. As a result, the demands of the gas exchange (uptake of oxygen and release of CO_2) also increase greatly above those of the dry seeds. As an example it may be mentioned that the release of CO_2 by dry barley grains which contain 10%-12% of water amounts to only $0 \cdot 3 - 0 \cdot 4$ mg/kg barley in 24 hours, and at 14%-15% of water rises to only $1 \cdot 4 - 1 \cdot 5$ mg, whereas at 33% it increases to the enormous amount of 2,000 mg. The seed coat may retard germination more by its low permeability to oxygen and carbon dioxide than by its resistance to wetting. It is an old experience that small seeds, on account of their greater relative surface, run little danger of suffocating in still, deep water. Even seeds of water plants do not germinate in water with little oxygen. In some species, e.g. *Typha latifolia*, a reduction of the oxygen content, but not complete absence, has a stimulating effect (MORINAGA 1926).

2 TEMPERATURE AND CHEMICAL FACTORS

It is generally known that the optimal germination temperature is especially characteristic of the species. This is not due to an effect on swelling, but to biological effects.

The temperature response always follows an optimum curve. The position of the optimum, which lies for cereals between 25° and 31°C and for peas between 37° and 44°C, is however less characteristic than the position of the minimum. This for cereals lies at 0°-5°C, but for cucumbers and melons at 16°-19°C (see DETMER 1880). The optimum also can show very low values. e.g. with meadow grasses 12°C (*Poa pratensis*, *P. nemoralis* and *P. trivialis*; GASSNER 1930). In cereals some connection between the germination temperature and photoperiodism has been found (PURVIS 1934).

With many seed fluctuations between high and low temperatures, or even periodic freezing, have a stimulating effect on germination (DOERFEL 1930, GASSNER 1930). In isolated cases distribution arrangements may be concerned, as in *Alisma* and *Plantago* (SCHAUMANN 1926); but usually it is a matter of switches between biochemical processes, as in vernalisation (see Chap. 10). This may apply also to the germination of *Neurospora* spores which was studied by GODDARD (1935). The germination of these spores is stimulated by heating to 52°-60°C for several minutes and the stimulation is accompanied by a remarkable increase in respiration.

Among the chemical factors the importance of oxygen supply has already been mentioned. Aerobic respiration is necessary for the synthetic processes e.g. protein formation, without which there can be no meristematic activity. Special chemical influences on germination appear to be rare in nature, apart from the unique contact effects between the seeds of orchids and their symbiotic mycorrhiza fungus (cf. p. 243). A stimulation of germination by growth substances has not been definitely established (cf. LUNDEGÅRDH 1943). According to certain data the germination of a number of water plants (*Sagittaria*, *Alisma*, *Hippuris*, *Scirpus*, etc.) is stimulated by acids and alkalis (CROMER 1916). Some chemicals, e.g. boric acid, have been found to affect germination especially of pollen grains. Here biological supplements appear to be involved, similar to those that have been found in the symbiosis between micro-organisms. It is often difficult, however, to distinguish substances which participate at the start of germination from those that stimulate continued growth. The latter include the nutrient salts. It may be mentioned that rice, for example, germinates best in distilled water, but that for the further development of the seedling nutrient salts must be supplied. Seeds of cereals and sugar beet are stimulated by thiamine, especially in combination with magnesium and phosphate, which may be due to the formation of cocarboxylase (LUNDEGÅRDH 1943).

Though actual chemical priming is thus relatively rare and usually uncertain (see also SÖDING and WAGNER 1955), the suppression or the removal of chemical inhibitors is a frequent condition for germination. After-ripening may involve the production of an inhibitor which then gradually decomposes spontaneously or alternatively is removed before germination (e.g. by elution, oxidation or adsorption in the soil). After-ripening may also be connected with the slow synthesis of a substance necessary for germination. An example of this is the formation of sugar in the seeds of *Euryale ferox* (Nymphaeacae), and germination is hastened by an artificial supply of sugar (OKADA 1930). The acceleration of the germination of potatoes caused by partial removal of the skin (HEMBERG 1947) may be due to removal of inhibitors found in the outer layers.

3 GERMINATION AND LIGHT

Germination in many cases is initiated or accelerated by illumination, which appears as a rule to be connected with the removal of inhibitors (for earlier literature see KINZEL 1913, CROCKER 1916). Even unripe seeds may be made to germinate by light (IZARD 1956). Conversely, in certain cases inhibitors are formed in the light. There is no sharp difference between light-germinating and dark-germinating seeds, since the light effect can sometimes be replaced by prolonged after-ripening. *Ranunculus sceleratus*, for example, after a ten-month ripening period passes over from light- to dark-germination, and *Poa pratensis* behaves similarly (JÖNSSON 1893). Fresh seeds of the grass *Chloris ciliata* germinate in the light, whereas after about eight months after-ripening light becomes an inhibitor (GASSNER 1915). Here the light seems to influence the oxygen permeability of the glumes, since their removal abolishes the light-sensitivity. According to GASSNER temperature affects the light-sensitivity of seeds of *Ranunculus* and *Chloris*. In the latter, light acts positively at the high temperatures of 33°-34°C, but negatively at temperatures below +20°C.

Chemical factors also may change the light-sensitivity. Cases are known in which treatment with proteolytic enzymes, weak acids or nitrogen salts converts light-germinators into dark-germinators. Nitrate appears to favour germination in general (GASSNER 1915, LEHMANN 1919). It cannot definitely be said whether such effects are associated with light-induced changes of permeability or stimulations in the embryo. KÜMMER (1932) believes that the light-sensitivity is in no way connected with the oil-content of the seeds, since light-germinators are generally low in oil.

There are numerous investigations dealing with the effect of wavelength and the alternation between light and darkness (FLINT and MCALISTER 1935, 1937; MEISCHKE 1936; ORTH 1937; RESÜHR 1939; MOHR 1955; CHAUDHRI 1956). It is usually found that certain regions of the spectrum favour germination and others restrict it. In *Lactuca* (FLINT and MCALISTER) the positive region lay at about 600-700 mμ, whilst a narrow band at about 750 mμ inhibited (Fig. 155). This spectral sensitivity reminds

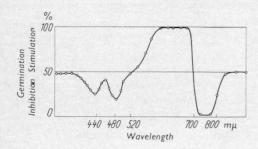

Fig. 155. The influence of different colours of light on the germination of *Lactuca* seeds (after FLINT and MCALISTER, from BÜNNING 1939).

one of the absorption spectrum of chlorophyll, since the strongest effect is observed in the red absorption band (about 670 mμ). A strong inhibition on the other hand appears at the strong absorption zone of carotene in the blue. Both chlorophyll and carotene are present in light-sensitive seeds. Inhibition is observed also in the infra-red. These investigations support the assumption of associated photochemical processes, such as photo-oxidations. Fluorescent substances also commonly occur in seeds. The fluorescence occurs only on swelling, i.e. in connection with the reviving biochemical activity.

Carotene appears to fulfil the function of a light sensitiser also in fern spores (ORTH 1937). The spores of Nostocaceae germinate in the light, whereas those of *Puccinia graminis tritici* germinate in the dark and are especially inhibited by long-wave light (DILLON-WESTON 1931).

4 BUD BREAK

Both in winter buds, which open in spring, and in resting axillary or adventitious buds, which remain in the resting state on account of correlative inhibitions, there are great similarities with seeds and seed germination. The real difference seems to be that in seeds, whether they are dormant or active, even though chemical factors co-operate, differences of water content are decisive, whereas in buds chemical inhibitors or their removal play the main part. The methods used in horticulture for forcing winter buds afford an example.

The simplest method of forcing is the warm bath (MOLISCH 1909). The higher the temperature the shorter the time of reaction; winter buds require 60-120 minutes at $+42°C$, 45 minutes at $+48°C$ and only about 15 seconds at $+55°C$ (VEGIS 1932).

The temperature effect may possibly be connected with the different Q_{10}-values of biochemical reactions, allowing some to forge ahead with rising temperature and so produce the substances necessary for bud break in adequate concentrations. There is an indication of this in the stimulating effect of a temperature fall on the sprouting of potatoes. MÜLLER-THURGAU (1885) observed that the tubers sprout only 14 days after harvest if the temperature is held at about 0°C. The equilibrium between sugar and starch is thereby shifted towards sugar formation, so that respiration increases (see below).

The sprouting of buds is not so much due to specific causes as to conditions which in one way or another produce a biochemical shock. This follows from the fact that even a wound stimulus can evoke an increase in activity. For this purpose one can, for example, pierce buds with a needle, cut the bud-scales or brush the epidermis of potatoes vigorously (SCHLUMBERGER 1926, JACOBI 1926, KOLTERMANN 1927). Mechanical disturbance of the protoplasm can also be attained chemically. Treatment with ether or gases such as acetylene or ethylene (WEBER 1916), hydrocyanic acid, etc., has often been used for this purpose. By treatment with ether lilac, for example, can be made to sprout as early as October (JOHANNSEN 1900). Water injection into buds, bathing in solutions of alcohol or mineral acids, etc., also have a similar effect.

The forcing by means of HCN introduced by GASSNER (1925) and others has led to the hypothesis that a stimulation of glycolysis, i.e. of anaerobic respiration relative to aerobic respiration, is concerned (BORESCH 1928, NIETHAMMER 1928, KAKESITA 1930 *et al.*). A number of intermediate- and end-products of glycolysis such as acetaldehyde, pyruvic acid and ethanol are in fact forcing agents. As however the most various means, e.g. even alterations of temperature and illumination, mechanical stimulus etc., lead to the same end, it is difficult to prove the glycolysis hypothesis.

The activation of buds is always accompanied by a large increase of aerobic respiration, and it is therefore likely that at least the formation of new cell substance which follows the sprouting is connected with the coming into play of the previously partially latent cytochrome system. Such an activation could certainly, as experience shows, result from various external causes. Only continued investigation can decide. That the glycolysis hypothesis, however, should not be rejected out of hand is clear from the forcing effect of a number of inhibitors of the cytochrome system, such as anaesthetics (which inhibit the electron transfer from cytochrome b to cytochrome c) (cf. p. 152) and HCN. Glycolysis may be regarded as the primarily effective agent, with stimulation of cytochrome respiration coming in only when the 'creative activity' of the protoplasm commences.

One can of course speculate about the sub-microscopic organisation of the protoplasm and imagine how, e.g. by its swelling, the relative positions and thereby the reaction rates of the enzyme systems are altered. Such speculations, however, do not get us much further. The same applies to a too facile application of the results with auxins. Before 1920 most workers were clear that the shoot activity was governed by nutrients but also by specific 'formation substances' which were translocated within the plant. After the discovery of the auxins it was readily assumed that the latent state of the buds was determined by concentrations of auxin above the normal (WENT and THIMANN 1937, THIMANN 1937, MICHENER 1939). WENT (1939) proposed an indirect auxin effect through secondary hormones, 'calines'. In the later development of auxin research specific inhibitors play an ever-increasing part (cf. above; SNOW 1940, OVERBEEK 1944, AUDUS 1953 et al.).

Before it can be finally decided whether and to what extent auxins or inhibitors and/or anti-auxins cause dormancy and the opening of buds, one must know more precisely how these materials are transported. It appears to be established (see Chap. 10) that the auxins are synthesised in the shoot meristem and migrate thence by diffusion, etc., basipetally in the parenchyma. The type of movement of auxins, etc., in the phloem is not yet clarified. Most of the organic substances necessary for bud break may migrate towards the apex in the phloem, at the same time that other substances also go in the same direction in the xylem (cf. Chap. 7).

Organic substances moving downwards are only found after the leaves have developed so far that there is an excess of formation over consumption of assimilates. In conformity with this one can assume that a correlative suppression of the lateral buds by the main shoot indicates that production of a special organic substance starts before the photosynthetic balance is reached. Such an auxin production, independent of their own carbohydrate production, is known in roots. The auxins produced in the root system seem, like a number of other organic products, to migrate into the xylem and thus to affect the stem tissue, etc. Auxin is also produced in the embryo and endosperm, which according to OVERBEEK (1942) prevents a premature development of the root primordia.

At the termination of dormancy nutrients begin to flow into the buds and root primordia. This suddenly aroused inflow of the sap streams has long been known and has caused much discussion. The opinion of some workers that the auxins have something to do with the stimulation of the sap movements is difficult to sustain. The experiments with active transport tend rather to show that, after the first activation (cf. above), the cytochrome respiration sets in to the full extent, and the active accumulation processes (Chaps. 6-7) begin to operate.

The sap flows emanate actively from the roots, but a continuous flow can be maintained only if a suction pressure, i.e. an active or passive consumption, also exists in the receiving shoot. A production of hormones that condition or inhibit dormancy thus supposedly takes place continuously and, together with the morphological placing of the buds and primordia, controls the complex, but strictly regulated morphological and physiological correlations which determine the structure of the plant. This complex hormonal balance undoubtedly prevails also during the complete rest of the winter sleep of trees. It is not seriously disturbed during the awakening activity of bud-break and still exists, even when the plant is fully active photosynthetically, although the total production of hormones is then raised to a higher level. The production and distribution of growth hormones is thus one of the most specific and fundamental properties of plants.

C. Growth—General

Whereas in animals growth and cell division are closely correlated, in plants one must distinguish between two phases, viz. between meristematic growth and extension growth or, otherwise expressed, between the *division phase* and the *extension phase* of growth.

In the meristem of shoots and roots the cells are mostly filled with protoplasm, and here the increase in volume is always accompanied by division. This is the division stage of growth. Whole organs, e.g. the coleoptiles of grasses, may be laid down meristematically in miniature. The extension stage is distinguished by a large increase in volume with little or no increase in protoplasm. A young organ can increase its volume very considerably without cell division becoming necessary. Both in shoot and in root the passage from one phase to the other is continuous (Fig. 156), and the meristem is renewed continuously also. The frequency of division quickly decreases away from the tip and in the extension zone gradually falls to zero.

Cell extension may be described as an osmotically regulated increase in volume, in which the surface of the cell walls is greatly enlarged. In this not only are water and osmotic substances taken up or produced, but the protoplasm also extends, although at a considerably slower rate than the cell sap (FREY-WYSSLING and BLANK 1952). This increase in protoplasm is mostly limited to the cytoplasm, while the cell nucleus remains in the 'resting' stage. The nuclear substance, however, also seems to increase. Accompanying very large extension growth distinct increases of nuclear mass and nucleic acid content have been found (SILBERGER and SKOOG 1953). If the cell lengths

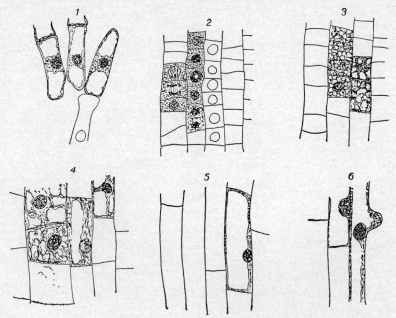

Fig. 156. Cell types in optical longitudinal section of a living wheat root of the second order, as shown by microphotographs. 1. Cells just released from the root cap. 2. The zone of cell division 0·2 mm from the tip. 3. Commencement of cell extension and vacuole formation 0·6 mm from the tip. 4. Continued extension, vacuoles 1·0 mm from the tip. 5. End phase of the extension 1·4 mm from the tip (2-5 from the cortex). 6. Primordium of a root hair 1·8 mm from the tip.

in different zones of a growing root are measured continuously it is found that extension sets in slowly near the meristem, and then as one moves upwards proceeds at increasing speeds, until at a distance of 1-2 mm from the tip an optimum speed is reached, which then just as quickly sinks again to zero. This is the *grand period of growth* first described by SACHS (Fig. 158).

Fig. 157. Microphotograph from the extension zone of a living wheat root.

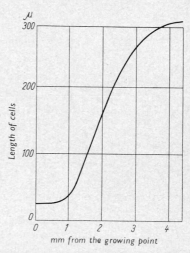

Fig. 158. The grand period of growth of cortex cells. The abscissa indicates the distribution of the growth stages in the root tips.

The cell wall generally retains its thickness during extension. Exceptions are, however, known in which a thinning occurs during extension (OVERBECK 1934 with Sporangiophores of *Pellia epiphylla*), which in other objects gives place to a thickening before the extension ends (WUHRMANN-MEYER 1939 with *Avena* coleoptiles).

The third phase of cell development consists of the onset of thickening growth of the wall after extension has ended, which is termed *secondary growth* (cf. Chap. 2). That the growth in thickness of the wall sets in usually only after extension ends is generally explained by the necessity for the extending wall to remain to some extent plastic. The hemispherical or parabolic tips of root hairs are on the other hand relatively rigid, and there are also other cases of growth in length of rigid cell walls. It may therefore be that the secondary growth in thickness of the wall is supplied with material that is unsuitable for growth in length. There are in fact certain chemical and structural differences between the primary and secondary wall layers.

D. Auxins and Other Growth Substances (Phytohormones)

1 THE IDENTIFICATION OF CHEMICAL TRANSMISSION OF STIMULUS

The existence of specific growth-regulating substances was asserted a considerable time ago (historical reviews are given by WENT and THIMANN 1937; HAAGEN-SMIT

1939, 1951; WENT 1943). The most important advances, however, have come from observations on movements evoked in higher plants by light or gravity (tropisms).

DARWIN (1880) and ROTHERT (1894) showed that the phototropic and geotropic stimulations are taken up (the so-called *perception* stage) by grass coleoptiles or roots, mainly at the tip and are transmitted thence to the elongation zone lying behind it, where the strongest curvature (the *reaction*) takes place. From his observations DARWIN drew the conclusion that with lateral illumination of a coleoptile the stimulus is perceived at the tip and that a *transmission* of stimulus proceeds basipetally. BOYSEN-JENSEN (1910, 1938) showed that the transmission of stimulus can also pass through a gelatine layer placed between the excised tip and the base. From this observation he drew the conclusion that a chemical substance takes part in the transmission. This conclusion was more clearly expressed by PAÁL (1914, 1919). He varied the experiment by placing an excised stimulated tip laterally on the stump of a coleoptile, which induced a curvature in the opposite direction. PAÁL assumed that a growth substance was formed by the light-stimulus and diffused from the tip downwards to the zone of curvature.

Further experiments of STARK (1921), SÖDING (1925) *et al.* confirmed PAÁL's conclusions. The decisive advance was finally made by WENT (1926, 1927), who followed the diffusion of the growth substance through small blocks of agar, by means of which an approximate molecular weight determination and later an isolation of the active substance were carried out. Among the more recent literature surveys THIMANN (1948), SKOOG (1951), SÖDING (1952) and AUDUS (1953) may be mentioned.

2 CHEMISTRY OF THE GROWTH SUBSTANCES

KÖGL and HAAGEN-SMIT (1933-5) isolated from urine two active growth substances, auxin a and b (auxentriolic and auxenolonic acids), derivatives of *cyclo*pentene-pentanoic acid. A third active substance, which they named heteroauxin, was also present and was identified as β-indolylacetic acid (abbreviated to IAA):

Indolyl-3-acetic acid

NIELSEN (1928) had already found an active substance in fungal cultures. It was particularly abundant in the pathogen *Rhizopus suinus* and caused curvatures of *Avena* coleoptiles. It was later identified as β-indolylacetic acid (THIMANN 1935). This growth substance is closely related to the amino acid tryptophan, from which it is probably formed via intermediate stages (KÖGL and KOSTERMANNS 1934, LARSEN and BONDE 1953; cf. also below, p. 369).

β-indolylacetic acid (IAA) is much more stable than auxins a and b and can be synthesised easily and cheaply. It soon found numerous applications in experiments on growth effects, and also in horticulture. It was initially believed that IAA occurred only in fungi. Later investigations, however, showed that it occurs in a number of higher plants, e.g. in maize cobs (HAAGEN-SMIT *et al.* 1942, BERGER and AVERY 1944), spinach leaves (WILDMAN 1947), pea epicotyls, beans, rock rose (LARSEN 1944), potato tubers (HEMBERG 1947), *Avena* coleoptiles (WILDMAN and BONNER 1948, TERPSTRA 1953), etc. In fact, on further investigation IAA has been found in all plants tested. Bacteria also produce it (STOWE 1955). IAA, which shows similar dissociation to auxin a and b (pK = *c*. 4·75), is therefore now considered the predominant plant growth substance (cf. for example WIEDOW-PÄTZOLD and GUTTENBERG 1957).

Most results, particularly the earlier ones, on auxins in plants are limited to physiological tests in which various active substances give similar reactions. VAN OVERBEEK (1944) introduced a scale of IAA equivalents, i.e. the effects of a growth substance were compared with IAA as a standard.

The attempts to characterise growth substances more precisely are mainly based on determining the rate of diffusion, inactivation by light, stability towards alkalis and acids, etc. Such characters however, are often inadequate, since frequently more than one active substance, besides inactive precursors and other inhibitors, cloud the picture. It is however interesting to see that determinations of molecular weight which are based on diffusion constants point to the existence of two classes of active substances, one with a molecular weight of about 175, as in IAA, and another with molecular weights between 300 and 400. The latter results, which could suggest substances similar to auxins a and b, have however not been confirmed.

For the indole derivatives there are also colorimetric methods, e.g. a modification of the SALKOWSKI method (BONNER and TANG 1951), best used in combination with paper chromatography (BENNET-CLARK *et al.* 1952, LUCKWILL 1952, BENTLEY 1952, LINSER 1952 *et al.*). Using these methods, investigations of the distribution of IAA as a growth substance made a considerable advance and at the same time countered the view that KÖGL's auxins occur generally. There are cases which can be quantitatively interpreted as due to the action of IAA (BENTLEY and HONSLEY 1952, BENTLEY and BICKLE 1952, TERPSTRA 1953). RAADTS and SÖDING (1957) by chromatographic methods found in *Avena* coleoptiles, as well as IAA, an inactive but not yet identified growth substance, and also an inhibitor.

The indole derivatives isolated from plants also include indolylpyruvic acid (THIMANN and STOWER 1953), indolylacetonitrile, indolylacetaldehyde and ethyl indolylacetate (REDEMAN *et al.* 1951), substances which were earlier prepared synthetically and which may possibly occur as active or potentially active auxins. It has also been thought that they participate as intermediate stages in the formation of auxin from tryptophan.

By means of paper chromatography it has been possible to show that tryptophan is the natural parent substance of IAA. The direct precursor of IAA is very probably indolylacetaldehyde; but tryptamine and free indolylpyruvic acid may not be intermediates in normal auxin synthesis. Also with paper chromatography (NITSCH 1956) it has been possible to separate acid and neutral indole compounds, e.g. indolylacetonitrile and ethyl indolylacetate (cf. REINERT 1957).

It is still not known to what extent growth substances resembling auxin are of actual physiological importance in plants. The following have been considered: cinnamic acid $C_6H_5 \cdot CH = CH \cdot COOH$, which is active in the *cis*-form and inhibitory in the *trans*; coumarin, the lactone of 2-hydroxycinnamic acid, its derivatives and many other substances mentioned below. The number of weakly active growth substances and inhibitors is quite considerable.

3 Relations between Structure and Growth-substance Activity

The minimum requirement for auxin activity, which was first put forward by KOEPFLI
et al. (1935) on the basis of observations on indolyl-, phenyl- and cyclohexane-
derivatives, has been formulated by THIMANN as follows:

1. a ring system as the nucleus,
2. a side-chain to the ring,
3. a double bond adjacent to the side-chain,
4. a terminal carboxyl group or a group easily convertible into carboxyl, which
   lies at least one carbon atom distant from the ring, and
5. a definite steric relationship between the ring and the carboxyl group.

The induction of cell enlargement may be taken as the primary auxin activity.
This is usually measured on etiolated pieces of pea hypocotyl or *Avena* coleoptile,
which are dipped into the aqueous solution of the active substance, or float on its
surface. This test is in general preferred to the older *Avena* test (WENT 1928), in which
the curvature caused by the lateral application of an agar cube containing the growth
substance is observed. Other test objects are roots or *Avena* epicotyls (see e.g. AUDUS
1953). The usual tests for auxin suffer from the drawback that they do not include the
rapid initial reaction to the active substance. In order to observe this a micro ciné
camera is needed. Such an instrument was constructed by LUNDEGÅRDH (1947, 1949);
with this one can reduce the time needed for measurement to minutes and seconds,
e.g. in recording the growth reactions of root hairs, or cells and cell groups in root
tissues.

With the simple test methods mentioned above, the steric characteristics of the
auxins were confirmed and extended. For example, the importance of steric variations
in the molecule of an active substance has been investigated (ÅBERG 1951, 1952, 1955).
The number of active substances include e.g. naphthylacetic acids (KATO 1951,
KEFFORD and KELSO 1957), α- and β-naphthoxyacids (BURSTRÖM and HANSEN 1955),
substituted phenoxyacids and benzoic acids (ZIMMERMANN and HITCHCOCK 1942,
HITCHCOCK and ZIMMERMANN 1943, OSBORNE *et al.* 1955, BURSTRÖM *et al.* 1956),
sulphonic acid derivatives (VELDSTRA *et al.* 1954) and many others.

In general, naphthalene and benzene derivatives are preferred for the synthesis of
the aromatic nucleus of the active substance. In horticultural and agricultural practice
naphthylacetic acid and halogen- or methyl-substituted phenoxyacids are predominantly used. The activity is strongly influenced by the nature and position of the
substituent groups. Phenoxyacetic acid is effective but its activity relatively low.
*Ortho*chlorophenoxyacetic acid is about twenty times more active, *para*chlorophenoxyacetic acid eighty times and 2,4-dichlorophenoxyacetic acid (commonly called 2,4-D)
about 650 times.

Substituted side groups can also influence secondary properties e.g. the speed of
transport in the tissue. This applies also to substituted ring atoms. C or O as a substitute for N in the indole ring does not remove the primary activity, but diminishes the
effect in the classical *Avena* coleoptile test, i.e. the polar transport of the active
substance is retarded. The importance of the position of the side-chain close to the
double bond in the ring is explained by the positive activity of the β-substituted and
the inactivity of the other cyclohexane acetic acids. The length of the side-chain can

be greater than two C atoms. Derivatives with four C atoms are more active than those with three. Even ten C atoms do not destroy the activity provided that the effect on the side-chain is compensated for by certain changes in the benzoic acid ring. Groups attached to the side-chain, e.g. esters, ethers and amides, block the activity, but such derivatives because of their fat-solubility can penetrate more easily (cf. also ÅBERG 1956 on the *para*-substitution in the phenoxyacetic acids). Subsequent internal hydrolysis may give rise to active compounds again. Use has been made of this also in practice.

Among the systematic attempts to put the problem of the connection between chemical constitution and physiological effect on a theoretically satisfactory basis, VELDSTRA and others have given attention to the physical properties of the active substances and also to their surroundings in the cell. VELDSTRA first believed that purely physical properties, e.g. surface activity and a given balance between hydrophilic and lipophilic groups in the molecule, might be decisive, but he later abandoned this view. The properties mentioned, however, undoubtedly have considerable secondary importance, viz. for the rates of entry and transport of the active substances. It is unfortunate that auxin research has largely neglected this important problem, apparently because of lack of interest in exact quantitative methods such as microcinematography.

Discussion of the possible collaboration of the physical properties mentioned above has, however, undoubtedly helped to clarify ideas (e.g. THIMANN 1951, VELDSTRA 1953). The activity of chlorinated benzoic and phenoxyacetic acids has been studied in detail by HANSCH and MUIR (1953) and NORMAN and WEINTRAUB (1953).

In speculations on the nature of the auxin effect, it has often been supposed that auxin reacts in the protoplasm with some carrier or receptor, and that only the auxin-receptor combination influences the biochemical processes concerned with growth. The auxin combined with receptor would therefore play the part of an enzyme, in which the auxin molecule would correspond to the prosthetic group. Unfortunately, however, more detailed experimental results are lacking, and nothing is known about the possible chemical nature of the receptor. The hypothesis can, however, to some extent provide a closer understanding of the observed phenomena of competitive inhibition.

Some investigators (MUIR and HANSCH 1951, BONNER and FORSTER 1956, BONNER 1957 and others) assume a two-point linkage of the auxin to the receptor, that is both to the ring and to the side-chain, and name as examples 2,4-dichloranisole and 2,4,6-trichlorphenoxyacetic acid. The former has a hydrogen atom in place of the carboxyl group of the active 2,4-D, and the second a chlorine atom instead of the sixth carbon atom in the ring (see the formulae below). Whilst 2,4-D is an active substance with about two-thirds of the activity of IAA, the two other derivatives are inactive.

$O \cdot CH_2 \cdot COOH$	$O \cdot CH_3$	$O \cdot CH_2 \cdot COOH$

2,4-Dichlorophenoxyacetic   2,4-Dichloranisole   2,4,6-Trichloro-
acid (2,4-D)   phenoxyacetic acid

2B

4 METHOD OF ACTION OF AUXINS AND OTHER GROWTH SUBSTANCES (AND OF ANTI-
   AUXINS AND OTHER INHIBITORS)

The idea of an auxin–receptor compound is easily linked with a hypothetical explanation of competitive inhibition. It is imagined that a material, in itself inactive, can
inhibit the effect of an auxin because it is structurally similar to the auxin in parts
of its molecule and can therefore replace it. Its dissimilarity in other parts of the molecule, however, cause its compound with the receptor to be inactive. A number of
investigations supply evidence for the exchangeability of the auxin linkages. We have
here rules similar to those for exchangeable ions and this is confirmed by the combined effect of two active hormones.

So far as quantitative measurements with the simple growth-substance tests are
possible, an approximately linear relation can be shown at low concentrations between
amount of auxin and increase in growth (BONNER and FOSTER 1955). With higher
doses, however, the curve bends, reaches an optimum at very high concentrations of
auxin, and then declines again. BONNER (1957) attempted to derive the optimum curve
of auxin effect from the hypothesis of a two-point molecular linkage. He believes that
at high auxin concentrations one linkage is loosened. This idea lacks clarity and overlooks the numerous possible complications at higher auxin concentrations, e.g.
changes in the auxin dissociation (cf. below). It must also be remembered that a
substance like auxin, which is translocated through the protoplasm, may well enter
in higher concentrations into other biochemical processes besides those that stimulate
growth. TONZIG and MARRÉ (1955) have shown, for example, that dehydroascorbic
acid behaves as an antagonist to auxin. As a result auxin may indirectly affect a number
of processes, as the ascorbic acid—dehydroascorbic acid equilibrium is involved in
oxidative processes.

A number of secondary functional changes may thus modify the final effect of an
auxin. Among the direct factors which competitively displace auxin from active
intermediate stages (such as a receptor compound) may be mentioned antiauxins and
auxin-antagonists. An *antiauxin* is formed from an active auxin if a group essential
for its effect is eliminated. One could for example explain the optimum curve by a
gradual transition of auxin into antiauxin. An auxin antagonist is any substance that
depresses, either competitively or non-competitively, the activity of an auxin or auxin-
receptor compound. It can also lead to regular inhibition. Competitive inhibitions are
of course the most interesting, since by their means information can be obtained about
the nature and the steric relationships of the active groups (cf. above).

Unlike many enzyme processes, auxin effects can only be studied in intact cells
and tissues, and to do this, as has been emphasised above, the rates of uptake and
transport of the auxin must be taken into account. Surprisingly few investigations
have been devoted to these important aspects of the process.

SUTTER (1944) and REINHOLD (1954) determined the decrease in concentration of
added auxin in the medium chemically, which, of course, could not observe the
extraordinarily low concentrations that are physiologically effective. SUTTER's conclusion, that the uptake of auxin proceeds to a diffusion equilibrium, has not been
confirmed. REINHOLD (1954) and JOHNSON and J. BONNER (1956), of whom the latter
utilised 2,4-D with ^{14}C in the carboxyl, found a process analogous to salt uptake,
i.e. an initial exchangeable adsorption and a continuing accumulation, probably in

the sap cavity. DE WIT (1957) finds that the initial uptake occurs quickly, whereas the 'fixation of the growth substance in the protoplasm' lasts 30-45 minutes (in *Avena* coleoptiles). One can therefore assume that the auxins are taken up by the general accumulation mechanism as anions. As with other organic acids, the undissociated molecules may, however, penetrate more quickly. It appears doubtful whether the amounts accumulated in the vacuole exercise any physiological activity. In general, one gets the impression that auxin is a material that must be continuously produced and transported to the site of operation.

In addition to the amounts of active substance possibly screened off in the vacuoles further quantities are probably continuously catabolised, and one can suppose that part of the catabolism is combined with positive activity. IAA is oxidatively inactivated by tissue preparations. It has often been assumed that 3-indolylaldehyde might be one of the decomposition products, but this appears not to be so (MANNING and GALSTON 1955, RAY and THIMANN 1955). As the auxin-destroying enzyme systems include peroxidase, and this enzyme occurs almost everywhere in plant tissues, particularly in roots, it may be one of the factors that make a continuous supply of auxin to the growing organs necessary. In the oxidation by peroxidase skatole (3-methylindole) may possibly be formed. Peroxidase, according to STUTZ (1957), may be supported in its effect by a phenolic activator with Mn ions. A peroxidase—auxin complex can be observed spectrophotometrically (LUNDEGÅRDH 1958). Auxin can also be decomposed photolytically with pigments, such as riboflavin, acting as sensitisers (BRAUNER 1953).

The stimulation of extension growth is one of the most striking effects of auxin, but there are others which fall more into the sphere of morphogenesis. This wide range of effects proceeding from one single group of chemical substances is unique. It should however be noted that the various effects usually are not comparable quantitatively or qualitatively. Some auxins have pronounced formative effects, such as change of leaf form. Naphthylacetic and indolylbutyric acids are outstanding as stimulators of adventitious root formation. Striking morphological effects have been observed after treatment with naphthoxy acids, halogen-substituted phenoxy acids and mandelic acid. Parthenocarpy is initiated chiefly by *para*chlorophenoxyacetic acid, e.g. in the production of seedless fruits, though it has only a small stimulating effect on extension growth (cf. NORMAN and WEINTRAUB 1953). Some auxin effect, particularly in formation, is exercised by the so-called 'carcinogens' which evoke tumours in animal tissues. To these belong e.g. 1,2-benzopyrene, tar, etc. (KISSER and LINDENBERG 1940). Very specific effects on *Chlamydomonas* are described for quercetin derivatives. A few molecules of quercetin-3'-methyl ether suffice to change the sexual behaviour of this organism (KUHN 1944), whereas 44 similar substances have no effect.

In certain fungi, e.g. yeast, growth is catalysed by small amounts of amino acids e.g. α-alanine (NIELSEN and HARTELIUS 1945). Pea roots also respond to amino acids, and it may be mentioned in this connection that amino acids usually specifically influence protoplasmic streaming. Some kinds of sugar can also have specific effects (see below). The distinction between substances which act in metabolism as nutrients and those that have only a catalytic effect is often not at all sharp.

Whether and to what extent the synthetic growth substances and inhibitors occur in intact plants is not known. The chromatographic investigations so far undertaken (cf. above) certainly indicate the occurrence of others besides IAA, even though the latter seems to be the most general growth regulator.

As with antibiotics, results keep turning up about compounds isolated from one organism and eliciting auxin effects in another. Such a substance is the *gibberellin* isolated from the phytopathogenic fungus *Gibberella fujikuroi*, which occurs in some modifications, e.g. gibberellic acid, $C_{19}H_{22}O_6$ (probably a tetracyclic dihydroxy-lactonic acid) (YABATA *et al.* 1939, KATO 1953, CROSS 1954, PHINNEY 1956, PHINNEY *et al.* 1957). The effects of the gibberellins are not identical with those of the auxins. They clearly stimulate cell extension but cause no reaction in the curvature test. The possible part played by substances resembling the gibberellins in natural growth and flowering of plants is still imperfectly known (BRIAN 1958).

Kinetin (6-furfurylaminopurine) and *carbanilide* (*N, N'*-diphenylurea) also have some auxin activities. Kinetin is prepared by treatment of desoxyribosenucleic acid (DNA) in autoclaves. It has been found that in the pith of tobacco stems a definite concentration ratio of kinetin and IAA is needed for the normal division of nucleus and cell (DAS *et al.* 1956). Kinetin also affects the growth of leaves (KURAISHI and OKUMURA 1956).

Originally a fairly sharp distinction was made between extension hormones, i.e. the actual auxins, and other substances, e.g. thiamine, biotin, etc., which may be considered rather as hormones of protoplasmic growth. Since it has been found, however, that auxins and similar substances also influence functions of the protoplasm, the above distinction can be maintained only if it is possible to define the effects quite sharply. An intermediate position is occupied by those substances which stimulate nuclear division, for example kinetin. A third group is formed by synergists, i.e. auxiliary substances such as gibberellin.

Thiamine (aneurin, vitamin B_1) appears to be formed in the leaves and shoot meristems and to be conducted thence to the roots (RYTZ 1939, BONNER and GREENE 1939), where it enters into carboxylase (HOROWITZ and HEEGARD 1941, LUNDEGÅRDH 1943). *Nicotinic acid* also has an established position in the culture of isolated roots (BONNER and DEVIRIAN 1939, AVERY 1942). Addition of IAA is often necessary in tissue cultures (GAUTHERET 1947). GAUTHERET found at a concentration of 10^{-7} a stimulation of cambial activity in artichokes, at 10^{-6} a stimulation of root formation, whilst at 10^{-5} cell division ceased and the cells expanded in all directions instead. ROBORGH and THOMAS (1948) and others investigated the effect of IAA on the alga *Chlorella vulgaris* and found that extension was stimulated at $10^{-6} - 10^{-7}$ and inhibition at 10^{-5}, whereas cell division remained unaffected. This alga itself produces auxin, of which each growing cell contains about 10 molecules.

Pyridoxin (cf. p. 236) appears to be a necessary factor for the growth of certain varieties of tomato (WHITE 1946, ROBBINS 1949).

GALSTON (1947) asserted a joint effect of *nicotinamide* and IAA such that both had to be supplied in root culture. *Riboflavin*, on the other hand, seems to be synthesised in the root tips (BONNER 1942). Among vitamins and vitamin-like compounds which usually need to be added to cultures (ROBBINS 1942), *biotin* (KÖGL *et al.* 1940; cf. DU VIGNEAUD 1942), *pantothenic acid, ascorbic acid, pimelic acid* (heptanedioic acid) and *inositol* may also be mentioned. The effect of para-*aminobenzoic acid* and *sulphonamide* on seedlings was studied by MACHT (1945).

Substances that are formed in the aerial parts and influence the growth of roots (LOO 1935) and conversely those that arise in the roots and influence shoot growth have been little investigated. The former are termed '*caulocalines*' (WENT 1929, 1943), and the latter '*rhizocalines*'. The formation of rhizocalines appears to be stimulated by good aeration of the roots (cf. Ropp 1946, Ruge 1957). This may, of course, often be merely an effect of auxin. For growth substances in heterotrophic plants see p. 243.

No sharp distinction can be drawn between growth-accelerating and growth-inhibiting substances, as even the typical auxins, e.g. IAA, may work in either direction according to their concentration, etc. The same applies e.g. to anaesthetics, which have a stimulating effect in minute doses, and to the trace elements which to some extent can be compared with the organic growth substances. It cannot however be doubted that typical inhibitors and antiauxins do exist. It is usually considered (Funke and Söding) that normal growth is regulated by a balance between auxins and antiauxins, which easily pass over into each other.

In the mutual ecological relations of plants, inhibitors play a part which can be regarded as a kind of inverted vitamin effect. These are the *antibiotics* mentioned earlier. According to Knapp and Furthmann (1954) *coumarin*, which is generally poisonous, is excreted by *Melilotus albus*, but in this case plays no important ecological role. Seeds can excrete inhibitors which inhibit the germination of other seeds (Fröschel and Funke 1939). The germination of orchid seeds is influenced by substances which are excreted by a symbiotic fungus (Vermeulen 1943). The antibiotics are of course well known because of their effect on pathogenic bacteria. Inhibitors, e.g. *cinnamic acid*, are excreted by the guayule plant (Bonner and Galston 1944). An antibiotic, *anemonin*, occurs in *Anemone pulsatilla* (Baer *et al.* 1946, Larsen 1947); it belongs to the same group as crepin, penicillin, streptomycin, clavacin and others. Coumarin inhibits the germination of seeds and is used as a herbicide (Harrington 1947). According to Virtanen *et al.* (1957), anti-microbial materials occur in cereals and clovers. From rye, 2(3)-*benzoxazolone* (see formula below) has been isolated. Many of the materials mentioned, whose effect on plant growth is still insufficiently investigated, and also true inhibiting hormones (Larsen 1947), often contain an unsaturated lactone ring, as in coumarin, and have reactive double bonds. (For the effect

Coumarin
(1,2-benzopyrone,
(o-hydroxycinnamic
acid lactone)

2(3)-Benzoxazolone
(o-hydroxycarbanilic
acid lactone)

of streptomycin on *Avena* coleoptiles see Rosen 1954 *et al.*) In etiolated pea epicotyls (Tang and Bonner 1947) and in bean epicotyls (Wagenknecht and Burris 1950) there is an enzyme system which inactivates IAA by attacking its active side-group. This inhibitor is formed only when oxygen is present.

For the physiological effect of auxins both concentration and sensitivity to light are important.

The optimum curve of the auxin effect has been mentioned above. It is important for the explanation of the opposite geotropic reactions of shoot and root. According to a hypothesis first put forward by CHOLODNY, geotropic reaction is due to a lateral shift of the auxin, so that the lower side of the organ gets more than the upper side. Shoots and roots react to gravity in opposite directions. In shoots increase of auxin concentration causes a unilateral stimulation of growth and a consequent upward growth of the shoot, whereas in the roots there is a corresponding inhibition of growth and the root bends downwards (see also Chap. 10). The phenomenon is usually interpreted as meaning that the effective auxin concentration in the shoot lies below, and in the roots near or above the optimum. CHOLODNY's hypothesis has given rise to extensive experimental work. Even though criticisms have been raised, CHOLODNY's hypothesis still seems to be maintained (cf. e.g. ÅBERG 1957). We return to this question in Section E.

In explaining the effect of light on growth and curvature, the sensitivity of auxin to light takes a foremost place. It has been found that auxin a occurs also as a lactone with about the same activity, and the equilibrium auxin a⇌auxin-a-lactone is reversible. Unlike auxin b, which shows a characteristic absorption band at 250 mμ, auxin a shows no absorption in the ultra-violet (KÖGL et al. 1944). On illumination auxin-a-lactone passes over into the inactive lumi-auxone. This photoreaction depends to a large extent on the wavelength of the light. For the conversion of 50% of active auxone-a-lactone into inactive lumi-auxone the light energy required increases greatly with the wavelength, as one passes from 313 to 578 mμ. Since auxin a in itself is colourless, the spectral sensitivity may be due to sensitising impurities. Thus, for example, the utilisation of light increases strongly in the blue part of the spectrum if some β-carotene is supplied. These results have a certain relevance in explaining the spectral sensitivity of phototropism (see Chap. 10, section C).

Some insight into the biochemistry of auxin is given by a study of the extraction process. The original extraction method is based on the diffusion from a tissue into an agar cube. Later extraction with ether or chloroform was investigated. This extraction takes place very slowly and, e.g. in *Lemna* (THIMANN and SKOOG 1940), may require several months. Roots also resist extraction, whereas oat coleoptiles are completely extracted by cold ether within 24 hours. GUSTAFSON (1941) recommends the following procedure: first freezing, then comminution, then boiling for one minute, and finally extraction with ether.

These facts remind one to evaluate carefully all data, and especially the earlier ones, on the absolute auxin content of an organ. Since auxin has a low molecular weight and dissolves easily in various media, the slow extraction must be due to fixation in the cell. SKOOG (1942) assumes a high-molecular mother-substance ('precursor') from which the auxin is only gradually released. Thus in seeds and storage organs 90%-95% of the auxin is inactivated in this way and is almost immovable, while only 5%-10% is mobile and active. The separation of the auxin is facilitated by hydrolysis at pH > 7, heat, ether, etc. Proteolytic enzymes also release the auxin (SKOOG and THIMANN 1942). As well as this inactive fixed auxin there probably also occurs in green tissues an active auxin complex which has less mobility than the free auxin and is probably of a protein nature. Here one is again reminded of the close connection between tryptophan and auxin. Tryptophan itself has no auxin effect but probably serves as the parent compound for auxin (SKOOG 1937, WILDMAN et al. 1947; according to ÅBERG 1957 evidence for this in roots is still lacking). The formation of auxin occurs only in presence of oxygen. According to LARSEN (1944, 1947), the auxin can occur as the neutral aldehyde (β-indolylacetaldehyde) which is converted by aldehydases into the active carboxyl form (see also ENGARD and NAKATA 1947; literature review in SKOOG 1947 and LARSEN 1951).

This interpretation of the presence of bound auxin or of auxin precursors is generally recognised. There is also the possibility that auxin accumulates by active ion transport in the vacuole and so is, in the main, rendered inactive. The idea of a receptor complex should not be confused with these inactive forms of auxin (see above). The hypothetical receptor linkage is analogous to the initial linkage of salt ions to large carrier molecules in the protoplasm, and must therefore be imagined as an exchangeable adsorption linkage. This linkage may be dissolved by electrodialysis (cf. WILDMAN and GORDON 1942). GORDON (1946) assumes that in wheat grains the auxin occurs as 'precursor' bound to the five predominant proteins; chiefly with albumin, globulin and proteoses in the embryo, and less with prolamin and glutelin in the endosperm. The parent substance of the auxin present in the endosperm may possibly be of a simpler kind, since it diffuses through a dialysis membrane made of cellophane (see OVERBEEK 1944). Such substances, soluble in water and in 95% methanol, have been isolated by paper chromatography. They are all inactive in the *Avena* test but give IAA by treatment with alkali.

These experiences of the multifarious occurrence of auxin have aroused strong doubt about the reliability of the usual physiological tests for auxin. The *Avena* test has been described above. An *Avena*-unit, according to KÖGL and HAAGEN-SMIT (1931), is that amount of a growth substance which under standard conditions of temperature and humidity and in an agar cube of 2 mm³ causes a curvature of 10°. The previously described coleoptile test, using pieces of coleoptile in solutions, is more reliable, but should be supplemented by determination of the amounts of auxin taken up. In this spectrophotometric determinations may give valuable help. If the determination of the amounts of auxin taken up is omitted, a number of factors difficult to control become significant, such as varying wettability of the coleoptile epidermis, factors of permeability, etc. The test substance appears to pass relatively quickly out of the solution into the coleoptile tissue; whereas in the older experiments with lanolin paste, according to ZIMMERMANN (1942), only one part in 25,000 of the IAA penetrates in six hours. Segments of the extension zone of *Avena* coleoptiles offer the advantage that auxin is not produced in them. In the root test, however, auxin is produced in the root tip itself (VAN OVERBEEK 1939, NAGAO 1939), though auxin uptake undoubtedly takes place more easily through the root surface than through the coleoptile epidermis. The roots' own auxin production always causes some uncertainty (about root tests see LEOPOLD 1954, AUDUS 1953, ÅBERG 1957). In roots also the superoptimal or inhibitory effects of the auxin become too pronounced, and this, with the general lack of knowledge about the true form of the auxin optimum curve, introduces still further uncertainty. In general, therefore, shoot tests are to be preferred, since in these the auxin usually operates in the steeply rising branch of the curve.

Finally, there is also the difficulty that the auxins already present in the tissues are often in reversible combinations dependent on the metabolic processes.

E. Growth Mechanisms

After the discovery of the auxins and other growth substances the interest of plant physiologists was strongly directed towards the parts played by them in the growth, form and movements of plants. It is at once clear that metabolism participates in growth as a whole, since both wall substance and protoplasm are consumed and must be produced afresh by it. The grouping of this side of growth physiology under the term 'food factor' (according to WENT and THIMANN 1939) appears to be too schematic. It is better to think of the auxins as one group among many which supervise and direct the phases of growth and of cell differentiation.

1 GROWTH AND RESPIRATION

As growth, with few exceptions, involves a synthesis of cell material, it is naturally closely connected with the turnover of energy. The energy produced in respiration is coupled with the energy consumed in the synthesis of cell material.

Theoretically it might well be possible to build up new cell substance by a series of dismutations, coupled, for example, with intra-molecular respiration or fermentation. Such a process, however, would probably mean considerable expenditure of material and the formation of by-products difficult to dispose of. Some anaerobic organisms have specialised on these inconvenient and expensive methods, and for obligate anaerobes oxygen may even be a poison. *Clostridium butyricum* for example is said to be damaged by oxygen pressure of even 0·001 atm. In higher plants growth is connected almost 100% with the presence of oxygen, and active growth is always accompanied by intensive aerobic respiration, through which with a slight expenditure of material much more free energy is made available than by intra-molecular dismutations. In aerobic bacteria also growth and aerobic respiration usually run parallel. KEILIN and HARTREE (1947), working with a cytochrome system, have shown this for the *Bacillus subtilis*. They found, however, that certain inhibitors, e.g. 8-hydroxyquinoline, inhibit only growth and not respiration.

A certain general conformity between growth and respiration is evident in root tips. MACHLIS (1944) and WANNER (1945) have determined the respiration in different zones. They found the greatest intensity of respiration in the primary meristem, although the extension zone also respires more than the developed zones. According to KOPP (1948), on the other hand, the extension zone respires more actively per unit of protoplasmic volume than the primary meristem (the zone of cell division). The increase of respiration associated with nuclear division and protoplasmic growth has been observed in the most varied objects, e.g. sea-urchins and stamens. The anthers show variations in respiration occurring synchronously with the reduction divisions (ZEUTHEN 1947, ERICKSON 1947).

It is, however, a peculiar fact that growth continues usually even with oxygen pressures low enough to restrict respiration severely. This suggests that only a part of the redox mechanisms active in oxygen respiration is necessary for growth. That growth increases or decreases at times without a corresponding variation in the respiration is probably less surprising, since growth requires not only the synthesis of energy-rich substances but is also regulated by auxins, etc., which certainly do not enter directly into the respiratory metabolism. It can be imagined that respiration and synthetic processes continue for a time even when the growth accidentally decreases because of shortage of auxin, etc. In cell extension much osmotic material is consumed, which explains, for example, why a correlation between growth and sucrose production can occur in barley (ARCHBOLD 1940).

In many investigations on growth one misses a distinction between the dividing and the extension phases. In general, e.g. in the root test, only the total volume increase or the forward movement of the tip of the organ is measured. Here the advantages of a ciné technique become evident, since measurements at short time-intervals refer almost solely to the extension phase.

As early as 1883 WIELER found that aerobic higher plants would grow exceptionally even under very low oxygen concentrations (down to 10^{-11} atm). The minimum usually lies at $0 \cdot 1\%$-3% by volume. In roots the sensitivity to oxygen differs in root hairs and the growing point. The hairs burst at oxygen pressures below the minimum, which suggests that even the deposition of the wall substances had been disorganised. Bursting occurs also at pH values under about $3 \cdot 5$, but here it may be due to solution of the necessary calcium from the pectin (cf. p. 80). According to KOPP (1948), the growth of root hairs of wheat ceases at an oxygen content of $0 \cdot 5$-1 mg per litre, which corresponds to about one-tenth of the normal content in water. They only burst, however, in almost complete absence of oxygen. The sensitivity is about the same in the dividing and the extension zones. Yeast, which operates to a great extent anaerobically, requires oxygen for growth and multiplication. The necessary concentrations however are, according to LIBBRECHT and MASSART (1935), extraordinarily low, from which one may conclude that the oxygen is used more to maintain the activity of certain redox systems than to serve as the general H-acceptor.

There are numerous examples of steady rates of aerobic respiration even when the speed of growth is varying. The growth of roots is greatly dependent on the pH of the medium (LUNDEGÅRDH 1942), but their respiration is not (LUNDEGÅRDH and BURSTRÖM 1944). The inside of the root is protected against fluctuations of pH by its exceptional buffer capacity, whereas it is the exposed outer wall of the epidermis which to a considerable extent regulates the growth, so giving rise to tension in the tissue. Grass coleoptiles appear to behave similarly. In *Aspergillus niger*, according to YAMAMOTO (1933), respiration is little affected by phenylurethane, NaF and CO; but these substances do, on the other hand, restrict growth. The utilisation of lactose for growth fluctuates also with temperature and attains an optimum at 25°C.

In many heterotrophic micro-organisms, e.g. *Aspergillus oryzae*, differences in 'economic coefficients' are clear, i.e. the energy requirement of growth changes with age. According to TAMIYA (1933), for the formation of a given amount of fungal substance more energy is consumed the older the mycelium is. The 'endogenous respiration' (cf. Chap. 4) also changes in a similar way.

A certain insight into the connection between respiration and growth is provided by investigations into the effect of IAA on protoplasmic streaming. The positive effect is increased by malate (OLSON and DU BUY 1940; SWEENEY 1941, 1944; SWEENEY and THIMANN 1942; VAN OVERBEEK 1944), and according to ALBAUM and COMMONER (1941) and COMMONER and THIMANN (1941) also by fumaric acid and succinic acid as well as by malic acid; but iodacetic acid has an inhibitory effect. In the view of these authors the observations support the assumption that auxin participates in the tricarboxylic acid cycle, which is said to supply 10% of the total respiration of the *Avena* coleoptile. They think that the auxin acts as an activator in the transfer of H. It might be supposed that the redox processes influenced by auxin act as a shunt synthesising wall material, whereas the main part of the respiration remains devoted to other functions. This would explain the usually indirect connection between respiration and extension growth. It has also been surmised that auxin accelerates the mobilisation of carbohydrate reserves. CARLIER and BUFFEL (1955) found an increase in synthesis of wall material, especially pectin, occurring simultaneously with the rise of respiration.

That growth substances of the category of biotin, thiamine, α-alanine, etc., exert their effect through the fundamental metabolic mechanism has already been emphasised. Further examples of such effects are given by investigations of SCHULTZ et al. (1940) with yeast, which show that the substances mentioned influence the utilisation of various nitrogen compounds.

2 CELL EXTENSION

For a considerable time the view has been defended that in cell extension the wall is stretched osmotically beyond the elastic limit so that at the same time new wall material can be deposited. According to this interpretation, the protoplasm is not notably increased, but the increase in volume depends especially on accumulating osmotically effective substances, such as sugars and salts. According to this the 'plastic extension' of the wall would be the main factor in the stretching. This interpretation has, however, suffered considerable modification and correction by later investigations.

BLANK and FREY-WYSSLING (1941) have shown that the protoplasm itself is considerably increased during stretching. The expansion of the cell volume, however, also requires active formation, or at least active accumulation, of other substances as wall material. The accumulation of osmotic substances in the vacuoles as a result of aerobic respiration is a general property of plant cells, even in the mature parts of the root (Chap. 6). It is never absent from extending cells and must of course always support growth, even when the turgor extension as such is not an instrument of the wall stretching.

It is still unknown whether the auxins directly stimulate salt accumulation, as COMMONER (1942) believed. It may not be necessary to assume, with OVERBEEK (1944), a special effect of the auxin on the 'non-osmotic water uptake'. As discussed in Chaps. 6 and 7, a 'non-osmotic water uptake' can only involve trifling amounts. The water uptake necessary for turgor pressure is based entirely on osmotic processes accompanying the active uptake of salt, sugar, etc. Added auxin, according to recent investigations, influences the active salt uptake in concentrations of $10^{-9} - 10^{-4}$ M very little, stimulates weakly at about 10^{-3} M, and inhibits strongly at higher concentrations. The fairly complicated effect of auxins on the bleeding of wheat roots (LUNDEGÅRDH 1949) follows other pathways, but affords no support for the hypothesis of a 'non-osmotic water uptake'. Neither the effect of auxin on salt uptake nor that on bleeding runs parallel with the growth effect, but rather in the opposite direction.

The view of COMMONER (1942) that the osmotic pressure increased by active salt uptake may act as an instrument of growth, is also refuted by the fact that a very large stimulation of growth (up to 10 times) by IAA is continued even during a subsequent treatment in distilled water. The necessary osmotic materials must arise through the decomposition of large-molecular inclusions of the cells, about which no detailed observations are available. The results and hypothesis of THIMANN (1951) and HACKETT and THIMANN (1953) about a 'non-osmotic water uptake' governed by an auxin-stimulated metabolism are ambiguous. In later investigations THIMANN and SAMUEL (1955) even turned against the hypothesis. They found that the synthesis of wall material increases at the time of stretching, and that the pectins are thereby favoured. THIMANN and SAMUEL worked with heavy water (tritium hydroxide THO).

The absence of any direct parallel between water uptake (from outside) and extension, and between extension and total respiration, follows from later work by BURSTRÖM (1953), ELIASON (1955), BUSSE and KANDLER (1956) and others. BURSTRÖM used mannitol, which does not penetrate cells, to change the osmotic value of the medium. NEWCOMB (1953) found that the increase in respiration caused by auxin precedes cell extension and water uptake, and that respiration continues even if the latter processes are inhibited by phenyl-thiourea.

The simultaneous increase of the negative surface charge (Fig. 159) with the increased rate of cell extension is an expression of the intensified ionic activity at the interface between protoplasm and cell wall. This fact suggests a strong acidification of the surface layer, which may be due both to the increased amount of acid pectins in the wall and to increased dissociation of the protoplasmic membrane. Alterations in the elasticity of the wall occur at the same time. According to BURSTRÖM (1942, 1956) elasticity increases at the beginning of extension (Fig. 161). This starting phase of extension is increased by a rise of temperature but is fairly independent of a special supply of sugar. The starting phase is increased in wheat roots also by IAA in the range of concentration from $10^{-11} - 10^{-6}$ moles per litre.

According to early observations (HEYN 1940), the first effect of auxin is a softening of the wall; but the interpretation put forward by RUGE (1939), that auxin might favour swelling of the pectins, does not seem to be valid (BLANK and DEUEL 1943). The assumption of a loosening of the wall structure by auxin is supported also by later investigations (CLELAND and BONNER 1956). ORDIN et al. (1957), on the basis of experiments with methionine marked with ^{14}C, assert that, under the influence of auxin, the carboxyl groups of pectin are esterified (transfer of the marked methyl groups of methionine). Earlier WILSON and SKOOG (1954) put forward the view that in the medulla of tobacco, which contains a lot of alcohol-soluble uronides, there are converted under the influence of auxin partly into pectin, and the pectin methyl esterase activity is also increased (BRYAN and NEWCOMB 1954). The enzyme is located in the wall fraction of the homogenates and, according to the view of the workers mentioned influences pectin hydration.

In the second phase of elongation (BURSTRÖM 1942) the elasticity (turgor extension) is reduced. This observation is important since it directly contradicts the older view about extension growth. With the use of X-rays, the polarisation microscope and the electron microscope, sub-microscopic cellulose strands have been found in the

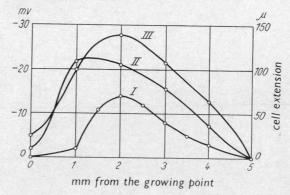

Fig. 159. Rate of growth and surface potential in the root tip of wheat. 1. The rate of cell extension (cf. Fig. 158). 2. The surface potential in 0·001 M CaCl₂. 3. The surface potential in 0·0001 M HCl. (after LUNDEGÅRDH 1942).

primary wall (HESS *et al.* 1939, DIEHL *et al.* 1939, FREY-WYSSLING 1945). In elongated cells these microfibrils, whose presence had already been suspected by NÄGELI, are usually orientated transversely in the so-called vessel structure. In the secondary wall they can also be orientated in other directions (Chap. 2). In bast fibres they lie parallel to the longitudinal axis (fibre structure), and in cotton hairs and the tracheids of conifers in a spiral; but in the thickenings of the ring tracheids, on the other hand, they are again transverse as in vessel thickenings.

It has been maintained that the cellulose fibrils do not cross each other but run in an interweaving wave formation adhering to each other at the peaks of the waves. In this way a reticulum is formed which is most readily extensible in a direction at right angles to the main orientation of the fibres. Plaiting together of the fibrils as in a tissue has been observed with the electron microscope.

According to a common interpretation, the wall may be stretched so much that new fibrils can be built in between those already existing. It has also been supposed that a kind of plastic extension with subsequent insertion of new fibrils at local points or surfaces may take place (so-called mosaic growth; FREY-WYSSLING and STECHER 1951). This has been said to explain the thickening of the primary wall which is sometimes observed. The observation of BURSTRÖM that in the stage of most rapid extension the elasticity of the wall decreases, whereas the turgor pressure remains approximately constant, does not however support the hypothesis of a plastic extension

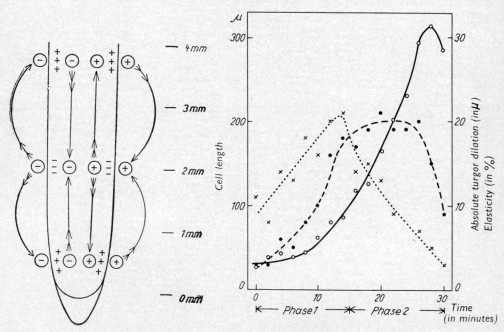

Fig. 160. Diagram of the boundary layer potential and the electrical microcurrents in growing root tips of peas. The zone of maximal extension (2 mm from the growing point) is electronegative in relation to the growing point and the mature part (4 mm and upwards). The directions of current are determined by measurements with unpolarisable microelectrodes inserted in the roots (after LUNDEGÅRDH 1942).

Fig. 161. The changes in the properties of cell walls during extension (in wheat roots). . . . increase in length of the cells, - - - the absolute turgor extension, ——— the elasticity (percentage turgor extension) (after BURSTRÖM 1942).

being the fundamental process of extension growth. On the other hand the observed facts can be brought well into line with the results on the positive effect of nutrients added during the volume increase.

The discussions on the importance of the sub-microscopic wall structure for the mechanism of extension growth have probably taken too little account of the difficulties which arise in testing the hypothetical structures by physiological experiments. It is, moreover, an open question how far observations on the sub-microscopic structure of dried cell walls can be applied to the living wall. KERR (1951) directed attention to the alternative interpretation which had already been suggested, viz. that cellulose might be present as a discontinuous phase which stiffens the wall structure like a cement but without forming a reticulum. He pointed out the suitability of such an interpretation for understanding a number of properties of the wall which otherwise would be difficult to explain.

In the growth of root hairs (LUNDEGÅRDH 1946, EKDAHL 1953) the starting phase and the extension phase cannot be separated. The growth takes place in the cone at the tip, and no stretching of the cylindrical part of the hairs occurs. In spite of the high osmotic pressure (in wheat root hairs 7-8 atm) no turgor extension can be detected even in the growing tip. In tip growth, as shown in Fig. 46 (p. 78), the wall formation must be fastest at the zenith, and then decrease along the parabolically curved side towards the cylindrical part. With changes in the surroundings (reduction in pH, deficiency of oxygen, etc.), which inhibit growth, the wall substance tends to be deposited lenticularly just at the tip, since normally the strongest deposit is formed there.

Observations on growth in relation to the osmotic value of the medium show that turgor extension is not a factor in wall formation during the growth of root hairs. Even in 0·1 M glucose, that is with an external pressure of 2·6 atm, there is no change in growth rate. Only after several minutes, when the sugar has penetrated and affected metabolism, does the rate of growth increase. An inhibition begins only at 0·2 M, that is at 5·3 atm pressure. It has already been indicated above that, in extension growth and in tip growth, the fibrils of cellulose and pectin are arranged according to two different principles, and this suggests differences in the participating enzyme systems and possibly also in the hydration.

Root hair growth shows clearly that 'plastic extension' is not necessary for growth in area of the cell wall, and similar arguments have been applied to the extension growth of parenchymatous cells. Here one is reminded of PFEFFER'S experiment of enclosing growing roots in plaster of Paris. Growth of the surface continues for a time, in spite of the high opposing pressure, until the walls are folded like a bellows.

The true nature of the processes controlling wall growth are still unknown, but one may suspect that the molecular configuration, that is fibrillar molecules with relatively weak lateral linkages, together with the presence of two oppositely working enzyme systems, one synthesising and stiffening and the other breaking down and loosening, could well cause a type of balance such that a maximum limit of wall thickness was not exceeded. What part pectin fibrils may play in this is not known. They seem to form a more irregular and therefore more plastic structure, which probably causes the looseness of the wall that seems to be so important for the insertion of new cellulose fibrils. In root-hair growth also pectin takes part. The indispensability of the calcium ion for maintaining a suitable plasticity of the pectin was discussed in Chap. 2. The importance of calcium ions for root growth was demonstrated by LUNDE-GÅRDH (1942). Even very small concentrations of calcium are effective (BURSTRÖM

1955, 1956; optimum concentration 10^{-7} M) especially in the first phase of growth. This phase is also accelerated by IAA, according to BURSTRÖM, while the inhibiting effect of auxin in roots is exercised during the second phase of growth. The first phase is inhibited by coumarin.

That glucose, which in the normal life of roots is conducted from the phloem of the leaves, is actually present in the surface of the cell, follows from the fact that the living root always exudes some glucose into the medium, although considerable losses are avoided by an accumulation mechanism working in the opposite direction. Whether the synthesis of wall material (pectin, cellulose, etc.) actually takes place in the surface of the protoplasm, which seems to be partly interwoven with the wall structure, or in deeper layers is a much-discussed question. SISSON (1941) and FARR (1941) believed that cellulose is synthesised in the interior of the protoplasm, possibly in special plastid-like organelles (mitochondria?), and that it migrates in plastic form to the surface where it 'crystallises' in fibrils. This interpretation has so far not been convincingly confirmed. More recent results suggest a particularly active metabolism of carbohydrates, including polysaccharides, at the protoplasmic surface. Importance is therefore given to the interweaving of the wall reticulum and the protoplasmic surface (PRESTON 1952). It may be remembered that a number of enzymes have been found in the protoplasmic layer near the wall (NEWCOMB 1951, 1953; MANDELS 1953; HONDA 1954; GODDARD and STAFFORD 1954).

The question of the biological effect of auxins in wall growth is still unsolved. The predominant view is undoubtedly that auxin induces a loosening of the pectin and cellulose structure and so makes the insertion of new wall material easier. Earlier it was also believed that the inhibiting effect of excessive doses of auxin was due to the loosening going too far. THIMANN and BONNER, on the other hand, directed attention to the extraordinarily small amounts of auxin which sufficed to produce a positive effect. They are of the opinion that an auxin molecule acts on several hundred cellulose micelles, which appears to exclude a direct chemical effect. These calculations are, however, insecurely based, as very few facts are known either about the total amounts of auxin taken up or about those needed for activity.

The following alternatives may be considered. The cellulose molecules grow in length by successive addition of glucose units. According to CORI and CORI (1946), the length of the polysaccharide molecules depends on the amount of activator present. At high concentration short molecular chains are formed, and at lower concentrations longer chains. This is reminiscent of the optimum effect of auxin. Whether auxin takes a part in the building of the primary valency chain, or only influences the few lateral linkages, in either case only a very small amount of auxin would be necessary. A third alternative would be an effect of auxin starting several stages before the final wall formation. Here it may be mentioned that auxin does influence a number of enzyme processes; for example an influence on the nucleic acid content of cells has been found. LEOPOLD (1953) found that auxin in the presence of coenzyme A and of ATP catalyses the fixation of SH-groups. Any stimulation or inhibition by auxin of an individual key process concerned in any way with the synthesis of wall materials may, of course, be supposed to affect the balance between the final synthetic and loosening processes.

The idea of an effect of auxin more deeply seated than in the end-stages of wall formation is supported by the previously described biochemical observations, by the opposed effects on growth and flowering (LUNDEGÅRDH 1949), and by observations on *adaptation to auxin concentrations*. Even a concentration of 10^{-10} M auxin inhibits the growth of wheat roots. After a considerable time (1-2 days), however, adaptation takes place, so that concentrations as high as 10^{-8} M accelerate growth. This adaptation is not due to the consumption or inactivation of the auxin taken up, but is observed also after repeated or continuous change of the auxin solutions.

This adaptation has been observed by several later workers (see the review in ÅBERG 1957). It is reminiscent of the adaptation to cyanide concentrations which was mentioned earlier (Chap. 4). As a possible explanation enzyme adaptation was suggested, that is selection of the most stable configuration in the given conditions of a protein combined with a given prosthetic group. The position of the auxin optima varies greatly in different plants and organs, as well as in different parts of the cell. *Avena* coleoptiles, for example, react positively with 10^{-5} M auxin, whereas the root hairs of wheat do not react with this concentration at all, and parenchymatous cells react strongly negative. The difference of sensitivity between roots and shoots is ascribed mostly to variations in the internal level of auxin, but the difference between root hairs and root cells must be due to specific differences in the wall-formation mechanism, in the case given obviously to different degrees of loosening of the wall structure. This is certainly suggested also by BURSTRÖM's observations on the opposed reactions to auxin in phases one and two of cell extension. We thus conclude that a certain extensibility (loosening or swelling) of the wall is a precondition for the positive auxin effect, which of course does not mean that the auxin acts directly in the end-stages of wall formation.

The behaviour of the root hairs seems to indicate that they possess a type of growth which operates well even without auxin. The circumstances also indicate that certain anti-auxins affect the enzyme processes regulating growth. In every young (unlignified) cell there are obviously two systems operating, one anabolic and the other catabolic, between which there is a steady state. One can observe changes in this balance in root hairs, in which growth may cease and be resumed later. In regeneration processes the growth of resting parenchymatous cells is again resumed, but this activation is not necessarily initiated by auxin (SÖDING 1940, GOUWENTAK 1941). Activation by auxins can of course be effected also by removal of an inhibiting factor. This possibility should be considered wherever there are differences of response e.g. in the twofold effect of auxin in the extension phase, and in adaptation phenomena, etc.

It was sometimes maintained that the growing cell wall is composed chiefly of pectin; but later investigations (WIRTH 1946) showed that hemicellulose, and especially cellulose, are the chief components. In very young maize coleoptiles the proportion of pectins is estimated at about one-quarter of the cellulose content. The characteristic method of formation of cellulose micelles from long chain molecules, described above, must consequently impose itself on the construction of the wall.

The importance of a proper coordination of several processes working together is clear from the growth of the root hairs. Disturbing influences can cause either an increased secretion of cellulose, combined with a decrease in the cell volume, or a diminished secretion of cellulose, with an increase in volume. In the former case growth ceases because of local thickenings of the wall, and in the latter case the wall bursts unless there is a simultaneous decrease of turgor. Locally differentiated surface activity of the cytoplasm leads to hair-like cells. In the cells of the root tip and probably also in other elongated organs the apparently continuous growth takes place in the individual cells very anisotropically or in a mosaic.

The earlier ideas of KRABBE (1886) on 'sliding growth' were soon dropped, and today it is believed that the middle lamella remains fixed. In specialised cells, e.g. bast fibres, there is a differential growth of adjacent cells with different rates of division, so that an elongated cell is surrounded by a number of shorter ones. PRIESTLEY (1930) calls this 'symplastic growth'. Such a symplastic growth takes place e.g. in the root epidermis, where cells with and without root hairs (trichoblasts and atrichoblasts) alternate irregularly. According to VAN ITERSEN and MEEUSE (1941; see Chap. 2) the basic form of the meristematic cells is a combination of octahedra and hexahedra with fourteen faces.

3 SPECIAL EFFECTS OF THE GROWTH SUBSTANCES

The differentiation of the surfaces of living cells in regions of different growth rates is a basic phenomenon through which various cell forms arise, organs grow in length or in width, and so on. The genetic cause of the differentiation still completely eludes our knowledge. Experiments with growth substances have, however, revealed the surprising plasticity of cells and tissues to an extent that earlier had been known only from plant pathology, especially in gall formation.

Gall formations arise as reaction to a foreign substance introduced into the tissue. All kinds of abnormal cell shapes and even backward development are induced. As it is now possible to reproduce a similar pathogenic morphogenesis by application of high auxin concentrations, the conclusion has been drawn that attacks of insects and pathogenic fungi might involve the transfer of growth substances. Some investigations on crown galls and their progenitor *Agrobacterium tumefaciens* suggest that the tumour-inducing agent is a substance related to nucleic acids (KLEIN 1953; for kinetin see p. 374), which in its turn induces a high auxin production in the tissues attacked. Addition of IAA also seems to cause a rise in the nucleic acid content.

In general, the known chemical growth factors are divided into two main groups according to whether they preferentially influence cell extension or cell division; though for the reasons mentioned above a sharp distinction is not easy. The typical extension hormone, IAA, also induces root formation, tumour-like tissue swellings and other abnormalities. On the other hand there is no doubt that more specific 'morphogenic hormones' also exist, and it must be remembered that an immense variety of forms can arise from the changing interaction of hormonal factors.

The *carcinogenic substances* which cause malign tumours in animal tissues (KENNA- WAY *et al.* 1937-40) belong to a special type, since they evoke irreparable genetic changes, which cause an increased frequency of division and at the same time the loss of the power of specialisation; that is, a kind of degeneration of the genes. In plants also a similar cancerous tissue with unrestricted power of growth has been observed (WHITE and BRAUN 1941). The problem of the ontogenetic determination that induces isolated root meristems, for example, to form roots was discussed in a previous chapter (Chap. 2). There it was emphasised that special processes are set in motion which finally cause an irreversible genetic block, so that a return to the primary meristem stage becomes impossible. SINNOTT (1942) put forward the idea that the nucleus does not participate in the detailed work of the cell, but only lays down the main lines. According to this interpretation the details may be worked out by the cyto- plasm, whose structural individuality is certainly passed from cell to cell. Support has also been expressed (cf. SKOOG 1954) for a more nearly universal domination by the nucleus, the view preferred by geneticists. The field is, however, still open to all kinds of speculation.

The most prominent property of the auxins is an unspecific regulation of cell extension and consequently of the general growth rate. By the unilateral effect of external factors, such as light and gravity, the curvatures which participate in so many ways in morphogenesis also come into the field of auxin effects. WENT (1942) believes that only the freely diffusable auxin takes part in the tropisms, whereas the general growth rate is determined by the 'combined auxin' (cf. above). LUNDEGÅRDH (1922) points to the different forms of the light intensity curves of growth and curvature of *Avena* coleoptiles (Chap. 10). Later ANKER (1955) published similar results on the auxin effect on growth and geotropism of roots. The opinion has, however, since been expressed that free auxin also dominates the growth process.

The sensitivity of root growth towards auxin has been demonstrated by several workers. The amounts necessary for negative reaction are sometimes extremely small (THIMANN 1937, LUNDEGÅRDH 1942, ÅBERG 1957). Comparative investigations on seedling roots of pure strains of maize show great differences in the sensitivity towards 2,4-D (BUCHHOLTZ and HANSEN 1953), and differences with IAA were still more pronounced. The roots of certain strains gave positive growth reactions at very low concentrations, but others were inhibited at all concentrations. No relation could be established between growth rate and the natural auxin content. There is thus a sharp contrast to decapitated coleoptiles in which added auxin elicits a reaction which varies approximately inversely to the natural auxin content (PORTER 1953). The peculiar reactions of roots are especially puzzling, and the behaviour of the maize varieties mentioned does not agree with the reactions to antiauxins or other inhibitors. The fundamental relationships in auxin research are thus still not completely clarified, and the attempts of BONNER *et al.* (1953, 1956) to refer everything to simple mathematical laws are to be regarded as premature.

The inhibitory effect of auxins on root growth, including the synthesis e.g. of nucleic acids, finds a counterpart in their inhibitory effect on buds, whose unfolding is inhibited also *in vitro* by IAA (SKOOG 1939). The concentration of auxin in leaves is in general too low to explain the inhibition of axillary buds, but high enough to influence growth and thus to determine correlations. A supposed inhibitory effect of its own auxin on the radical of the embryo is described by VAN OVERBEEK (1942). A number of observations support the general conclusion that quantitative relations between auxin concentration and growth hold only for distinct organs. In comparisons between different organs the level of sensitivity varies greatly. It is also probable that the balance between auxins and inhibitors is involved in determining the sensitivity level characteristic of an organ and that observed positive or negative reactions may be explained by variations of the inhibitors. A final decision is not yet possible because of the lack of experimental results. These points must also be taken into account in the practical applications of auxins as herbicides (e.g. CRAFTS 1946).

A further effect of auxins should probably be discussed, viz. their narcotic action. Such an effect appears to be exercised on the pistils of various plants leading to the formation of seedless (parthenocarpic) fruits. A morphogenic function of auxin occurs in fruit and leaf drop. Not only auxins (WETMORE and JACOBS 1953) but probably also other materials, e.g. ethylene (ROSETTER and JACOBS 1953), can be effective in this way. The occurrence of dwarf forms has at times been ascribed to shortage of auxin (VAN OVERBEEK 1938); but in only one case (*Epilobium hirsutum*), has it been possible to

2c

produce a normal plant from a dwarf by the supply of extra auxin. It is possible that the auxin concentration is usually so near its optimum that even reduction to a half is without noticeable result (SKOOG 1938).

The further fate of auxin in the plant has so far been little investigated. The possibility has been suggested above that large amounts of auxin are rendered inactive by accumulation in the cell sap, which could partly explain the discrepancy between the total auxin content of an organ and its method of reaction. Auxin is inactivated also enzymatically, i.e. by chemical degradation. It is however surprising that the plant auxins are so resistant that they pass unaffected through the digestive tract and the kidneys of animals in considerable amounts.

The ability to synthesise auxin appears to be a property of almost all young cells (in the growing points, leaves, etc.). External conditions, e.g. salt nutrition, of course exercise an influence here (GUSTAFSON 1946). Auxin is said to be inactivated or destroyed in absence of zinc (SKOOG 1940; cf. TSUI 1948). Another trace element, boron, has also been related to auxin activity (EATON 1940). Of the essential nutrients, nitrogen (AVERY and POTTORF 1945) and calcium (STRUCKMEYER 1942) have been especially mentioned. It should, however, be noted that the accelerated vegetative growth of the green parts with an abundant supply of nitrogen is not due to increased formation of auxin. A more influential factor on auxin content is light (THIMANN and SKOOG 1934), which, as already mentioned, causes a breakdown by which the delay of growth in light (in contrast to etiolation in the dark) can be explained.

In the cambium of trees, etc., auxin production is awakened in spring (see SNOW 1940, SÖDING 1940, AVERY 1942), though little is known about the possible production of auxin in the resting meristem. Tissue cultures of cambium, however, grow only after addition of IAA, and other stimulants also seem to be necessary (JABLONSKI and SKOOG 1954).

A distinct morphogenetic effect of auxin becomes evident in the formation of roots on cuttings. Here cell division is induced in resting cells; the swelling of the cortex and the changed orientation of cell divisions are striking (WENT and THIMANN 1937). BURSTRÖM (1942) found that 10^{-6} M IAA caused the resting sub-epidermal cells of the root to increase their volume by several times. The elasticity was increased two- or three-fold, especially in the radial direction, whereas the osmotic value sank. BURSTRÖM observed polyploidy in such extended cells, but no new cell divisions. A stimulation of cell division associated with swelling induced by IAA was on the other hand studied by CHOUINARD (1951) in onion roots. He and other workers found a resumption of cell division in mature parts of the organ. The relative number of tetraploid or polyploid cells was not higher than normal, but a change of up to 90° in the orientation of division was observed especially with high auxin concentrations. Root hair formation was also affected.

BURSTRÖM directed attention to the many similarities between the formative effect of high auxin concentrations and that of increased sugar uptake. There is, however, the difference that auxin always stimulates the initial phase of growth, whereas sugar mainly affects the total elongation. Experiments with various types of sugar showed that both the dividing and the extension mechanisms are extraordinarily sensitive towards steric differences in the sugar molecule (BURSTRÖM 1942, WÜRGLER 1942). Wheat roots utilise glucose best, then maltose, whereas sucrose is effective only after inversion and fructose is inhibitory. In maize roots maltose seems to be active, whilst galactose and lactose are inactive.

The reason why variations in carbohydrate metabolism have morphogenetic consequences may well be sought partly in the altered paths of diffusion of oxygen, carbon dioxide, nutrient salts, hormones, etc., caused by the changes of dimensions. Diffusion changes could affect both the differentiation of the cell surface and the polarity. It should, however, be emphasised that the properties of the living cell surface are determined by their chemical and physical properties. That the development follows a certain symplastic scheme is seen from the fact that the root maintains its symmetrical torpedo form however much the directions of cell division may vary. Correlative, i.e. symplastic morphogenetic, effects exist everywhere; but their material basis is still completely unknown. A further example of such correlations is given by the sloughed-off cells of the root cap. After their 'liberation' they grow strongly in all directions. They can continue to live a considerable time in the rhizosphere if nutrients are available (ROGERS et al. 1942). Cells isolated from the leaf mesophyll and the pith can also increase visibly in volume.

Thus, whereas unknown inhibitory factors contribute to keeping the size and the form of tissue cells within certain limits, on the other hand a number of factors are known which must be added to tissue cultures in order to maintain active growth and division. The methods and results of *tissue cultures* have been collected by WHITE (1951, 1954), GAUTHERET and others. The need for a supply of vitamins B_1 and B_6, niacin and biotin has already been mentioned above, but in many cultures other substances are also required. Ascorbic acid, biotin and other vitamins stimulate the growth of pea seedlings from which the cotyledons have been removed (VIRTANEN 1949, VIRTANEN and VON HAUSSEN 1949). The antagonism of auxin by ascorbic acid observed by TONZIG (1950) has already been mentioned. A stimulation of isolated plant tissues is difficult to bring about. An exception is afforded by the experiments with coconut milk, in which both sugar and unknown activators are effective (VAN OVERBEEK et al. 1944, MAUNEY et al. 1952). STEWARD and SHANTS (1952) report callus formation on carrot tissue under the influence of a crystallising but unknown substance. The coconut factor is heat-resistant.

Like the auxins, *vitamins* also have morphogenetic effects, though most clearly on the negative side, as deficiency symptoms. Pea roots become thinner in absence of nicotinic acid. With a deficiency of vitamin B_1, on the other hand, they become shorter and thicker, and irregular thickenings occur in the mature parts (ADDICOTT 1941). Flax roots similarly require B_1; tomato roots B_1 and B_6. The former can synthesise purine, sterol, imidazole, indole, flavin, etc., but not pyrimidine and thiazole. Flax leaves, on the other hand, produce all the components necessary for the synthesis of B_1.

Supply of B_1 seems to be necessary for all roots, and this vitamin is usually a growth-regulating factor. The root weight of wheat seedlings increases with thiamine concentration up to an optimum at 10^{-6} M. Whether the simultaneously observed acceleration of shoot growth is due to the increased salt uptake through the enlarged roots or to vitamin translocation is not known (cf. also BONNER and GREENE 1939). It has been asserted that 'humus plants', e.g. *Camellia* and *Azalea*, draw B_1 from the soil (WENT 1943). Conversely, certain roots (flax and tobacco; WEST 1939) appear to excrete thiamine and biotin, which stimulate the bacteria of the rhizosphere (cf. also p. 242). Nucleotides and nucleosides, which likewise are exuded by roots (LUNDEGÅRDH and STENLID 1944) but not, so far as is known, translocated in the xylem stream, serve as growth substances for certain strains of *Neurospora* (LORING and PIERCE 1944).

Growing leaves also require a supply of adenine or similar purine derivatives (WENT 1943), which also influence other organs (MILLER 1953). Numerous data show, however, that IAA and synthetic growth substances are carried in the xylem stream (SKOOG 1937, FERRI 1945, MITCHELL 1951; see section 4 below). Internally produced auxin therefore seems to be circulated.

The importance of a supply of growth substances from the leaves appears from the fact that root growth is at once almost halved if the green parts are removed, in spite of the presence of glucose and active ion uptake (LUNDEGÅRDH 1945, p. 32). Addition of thiamine to excised roots is without effect. The effective growth factor is thus probably a growth substance coming from the leaves.

WENT's (1943) conjecture that a specific factor X, or 'caulocaline', originating in the roots determined the growth of the stem has been doubted on the ground of recent experiments. WENT overlooked the effect of the uptake and production of nutrients in the roots (see Chap. 7). The effect of the cotyledons on seedling growth can also, at least partly, be a question of nutrition. In experiments on bud formation in segments of tobacco stalk the buds remained living on nutrient solutions for months, but opened only after the formation of roots. Here the growth begins immediately after the formation of the root-initials, and the effect is also independent of the nutrient uptake from the medium. The stimulating effect on the buds in this case does not depend on nutrition. The question of the existence of true 'caulocalines', however, is still not solved.

A number of other hormones, which up to now have been characterised only by their effects, may be found in the literature. A few examples are given here. According to VAN OVERBEEK (1942) ripe embryos are fully autotrophic with respect to hormones. Very young embryos, on the other hand, appear to require a low-molecular 'embryo factor' which occurs e.g. in coconut milk. If this hypothetical factor is lacking, the proembryo may degenerate to a mass of callus. In such phenomena auxin may of course always be involved as a growth substance, but inhibitory factors have also been found e.g. in tomato fruits (JUEL 1946, EVENARI 1949).

Some correlations, still unexplained biochemically, may be mentioned here. Removal of the mature leaves from the twigs of certain trees causes sprouting of the axial buds, even when the tip of the shoot remains intact. Removal of a leaf lamina of *Vicia faba* leads to decay of the adjacent leaves. The presence of the leaf laminae inhibits the unfolding of the axial buds. According to SNOW (1931, 1932), this inhibition is dependent on the developmental stage of the leaf. LOEB (1915) observed that dipping a root of *Bryophyllum calycinum* in water inhibited the growth of the remaining roots and assumed a purely trophic competition, but there can be no doubt that hormonal processes similar to those between leaf and axial bud, etc., are active here also.

The conversion of a growing point into a flower primordium is usually interpreted as being a result of the action of a *'flower-forming hormone'* formed in the leaves. Considerable advances, however, have been made since the time of SACHS. The statement of HAMNER and BONNER (1938) that the flowering hormone diffuses from the illuminated leaves to the growing point was not confirmed. WITHROW and WITHROW (1943) and MELCHERS and LANG (1948) have thrown light on this question by grafting experiments. HARDER and GÜMMER (1944) assume the existence of a 'metaplasin' which may determine the leaf type in the transition from short-day to long-day leaves. They assume that this substance migrates in the xylem, especially on the same side as the leaf.

4 THE TRANSLOCATION MECHANISMS OF THE AUXINS

The possible translocation pathways for growth substances were discussed in Chap. 6. Research workers on auxin appear in general to think of diffusion, but some (WENT and WHITE 1939; cf. VAN DER WEIJ 1932, 1934) state that the speed depends only slightly on the length of the pathway, and this suggests other mechanisms. Translocation along the surface film has also been considered (cf. p. 254). The fact that in the biological range of pH the auxins occur as acid anions supports the idea that ion respiration is involved. This would certainly explain the data on auxin translocation in the xylem, since free anions are seized more or less easily according to their size by the active mechanism that exudes salts into the lower parts of the stele. The relatively low molecular weight of auxin may not form an absolute barrier to its 'active' translocation. It must, however, be imagined that auxin migrates also in the phloem and parenchymatous tissues both by diffusion and with the help of metabolism. The auxin anions can also be transported electrophoretically wherever persistent bioelectric currents are active in an organ.

Such potential differences occur e.g. in root tips (Fig. 160, p. 382). If fine unpolarisable electrodes are inserted into the root tissue and connected with a measuring instrument, the bioelectric currents can be measured. They flow in the directions indicated in Fig. 160. The transport capacity of the electric currents is estimated at about 10^{-5} milliequivalents per hour. This capacity is quite enough to transport the amounts of auxin which are active in the root tip. As is seen from Fig. 160, the auxin anion can move electrophoretically in the interior of the root in such a way that it flows from the site of production, the primary meristem, towards the zone of maximum elongation, i.e. about 2 mm behind the tip. From there it is conducted into the surface of the root and probably partly exuded, if it is not removed by the surface current flowing in the opposite direction back to the tip. Auxin losses in the extension zone are probably increased if the medium is electrically conductive, e.g. if nutrient salts are present. Cations are obviously moved in the reverse direction to the anions. The electrical potential differences (cf. LUNDEGÅRDH 1940, 1941, 1942) also induce currents between the extension zone and the mature part of the road. These currents operate in the reverse direction to the tip currents, that is in such a way that the auxin translocated to the extension zone does not penetrate further towards the tip.

Because of the small dimensions involved it is very difficult to prove the actual existence of electrophoretic auxin translocation according to the plan sketched in Fig. 160. That the currents exist has been proved. It should be noted that the measurements apply to ohmic resistance and galvanic currents with which the impedance and the polarisation at the many biological boundary layers interfere. The size of the auxin anions may exert some retarding effect, but on account of the low hydration and the unimportant differences in molecular weight (175 for auxin as compared with 61 for nitrate and 96 for phosphate) does not retard translocation of auxin much behind that of nutrient salts.

The idea of an electrophoretic auxin translocation has been put forward also by other workers (WENT and THIMANN 1937, KINOSHITA 1939, SCHRANK 1951) but has seldom been experimentally checked. Earlier measurements were mostly technically inadequate, but there are some later measurements by SCOTT et al. 1955. Measurements of potentials in aerial organs (e.g. CLARK 1937) suffer from the drawback that the wax coatings lead to complications. Wrong conclusions are also easily drawn from experiments with potentials applied from outside, in which no auxin translocation was observed. The natural currents flow in opposite directions in the centre of the organ and in its periphery (Fig. 160), and one must also take into account the effect of the cell polarity on the ohmic resistance. The potential differences, according to the interpretation put forward here, are produced by differences in the concentration of cation carriers (R^-). What is particularly referred to is a high concentration of large molecular acidic substances, nucleotides, pectic acids, etc., at actively growing cell surfaces. The hypothesis put forward by SCOTT et al. (1955) that diffusion potentials are concerned is rather improbable. The assumption that the maximal extension zone coincides with a zone of maximal salt uptake is in any case wrong, since it has been shown experimentally that there is no close parallel between salt uptake and growth (see Chap. 6).

Even though a biological electrophoresis is probably concerned in the distribution of auxin within a growing organ, it does not of course follow that this is the only, or even the main, mechanism of translocation. It is, of course, excluded if the growth substance is insufficiently ionised, which does not apply to auxin. One can also imagine that the auxin is accumulated by localised chemical fixation e.g. in the surface of the cell at particular points. We have already discussed above the possible existence of an active auxin—receptor linkage. An experiment with a localised supply of an artificial growth substance, 2-iodo-3-nitrobenzoic acid, to a bean plant gave the following results (WOOD et al. 1947). If the growth substance was applied to a leaf tip, after three days the main amount was recovered in the apical bud, less in the base of the stem and very little in the other leaves. The translocation thus seems on the whole to follow the same paths as that of organic products produced in the leaves.

5 POLARITY

The active transport mechanisms may represent causes involved in the polarity phenomenon. By polarity is meant the tendency exhibited by cells and organs to behave either physiologically or morphologically differently at two opposite ends and to adhere to this tendency even when external conditions are changed. The polarity phenomenon, however, has many aspects, as may appear from the examples selected below (detailed literature review in BLOCH 1943).

A classic example of polarity in algae is given by the differentiation of the eggs of *Fucus*. The egg originally has a radial construction, but is polarised by the formation of a bulge bounded by a new wall. This outgrowth develops into a rhizoid while the remaining part of the egg becomes a thallus. This polarisation can be induced by a number of factors, e.g. a light gradient, temperature differences, auxin, an electrical field, centrifugal force, etc. The induction is fixed in the first 12-13 hours of the life of the fertilised egg and can then no longer be reversed, although the visible rhizoid formation begins only after 17 hours. In the Florideae and Siphonocladiaceae the polarity is less firmly anchored. *Cladophora* cells on the other hand are polarised and, after plasmolysis, develop into new algal filaments in which each cell maintains the tendency to rhizoid formation at its base. In this case, however, the polarity can be reversed by centrifuging.

The cells of the liverwort have no pronounced polarity. In *Equisetum* spores polarity is induced by light gradients. More detailed investigations on the inversion of polarity have, however, not been carried out. One gets the impression that polarity is connected with a certain arrangement of the cell content, possibly with anisotropy of the protoplasmic structure. Electrical potential gradients which could affect the flow of dissociated substances are probably also concerned (cf. above). Dissolution or rearrangement of the structure should also change translocation.

In higher plants the fundamental polarity, i.e. the differentiation into root and shoot, is already laid out in the embryo sac. A number of distinguished early plant physiologists, such as SACHS, VÖCHTING, PFEFFER and KLEBS, made valuable contributions to this subject. The work of VÖCHTING in particular is classic. Polarity was studied preferably in cuttings, in which it is expressed in many ways. Excised root and shoot tips show their polarity by their meristems being specialised solely for root or shoot formation respectively. Some cases of inversion of polarity originate with the data of BEIJERINCK, but were on the whole rarely observed (cf. also Chap. 2). Tomato roots have been cultivated for ten years with a total of 125 transfers without any inversion being observed (ROBBINS 1946). The fixation of a particular course of development also occurs chemically; roots synthesise biotin and pyridoxin, but not thiamine or thiazole. The latter must therefore be supplied continuously. On the other hand the roots seem to be able to prepare for themselves the pyrimidine components of thiamine (BARTLEY 1937). In a similar way, this is by addition of the growth substances mentioned, isolated stem tips of *Cuscuta* can be caused to grow, and produce lateral buds and flowers (LOO 1946).

In cuttings the potential ability to form roots is never absent, but the polarity expresses itself through the conditioning substances, e.g. auxin, moving in a definite direction. Individual parenchymatous cells do not reverse the polarity of the cutting; on the contrary, in the undifferentiated callus cells at the tip of a cutting stood upside down, a new polarity is induced (VÖCHTING, NEEF et al.). According to WENT (1941), no case of inverting the direction of movement of auxin is known. In overcoming the visible polarity of inverted cuttings a new auxin polarity is apparently gradually formed in the new tissue elements, whilst the old polarity still persists in the old tissues. On the other hand, the polarity of stem segments can be reversed without difficulty by treatment with 2,3,5-tri-iodobenzoic acid and phenylacetic acid. In this case also the reorientation is mediated by the formation of callus. IAA in high concentrations can also invert polarity in the same way.

The real basis of the cell- and tissue-polarity is unknown. One can only deduce that differences exist between opposite cell surfaces, that are formed during ontogenetic development under the influence of gradients of nutrients, oxygen, carbon dioxide, etc. Polarity can therefore be considered from the same point of view as irregular cell growth, i.e. as the existence of local differences in the wall-forming protoplasmic surface layer. The cell surface, in other words, operates in special ways at different points (cf. for example, root-hair formation and cortical cell growth). Active salt transport through a tissue is also an expression of polarity.

A possible cause of polarity is the membrane charge which leads to ionised materials migrating more easily in one direction than in its opposite. With a potential gradient across a membrane which goes from strongly negative to weakly negative, anions migrate more quickly in the direction of the gradient than against it, and so on. Such a potential gradient across the common wall of two cells could easily arise by the membrane components of one cell having a different degree of dissociation from those of its neighbour. Chemical differences in the surface layer may also be able to influence the migration of sugars, proteins, etc. Examples of specialised directions of migration are afforded by the sieve tubes. It may be remembered that, according to numerous data in the literature, accumulation of nutrients takes place at one end of cuttings.

There are thus several chemico-physical analogies which make the material bases of polarity more comprehensible. Recently it has been imagined that the polar transport of auxin depends on a sliding movement along an adsorption track, i.e. is guided in a given direction by the protoplasmic structure. It may be mentioned in this connection that auxin polarity is destroyed by ether, ethylene and respiratory inhibitors, which also interfere with the initial carriers of salt ions (cf. p. 261). Auxin polarity can also be destroyed by competitive inhibitors, which prevent the sliding of the auxin molecules along the structural paths by displacing them from their carrier linkages.

Polarity reflects various aspects of differentiation and regeneration. It can, as we have seen, be induced by the most varied factors, but it is common to them all that they create gradients e.g. of light, nutrients, oxygen, auxins, etc. The gradients then effect a polarisation of the sub-microscopic organisation of the cells and tissues. Consequently polarity is reversible whenever the capacity for sub-microscopic differentiation can be regenerated. Multicellular organs seem to be distinguished by the fact that in them only individual cells or cell groups possess this capacity for regeneration. In small fragments of tissue polarity is more easily supplanted by callus formation.

F. The Dependence of Growth on External Factors

Those internal factors have been mentioned above, which regulate the growth rate: respiration, nutrient supply, water supply and growth substances. The large specific differences in growth rates can occasionally be attributed to one of these factors, e.g. to auxin as regards dwarf forms; but generally one has to be satisfied with mere supposition.

Most of the higher plants attain growth rates not much higher than a couple of centimetres per 24 hours, but the range of variation is wide and, for example in *Asparagus officinalis*, values up to 30 cm per 24 hours have been found. All these results refer of course to optimal temperatures. High values exist for *Eucalyptus*, *Cupressus*, *Grevillea*, *Parkinsonia*, *Campsis* and others (OPPENHEIMER 1945). *Phyllostachys* is said to be able to grow 18-54 cm in 24 hours. Here a prolonged meristemic activity is of course essential. Extension can also take place at a considerable speed e.g. in the filaments of stamens.

Genetic differences affect reactions towards external factors. Different reactions have also been observed at different developmental stages of the same organ. The effects of external factors are most clearly observed in the study of roots and shoots over short periods of time. The majority of investigations on the relations between growth and external factors have used such objects.

1 TEMPERATURE

As both photosynthesis and respiration show optimum curves, every growing cell or organ also shows a temperature optimum whose level is usually, as in respiration, a function of the time of observation. This applies not only for the growth rate with optimal food supply, but also for longer periods in which photosynthesis is a consideration. The removal of the assimilates from the leaves is also affected by temperature (CURTIS and HERTY 1936). The temperature sensitivity of the growth of pollen tubes is important in fertilisation (NOGUCHI 1931). Ecological effects also arise as with the microbiological processes in the soil. Lignin for example is quickly degraded at $+37°C$ but very slowly at $+9°C$. The dependence of nitrogen metabolism on temperature is the reason why humus soils in cold regions are richer in nitrogen than they are in warmer regions (WAKSMAN and GERRETSEN 1931).

The influence of temperature on the germination of seeds and spores has been dealt with above. There are numerous examples of differing temperature responses at different stages of development. Thus according to SETCHELL (see STILES 1936, p. 345). *Zostera marina* still grows vegetatively at $+10°C$, whilst the minimum of sexual reproduction lies at $+15°C$. *Crepis* conversely shows a lower temperature optimum for fruit formation than for vegetative growth. In many fungi and green algae there are also different temperature responses by vegetative growth and spore formation.

The occurrence of the temperature optimum, its change with time and its very different values in different species, organs or stages of development—all this is explained in general by the different temperature coefficients of the partial reactions concerned in growth. The relations between sugar$\rightleftharpoons$starch may be remembered. A further example is the colour of the flowers of *Erodium gruinum* and *E. ciconium*, which is blue at low temperatures, but at more than $+20°C$ changes over reversibly to pink (FITTING 1912). Similar inflection points or optima may also occur in growth.

As an example of the morphogenetic effects of temperature it may be mentioned that the base of tulip flowers becomes broader at low temperatures and forms more flowering organs than at higher temperatures. Alterations in the direction of cell division and in cell extension caused by temperature changes were demonstrated by BURSTRÖM (1941, 1942). These investigations confirmed earlier observations of VOGT (1915) on the growth of darkened *Avena* coleoptiles. Here an optimum temperature giving growth of 20 mm per 24 hours was attained at about $+20°C$, whereas the maximum lies at $+42°C$. The largest final length of the coleoptile, however, was attained as low as $+12·8°C$. The whole growth period is reduced continuously from 30 days at $+7·5°C$ to $2\frac{1}{2}$ days at $+35·1°C$. In other cases, e.g. in the sporangiophores of *Phycomyces blakesleanus*, the final length may be independent of the temperature.

Among other examples of formative effects, it may be mentioned that the alga *Stigeoclonium* at low temperature passes over to the palmella stage, whereas at higher temperatures it assumes the filamentous form. Cytologically both chromosomes and protoplasm are so affected by extremely low or high temperatures that anomalies occur in division.

In recent investigations attention has been directed to the after-effects of low temperatures on the rate of development. It has been known for a considerable time that regularly occurring changes in temperature, e.g. in the 24-hour rhythm, create an advantageous environment for normal development. There are great variations among species (WENT 1953) and one speaks of a specific *thermoperiodism* of plants (see ARTHUR et al. 1941). The correlation between the vegetative and floral organs is changed by a low germination temperature or a cold period during germination (MAXIMOV 1929). The temperature conditions during fruit formation also extend their effect to the development of new plants (BÜNNING 1939). Through appropriate pretreatment of the germinating plants attempts have been made to hasten the later development ('jarovisation' or *vernalisation*). MAXIMOV (1934) recommends soaking and germination at a temperature somewhat above 0°C. By this treatment winter cereals can be converted into summer cereals. In other cases, e.g. in maize, heat treatment at 20-25° or 25-30°C serves the same end. According to HARDER and STOERMER (1936), an initial cold treatment at $+0.5°$ to $+1°C$ for 10-30 days shortens the time of development of *Sinapis alba*. The length of day, however, is also involved. The after-effect of a cold treatment is increased 30% by a nine hour day-length but only 15% by a day-length of more than 12 hours. The after-effect of cold periods can of course be of great ecological importance (NICHOLS 1934, LAIBACH 1940, 1943). Cold treatment can also have morphogenetic results. VÖCHTING (1902) reported experiments which showed that one variety of potato after storage for 4-5 weeks at $+6°$ to $+7°C$ produced daughter tubers instead of green shoots. FINCH and CARR (1956) have investigated the possible chemical changes in vernalisation of winter rye. They found no alteration in the content of nucleic acid and other phosphorus compounds. HIGHKIN (1956) reports that an initial warm period has some effect on the capacity of peas for vernalisation.

The explanation of vernalisation may be that the formation of 'flowering hormones' is favoured by a prolonged juvenescence or temperature fluctuations (cf. GREGORY 1948). Similar accelerating or retarding effects result also from other factors, e.g. air humidity and the nutrient balance during germination.

2 LIGHT

The spectral composition of light to a great extent influences the kind and the intensity of its biological effects. This includes X-rays (γ-rays) and the corpuscular (α-) and β-rays, about whose effect on plants little is so far known. Apart from the infra-red rays, whose action is limited to their temperature effect, there are the photochemical reactions induced by the visible and ultra-violet rays, which influence the protoplasm and thereby also growth. The photochemical effect consists either of an acceleration of the intramolecular atomic vibrations, whereby the barriers to reaction are more easily overcome, or in a direct ionisation, enabling electrons to be transferred to adjacent molecules (cf. Chap. 3). The ionising effect of the radiation increases with decreasing wavelength.

(a) *The Effect of Short-wave Radiation*

Living protoplasm does not tolerate any considerable amount of short-wave radiation (X-ray and ultra-violet radiation below 250 mμ). From time to time, however, statements appear about the favourable effects of ultra-violet radiation. According to LOOFBOURROW *et al.* (1941), the production of nucleic acid and the rate of division in yeast are favoured. Everything of course depends on the dosage, and in this case it seems that the ultra-violet radiation behaves like certain poisons, which in minute doses have a stimulating effect. The so-called 'mitogenetic rays' said to exist by GURWITSCH *et al.* with a wavelength of 190-250 mμ, and, according to him, produced by dividing cells and able to stimulate other cells, are still however very hypothetical (HOLLAENDER and CLAUS 1935). Here we can mention only briefly the bactericidal effect of ultra-violet rays. According to WYKOFF (1932) the 'harmfulness' of X-rays may be at least a hundred times greater than that of ultra-violet radiation of 250 mμ wavelength. The bactericidal effect of UV-radiation usually shows a maximum at about 260 mμ, where the absorption is considerable (GATES 1930). There is also a maximum toxicity with *Chlorella vulgaris* at this wavelength (MEIER 1936). Illumination with light of 253·7 mμ inhibits rhizoid formation in *Fucus* eggs, whereas white light has a healing effect (WHITAKER 1942). This is probably connected with the inhibition of certain enzyme reactions by UV-radiation, and the favourable effect of visible light (MURAKAMI 1939; cf. POPP and BROWN 1933, PRÁT 1936). The strong absorption of the nucleic acids at 260 mμ may be involved in this effect. The proteins have a relatively weak UV-absorption, with a maximum at 280 mμ. According to THOMPSON and HUSSEY (1932), amylase and pepsin are especially strongly inhibited by UV-rays. In higher plants harmful effects seem to occur also at longer wavelengths; e.g. according to STEWART and ARTHUR (1934) at 290-313 mμ; the latter wavelength causes erythema of human skin. According to PIRSCHLE (1941), most plants die after long-continued illumination with 280-320 mμ, except high alpine types, which seem to be specially adapted to ultra-violet light. Inhibition of growth, however, occurs also in alpines, and the N- and P-contents assume high values (cf. also ARTHUR *et al.* 1930).

Higher plants in general withstand UV-radiation better than unicellar plants, since the UV-light is strongly absorbed by the epidermis, which thereby protects the internal layers of tissue. Among unicellular organisms the lethal effect of UV-radiation increases so strongly with the ratio of surface to volume that a very effective method for the removal of bacterial contaminations in algal cultures has been developed on this basis (ALLISON *et al.* 1937).

(b) *The Effect of Light*

The effect of visible light on growth depends, like that of temperature, very much on the duration of treatment. Photosynthesis supplies building materials and is thus the means by which visible light affects nutrition. In *Commelina* (MEVIUS 1930) a connection has been found between illumination and the formation of adventitious roots. SKOOG (1952) reported similar results with segments of tobacco stem. This may be due to a photochemical synthesis of hormones. Apart from such possible long-range hormone effects, both the elongation rate and the morphogenesis of the shoot are governed by photoreactions, so that the total effect of light can appear very complicated (cf. Fig. 162). The growth effects evoked by light show a different spectral sensitivity from those of photosynthesis, and separate photo-chemical processes can thus take place simultaneously in the same organ.

Fig. 162. Diagram of the effects of light of various wavelengths in experiments with peas (after WENT 1941).

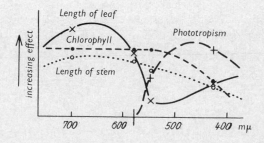

At this point some observations may be mentioned which incidentally bear on the teleological viewpoint that everything which happens must have a purpose. The sun-leaf structure, which is so advantageous for the life of sun plants, according to some observations, is not always evoked by strong light, but by increased internal salt concentration resulting from increased transpiration. The differentiation of sun and shade leaves on a tree usually takes place in the bud primordium, i.e. in the previous year. The suitable orientation of the unfolding shoot to light is determined, not by the yellow and red rays which are effective in assimilation, but by blue and ultra-violet rays which are of little benefit to the plant's nutrition.

(c) *Etiolation and Photomorphosis*

The influence of light on the growth of shoots extends to both the dividing and the elongating zones. According to investigations by LANGE (1929), the mesocotyl (that is the first internode) of the oat seedling elongates several centimetres in the dark. After illumination with white or red light development, including cell division, is strongly inhibited. The well-known phenomenon of *etiolation*, i.e. the abnormal elongation of the shoot in darkness, is thus of a negative character, due to the absence of inhibition by light. That the leaves conversely are stunted in darkness only shows how multifarious photoinductions can be.

PRIESTLEY (1923-6) found anatomical differences between etiolated and green shoots. In the former the vascular strands are relatively weakly developed and an endodermis occurs like that in roots. Etiolation may however occur in very different degrees, e.g. in *Vicia faba* strongly and in *Phaseolus multiflorus* weakly. It was soon discovered that the phenomenon is not directly connected with the absence of photosynthesis or of chlorophyll. It occurs also in coniferous trees, which form chlorophyll even in the dark. According to BÜNNING (1939), etiolated plants do not possess more auxin than green plants. Etiolation is typically local and is thus not due to the bringing up of growth substances. Even though the annulment of etiolation by light cannot be considered as a mere photo-destruction of auxin, a photo-inactivation of the auxin undoubtedly takes place in organs which contain sensitising pigments. THIMANN and SKOOG (1934) interpreted the annulment of etiolation by light as a reduction of sensitivity towards auxin. Chlorophyll and carotenoids undoubtedly serve to a certain extent as transferers of light energy, but riboflavin appears to be particularly suitable for this purpose both in its absorption spectrum and in its distribution in the plant (GALSTON and BAKER 1949, REINERT 1952).

Following from what has been said above it is not surprising that etiolation can occur also in chlorophyll-free organs. Isolated *Datura* roots for example elongate less in the light than in the dark. To emphasise the many-sided effects of light we may mention that the root-hair growth of this species is favoured by light (ROBBINS 1940). The regular alternation between day and night is thus reflected in separate zones of hairs along the growing root. In most roots, however, the growth rate is not influenced by light.

As an example of organs which grow more quickly in the light than in the dark the sporangiophores of *Phycomyces* (BLAAUW 1918) may be mentioned. A positive effect of light on the frequency of cell division was described by KLEBS for the prothallia of *Pteris longifolia*. He asserted that light acts both trophically through photosynthesis, and as a stimulus by means of a special growth factor. Red light stimulated elongation and blue light increased the frequency of cell division. The effect of continuous illumination on cell growth is always combined with effects on the direction of cell division and with the relation between increase in length and breadth, which in turn alter the forms of the organs.

A characteristic trait of etiolation is the elongation of supporting organs such as the stem, and a stunting of photosynthetic organs, such as the leaves. The positive light effect is thus expressed as an inhibition of stem growth. Among lower plants which show typical shortening of the internodes in light, may be mentioned the Characeae and mosses. In toadstools the etiolation is expressed by a lengthening of the vegetative body and a shortening of the spore-carrying organs, although here there are great differences between species. The synergistic effect of light and mechanical stimulation on *Coprinus* have been studied by STIEFEL (1952).

Of special interest is the result of BORRIS (1934) according to which the formation of the fruiting body of *Coprinus* can be evoked partly by light, partly by increase in temperature and partly by contact stimulus. Here, as in other cases, the course of development is fixed by a given sequence of protoplasmic processes, which are set in operation by an unspecific change in the balance. Even in higher plants it is found that the size of leaf and the internode growth are regulated not only by light but also by moisture, temperature, etc.

According to GORTER and FUNKE (1937), the decreased growth of *Raphanus sativus* in dry culture is due to a reduced hydration and extensibility of the cell walls; and the sporangiophores of *Phycomyces*, according to WALTER (1927), show accelerated growth in damp air. That hydration is concerned here seems to follow from the fact that the moisture has a local effect and, acting unilaterally, can cause curvatures. One can even suppose that the similar tropistic effects of light and temperature are connected also with a local change in hydration, which e.g. could be caused by an increased ionisation.

Well-known effects of light on form are the induction of dorsiventrality in the gemmae of *Marchantia*, the leaf-like form of the stem in the Phyllocacteae, etc. (see FITTING 1936, or GOEBEL 1928, p. 614). The dorsiventrality of the leaf-like branchlets of cypresses is also induced by light and can be reversed by change in the direction of the light (FITTING 1942).

The effects of light on form result in general from long-term exposures, which explains their very complicated nature; many trophic and hormonal effects collaborate. The stimulus effect of light, particularly in elongation, is more clearly seen in short-duration experiments.

(d) *Light Growth-reactions*

The course of the *light growth-reaction* was studied in detail by BLAAUW (1914, 1915, 1918) and a number of later workers (see the literature in NUERNBERGK and DU BUY 1932-5). In order to avoid phototropic movements in these experiments, uniform illumination, e.g. from four sides, is used, or one-sided illumination combined with a slow rotation of the object on its longitudinal axis. The light growth-reaction takes place in three stages or phases: (1) *perception* (that is, receiving the stimulus); (2) *transmission* (that is, passing on the stimulus to the growth zone); and (3) *reaction*.

The nature of the transmission depends entirely on the differentiation of the organ, i.e. whether a special region of perception is available or not; even in the latter case there is always a certain time lag between the start of stimulation and the commencement of reaction (that is, the *reaction time* or latent time). The reaction time usually becomes shorter with increasing intensity of illumination (CASTLE and HONEYMAN; and Fig. 163). With sporangiophores of *Phycomyces*, one of the objects used by BLAAUW,

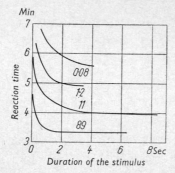

Fig. 163. Light growth-reaction of the sporangiophores of *Phycomyces*. The intensities are expressed in units of about 10 lux. The reaction time changes with the illumination (after CASTLE and HONEYMAN).

the reaction time was 8·5 minutes with the least quantity of light that induced any reaction, i.e. 4×0.25 metre-candle-seconds (mcs, also known as lux-seconds), but fell to 3·5 minutes with stimulation of 4×210 lux-seconds. The *speed of reaction* also increases with the amount of stimulus and the size of the reaction. A light growth-reaction of 21% is completed in 10·9 minutes and a reaction of 153% in 7 minutes.

Similar to these positive light growth-reactions, those in green shoots are usually negative, e.g. in the hypocotyls of *Helianthus* and the coleoptiles of *Avena*. Here, however, the reaction picture is somewhat more complicated because light stimuli are received both at the tip and at the base. Induction at the tip is generally the most powerful, although the reaction time is longer, probably due to the more extended transmission.

The light growth-reaction is regularly followed by a *counter-reaction* which takes place in the opposite direction to the primary reaction. After a positive light growth-reaction, as in the sporangiophores of *Phycomyces*, there follows a negative counter-reaction; after a negative primary reaction, as in *Avena* coleoptiles, there is a positive counter-reaction. After the first swing over, a second, third, etc., reaction wave with diminishing amplitude may follow. Similar relationships are encountered in *temperature growth-reactions* (SILBERSCHMIDT 1925, ERMAN 1926). Even under completely constant conditions, the growth does not proceed with absolutely constant speed but shows small fluctuations round a median value. These fluctuations are referred to again in Chap. 10, since they become clearer in the tropisms.

The actual cause of the negative light growth-reaction in the *Avena* coleoptile has been sought in the photo-inactivation of the lactone of the auxin (cf. p. 376); there are also data which suggest that growth-reactions can occur without change of the auxin content or of auxin transport. According to some workers, an effect on auxin transport occurs only in the tropisms. As the auxins absorb visible light only weakly, destruction of auxin requires a photoreceptor, that is a pigment such as chlorophyll, carotene, flavoprotein or haemoprotein. Against a general activation of auxin by light there is the evidence of the positive light growth-reactions.

Some insight into the nature of the primary light perception is yielded by investigations on the *spectral sensitivity* of the light growth-reaction. Detailed experiments have been carried out by TEODORESCO (1929) and later by JOHNSTON (1934) and other workers. *Avena* coleoptiles have a maximum sensitivity in the blue (about 440 mμ) and blue-green (about 475 mμ) and are practically insensitive towards wavelengths longer than about 500 mμ. The sporangiophores of *Pilobolus* also show a similar spectral sensitivity. The sensitivity diminishes towards the ultra-violet, without actually sinking to zero.

It is tempting to ascribe the spectral sensitivity to the presence of a pigment which functions as a sensitiser and energy transferer in the light growth-reaction. Carotene and riboflavin (flavoprotein) have been considered most as, unlike chlorophyll, they are present also in etiolated parts of shoots. They are most abundant in the sensitive tip, where the absorption spectrum coincides approximately with the spectral sensitivity of the phototropic reaction. Carotene has also been found in the light-sensitive parts of *Pilobus* and *Phycomyces*, and in the stigma of flagellates and Volvocaceae. A phototropic curvature may be induced in the sporangiophore of *Phycomyces*, according to WASSINK and BOUMAN (1947), by one light quantum. As an interesting parallel to the hypothetical function of carotene in light perception by plants, it may be mentioned that the red pigment in the retina of the eye is related to the carotene derivative, vitamin A. In the purple bacterium *Rhodospirillum rubrum* on the other hand photo-taxis is induced by changes in intensity of photosynthesis (MANTEN 1948). The light-perceiving pigments here are bacteriochlorophyll plus four carotenoids. There is, however, the possibility that the light energy taken up by the pigments influences a separate movement-reaction via a shunt.

Carotene is probably involved in certain redox reactions which could well be involved in the formation, liberation or destruction of auxin. In certain cases inhibition of growth undoubtedly appears to be connected with a photocatalytic destruction of auxin. Auxin destruction has also been observed *in vitro* after sensitising with eosin (SKOOG 1935). OPPENOORTH (1941) doubted these results. New experiments of KOLTERMAN and SKOOG (1954) have, however, shown that such photosensitised destruction of auxin occurs very rapidly in acid solutions, though only slowly in alkaline. At pH 4 a solution of 40γ of IAA per litre is completely inactivated by irradiation with 3,000 mcs. Pigments other than eosin also have similar effects. In living objects carotene or perhaps preferably riboflavin can thus promote a photo-inactivation of auxin. In peas and beans an IAA-oxidase system seems to be active, in which flavoprotein and peroxidase are included (Chap. 4). In this inactivation process one mole of CO_2 is said to be formed per mole of oxygen consumed.

Conversely, the collaboration of light in auxin formation, e.g. in *Vicia* (THIMANN and SKOOG 1934) or in *Nicotiana* leaves (AVERY *et al.* 1937), is probably an indirect effect via photosynthesis. A more direct influence of light on the formation of active auxin is less likely (THIMANN and WENT 1937), even though it would not be easy to show that light in some way or another regulates the balance between combined and free auxin.

Auxin is produced in callus cultures of *Nicotiana* both in the light and in the dark (SKOOG 1944). In cultures of isolated roots also auxin is formed on suitable nutrient media in the dark (NAGAO 1938), and the same can be observed in cucumber seedlings (KRIBBEN 1940, LAIBACH 1941). From what has been said it can be concluded that light affects auxin metabolism in several ways (SKOOG 1947). To pass a final judgment on the mechanism of the light growth-reaction is thus at present impossible (see also the observations of GALSTON 1953).

Light can of course influence growth by other means, e.g. through light-sensitive systems other than those already mentioned or by an absorption of ultra-violet light in the colourless ground substance of protoplasm. It may be recalled that the base of the coleoptile reacts towards light differently from the tip (HAIG 1935). It is possible that some biochemical systems as a result of illumination affect only the extensibility of the cell wall, while others cause an increase of the protoplasm and osmotic materials. Inhibitions of growth may be caused by the generally lethal effects of UV-radiation. The influence of light on protoplasmic viscosity may also be mentioned, since imbibitional phenomena play such a considerable part in the extension of the cell wall.

It is a general experience that every physiological reaction following an external stimulus changes the sensitivity of the organ towards renewed stimulation. There is usually a depression of sensitivity, similar to physical fatigue. The reduction of sensitivity is evident both with continuous stimulation, where it expresses itself in a constantly diminishing strength of reaction, and with intermittent stimulation with impulses of equal intensity, where the effect of each successive stimulus becomes weaker than that of the immediately preceding one. The decrease of sensitivity may go so far as complete inactivity, i.e. to a refractory stage. After stimulation has ceased the organ gradually recovers, until the original sensitivity returns.

If the recovery takes place quickly it may happen that with the choice of suitable intervals the effect of an intermittent stimulation becomes greater than that of a continuous, equally strong stimulation (GÜNTHER-MASSIAS 1928). The precondition for a summation of intermittent stimuli is of course that the induction persists through each interval.

For small amounts of stimulus which do not reduce sensitivity TALBOT's principle applies, which states that an intermittent stimulation has the same reaction effect as a continuous stimulation of the same amount. An increased response with intermittent stimulus only occurs when the total stimulus is strong (for similar relationships in photosynthesis see Chap. 3).

The biochemical cause of the reduction of stimulation is probably the consumption of chemical stimulus-acceptors, which in accordance with the rules for reactions of the first, second order, etc., leads to a continually decreasing speed of reaction. The regeneration of the acceptors in metabolism is a time reaction. Before the start of stimulation the acceptor substance is present in an amount determined by biochemical equilibria. The induction process, according to this interpretation, reflects the simple rules that apply to chemical reactions. Because of the linking together of several biochemical systems other reactions follow the initial induction, until the whole reaction chain has been traversed. It can also be imagined that counter-reactions are set in motion at the same time which may eventually set a limit to the response. We shall return to these matters in Chapter 10.

3 PHOTOPERIODISM

Under this term are included some phenomena connected with the dependence of development on the length of day or, more correctly, on the periodic alternation between light and darkness. GARNER and ALLARD (1920 and later works) were the first to study in detail the effect of day-periodicity on the transition from vegetative growth to flowering. They varied the length of day from five hours to twelve or more (in the latter case by supplying electric light) and found that sexual reproduction occurs only with a definite relation between the length of the light and dark periods. They divided their plants into three groups: *long-day plants, short-day plants* and *intermediate plants* (day-neutral plants) (reviews in GARNER 1929, LANG and MELCHERS 1943, HAMNER 1944).

In typical short-day plants flowering failed altogether if they were illuminated for 12-14 hours a day. With long-day plants the same failure occurred when the daily illumination was shortened to less than twelve hours. Among short-day plants may be mentioned *Cannabis sativa, Chrysanthemum indicum, Dahlia variabilis, Helianthus tuberosus, Phaseolus multiflorus* and the soya bean. Among long-day plants are *Allium cepa, Lactuca sativa, Papaver somniferum, Sinapis nigra,* oats, rye, carrots, beetroot and horse beans. The distinction is often not very sharp, and generally only a delayed or advanced flowering is involved. Thus for example the potato flowers late as a short-day plant in the north. It may further be noted that varietal differences may result in considerable variation. This is an important practical consideration in the adaptation of cultivated plants imported to new climates. On this account it has been possible to introduce the short-day soya bean plant into northern countries. BLAAUW *et al.* (1930) have reported on the adaptation of hyacinths and tulips to more southerly areas. WASSINK and WIERSMA (1955) worked on photoperiodism in trees Even nearly related species can react very differently in their photoperiodic behaviour. The distribution of short- and long-day plants throughout the world seems to be governed by certain photoperiodic rules (JUNGES 1957).

The most striking fact in photoperiodism is that the flowering of short-day plants is completely suppressed by continuous illumination. In this way, for example, rice can be induced to grow vegetatively for years at a stretch (KONDO *et al.* 1932). When it is taken back to normal conditions flowering occurs.

Attempts have been made to explain photoperiodic induction by assuming the formation of hormones necessary for flower formation (WENT 1943, SANDE BAKHUY-SEN 1947, HARDER 1948). There are also speculations about receptor substances for radiation (SALISBURY and BONNER 1956). MURNEEK (1937) found certain chemical differences; e.g. in oats (long-day plants) he found more dry matter under short-day illumination, whereas millet (long-day) behaved conversely, though both showed the same photosynthetic activity. (Discussions about the various chemical effects of day and night phases are given in BÜNNING 1944.)

These and other observations (ARTHUR *et al.* 1930) seem to show that photoperiodic induction occurs independently of photosynthesis and carbohydrate formation. The experiments of ROODENBURG (1937) showed that an adequate day-length could be attained by extending the natural day with artificial light of the low intensity of 20 lux. HARDER *et al.* (1936, 1937) found an effect as low as at 0·25 lux. Even moon-light suffices for photoperiodic induction (GAERTNER *et al.* 1935).

The induction takes place in the leaves; without leaves there is no influence on flowering. The age and the position of the leaves are also of importance. If one retains two leaves standing one above the other on a plant and exposes them to opposite lengths of day, the inhibition of flowering proceeding from the leaf exposed to long-day conditions is effective only if the long-day leaf is the upper one (HARDER and BÜNSOW 1958). A short, even a single cycle, induction period often suffices to provide the impetus to development (see HAMNER 1944, NAYLOR 1953).

The question has been discussed whether the buds also participate in photoperiodic
    2D

induction. LONA (1949) was able to transfer the photoperiodic induction by grafting a separately induced leaf. On the other hand CARR (1953) mentions that such a transfer is possible only if the induced leaf has a bud. The transmission of stimulus from the leaves to the shoot tips proceeds relatively slowly, which leads to the assumption that it is diffusion through living cells that is concerned.

Investigations of the effect of different spectral regions (ROODENBURG 1940, WITHROW 1940, PARKER et al. 1946) have shown that the photoperiodic induction is initiated by long-wave light. The upper limit is stated to be 720 mμ, or by WHITROW even as high as 900 mμ, with a maximum at 600-680 mμ and a minimum at 480 mμ, with some increase in the UV-region. For this reason it has been surmised that chlorophyll in some way collaborates as acceptor, but the answer is still obscure. By some a collaboration of photosynthesis and sugar supply is still thought of (see HAMNER 1944), but the data on hormone effects are increasing.

Auxins are formed in leaves under the influence of light. In experiments with pineapple VAN OVERBEEK et al. (1947) found that adding small amounts of auxin induced flowering. The stem tip contains auxin in the free form, whereas the base of the leaves may contain much combined auxin. The induction to flower formation may thus be due to an increased conversion of combined into free auxin; but there still remains some doubt whether such a complicated phenomenon as the transformation of a growing point into a floral axis can depend only on increased supply of the general growth hormone. LIVERMAN and LANG (1956), however, reported some experiments with the long-day plants *Hyoscyamus niger* and *Silene armeria* which could be caused to bloom by application of IAA. Gibberellin on the other hand seems to have no very marked effect (HARDER 1958).

Photoperiodic induction is greatly dependent on certain general factors such as temperature (KNOTT 1939, LEIMWEBER 1956, LANDAU 1956). The age of the plant (HARDER and WITSCH 1942) and vernalisation phenomena may also be concerned (HARDER and DENFFER 1937, LANDAU 1956). For the interaction with temperature changes the term '*photothermic induction*' has been suggested. The long-day plant *Hyoscyamus niger*, for example, can be caused to bloom in short-day illumination by a drop in temperature. A general thermoperiodic modification from long-day to short-day plants, however, does not seem to take place; but cases of an increase in photoperiodic sensitivity by previous vernalisation are known.

WENT (1945) and others have drawn attention to *thermoperiodism* in which individual variations are fairly considerable. COSTER (1927), who investigated the effect of the diurnal rhythm on tropical plants, found that there are plants which show their greatest growth rate during the day, whereas others grow better during the night. Here the daily fluctuations in the water balance seem to be active, and an endogenous diurnal rhythm of growth has rarely been found (cf. also Chap. 10). On the other hand there are some results indicating the existence of an endogenous annual rhythm regulating the flowering of the short-day plant, *Amaranthus caudatus* (CHAUDHRI 1956).

The photoperiodic effect is not restricted to flowering. Other effects on development have also been observed. Thus short-day plants may have a more compact structure, with shorter internodes and more succulent leaves than long-day plants, which naturally brings with it changes in the water balance (DENFFER 1941, HARDER and WITSCH 1942). In wheat seedlings also photoperiodic effects on form have been observed (HURD-KARRER 1930).

4 INFLUENCE OF THE CHEMICAL COMPOSITION OF THE MEDIUM (pH AND ELECTROLYTES)

The influencing of growth by the chemical composition of the medium surrounding the growing cell is of two types: (1) through raw materials for the synthesis of proto-plasm, cell wall and vacuole, and (2) through chemico-physical regulators which influence auxin activity, etc.

The importance of a suitable supply of raw materials was dealt with in Chapter 7. One should not overlook the fact that raw materials can also have formative effects. Thus, for example, cacao trees, short of iron or manganese, form indented and lobed leaves instead of the normal entire leaves (GREENWOOD and POUSETTE 1947). In the carbohydrate metabolism of green plants there is, as would be expected, a general connection between the intensity of illumination and the production of dry matter (GAST 1937, FILZER 1939). The water-balance usually enters as a complicating factor; since it regulates both gaseous exchange (stomata) and salt uptake, and for this reason any attempt to deduce climatic conditions from the sizes of the annual rings in woody stems is unconvincing (GLOCK 1941). It is found also in short-period investigations with suitable plants that the atmospheric humidity strongly affects growth and form. Thus, for example, *Taraxacum* leaves become up to five times longer if grown in damp air instead of under normal conditions, and their indentation is also influenced by the humidity. The overall water-balance determines the form; but the thickness of the cuticle, on the other hand, is determined directly by the atmospheric humidity.

Just as light directs the overall growth of green plants by way of carbohydrate production, so salt supply regulates growth and to some extent morphogenesis through root action and transpiration. With these continuously operative factors both cell division and cell extension are involved and morphogenesis is particularly deter-mined by the course of division. If the growth of a shoot- or root-tip is investigated with a horizontal microscope one is obviously following the summation of the divisions and extensions in growth. With long periods of observation the frequency of division has a great influence. In measurements at short intervals (seconds to minutes), on the other hand, extension growth is predominant to such an extent that the total growth is approximately the same. Only exact microcinematographic measurements on trans-parent organs, e.g. cereal roots of the second order, can reveal all the individual phases of growth of a tissue.

In the absence of the hormones which often migrate together with the nutrients, the influence of the latter cannot of course be successfully studied. About the auxins, synergistic substances, antiauxins and other competitive or non-competitive inhibitors, which have been dealt with in the previous sections of this chapter, something is known, but by no means everything. These substances belong to the *rate regulators* which develop their full effect only when the raw materials are at their optimum. The auxins have the properties of catalysts, but they are distinguished from the enzymes in that, as far as is known, they do not possess apoenzymes (proteins).

The electrolytes in the surrounding medium are also rate regulators. Some ions have in addition a more specific function as activators. The effects of ions occur most strikingly in plants and organs which live in constant contact with an aqueous medium e.g. in roots. It may, however, be assumed that the solutions circulating in the cell walls of the aerial organs have a similar general effect.

Because of the usually predominant acid dissociation in the protoplasmic surface layer, due apparently to proteins, nucleic acids and the acid dissociation of the cell wall pectins, the effect of inorganic cations is especially marked. By exchange with the hydrogen ions dissociated off they largely determine the surface potential. The importance of the interaction between the dissociated but adsorptively-retained H-ions in the cell surface and the free metallic cations of the medium was dealt with in detail in Chap. 5. The concentration (activity), charge and hydration of the free cations and the specific adsorption constants of the cell surfaces govern the relevant exchange reactions.

The growth of cereal roots (wheat) follows a single-peak pH curve with the optimum at pH 3-4 (Fig. 164). It has been found that the position of the optimum is shifted to higher pH values by the presence of metallic cations in the medium (LUNDEGÅRDH 1942). The extension growth of *Avena* coleoptiles also follows single-peaked pH curves (VAN SANTEN 1938; for salt effects on the growth of coleoptiles see also WUHRMANN 1937).

If the growth of wheat roots is recorded at short time-intervals (cinematographic method; LUNDEGÅRDH 1946, 1949), it is seen that the effect of pH and of salt ions changes with time and that the extension of the root cells and the growth of the root hairs react with these factors in different ways. In the first few minutes after a change from distilled water to a very dilute mineral acid solution (that is in a pH series without metallic cations) the pH optimum lies towards the acid side, and then gradually shifts somewhat towards higher pH values. In root hairs the pH optimum already lies considerably higher at the beginning.

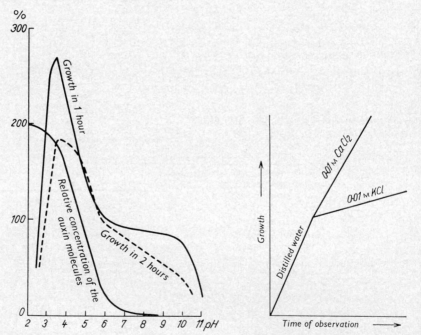

Fig. 164. Relations between the extension growth of wheat roots and the pH value of the medium. There is some similarity with the dissociation curve of auxin, that is a correlation between growth and suppression of dissociation.

Fig. 165. Strong inhibition of growth by KCl, little influence of $CaCl_2$ as compared with distilled water; experiments with wheat roots.

Rapid changes reflect the growth reactions of the epidermis, which is stretched like a skin round the cortex which is under a negative tissue tension. The first recorded pH optimum thus applies to the direct effect of the medium. The higher pH optimum recorded later applies to the reaction of the cortex, which is always buffered against the medium.

If a root is transferred from distilled water or a very dilute solution of a mineral acid into a solution of a neutral salt, an ion exchange $H^+ \rightleftharpoons M^+$ sets in at once at the root surface. In this way the pH of the cell surface (p. 49) sinks; but in addition, certain metallic cations, e.g. calcium (p. 299 ff.), have specially marked effects and can be termed growth activators. The best known is the effect of the calcium ion (BUR-STRÖM 1955), which, because of the time lapse of the modified potential differences, is considered to be biochemical. The calcium ion appears to raise the acid dissociation of the cell surface to the level that seems necessary for normal growth (LUNDEGÅRDH 1940, 1941, 1942, 1949, 1950). If the calcium ions are removed from the cell surface, e.g. by exchange with the potassium ions of a KCl solution, the growth rate consequently falls (see Fig. 165). In root hair growth the activating effect of Ca-ions is probably connected with the formation of calcium pectate.

Together with special ionic effects on growth, of which those described above for calcium are the only ones so far well known, there must also be considered the strong influence of ion exchange on surface potentials. As mentioned on p. 382 (Fig. 160), one must assume that the microcurrents induced by the potential differences take an active part in auxin transport.

The auxins at the ordinarily occurring biological pH values are almost totally dissociated (IAA has $pK = 4 \cdot 75 \text{-} 5 \cdot 0$; the normal pH of wheat roots is $6 \cdot 2$). The potential differences at the root tip are continuously regenerated by metabolism, and the microcurrents indicated in Fig. 160 therefore flow continuously as long as the root grows. The dissociation of the auxin found in the external surface of the epidermis is also directly influenced by cation exchange, since this regulates the local pH of the boundary surface. More important, however, is the auxin transport inside the root tissues. Other things being equal, a change in the potential differences between the tip and the extension zone must induce changes in growth. Electrophoretic auxin transport can also be accelerated or decelerated by electrical currents applied from outside, with consequent changes in growth. Whether similar electrophoretic currents occur in shoot tips is still uncertain (cf. RAMSHORN 1934, CLARK 1937, SCHRANK 1951), although it is *a priori* probable. If they do occur, the external circuit must flow through the surface of the epidermis, as an external water phase is absent. The ideas about electrophoretic auxin transport were developed by SCHRANK (1950, 1953) and treated experimentally. Thus although electrophoretic transport definitely plays a part on short stretches, as in root tips, long-distance transport, on the other hand, depends on the conducting tissues.

A requirement for electrophoretic transport is, of course, an adequate dissociation of the free, fairly low-molecular auxin. If auxin is combined with a carrier or receptor, having an adequate dissociation, this may also migrate electrophoretically. As this involves much higher molecular weights, such translocation must remain very modest.

The question of the dissociation of auxin also has another aspect, viz. whether the activity is a property of the undissociated molecule or of the anion. Those arguments that have hitherto been adduced (BÜNNING 1939, AUDUS 1949, 1953) in support of the hypothesis that the undissociated molecule is the active form are not convincing·

Recently a number of sulphonic acids which show auxin activity, e.g. indolyl-3-methanesulphonic acid and 2,3,6-trichlorophenylmethanesulphonic acid, have been synthesised. Because of the strong dissociation of these substances the anion must obviously be their active form (VELDSTRA et al. 1954). It would also be difficult to understand why the carboxyl group present in all active substances should occupy a key position, if it did not, for example, make linkage to a receptor possible through an anion stage.

If now the auxin anion represents the active form of the growth substance, it follows that changes in the hydrogen-ion concentration, which depress the auxin dissociation, must inhibit the hormone effect (LUNDEGÅRDH 1942, 1946, 1949). It is now known that fairly considerable changes in the H-ion concentration of the medium influence the internal pH remarkably little because of the strong buffering capacity of most tissues including those of roots. The root epidermis, and particularly its outer wall, is directly exposed; but, on account of the rapid penetration of dissolved substances into the network of cell walls (cf. the 'free phase'; Chap. 6), it can be expected that the surfaces of the internal protoplasts will also be influenced by pH changes in the medium.

With the aid of a special cinematographic technique the growth reaction of intact wheat roots was studied (1) at rising concentrations of IAA; (2) with the sodium salt of IAA; and (3) with rising concentrations of HCl to give a pH series without metallic cations. The roots lying in a vessel with solution flowing through it were micro-cinematographically photographed at intervals of two or four minutes. Standard growth was measured in distilled water, and changes of solution were made in a few seconds. A concentration of 10^{-9} M IAA (pH $= 6\cdot9$) was without effect on root growth even when the medium had been flowing for several hours. From this it was concluded that 10^{-9} M IAA corresponds to the normal concentration of auxin in the root.

Even with a very small increase of the auxin concentration above this limit strong inhibition of growth at once occurs (see Fig. 166). 10^{-8} M IAA lowers the growth rate to one-third. As the inhibition sets in almost instantaneously (in less than one minute), one must assume that the reaction of the outermost cell layer is concerned. The inhibition in concentrations up to 10^{-5} M IAA remains constant at about one-third, even when the duration of the observations is lengthened to sixty minutes.

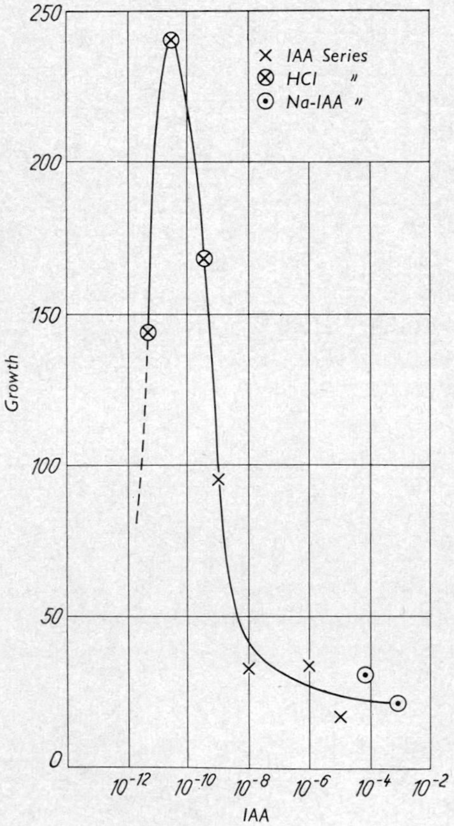

Fig. 166. Effect of various concentrations of IAA and HCl on the extension growth of wheat roots. Normal growth in distilled water is taken as $=100$ (after LUNDEGÅRDH 1949).

If the auxin concentration now increases to above 10^{-5} M the growth begins to rise again from the minimum and in 10^{-4} M IAA reaches almost normal values. At 10^{-3} M IAA the inhibition changes over to a stimulation, which in the first 6-8 minutes amounts to more than 50%. The explanation of this inversion is clear from experiments with the neutral sodium salt of IAA. In this the strong inhibition is maintained in 10^{-4} and 10^{-3} M and even somewhat strengthened (see Fig. 166). The inversion in the growth-reaction between 10^{-5} and 10^{-4} M pure IAA must therefore be connected with the fall in pH, which takes place with the increased concentration of the pure acid. To confirm this assumption the experiments with dilute mineral acids were repeated (Fig. 166).

The experiments with dilute solutions of HCl, that is a pH-series without metallic cations, show convincingly that the growth remains unaltered during the first six minutes with a reduction from about pH$=6$ (that is, distilled water) to pH$=4·7$ (2×10^{-5} M HCl). Only after ten minutes does a growth stimulation commence. The stimulation is however much more pronounced at pH $3·4$ (4×10^{-4} M HCl), where an acceleration to 125% (against 100% in distilled water) occurs in the first minute, to 210% in the sixth minute and in the tenth minute to 302%. These accelerations are in no way pathological, since the roots die only at pH values below $3·0$ after thirty minutes. During the first few minutes at pH$=2·7$ (2×10^{-3} M HCl) there is a great acceleration of growth of the still undamaged root, which after thirty minutes ceases because of the death of the root. The experiments show that the pH growth-optimum lies at about $3·4$, which also agrees with the results of direct culture experiments (LUNDEGÅRDH 1942).

A conceivable explanation of the acceleration of growth at pH values below about 5, in accordance with the interpretation given above, may lie in a gradient reduction of the dissociation of the auxin in the root. The lowering of the concentration of the active auxin anions thus caused would accelerate growth under the postulated conditions, since the normal auxin concentrations of the root, which we calculated at 10^{-9} M, is on the rising branch of the auxin growth-curve. Any decrease of the concentration of the free auxin anions would therefore evoke an acceleration of growth. It can be calculated that at pH$=4·7$ the auxin dissociation (at an assumed pK of $5·0$) sinks to about one-third, that is from 10^{-9} to $10^{-9·47}$, and at pH$=3·4$, corresponding approximately to the pH optimum of growth, to $10^{-10·6}$ (see Fig. 166).

If we now transfer the results of this analysis to experiments with auxin supplied from outside, there is good agreement in the shape and position of the pH curves of growth; that is to say, in the high auxin concentrations, where the pH falls on account of its dissociation, there is an acceleration of growth in about the same pH range as in pure HCl solutions. Since, however, in the stronger IAA solutions the internal auxin concentration undoubtedly rises far above the normal value of 10^{-9} M, the observed acceleration of growth cannot be due to depression of the internal auxin dissociation. Some special pH effect is involved here, which develops quite independently of the auxin concentration. This conclusion does not invalidate the hypothesis of the activity of the auxin anions; but for a final explanation new experimental result are needed.

About the nature of the special effect of pH on growth we at present know nothing with certainty. It is known that acid substances, e.g. pectic acid, occur among the structural materials of the cell wall. Another possibility is an effect on the dissociation of the hypothetical receptor substance or auxin carrier. A depression of this dissociation would probably be able to restrict the possibilities of binding active auxin. This explanation may also be applicable to experiments with auxin added from outside.

Some elucidation of the part possibly played by pH-sensitive substances other than auxin can be obtained by experiments with root hairs. These, in marked contrast to the whole root, are practically insensitive to addition of auxin (LUNDEGÅRDH 1946); but, on the other hand, are just as sensitive as the root to pH (Fig. 167).

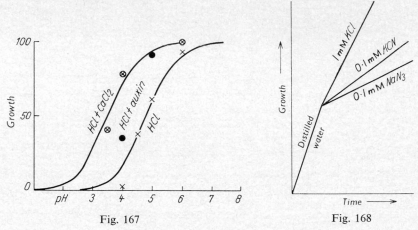

Fig. 167   Fig. 168

Fig. 167. The dependence of root-hair growth on pH, Ca-ions and 10^{-5} moles per litre of IAA. In pure acid solutions growth ceases at pH=4, but in presence of Ca-ions higher H-ion concentrations are tolerated (after LUNDEGÅRDH 1946).

Fig. 168. The inhibition of root growth in very dilute solutions of cyanide and azide in comparison with chloride. Recording of growth during an hour.

The pH-curve of root-hair growth is similar in shape to a dissociation curve, and one can therefore certainly say that in this case the dissociation of other growth-regulating substances is decisive. The experiments also seem to show that the pH-curve in itself is not due to lack of calcium, since after addition of $CaCl_2$ the pH-relation is moved as a whole about one unit downwards, but the form of the curve remains unaffected. Addition of calcium thus cannot prevent a reduction of the dissociation of the important but unknown components in the wall. The minus-calcium effect appears strongly, however, in the root hairs.

Application of results obtained with root hairs to the growth of whole roots should therefore be made only with care, since the two types of growth differ fundamentally both as regards the physical properties of the cell wall and the auxin effect. The calcium effect on root hairs is usually thought of as a salt-fixation with pectic acid. In the whole root, however, this effect does not appear so clearly. The considerably greater sensitivity of the root hairs towards a fall in pH may be connected partly with a weaker buffer capacity. The tissue cells are certainly much better screened from changes in the surroundings. Considerable buffering against changes in pH of the medium is shown, however, by bacteria and by many thin-leaved water plants, such as *Elodea* and *Ceratophyllum*, whose growth, according to STEEMANN NIELSEN (1944), is independent of pH variations between 4·5 and 8·2. Their photosynthesis is, however, eventually affected by the changed bicarbonate balance of the medium.

The cation effects that have now been described refer to concentrations usual in plant substrates. At high salt concentrations, osmotic effects are added, which may lead, among other things, to a reduced swelling of the cell wall. The danger of chemical toxicity naturally increases with the concentration. The poisonous effects of a number of heavy metals, which are also recognisable as inhibitions of growth, are mostly due to secondary effects on metabolism.

In summarising ionic effects on growth, the extraordinary complication of the reactions induced by cations must be emphasised. The concentration of hydrogen ions determines the degree of dissociation of a number of weak acids in the cell surface such as auxins, auxin-receptors, pectic acids, cation carriers in the surface layer, etc. To the extent that the activity of the auxin depends on the relative concentration of its anions or on the degree of dissociation of the receptors, this hydrogen-ion effect must be of the first importance. H-ions also exercise a further influence through exchange with the metallic cations, e.g. K, Ca and Mg, which are adsorbed on the cation carriers of the cell surface. This influence of course increases with rising pH value and thereby influences e.g. also the special ionic effects such as that of calcium. The effects of the pH of the medium mentioned here refer to very short periods of observation, which may not always have been adequately taken into account in the literature. With a longer period of action an increase in pH leads to a stimulation of auxin production (RUFELT 1957).

All cations influence the surface charge of the protoplasm and thereby the potential difference between the root tip and the extension zone. The microcurrents, to which we have ascribed a function in the internal transport of auxin, are weakened by strong intake of metallic cations. In the range of concentration of the usual nutrient solutions, however, this cation exchange cannot exercise any decisive effect on the relative potential differences. More important here are the specific effects of cations such as the antagonism between K and Ca, in which the effect of K is to cause a deficiency of Ca.

Among chemical influences on growth rate the respiratory poisons should finally be taken into account. Haem-blocking poisons such as cyanide and azide are effective, since inhibition of the cytochrome respiration reduces the growth rate to a small percentage of the normal (cf. Fig. 168). Growth is inhibited by high CO_2 concentrations (CHAPMAN et al. 1924), and by ethylene (GUSTAFSON 1944), substances which also interfere with the cytochrome system.

Chapter 10
THE MOVEMENTS OF PLANTS

A. Review of Movements in response to Stimuli and their General Mechanism

There is no sharp boundary between growth and movement, since roots pressing forward in a straight line carry out a kind of growth movement, which is comparable with the locomotion of animals as a means of nutrition. The growth movements proper are, however, the curvatures and rotations of organs initiated by external or internal stimuli.

Movements which are due to one-sided (anisotropic) growth acceleration or retardation are called *tropisms*. According to the kind of stimulation, one distinguishes photo-, geo-, hapto-, traumato-, hydro- and chemo-tropisms. In all of these a stimulus coming from a definite direction causes a change of postion, which usually places the organ in a posture more favourable for its function. Ecologically one speaks of *orientation movements*, although under this term are grouped all movements induced by an external stimulus. If the initiating stimulus comes from within, one speaks of *autonomic movements*. An example of an autonomic movement is *autotropism*, by which a shoot- or root-tip that has moved in response to an external stimulus is led back to its earlier erect position. The *nutations* of shoot tips and leaves are usually autonomic.

Mature organs are usually no longer capable of movement, and it is the active meristems, especially the extension zones, that have the ability to move. Examples are known, however, of slow curvature of lignified stems, where the cambium plays the part of the motor organ. In special cases, e.g. in the curvature of the joints (nodes) of grass stalks under the influence of geotropic stimulation, growth that has ceased is taken up again. In the pulvini of the leaves of Leguminosae and Oxalidaceae the mature cells remain permanently extensible. Movements are brought about by changes in osmotic pressure in the upper and lower parts of the pulvinus.

In the tropisms the organ orientates itself in accordance with the direction of the stimulus. The construction and orientation of the organ in this case have little to do with the direction of movement, and thus behave more or less isotropically with respect to the stimulus. In the large group of *nasties* on the other hand the direction of movement is determined by the structure of the organ itself even when the stimulation comes from a definite direction, and the organ behaves anisotropically with respect to the stimulus. Whilst in phototropic movements the leaf places itself at a certain angle to the incident light, photonastic movements, as in bean leaves, consist in raising and lowering the lamina by day and night independently of the direction of the light rays. In the characteristic thermonastic movements of spring plants (tulips, *Anemone nemorosa*, etc.) temperature changes induce different growth rates of the upper and lower sides of the petals. The stomata are photo- and hydro-nastic, etc. The structural anisotropy characteristic of nasties may, as in the examples quoted, be based on the construction of the organ. In other cases, a nastic anisotropy can be induced by long-continued unilateral illumination or by gravity.

Only unicellular or colonial plants are provided, like animals, with locomotive mechanisms. Only the male gametes retain in early phylogenetic stages their capacity for locomotion (e.g. the spermatozoids of the mosses, ferns and cycads). Protoplasmic streaming occurs as a relic of the amoeboidal movements of naked protoplasts. The gliding movements of Diatomaceae are of a similar unspecialised kind, whereas the cilia of bacteria, unicellular green algae, swarm spores and spermatozoids represent more specialised organs of locomotion. These movements can undoubtedly be termed autonomic, when they express themselves as an aimless wandering about in a uniform environment. Ecologically they appear as a *taxis* if the movement, because of unilateral stimulation (light or chemical stimuli), takes a definite direction.

The movements of living cells or tissues are stimulus phenomena. Even dead cells and tissues can, however, carry out biologically valuable movements. To these belong many hygroscopically regulated mechanisms for the dissemination of spores or seeds, and the mechanism of fern sporangia depending on the cohesion of water. These movements are reminiscent of nasties in that their direction is determined by internal structural relationships; but none of those characteristics is connected with stimulus-perception in living cells. Mechanical tensions which can be suddenly released may also arise in living tissues. An example is the seed-dispersal mechanism of the squirting cucumber *Ecballium elaterium*.

These mechanisms are reminiscent of the trigger mechanism of a rifle. The force necessary for pressing the trigger is much less than the motor force of the spring which is released. Such trigger mechanisms are examples of the 'all or none' principle, i.e. there is no quantitative relation between the energy needed for the release and the energy developed during the reaction. If there is any reaction at all, the full reaction energy is released, and the total reaction starts immediately the stimulation reaches a certain threshold value. In the *Ecballium* fruits, or the annulus of the sporangia of *Pteris*, motor energy is stored behind the motor barrier of the trigger. Examples of all-or-none reactions in living tissues are the trap mechanisms of *Utricularia* and *Dionaea*, to some extent the tentacles of *Drosera*, the mobile stamens of *Centaurea*, the seismonastic movements of *Mimosa* leaves, and some movements of tendrils and climbing plants. In processes which involve an induction in the living protoplasm, the ability to react does not usually depend on a previous accumulation of energy behind barriers suddenly removed by the stimulation. The stimulus usually sets in train a series of biochemical reactions which, after the cessation of the impulse, continues spontaneously as long as the available energy lasts.

The most usual and by far the most important type of movement mechanism works on similar principles to the accelerator of a car, i.e. the intensity of the reaction has a definite relation to the intensity of the stimulation, although the amount of energy converted by the reaction is usually far greater than the energy of the stimulus. In the theoretically simplest case the stimulus links on to the initial reaction of a long biochemical chain of causation, which ends with the movement. In the more highly specialised mechanisms two separate complexes can be distinguished, *perception* (or induction) and *reaction*, which are connected by the *transmission* of the stimulus.

A proportional induction distinguishes almost all tropisms and some taxes, whereas the nastic movements usually belong to the all-or-none type. A proportional induction presupposes partly a more complicated receptor mechanism and partly a definite quantitative connection between it and the reaction mechanism. The two are often united by a similarly variable transmission of stimulus. To make this important type of stimulation process more understandable one may imagine that a stimulus-receptor substance is formed during induction, which, after translocation to the site of reaction, releases the visible movement. In the highly developed movements due to proportional stimulation one can thus distinguish two phases of the release mechanism, of which the former (that is, the induction) is regulated by the stimulus and the latter (that is, the reaction) is regulated by the transmission. If one wishes to schematise the stimulus-reaction chain to the limit, one may also distinguish between the primary induction or perception and the excitation. By the latter term is then understood the biochemical processes which are set into operation in the organ of perception. Ordinarily the term perception includes excitation.

A sharp distinction between proportional induction and the all-or-none processes cannot be maintained. In all stimulus processes there are initial barriers, which must be overcome or set aside before there is any result. Here one speaks of the *stimulus threshold*. In the all-or-none process, on passing the threshold a powerful increase of induction occurs. More precise investigation, however, often shows some gradation, although the maximal stimulation is reached very soon. With proportional induction the optimal stimulation is attained only after a longer rise. The optimum region, on the other hand, is less definite, since variations in the intensity of stimulus here have very little effect. At the optimum the full capacity for perception is utilised and cannot be further increased.

All stimulus processes are complicated both by *fatigue* and *recovery* and by auto-nomic *counter-reactions*. Fatigue and recovery were dealt with in connection with externally stimulated growth reactions (p. 402). Fatigue, which ultimately leads to a non-responsive stage, can usually be referred to the consumption of one or more chemical substances necessary for the stimulus chain. The formation of these sub-stances is limited by the time factor, among others, so that the effects of rapid repeti-tions of stimulation are accumulated. In this one can see an expression of the biological relativity law. The complete exhaustion of the non-responsive stage occurs most clearly in some nastic movements, e.g. in the capture movements of carnivorous plants. The reaction mechanism here discharges itself completely, and it requires a definite time before the necessary energy level is again attained.

With proportional stimulation mechanism fatigue becomes evident in the pro-gressive delay of the reaction as it approaches the optimum, and also in the falling off of the response. This is expressed in the WEBER-FECHNER law which is concerned with the ability to distinguish between two stimuli, i.e. whether a stimulus *a* is stronger or weaker than a stimulus *b* applied at the same time or shortly after. It has been found that the difference can be verified if the ratio of *a* : *b* reaches a given minimum; that is to say, it is the relative, not the absolute, difference *a-b* between the two stimuli that matters. The latter rises with increasing intensity of stimulus and so to some extent reflects the damping of perception. The WEBER-FECHNER law was originally established for the sensory physiology of man, but was later also applied e.g. to the phototropic and taxic movements of plants.

The WEBER-FECHNER law is, however, only an approximation, since various links in the long chain between perception and reaction may be relaxed by fatigue. The processes accelerated by a stimulus may follow a time schedule different from those leading to recovery, through which the sensitivity to stimulation is restored. The time needed for recovery is not necessarily the same for all partial reactions. It is thus comprehensible that, with a given relation between stimulus and interval, intermittent stimulation may have a greater effect than the same amount of stimulation applied continuously; and, conversely, that too long a rest period between the individual impulses may depress the total effect below the normal (cf. also BÜNNING and GLATZLE 1948).

A fundamental property of living substance is its functional elasticity, i.e. its ability to restore disturbed equilibria. The phenomenon forms a counterpart in stimulus physiology to buffer capacity in nutritional physiology. Functional elasticity can be referred to thermodynamically reversible chemical equilibria or, what is commoner, to steady states like those of oxidative processes such as respiration. It occurs extensively in stimulus phenomena, partly in recovery after fatigue and partly in counter-reactions (autotropism, etc.).

The *counter-reactions* manifest themselves in growth as a slowing of the rate of reaction in tropisms even by a reversal of the direction of movement, and in nasties by a return to the original position. They amount to counter-reactions with complete induction-response sequences. A counter-reaction is triggered off by the internal changes caused by the externally induced primary reaction. For this reason autotropism can be considered as a kind of internal chemotropism. Autotropism, especially in geo- and photo-tropic primary reactions, is associated with externally induced reactions, as e.g. when a shoot tip on erection passes the vertical and receives an external stimulus on the opposite side.

In all counter-reactions the time factor exercises a great influence, since the counter-reaction is induced only by a stimulation occurring in the primary reaction chain. Temperature and nutrient factors are also concerned. The time course of a reaction is made up of the *presentation* time, the *transmission* time or 'latent period', and the *reaction* time. Their durations are partly determined by the intensity of the partial reactions; the latent time, for example, decreases with increasing intensity of perception. Conditions such as temperature, water balance, etc., may also affect the courses of the individual reactions, though little is known about this.

The tonic phenomena exhibit damping effects of a special kind. By *tonus* is understood the general sensitivity or capability of an organ to react. It is known, for example, that it changes with age, state of nutrition, illumination, etc. Usually only a detailed analysis can determine whether an observed change in sensitivity is due to an interaction of two opposed reactions or to an inhibition or acceleration within the reaction chain. Only in the latter case does one speak of tonic effects.

B. Geotropism

Geotropic movements are initiated by gravity or, more correctly, by mass acceleration, including centrifugal force, and cause an orientation of the organ in a given relation to the horizontal.

The main types are *orthogeotropism* and *plagiogeotropism*. In the first the organ sets itself vertically and in the second at an acute angle to the earth's surface. The terms *positive* and *negative geotropism* imply that the organ in the stimulus-free state turns downwards or upwards respectively. Applying the trigonometrical angular terminology (see Fig. 169), $-90°$ indicates the positive orthogeotropic position of rest and $+90°$ the negative orthogeotropic. The corresponding plagiogeotropic positions of rest lie within the region $-0°$ to $-90°$, or $+0°$ and $+90°$ respectively. *Diageotropic* or *transversely geotropic* organs place themselves in the position $\pm 0°$ or $\pm 180°$, which in nature corresponds to the horizontal. An alternative term, therefore, is *horizontal geotropism*. Special forms of geotropism occur in climbing plants as *lateral geotropism*.

Of special importance for geotropic and particularly plagiogeotropic movements are the tonic effects induced by gravity (*geotonus*). These special gravity perceptions are not of a nastic type, but are just as dependent on the direction of stimulus as the tropistic inductions. The most important are those induced in root- and shoot-tips in the vertical position with gravity acting as a 'longitudinal force'.

1 GEOTROPIC PERCEPTION

As protoplasm has a fluid to semi-fluid consistency, gravity must always tend to cause a separation of dispersed particles (microsomes, molecules and ions) according to their specific gravities, a fact which was pointed out by PFEFFER (1897-1904). This sedimentation is most conspicuous when the protoplasm is 'resting', that is non-streaming. One may therefore surmise that it occurs more in the primary meristem cells filled with resting protoplasm than in the vacuolated cells of the extension zone; though the protoplasmic membrane tends to be quite immobile in the latter also. A sedimentation of particles, molecules or ions must obviously have biological effects, since separation of materials may, for example, cause concentration differences between the upper and lower surfaces of horizontal membranes. The purely mechanical effect of gravity may thus accelerate reactions at some surfaces and inhibit them at others, according to the make-up of the biochemical systems involved.

Sedimentation under gravity naturally makes itself most evident with the larger inclusions in the cell, particularly when their specific gravity differs considerably from that of the surroundings. Usually it is easy to separate fat droplets, starch granules or crystal druses from the remaining cell content by weak centrifugal forces. The whole protoplasm is likewise easily stratified in a centrifugal field, a phenomenon commonly utilised for the measurement of the viscosity of protoplasm. Under such treatment the nucleus also changes its position in the cytoplasm. Under the normal acceleration due to gravity no stratification of the nucleus is found; but on the other hand a stratification of starch granules (together with leucoplasts) is easily observable. These react in

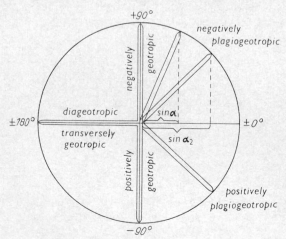

Fig. 169. Diagram showing the trigonometrical angular terminology for describing the geotropic equilibrium positions.

the gravitational field roughly like the statoliths in the organs of hearing of animals. This analogy has caused the so-called *statolith theory* to be put forward.

NĚMEC (1900, 1902) and HABERLANDT (1900) observed that the starch granules, which often occur in certain cells and cell layers, form a sediment on the lower walls on account of their high specific gravity. This displacement of the 'statoliths', according to these workers, gives the impulse to geotropic perception. While, as pointed out above, there is no objection to assuming biochemical consequences from partial sedimentation, the weak point of the NĚMEC-HABERLANDT theory is that only the stratification of starch granules is taken into account. Among ergastic inclusions there are also many other sedimentable particles. PRANKHERD (see STILES 1936, p. 47) gives as an example the calcium oxalate crystals in the nodes of the wheat stalk.

The statolith theory was formerly much discussed. It can scarcely be said that it has been finally proved, though a large number of observations have shown a striking parallelism between the occurrence of mobile starch grains and geotropic sensitivity. Mobile starch also occurs regularly in the root cap, in coleoptile tips and in the parenchymatous sheaths of conducting strands. The fungi, which are usually strongly geotropic, lack mobile starch grains, however, and certain discrepancies in the occurrence of starch and of geotropic sensitivity have been found also in the higher plants (JOST, VON UBISCH et al.). Very striking arguments for the theory have nevertheless been adduced (VON GUTTENBERG, HAWKER, ZOLLIKOFER et al.). These arguments generally aim at showing that the development and re-formation of statoliths run parallel with geotropic sensitivity. Careful investigations on the relations between the rate of sedimentation of the starch grains and the length of the presentation time, however, are lacking. Against the theory may be quoted also the experiments of JOST, according to which a geotropic effect was observed with such weak centrifugal force that the starch grains were not sedimented.

The statolith theory is a typical example of the method by which physiological processes are explained in terms of visible structural changes in cells. How the induction, i.e. the conversion of statolith impacts against the protoplasmic membrane into biochemical processes, actually takes place, naturally remains an unsolved question. At present one can only assume quite hypothetically that any sedimentation of molecules and ions in a biochemical system with ultramicroscopic structure must cause changes in reaction rates.

After the discovery of the collaboration of the partly dissociated *auxins* in the transmission of stimulus, more constructive possibilities for such speculations were opened up. According to the train of thought started by CHOLODNY and followed by most later workers, geotropic curvatures are due to a redistribution of auxin between the upper and lower sides of an organ; as, for example, when more auxin is conducted from the tip to the lower side. There are also other hypotheses about the differential effect of auxin, such as a change in the sensitivity of the opposite sides (cf. BRAUNER 1954).

The values in Table 25 given by AMLONG, BOYSEN-JENSEN et al. are an example of the anisotropic distribution of auxin in horizontally placed organs.

As the speed of migration of auxin is influenced by local potential differences (see above), the discovery of changes of potential induced by gravity in living organs must be considered an important advance in the study of geotropism. This *geoelectric effect* was first observed by BRAUNER, who referred it to the already known physical phenomenon, that potential differences can arise at the horizontal boundary layer of

Table 25

	Percentage of auxin	
	Upper side	Lower side
Oat coleoptiles	38	62
Root tips of maize	25	75
Hypocotyl of *Lupinus*	32	68

a salt solution due to the positive and negative ions having dissimilar weights. The geoelectric effect measured by BRAUNER seldom attained values higher than 2-10 millivolts. A more exact study of the potential distribution at the surface of root tips, however, revealed considerably higher geoelectric effects (LUNDEGÅRDH 1942).

The geoelectric effect is strongest in the root-tip, where its direction is the opposite of that in the extension zone. Stimulation by gravity rearranges the electrical poles and produces a steep potential gradient along the lower side of the root tip. This increase of the electromotive force might be sufficient to accelerate electrophoretic auxin transport along the lower side relative to that along the upper side. The latter remains unchanged also after the stimulation. Figure 170 shows the geoelectric effect

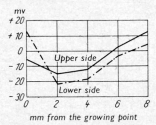

Fig. 170. The geoelectric effect in a root-tip. The tip, from 0 to 2 mm, reacts inversely to the remainder of the root (after LUNDEGÅRDH 1942).

in pea roots, which were placed in the horizontal position; the potential difference between the tip and the middle of the extension zone (a distance of 2 mm) rises on the lower side to about 35 millivolts, that is to more than four times the 8 millivolts difference on the upper side. Thus considerably more auxin anions could be transported electrophoretically from the tip to the extension zone along the lower side of the root than along the upper. A similar, though weaker, geoelectric effect was also measured in wheat roots, which react geotropically much more weakly than pea roots.

Geotropic induction causes in all elongating organs an increase in the auxin concentration on the lower side and a diminution on the upper side, that is a change in the distribution of the auxin production constantly flowing from the primary meristem. In negatively geotropic organs, such as stems, which react positively to auxin, the increased auxin current along the lower side causes a curvature upwards. In roots, which react negatively to auxin, the relative increase of the auxin concentration along the lower side evokes an inhibition of growth on this side, i.e. a curvature downwards. Because of the changed distribution the upper side also suffers a change in its auxin supply, usually a diminution. Consequently the average growth during curvature seldom remains unchanged. It is therefore not surprising that the auxin concentrations necessary for optimal growth do not coincide with those which give optimal geotropic reaction (ANKER 1955), a phenomenon also observed in phototropism (see below). According to GEIGER-HUBER (1945) repeated decapitation of the root-tip may cause the auxin concentration to sink so far that the geopositive reaction changes over to a negative reaction. It must, however, be remembered that other growth substances besides auxins are active, which have to do with the normally depressed negative geotropic reaction (cf. below).

The strong geoelectric effect in the primary meristem, which is rich in protoplasm, apparently depends on the pressure of heavy elongated anions, e.g. those of nucleic acids, which become reorientated under the influence of gravity. It can be imagined that such elongated molecules or perhaps even micelles are built into the protoplasmic surface layers in such a way that they partly retain their mobility. If one end of a long ion is heavier than the other, it will have a tendency to rotate with changes in position of the membrane; and the membrane charge will thus be changed. The potential change will be particularly great if the ionic rotation leads to a screening of the charge. It may be mentioned that such gravitational rotations of elongated molecules and ions may complicate work with the ultra-centrifuge. The probable connection of the strong geoelectric effect observed in the primary meristem with the presence of large elongated molecules follows from the fact that a corresponding effect arises also in filter paper that has imbibed a solution of thymonucleic acid. Impregnation with neutral salts gives only the weak geoelectric reaction observed by BRAUNER, which also occurs in the mature part of the root, but is probably quite unimportant for geotropic induction.

The geoelectric effect develops very quickly (in less than two seconds), which makes the summation of short-duration gravitational stimuli comprehensible. The idea of an electrophoretic translocation of auxin does not of course exclude the possibility that the translocation of other ionised organic substances also undergoes differentiation. More direct potential effects could also take part without transmission. A further possibility is a direct geoelectric effect on auxin formation or activation (cf. also SCHRANK 1950, 1953). Change in the local pH is a direct geoelectric effect. Rising negative potential means for example an acidification of the outer side of the protoplasmic membrane interwoven with the growing cell wall. Enzymic processes, which are always highly sensitive to pH, may react at once on such a change.

The great uncertainty which still remains about the mechanism of tropic movements is illustrated by the recent experiments of AUDUS and BROWNBRIDGE (1957). They doubt CHOLODNY's theory of the redistribution of a growth substance flowing from the tip zone, and believe that the inhibition of growth at the lower side of the geotropically stimulated root is due to the formation of an inhibitor, which may not be identical with IAA. It would thus be a question of a direct local effect of geoelectric perception, such as has been discussed above. The participation of growth substances other than auxin in geotropic movements is clear from the existence of the geotropic counter-reaction to be discussed below.

The above points about geotropic perception also have a certain interest for the theory of the *klinostat*, the instrument that has been industriously used since the start of modern plant physiology to eliminate geotropic stimulation. On this instrument plants rotate slowly about a horizontal axis. Complete absence of stimulus is of course not possible, since the minimum time of a geotropic induction is so small (less than two seconds), that a complete elimination of stimulus would only be possible at a speed at which centrifugal force would begin to have an effect. The practical value of the klinostat therefore lies in an elimination of reaction by equally strong counter-reaction. An appropriate speed of rotation must still be chosen, of course (cf. also LARSEN 1955). The observation usually made, that in geotropically sensitive organs

2E

the speed of growth is not changed by rotation on the klinostat, obviously supports the interpretation that auxin production is not altered in geotropic perception, but only auxin distribution.

2 PERCEPTION, TRANSMISSION AND REACTION

It was very early recognised that geotropic perception is restricted mainly to root-tips or shoot-tips. CIESIELSKY (1871) found that curvature did not take place in roots if the tip had been removed. This experiment was confirmed on a larger scale by the DARWIN father and son. The experiment of FRANCIS DARWIN with young seedlings of *Panicum* and *Sorgum* is especially well known. Here the coleoptile is several millimetres long and is borne on a mesocotyl. If the former is fixed in a level position in a horizontal glass tube, the mesocotyl curves continually in spirals, since the perception is in the coleoptile and this is continuously stimulated. The following experiment of PICCARD (1904) is also well known: a root is placed obliquely across the turning point of a centrifuge disc in such a way that the tip protrudes a short distance beyond the centre (Fig. 171). The tip is thus stimulated by the centrifugal force in the opposite direction to the growth zone, and the resulting curvature shows that only the tip functions as the perceptive organ.

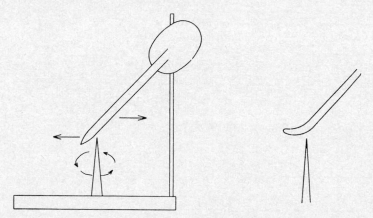

Fig. 171. PICCARD's experiment with opposed centrifugal stimulation of tip and basal end of a root. The reaction follows the induction in the tip.

In *Avena* coleoptiles the tip is on the average about six times as sensitive as the base. In tips of stems the perception zone is usually longer and may partly coincide with the reaction zone. Even in root-tips and coleoptiles there is a gradation of sensitivity rather than a sharp distinction between perception and reaction zones. The reaction usually begins as a weak asymmetry of the extreme tip. The asymmetry spreads towards the elongation zone and attains its maximum where elongation is fastest. In other cases the curvature is first noticeable in the elongation zone itself (Fig. 172).

With persistent stimulation the curvature finally becomes fixed at the boundary between extending and mature cells. It must thus be supposed that a re-orientation of the growth substances begins in the induction zone and that transmission causes this anisotropic distribution of the growth substances to move towards the base. The total course of the reaction is thus a complicated summation of the reactions of all growing cells to the transmission of the stimulus. The theoretically correct measure for the curvature of a cylindrical organ is the angle between the tip of the organ and the middle line of the immobile base. This angle of curvature is proportional to the difference of growth rate between the convex and concave side of the curved organ.

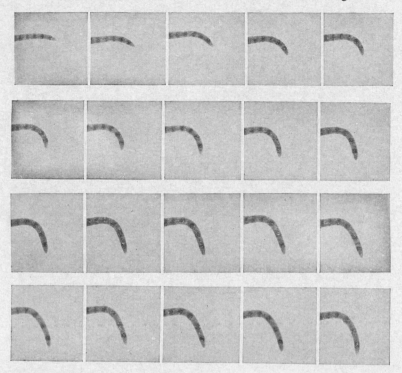

Fig. 172. The course of the geotropic curvature of a pea root, with a magnification of about 2, recorded cinematographically. The markings in Indian ink were made at distances of 1 mm (after LUNDEGÅRDH 1916).

An exact study of the tropisms requires more precise methods of measurement than the hitherto customary semi-quantitative estimates, e.g. 'just visible reaction', etc. Since the introduction of the cinematographic recording technique for measurements of angle (LUNDEGÅRDH 1916-18) one is better equipped to analyse the course of the reaction and the interplay of different stimuli which takes place even in apparently uncomplicated orthogeotropic curvatures (cf. Fig. 172).

The simple tropistic reaction follows a sigmoidal curve. The middle part of the curve is almost a straight line (Figs. 173 and 174; LUNDEGÅRDH 1922, 1926) and may be termed the *eumotorial phase*. The uniform progress of this phase can be interpreted as meaning that the cell growth is governed by a factor uniformly supplied and that this is directly proportional to the reaction. This explanation can be combined with the idea of an auxin stream. As every single cell passes through a grand period of growth, the reaction may be conceived as a wave of extension accelerated or inhibited by hormones slowly progressing basipetally. As in other cases, the individual cells act symplastically together (LUNDEGÅRDH 1917, p. 52 ff.).

The uniform progress of the eumotorial phase also supports the idea of an electrophoretic auxin translocation. In diffusion, according to the formula of PERRIN, distance traversed is proportional to the square root of time. If the auxin were dependent on diffusion alone, there would not be an almost rectilinear eumotorial phase. In

---

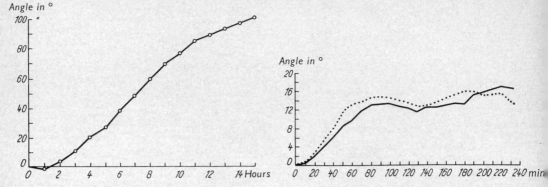

Fig. 173. Negatively geotropic reaction of the main shoot of *Coleus* laid horizontally, according to cinematographic recording of the angle of inclination. The abscissa gives the time in hours. Over-curvature at +90° (after LUNDEGÅRDH 1926).

Fig. 174. Positive geotropic curvature of two lateral roots of *Pisum* placed horizontally, after pre-treatment by a long period of rotation on the klinostat (that is, absence of stimulus). Because of plagiogeotropic induction the reaction ceases at a certain angle of inclination (after LUNDEGÅRDH 1926).

electrophoretic translocation, on the other hand, the distance traversed is directly proportional to time.

Tropistic reactions are always distinguished by a latent period or 'starting phase' during which the rate gradually increases from zero to the value maintained in the eumotorial phase (Figs. 173 and 174). From the standpoint of a geoelectric induction, the starting phase may be conceived of as the time that elapses before the modified auxin streams reach the elongation zone. In a root growing vertically an isotropic auxin stream flows from the growing point towards the elongation zone. If the root is laid horizontally, induction starts almost at once; but it takes a considerable time before the auxin streams can develop their full effect in the elongating zone. Even in genetically pure material the reaction time naturally varies (Fig. 175). In a considerable

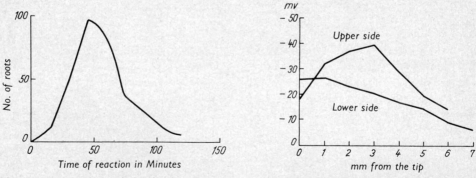

Fig. 175. The curve of variation for the geotropic time of reaction of the main roots of *Pisum*. Constant temperature, 20° C (after LUNDEGÅRDH 1917).

Fig. 176. The distribution of the potential on a pea root placed horizontally, measured 15 minutes after the commencement of the stimulation. The potential distribution on the upper side corresponds to that of an unstimulated root (cf. Fig. 159); the potential distribution on a lower side with inhibited growth behaves anomalously.

series of experiments with pea roots the following percentage values were found for the latent time:

Table 26

Duration of the stimulus (in minutes)	Percentage of the roots just reacting	
	In soil	In damp air
5	43	19
10	70	—
15	92	72
18	94	—

The time of reaction varies approximately according to a Gaussian curve (Fig. 175). Humidity has a marked effect on the course of the reaction. The geotropic sensitivity is considerably reduced if the roots grow in damp air instead of in damp ground (see the above Table).

The end phase of the tropistic reaction is a reversal of the starting phase, that is a gradual decrease of the rate of curvature towards zero (Figs. 173 and 174). After very weak stimulations and slight curvatures, the end phase starts early; after stronger stimuli on the other hand a regular relationship between the time of onset of the end phase and the intensity of stimulus can scarcely be detected. This is because the reaction proceeds more quickly, the stronger the stimulation, whereas the total time of the curvature is relatively little affected. The average rate of growth of the organ is influenced by the geotropic curvature. This certainly has its cause in the relative changes of the rate between the two opposite sides. The time of reaction is determined by the time course of the grand period of growth of the cells, and this contributes in a large degree to fixing the time of onset of the end phase. The end phase as a rule is only an interphase between a reaction and its counter-reaction, which appears especially clearly in the periodic phenomena (see below).

3 THE QUANTITATIVE RELATIONS BETWEEN STIMULUS AND REACTION

According to the well-known interpretation by CHOLODNY, the geotropic reaction is due to a redistribution of auxin, so that the lower side of the organ receives more than the upper (see also BARA 1957 and the literature quoted there). The rule is that growth is regulated at every moment by the concentration of auxin flowing in.

The orthogeotropic reaction of roots can be inferred from electrical potential differences which have nothing to do with the primary geoelectric perception, but merely reflect the different growth rates of the upper and lower sides.

On the diagram in Fig. 160 (p. 382) there is round a normally growing root a negative potential gradient extending from the maximum of the extension zone to the growing point. It has been found that the gradient increases and decreases with the intensity of growth (LUNDEGÅRDH 1942). In a geotropically curving roof, however, the upper side grows more than the lower side. One can therefore expect in the former a steep potential gradient and in the latter a weak one. As Fig. 176 shows, this is actually the case. This strong local differentiation of the potential gradient opposes the hypothesis propounded by SCOTT et al. (1955), that the potential gradient is determined by local differences of salt uptake. These potentials are firmly based on the dissociation of the organic components of the cell surface (that is, of the type

$H^+ \cdot R^-$). As possible R^- groups we have referred to the nucleotides, phosphatidic acids, pectic acids and others. Other chemical differences between the upper and lower sides of geotropically curved organs have also been found, e.g. in the pH value, the catalase activity, the content of sugars and osmotically effective substances, of chromogens, etc. These results, however, have not afforded any deeper insight into the biochemical mechanism of growth.

During geotropic perception and response in roots, surface potentials behave according to the following scheme:

In the primary geoelectric perception the already existing (isotropic) potential gradient, characteristic of growth, changes in such a way that it momentarily rises on the lower side while it remains unchanged on the upper side. Thus, on the lower side, a geoelectric potential gradient is superimposed on the one already existing. As a result of the increased supply of auxin to the lower side of the growth zone, the growth there is inhibited. Thus less of the R^- substances collect there than on the upper side and the potential gradient falls again. The weakening of the geoelectric perception occurring with increasing curvature contributes to the same result.

The strength of the geotropic stimulation can be changed by variation of the acceleration (i) or of the presentation time (t). The product $i \cdot t$ is the *amount of stimulus*. In the geoelectric effect the number of ions deposited naturally increases with the acceleration (g) and the potential gradient between the primary meristem and the extension zone is increased accordingly. From the point of view of the statolith theory also, it is understandable that higher g-values exert stronger pressure on the sensitive surface layers.

It was shown in a number of early investigations that the threshold value of the gravity stimulation ('just visible reaction') is attained when the stimulation $i \cdot t$ reaches a certain size, even when i and t vary within wide limits. The value of g can easily be altered, as required, by centrifugal force. Values of g less than unity are obtained most simply by placing the organ in a more or less steeply sloping position to the vertical. If the force of gravity, in conformity with the parallelogram of forces (see Fig. 181), is split into two components, of which one operates vertically to the axis of the organ whilst the other coincides with it, only the former, of course, exerts a geotropic stimulus. This component and thereby also the intensity of the geotropic perception varies with the sine of the angle to the vertical. In stimulus-physiology one consequently speaks of a *sine law* of geotropic stimulation.

As an illustration of the law governing the amount of stimulus, one of the series of results obtained with *Avena* coleoptiles by RUTTEN-PEKELHARING (1910) may be given. The amount of stimulus necessary to attain 'just visible' reaction was determined in experiments using centrifugal forces.

Table 27

Centrifugal force (i)	Period of stimulus in seconds (t)	Amount of stimulus ($i \cdot t$)
0·08	3900	312
0·25	1300	325
1·04	310	322
3·00	100	300
10·08	31	312
41·76	7	292
58·43	5	292

This regularity is called the *product* or *reciprocity law*. Of course it does not apply under extreme conditions, since with very long periods of stimulation at low intensity, the time factors for reaction and counter-reaction are also involved. It may also be assumed that at very high accelerations perception does not increase to an unlimited extent proportionally to i. It should also be noted that with very low intensities of stimulus the time of reaction is disproportionately prolonged.

The validity of the sine law was already surmised by SACHS and was demonstrated experimentally by FITTING (1905) and RUTTEN-PEKELHARING (1910). With *Avena* coleoptiles the latter obtained the following values:

Table 28

Stimulus angle in degrees (α)	Sine of the angle α	Duration of stimulus in seconds (t)	Amount of stimulus ($t \cdot \sin \alpha$)
10	0·174	1415	246
30	0·500	540	270
45	0·707	366	259
60	0·866	326	282
90	1·000	269	269
120	0·866	332	288
150	0·500	538	269

The sine law applies also to the negative geotropism of *Coleus* shoots (LUNDEGÅRDH 1918). Shoots were stimulated alternately at 0° and 120° by means of an automatic device. The shoots remained straight if the period of stimulus was 20 minutes in the first case and 20/sin 120° minutes in the latter.

In these experiments the threshold value, that is 'just visible' reaction, was taken as criterion. LUNDEGÅRDH (1918) further investigated the relation between the amount of stimulus and reaction, when the amount of stimulus was increased above the threshold value.

The main roots of *Pisum* gave the curves reproduced in Fig. 178. The time of stimulation by gravity varied from 10 to 60 minutes and the roots were then transferred to a klinostat, which was so constructed that the movements of the roots during rotation were recorded photographically. The progress of the

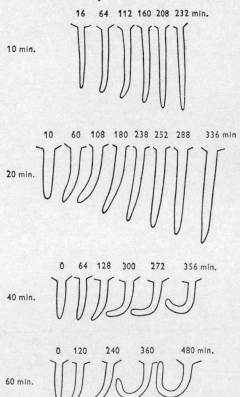

Fig. 177. Relations between duration of stimulus and intensity of the geotropic reaction of main roots of *Pisum*, cinematographically recorded after stimulation in the horizontal position on the klinostat (after LUNDEGÅRDH 1918).

movements of the root tip could then be measured with great exactness, as the angle of deviation on the recording film.

Fig. 177 shows that both the extent of curvature and the rate of reaction increase with the amount of stimulus.

With varying intensity of stimulus (g) at constant time (Fig. 179) the reaction also initially increases with rising amounts of stimulus (that is, g-minutes). If one takes as a measure of the amount of reaction that point in the curve at which the eumotorial phase passes over into the end phase (see Fig. 173), one finds that the reaction increases approximately in proportion to the amount of stimulus ($i \cdot t$) up to a value of 30 g-minutes, and then rapidly declines (Fig. 179) if the amount of stimulus is increased further.

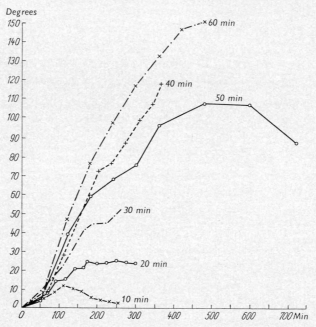

Fig. 178. The geotropic reaction of the main roots of *Pisum* with different times of stimulation (cf. Fig. 177). Recording on the klinostat (after LUNDEGÅRDH 1926).

The rate of reaction also increases with the amount of stimulus, to remain at an optimum value at about 90 g-minutes. This fact is easily explicable, since the growth movements are dependent on the capacity of the general cell metabolism and thus cannot exceed an optimal rate, even when e.g. the auxin difference between the upper and lower sides would permit it. An upper limit has also been observed for the relation between amount of stimulus and the time of reaction.

If one compares the two series in Figs. 178 and 179 the surprising fact is noted that a clear decrease of reaction beyond the optimum only occurs with higher amounts of stimulus than those obtainable with gravity alone. In the general conditions selected in these experiments it is in fact not possible to exceed the limit of about 60 g-minutes, since the reaction is clearly perceptible after an hour (Fig. 177). The experiments show that with amounts of stimulus up to about 60 g-minutes only an uncomplicated positive geotropic reaction is induced.

At higher amounts of stimulus, which can be effected only by utilising centrifugal force, a negative geotropic reaction is also induced (along with the positive), by which the actual curvature is restricted. This may be termed the *geotropic counter-reaction*.

The first indication of the negative reaction is found with pea roots after a stimulation of 40-50 *g*-minutes. It appears as a weak transient reduction of the course of curvature. With amounts of stimulus over about 90 *g*-minutes (see Fig. 179) the counter-reaction appears with increasing clarity.

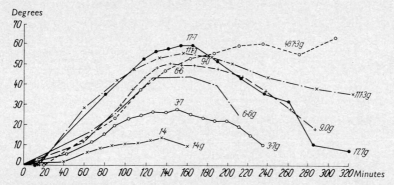

Fig. 179. Effect of the centrifugal stimulation (given as acceleration in *g*) on the development of the positive geotropic reaction of *Pisum* roots. Period of stimulus 5 minutes (after LUNDEGÅRDH 1926).

A corresponding geotropic counter-reaction, although in this case positive, is undoubtedly induced also in shoot-tips. The apparently simple orthogeotropic reaction, the downward curvature of a main root or the upward curvature of a stem tip, is thus the result of two opposite impulses, of which the counter-reaction is considerably the weaker. Under natural conditions its effect is small. In the plagiotropic lateral roots and side shoots on the other hand the geotropic counter-reaction plays a more important part. In phototropism, where the amount of stimulus can without difficulty be pushed to considerable heights, the counter-reactions may sometimes get the upper hand.

The existence of a negative geotropic reaction in the main roots was confirmed by the investigations of RUFELT (1957). He was also able to find certain differences in the sensitivity of the positive and negative reactions towards external conditions. The negative reaction is in general more sensitive, e.g. towards pH and temperature changes, and it is supposed that it is induced not by auxin but by an unknown, less stable growth substance. The negative reaction is insensitive to α-indolyl-3-isobutyric acid, but on the other hand is inhibited by α-phenylisobutyric acid.

Fig. 180. The relation between the amount of stimulus (*i.t*) and the reaction optimum with geotropic stimulation of pea roots. The gravity series (*g* constant at unity and with varying duration of stimulation; cf. Fig. 178) is shown with a dotted line. The curve of the centrifugal force series (with a constant 5 minutes duration of the stimulus and varying *g* values) is shown with a double line. The identical course of the curves illustrates the product law of stimulus (after LUNDEGÅRDH 1926).

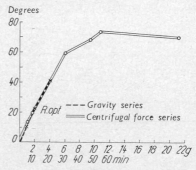

The geotropic counter-reaction can be regarded in a simplified way as the return swing of a pendulum. A chemical analogy is the phenomenon of solarisation of a photographic plate. These, however, are only superficial analogies as we do not yet know whether the growth substance necessary for the counter-reaction has anything to do biochemically with the formation or decomposition of auxin. A simple hypothetical explanation might be the gradual formation of an active decomposition product of the primary growth substance. One can also conceive of secondary effects released by the geoelectric reaction. In the geoelectric primary effect the potential of the upper side of the tip zone does indeed change to positive (Fig. 170). In this way the accumulation of acidoid materials is favoured, which gradually prepare a return to the original charge. During the full development of the geotropic reaction, as Fig. 176 shows, changes in the surface layer potential also occur, which give evidence of biochemical changes. There are thus many indications of a changed biochemistry as between the lower and upper sides of a curving root, which might be connected with the formation of secondary growth substances. One should also keep in mind that growth gradually moves the stimulated and reacting cells backwards from the tip and gradually changes their biochemistry.

4 AUTOTROPISM

The geotropic counter-reaction induced at high accelerations (in roots negative, and in shoots positive) should not be confused with the *autotropic reactions* induced after every curvature. The autotropism is induced independently of the kind of curvature. Even mechanical curvatures, according to SIMON (1912), initiate autotropic straightening. Autotropism is thus an expression of the tendency of a cylindrical organ to remain straight. Autotropism has been most thoroughly studied in connection with geotropic curvatures (LUNDEGÅRDH 1918).

A precondition for the straightening of a geotropically curved organ is, of course, that the curvature still remains in the growth zone. We see from Fig. 171 that every cross-section of a root passes through a maximum curvature and then straightens itself. With a weak induction all sections have time to react autotropically before the extension phase of the cell ends. With stronger induction the curvature in the mature part remains more or less fixed (see Fig. 177). These data refer to roots which were rotated on the klinostat after stimulation. In the normal position of the plant the induction continues until the tip of the organ has arranged itself in the direction of stimulus (Fig. 172).

Weak geotropic induction evokes only an asymmetry of the tip. Strong stimuli quickly spread basipetally and bring almost completely mature cells under their influence. In shoots, especially those of trees, the geotropic reactivity persists long after the termination of growth in length, due to the activity of the cambium. The curving of a root tip can continue after very strong stimulation for more than ten hours, in which time cells entering the extension zone from the primary meristem are induced.

The durability of the geotropic perception is therefore quite considerable; and curvatures of 180° and more can arise as residual effects on the klinostat (Fig. 177). In nature also over-curvatures occur normally, but these are eliminated by new geotropic inductions in the opposite direction until after several oscillations the equilibrium position is attained.

The *autotropic counter-reaction* in pea roots also becomes perceptible even in the tip and is thus a condition for the maintenance of the symmetrical conical form. Even in the tip, however, an autotropic reaction can be balanced out by a new one. In auto-tropism, therefore, one must assume a linking of perception and reaction just as in movements induced from outside. Side roots remain straighter on the klinostat than main roots do. It has also been found that geotropic sensitivity is higher on short roots than in long ones.

The independence of the autotropic counter-reaction is clear from the fact that it is practically independent of the intensity of the preceding geotropic stimulation. The following table shows that the autotropic reaction is about the same in spite of large variations in the preceding geotropic reaction. The movements were recorded on the klinostat:

geotropic primary reaction $20°$ $30°$ $40°$ $50°$ $60°$ $70°$ $80°$
autotropic reaction $20°$ $25°$ $20°$ $31°$ $30°$ $30°$

The reversal of the primary geotropic curvature is caused by autotropism, and there is an obvious positive correlation between the tip curvature and the straightening of the extension zone. Any form of a root or shoot tip deviating from the vertical thus induces an autotropic reaction which seeks to eliminate the deviation. The factors effective here are still unknown, but it would certainly not be wrong to assume that auxins are not directly concerned. Autotropism is related to morphogenic phenomena and to those factors which cause local differences in growth between individual cells of a tissue and even between individual zones of one and the same wall to become correlatively or 'symplastically' adjusted.

The autotropic counter-reaction of the shoots usually takes place fairly slowly. With *Coleus hybridus* a time of 1-2 weeks has been observed. The reaction is very effective, however, and with sufficiently prolonged rotation on the klinostat always ends with the complete straightening of the organ. This prolonged period of time is due partly to the considerable length of the extension zone and partly to the property, characteristic of shoots, that the ability to respond is retained long after the conclusion of normal cell extension. With roots this is not the case.

The mechanism of tropistic curvatures in mature parts of stems has not been clari-fied. In stems with secondary thickening, the cambium, as already mentioned, is still active. By differential growth the lower side can be gradually elongated. With herbaceous shoots, e.g. *Coleus*, the reaction of the mature part may be brought about by turgor differences, although a resumed cell extension in the parenchyma and collenchyma is certainly not excluded.

5 NUTATIONS. LATERAL GEOTROPISM

Not all cylindrical organs remain straight on the klinostat. The lateral roots of peas remain quite straight, whereas the main roots may show all kinds of minor curvatures. By *nutations* are understood the more or less irregular fluctuations round a median position. Normally the nutations are corrected by geotropic reactions, and this is the reason why they are so conspicuous on the klinostat. The similarity between nutations and autotropic reactions has been mentioned above, as well as the induc-tions due to shape.

Leaves also undergo nutations; well-known examples are the small leaves of

Desmodium gyrans and *Eleiotis soraria*, whose tips rotate in an ellipse. Here one speaks of *variation movements* and it is generally supposed that turgor variations are involved.

CHARLES DARWIN in his books *Climbing Plants* and *The Power of Movement in Plants* has described many nutations. *Circumnutations*, that is a rotation of the organ tip during growth, ordinarily takes place very slowly, one rotation requiring 2-24 hours. The variation movements usually take place much more quickly, e.g. the leaves of *Desmodium* and *Eleiotis* complete a rotation in about four minutes. Most of the leaves equipped with pulvini, e.g. *Oxalis*, *Trifolium* and *Phaseolus*, also show autonomous movements, which usually cannot be so easily distinguished from induced 'sleep movements'.

Nutations are not merely an expression of the unavoidable fluctuations of symplastic growth about an equilibrium position (a factor which increases the difficulty of exact measurement in stimulus physiology); they may also help to orientate the plant. We have already met a spiral tendency in root formation in the distribution of the trichoblasts and atrichoblasts. A spiral tendency in the sphere of movements expresses itself in the *cyclonasty* or circumnutation of many shoot tips. A zone of stronger growth moves gradually round the stem so that the tip describes a tight spiral. The spiral movement usually runs from right to left, i.e. counter-clockwise. Tendrils also can show active circumnutation, which aids them in seeking out supports. Powerful nutations are also shown by many seedlings; the nutations are strongest in the twining plants where, however, they are usually accompanied by geotropic inductions.

If a geotropically sensitive growth zone shows at the same time considerable circumnutation, the assumption is obvious that the spirally migrating growth zone is influenced by gravity. In circumnutation the migrating zone of accelerated growth always forms the convex side of the spiral curvature. An activity of the migrating zone increased by gravity is termed a *lateral geotropism* (cf. KONING 1933).

Laterally geotropic stems are also negatively geotropic, i.e. the tip laid horizontally curves upwards. The existence of two separate perceptions is clear from the fact that the lateral geotropism may have a shorter induction period than the negative geotropism. The reaction zones may also have different positions (ULEHLA 1920). There are thus similar relations here to those between straight growth and geotropic curvature, whose physiological characteristics also differ.

Lateral geotropism is more or less strongly developed in various twining plants. Some show outstanding autonomous cyclonasty and continue the twining on the klinostat. Their negative geotropism usually protects them in nature from twining round horizontal supports. Individual cases of such behaviour have, however, been observed. As the spiral tendency persists during the whole growth period, the older parts of the stem rotate about their axis, whereby the twists lie closer to the support. The spiral tendency has also been observed in the sporangiophores of *Phycomyces*.

6 PLAGIOGEOTROPISM AND HORIZONTAL GEOTROPISM. GEOTONIC INDUCTIONS

(a) *Orientation of Side Roots*

We have seen in Chap. 9 examples of one and the same external stimulus being able to induce several simultaneous or successive reactions. In the positively geotropic main roots a negative reaction is also induced, which with high amounts of stimulus weakens the effect of the positive reaction. In the main shoots of *Coleus*, however, no such geotropic counter-reaction has been observed. In the roots the two reactions operate in the direction of the axis, and the end result is thus a partial weakening of the primary reaction. In twining plants lateral geotropism and negative geotropism operate at different levels. The end result here is a resultant movement, in which the revolving lateral geotropism and the negative orthogeotropism are combined to produce a rising spiral movement.

The orientation of plagiotropic organs with respect to gravity likewise results from the interaction of different impulses. The two reactions also found in orthogeotropic roots, positive and negative geotropism, are here accompanied by a third induction of a tonic type, the so-called *longitudinal force*, whose direction of induction lies at 90° to that of the two first reactions.

The geotonic induction differs from the geotropic not only in its direction but also in the response. As the name indicates, the tonic stimulus does not induce an independent curvature, but merely affects the intensity of the geopositive primary reaction. The geopositive induction is strongest when the root is horizontal ($\pm 0°$ and $\pm 180°$) and becomes weaker the more it approaches the vertical position ($-90°$) (cf. Fig. 181). The geotonic induction of the roots is strongest at $-90°$, and at $\pm 0°$ becomes nil.

Thus while the geotropic induction varies with $\sin \alpha$, the geotonic 'longitudinal force' varies with $\cos \alpha$ (Fig. 181). The geopositive reaction tends to direct the root tip straight downwards. As the geotonic longitudinal force impedes this reaction and its effect becomes greater as the root tip approaches the vertical, the curvature ceases at a given angle of inclination where the two impulses are balanced. The negative geotropic induction which is well developed in lateral roots also contributes to the position of equilibrium. Three different causes (1) *positive geotropism*, (2) *negative geotropism* and (3) the *geotonic longitudinal force*, thus determine between them the angular position of side roots of the first order. This

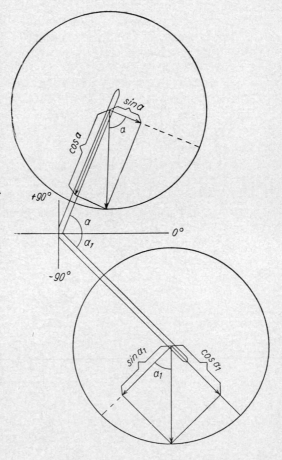

Fig. 181. Diagram to show how the effect of gravity is resolved into two components, of which one in the transverse direction varies in accordance with the sine of the angle of inclination α, and the other in the longitudinal direction varies in accordance with the cosine of the same angle. The quantitative relation between the components changes with the angle of inclination, α.

analysis of plagiogeotropism was first carried out by LUNDEGÅRDH (1917, 1918, 1926), and has later been confirmed in general by a number of workers (ZIMMERMANN, VON UBISCH, METZNER, RUFELT).

There is no fundamental difference between the reactions of main and side roots induced by gravity. The positive and negative orthogeotropic inductions are fundamentally the same for both (see also RUFELT 1957). It was shown by RISS in 1913 that the geotonic 'longitudinal force' inhibits the geopositive reaction in main roots also. The following experiments carried out with *Pisum* roots (LUNDEGÅRDH 1917, p. 18) illustrate the effect:

Table 29

Duration of the stimulus in minutes	Reaction (per cent. curved)	
	with 'longitudinal force' (placed vertically)	without 'longitudinal force' (on the klinostat)
3	—	38
5	19	60
10-12	72	81

Whereas 50% of the roots react when they are stimulated for seven minutes and then placed vertically, they require to be stimulated for only four-and-a-half minutes to attain the same effect when they are put on the klinostat after the stimulation. The 'longitudinal force' does not operate strongly enough in main roots to force these to an equilibrium position different from $-90°$. In lateral roots the geopositive reaction is weaker than the geonegative, and the 'longitudinal force' effect is much stronger.

The liminal angle of side roots of the first order varies with the external conditions (on this cf. also RUFELT 1957). Soil moisture, temperature, pH etc., exercise an influence; also correlations and age (cf. SNOW 1945). It is of special interest that the liminal angle decreases with the intensity of the geotropic stimulation (Fig. 182), since it provides an argument for assuming that the individual reactions, especially the geopositive and the geonegative, are governed by different growth substances. Even minute changes in the complex of conditions can induce considerable differences in the liminal angle which also varies with the species. The same applies to the inclination

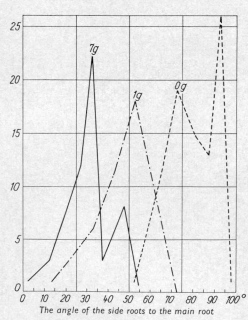

The angle of the side roots to the main root

Fig. 182. The dependence of the plagiotropic angle of inclination on the intensity of the gravitational force. Og = on the klinostat.

of side branches which, in principle, are controlled by the same reaction complex, though the signs of the individual reactions are opposite.

If the tip of the main root or shoot is cut off, the angle of inclination of the nearest root or branch diminishes. This is a correlative adjustment which does not affect side organs which are already mature, but only the embryonic primordia (LUNDEGÅRDH 1916, 1918). Even in the absence of a geotropic stimulation the side axes assume a fixed position with respect to the main axis. To demonstrate this the organs must be kept on the klinostat both while they are forming and are elongating. In the lateral roots of *Pisum* (Fig. 182) the characteristic angle varies in a two-peaked curve, with maxima at 70-75° and 90-95°. The characteristic angle is thus considerably more obtuse than under the influence of gravity, where it amounts to about 50°. The lower maximum seems to be determined by the correlative effect exercised by the main root, particularly in the younger lateral roots. Morphologically the primordia of the lateral roots are set approximately at right angles to the main axis. With the side shoots there is from the first a tendency towards an acute angle of inclination to the main axis, since the bud lies in the angle between the leaf stalk and the stem. Side shoots of *Coleus*, which have been placed on a klinostat and developed, have a characteristic angle of only 30°-45°, and the plagiotropic equilibrium position is less steep.

Where there is no main root, e.g. in grasses, all roots of the first order tend to react more or less orthotropically. The lateral roots are almost ageotropic, and the same applies to lateral roots of the second or higher order in plants which have a main root. Ecologically this state of affairs results in a suitable spread of the root system, so that the largest possible volume of soil is exploited and full use made of chemo- and hydro-tropisms.

The different reactions to gravity differ considerably both in the length of the presentation time and in the persistence of the induction. For lateral roots of the first order of *Pisum*, the positive geotropic reaction has a presentation time of about 12 minutes, whereas the presentation time of the negatively geotropic counter-reaction amounts to 2-5 hours. If lateral roots are not held in a constant position of geotropic stimulus, the geonegative reaction cannot be induced at all, on account of the inhibitory effect of the longitudinal force. In main roots the geonegative reaction never develops under the stimulation of gravity alone; it can only be induced by centrifugal force.

Increasing the centrifugal force shortens the presentation time, as has been mentioned above (cf. Fig. 178). The positive and negative reactions behave differently, and with an increasing g the positive at first increases more strongly than the negative. Not only is the presentation time of the negative reaction often longer than that of the positive, but the reaction time is much longer also. As the tonic effect of the longitudinal force dies away very quickly, a lateral root which is taken from its equilibrium position and placed on a klinostat produces first a positive geotropic curvature, then an autotropic straightening and finally a negative geotropic curvature.

A main root taken away from its normal vertical position, on the other hand, shows no geotropic reactions on the klinostat. Its normal vertical position, unlike that of lateral roots, is in fact stimulus-free. The normal equilibrium position of lateral roots is dynamic. The stimulus impulses interacting at equilibrium become evident only when the object is transferred to the klinostat.

If a lateral root is moved from its plagiotropic equilibrium position into the vertical it receives no new geotropic impulse, but for this very reason the residual effect of the impulses received in the normal position can become evident. Because the longitudinal force now has its maximum effect, the geopositive curvature is suppressed and after a time the geonegative curvature becomes evident. Because of this, lateral roots placed vertically curve slowly upwards (in the opposite direction to the geopositive reaction), until they reach their former equilibrium position (Fig. 183).

Fig. 183. Curvatures of the side roots of *Pisum* after the main root has been placed at an angle of 45°

The lateral roots on the opposite side of the main root are brought in this experiment almost into the horizontal position and bend themselves downwards by positive geotropism, until they attain their earlier equilibrium position (Fig. 183). The longitudinal force shows a very rapid decline and reveals its full effect only with continuous stimulation. The final ecological result, i.e. the spread of the root system in space, is thus attained in different ways, thanks to the unique nature of the three interacting impulses due to gravity.

The effect of the geotonic longitudinal force finds expression, as explained above, in an inhibition of geotropic reaction, and not of geotropic induction, since the geotropic reaction becomes evident on removal of the longitudinal force effect. The inhibition of response by the longitudinal force occurs in roots only in the lower quadrants with a maximum at $-90°$. If the root is directed upwards, instead of an inhibition an acceleration of the geotropic reaction occurs. Instead of a deceleration, as in the lower quadrants, there is thus an acceleration in the upper quadrants. A root which, after geotropic stimulation, is directed upwards $(+90°)$, consequently curves more quickly than it would on the klinostat after an equal amount of stimulation. This fact has a certain interest with regard to the validity of the sine law. Exact measurement of the reaction shows that the sine law is only approximately correct. If, for example, the root is stimulated alternately at $+45°$ (or $+135°$) and $\pm0°$, and the times are chosen according to the sine law, it is found with exact observation that the reaction induced in the former positions exceeds the one induced at 0°. The deviations from the sine law are particularly apparent when the reaction follows rapidly after the stimulation. Because the longitudinal force quickly dies away, its effect, with intermittent stimulation in the positions named, becomes small if the reaction time is long in comparison with the presentation time. This often happens, for example, with side shoots. The varied effects of the geotonic longitudinal force may be regarded as an axial polarisation of a symmetrical organ.

(b) *Orientation of Side Shoots*

The orientations of aerial shoots under gravity are in principle determined by a similar joint effect of three elementary reactions, as in roots. In the plagiogeotropic side shoots of *Coleus hybridus* a *geonegative primary reaction* is induced with a presentation time of less than half an hour and a reaction time of about an hour. This reaction is well shown if the plants are first removed from the geotropic stimulation by a lengthy rotation on the klinostat (14 days or more). A short geotropic induction then allows the corresponding negative reaction to become evident on the klinostat. The negative geotropic reaction was observed in side shoots by BARENETZKY as early as 1901.

A *geotropic counter-reaction* is induced in side shoots as in side roots, but not in main stems. In the side shoots it is positive. It has a much longer presentation time (1-2 days) and reaction time than the geonegative primary reaction. It may take up to two weeks on the klinostat before the positive reaction dies away. The relations are thus fundamentally similar to those in plagiotropic side roots, although the signs of the individual reactions are inverted. The geotropic counter-reaction is also much stronger in side shoots. In *Coleus* the geonegative primary reaction dies away about six times faster than the geopositive counter-reaction, so that the after-effect of the primary reaction disappears rapidly on the klinostat (Fig. 184).

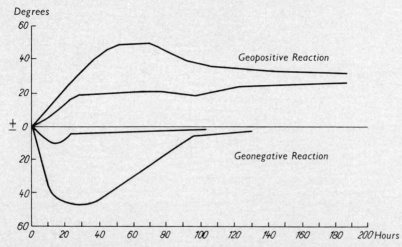

Fig. 184. The negative and positive geotropic reactions of the plagiotropic side shoots of *Coleus*. The plants have been made as far as possible stimulus-free before the experiment by a lengthy rotation on the klinostat. After stimulation for one hour in the horizontal position the plant was put back on the klinostat and automatically recorded there. The geonegative reaction developed in the course of a few hours, reached its maximum and then autotropically declined. The geopositive reaction has a presentation time of many hours, and develops if the plant is brought from the normal plagiotropic position on to the klinostat. This geopositive reaction also declines much more slowly and much less completely than the geonegative one (after LUNDEGÅRDH 1918).

The geotonic effects of the longitudinal force also appear in side shoots. An inhibition of the geonegative primary reaction makes itself felt when a side shoot stimulated in the horizontal position curves upwards, but the inhibition of the upward curvature is weaker than the corresponding tonic reaction in roots. This is seen from the fact that the stimulated side shoot at first places itself almost vertically. It only sinks gradually into the inclined plagiotropic position, because the geopositive counter-reaction comes into play. The plagiotropic equilibrium position is thus determined in side shoots to a greater degree than in side roots by the resultant effect between the two opposite geotropic reactions. Nevertheless, the geotonic effect is by no means absent from shoots.

2F

In the converse position (in the lower quadrants of Fig. 169) the longitudinal force makes itself perceptible. The shoots react, like roots, isotropically (radially), as is seen from the fact that the same plagiotropic equilibrium position is reached whether the plant is placed upside down or with the main shoot horizontal. In the latter position the geopositive reaction which dies away very slowly interacts with the newly induced reactions in such a way that the equilibrium position is moved sideways.

The various geotropic positions of the shoots of a *Coleus* plant are illustrated in Fig. 185. It is seen that in the positions between the normal and $+90°$ a convex curvature (away from the main shoot) arises. This is due to the fact that with any alteration of the reactions equilibrated at the normal position, the geonegative

Fig. 185. Orientation movements of the shoots of *Coleus hybridus*. The plant is inclined at 45°, at which the main shoot curves orthogeotropically upwards. The lateral shoots on the upper side show positive geotropic curvature outwards (geonastic supplementary effect). The shoots on the lower side have a negative geotropic curvature upwards (new induction) (after LUNDEGÅRDH 1918).

reaction, which would cause a curvature towards the stem, dies away much more quickly than the geopositive. In the two left quadrants (Fig. 169, +90° through ± 180° to −90°) the after-effect of a geopositive reaction works in unison with a newly induced geonegative reaction.

A number of herbaceous plants behave in the same way as *Coleus*. In some, e.g. *Tradescantia*, a morphotropic effect seems to co-operate with the geotropic reactions.

The *orientation movements of trees* afford examples of interactions between morphotropic effects (which we have already met in young side roots) and autotropism (rectipetality i.e., the tendency of cylindrical organs to straighten). These two directional impulses can to some extent replace the gravitational reactions. The side shoots of trees undergo developmental modifications of response much more extensively than the shoots of *Coleus*. Young shoots of beech, spruce and other trees are almost ageotropic and hang down more or less slackly. Later, the beech shoots straighten themselves autotropically and develop a weak negative geotropic sensitivity. The capacity for geotropic orientation is then shown by the shoots sprouting on branches previously rotated through 180° twisting and turning in such a way that the leaves come into the proper position. Beech shoots are also affected by gravity by its determining the orientation of the plane of symmetry of their bilateral growing points. The point of attachment of the leaf is always on the under side of the shoot.

During the development of spruces and pines the extensive reversals of the geotropic reaction of the side shoots can be studied. The upper side shoots of the first order in the spuce at first curve strongly downwards, more or less passively under their own weight. Soon, however, geotropic sensitivity is developed and both a negative and a positive geotropic induction can be observed, which together determine the equilibrium position. MÜNCH (1938) called this response *epinasty* (see below). Geotonic inductions appear to play only a minor part in spruce shoots. As may be seen from Fig. 186, the plagiotropic side shoots curve, in the main, like those of *Coleus*, although in the spruce the geopositive induction so preponderates that the lower shoots do not regain their earlier equilibrium position. The geotropic reaction of the main shoot is entirely negative. At the end of the growth period the capacity for geotropic reaction is lost, and only the autotropism remains.

As mentioned earlier, spruce trunks retain a limited geotropic sensitivity for several years, as was early observed by SACHS (Fig. 187). According to MÜNCH (1939), the geotropic erection of the side branches of conifers may be due to increased formation of wood on the under side, whereas with deciduous trees the upper side is shortened. In both cases of course the cambium is active. The influence of auxin on the activity of the cambium has been emphasised already. Other hormones also may co-operate, according to SÖDING (1940), especially cell division hormones.

The young side shoots of the pine are geotropically strongly negative; but an epinastic reaction also appears on the klinostat, which together with the autotropism finally determines the plagiotropic position. During the straightening geotropic sensitivity decreases.

Changes of geotropic sensitivity often occur in flower stalks or inflorescence stalks. The downward-curved stalks of certain varieties of tulip, which become negatively geotropic and raise themselves up during the ripening of the fruits, are well known. A typical example of a reversal occurring several times during development is given by *Calandrinia grandiflora* (BORRIS and BUSSMAN 1939). The young infloresence is at first curved downwards, then becomes erected, when even the individual flower stalks,

Fig. 186. Orientation movements of the young shoots of spruce, after they have developed geotropic sensitivity (after LUNDEGÅRDH 1916).

Fig. 187. Negatively geotropic upward curvature of the tips of a felled spruce (after LUNDEGÅRDH 1916).

which have basal pulvini, show a negative geotropic response. After fertilisation the flowers again bend vertically downwards, to become erect again when the seed ripens. It has been shown that these movements are connected with variations in the auxin content.

The correlative modification of the plagiotropism of the side shoots in spruce and pine is distinguishable only after a year and affects the position of the buds (LUNDE-GÅRDH 1916, pp. 14 ff.). The down-curved and rolled conditions of young tree shoots and inflorescence stalks may be due to morphotropic epinasty, i.e. the morphologically upper side keeps growing somewhat more strongly than the lower side, independently of the direction in which gravity has its effect. In other cases, e.g. in *Dryopteris*, the growing leaf tip is rolled up hyponastically, that is, the morphologically lower side grows the more strongly.

In these phenomena the differential rates of growth are regulated by internal factors. It is known that most anatomical and morphological differentiations are independent of external regulating forces. In only relatively few cases have purely geo- or photo-effects on development been studied in detail. The effects due to external causes seem to be mostly tonic stimulations or slow counter-reactions. The few known effects of gravity on form are strongly reminiscent of geotropic counter-reactions with very slow presentation and reaction times. The induction of dorsiventrality in *Marchantia* is extended over 10-20 hours according to DACHNOWSKI, or over 6 hours according to FITTING (1936). This presentation time is in fact shorter than that of the geotropic counter-reaction in *Coleus*. The dorsiventrality of *Marchantia* and beech shoots (see above), remains fixed, which however may be compared with a prolongation of the geotropic secondary reaction. In shoots this dies away very slowly and in trees can survive the whole period of growth, even if the apical bud has already been removed in the spring. Only in the following year does one see the result of the correlation of the buds (LUNDEGÅRDH 1916).

Correlative determination can thus be effective only if a true primary meristem is present, i.e. in bud primordia. In tree shoots the geotropic orientation is thus determined in those buds which open only in the following year, whereas the current year's growth tenaciously retains the determination which it received in its own primordium. The positive geotropic induction, which an emerging side shoot of a herbaceous stem receives, can also be fixed for a long time—months, perhaps years. This is observed in cuttings of side shoots. Although they develop morphologically into new main stems, they tend to retain for a long time their earlier geopositive (epinastic) induction, and consequently curve on the klinostat. There even seems to be a transfer of stimulus to the developing growing point from below. There are thus all transitions between short-duration geotropic movements, tenaciously retained epinasties (that is, geotropic secondary reactions) and fixed effects on form. The last sometimes seem to be accompanied by pressure or tension effects, e.g. in the asymmetric formation of the wood of side branches (PRIESTLEY and TONG 1927).

The plagiotropic orientations due to external factors have an important influence on the suitable shaping of the plant. In this they co-operate with morphotropic stimuli from within. We have already emphasised the importance of plagiotropism in the spreading of the root and shoot systems in space. Geotonic phenomena and gravitational effects on form also play a part. For example, the side shoots springing from the upper side of plagiotropic twigs grow more quickly than those on the lower side (Fig. 188). If the twigs are bent over, as seen in Fig. 188, the morphotropic factors (cf. LUNDEGÅRDH 1913) can supplement the geotonic induction. Side roots also do best on the outer side of convexly bent main roots. How the distribution of growth substances in mechanically curved organs behaves is still unknown. Otherwise it appears, according to JACOBS and MORROW (1957), that there is a complete correlation between xylem formation and auxin concentration.

Fig. 188. Unequal development of side shoots on the lower and upper sides of *Rosa canina* (after LUNDEGÅRDH 1916).

Light also has a regulating effect on the rate of growth (Chap. 9) and also a tonic effect on the plagiotropic liminal angle, which generally becomes more acute, as the light intensity diminishes, both in lateral shoots and in roots. This photo-adjustment contributes to the broom- or funnel-shaped habit of deciduous trees growing in deep shade. In this connection the prostrate (creeping) habit of growth of many plants on waste places, e.g. *Polygonum aviculare*, and sea-shores may be mentioned. There well-illuminated shoots grow almost diageotropically, but in the shade they are negatively geotropic and turn upwards. This phenomenon can easily be observed in *Rubus, Fragaria, Glechoma*, etc. Temperature changes can also modify the geotropic orientation, e.g. in *Lamium purpureum* and *Lysimachia nummularia*.

(c) Transverse Geotropism

Many runners and also the rhizomes of *Triticum repens, Carex arenaria, Agrostis stolonifera, Anemone nemorosa, Polygonatum*, etc., are transversely geotropic, or diageotropic. Leaves, e.g. those of beech, and flowers such as those of *Amaryllis* also show the same reaction. Transverse geotropism may be considered a limiting case of plagiotropism, in which the geotropic liminal angle reaches 90°. In these organs, as in the plagiotropic, geotropically positive (epinastic) reactions have been observed after changes of position. A geonegative reaction also seems to occur, which may maintain the balance with the positive.

The diageotropism of the rhizome of *Polygonatum*, according to CLAPHAM (1945), is due to a balance between negative geotropism and a dorsoconvex (epinastic) curvature, which according to him may be transferred from the illuminated base of the shoot to the rhizome. Any tonic effects of the 'longitudinal force' must play a more subordinate part. It is indeed difficult to understand how such longitudinal force effects could result in an equilibrium position at $\pm 0°$.

SACHS (1887) believed that a diageotropic organ was composed of a number of transversely placed orthogeotropic elements. This idea is, however, refuted by the fact that diageotropic and plagiotropic organs react anisotropically in different quadrants. It can thus scarcely be doubted that a balance between positive and negative reactions to gravity determines the reaction of the diageotropic organ. One may also assume hypothetically that the force of gravity induces a physiological dorsiventrality, which finds expression as a kind of 'geopolarity' of a type similar to tonic induction. Complicated hypothetical ideas about diageotropic equilibrium in rhizomes of *Aegopodium podagraria* have been developed by BENNET-CLARK and BALL (1951).

In diageotropic leaves there is indeed a pronounced morphological dorsiventrality, and here it might well be more suitable to apply SACH's idea. One could, for example, regard the palisade cells as vertical stimulus perceptors. Some leaves and leaf stalks, including those of *Liriodendron tulipifera*, are insensitive both to gravity and to light, and their orientation consequently comes about entirely autotropically or morphotropically. Most leaves react phototropically, and geotropic reactions are rarer. Beech leaves, however, are among those which are insensitive to light and oriented exclusively by gravity with some autotropism (LUNDEGÅRDH 1916).

Young beech leaves curve epinastically. Here, however, a supplementary effect of a geopositive induction received in the bud primordium may possibly be concerned. They are also governed by an autonomic factor which leads to the leaf system of a twig being spread out like a fan. Only towards the end of the extension period does one note in shaded leaves a clear diageotropic reaction. This collaborates with the epinasty and, after any necessary curvatures and torsions of the leaf stalk, the leaf shoot is finally fixed in the horizontal position. With stronger illumination, e.g. in the crown, the diageotropic sensitivity disappears and the spread assumes a more or less inclined position. Data on the geotropic movements of *Tropaeolum* leaves may be found in BRAUNER and VARDER (1950). GESSNER and WEINFURTER (1952) have investigated the reactions of *Nymphaea* leaves.

7 SUMMARY OF THE MECHANISM OF GRAVITY INDUCTIONS

The discovery of the auxins has brought a revolution in the methods of investigation. Whereas formerly stimulus phenomena were analysed according to the succession: perception—transmission—reaction, so that a number of complicated movements could be referred to the interaction of a few separate stimulus effects, the auxin researchers usually restrict themselves to the simple reaction effect, i.e. whether a movement can be referred to the supply or distribution of auxin. In spite of the impressive advances of auxin research one must, however, regret that, in their endeavours to simplify they often neglected earlier results of stimulus physiology. As may be seen from Chap. 9, very important questions are still unsolved, such as the conditions and methods of activation and inactivation of the auxins, the biochemical relations between auxins and antiauxins, and the occurrence of inhibitors as inter-mediaries of movements. Even concerning the transmission of stimulus, which actually gave the first impetus to auxin research, opinions are still divided.

The view was put forward by WENT, CHOLODNY, BOYSEN-JENSEN and others that tropistic curvatures are due to an unequal distribution of auxin in cylindrical organs. Together with the discovery of the geoelectric effect and the occurrence of electric currents in irritable organs which could collaborate in auxin transmission, it forms the basis for an auxin-transmission theory which cannot be dismissed out of hand from any discussion of tropistic movements.

There are, however, facts which suggest a more direct effect of the primary geotropic induction on the state of the growth substances in the stimulated organ. The geo-electric effect has to be considered not only from the point of view of electrophoretic auxin transmission, but also as a measurable indication of a separation or reorienta-tion of biochemically active ions caused by gravity. The biochemical separation and the resulting chemical processes would, from this point of view, be the primary stages in geotropic perception. Such a 'geopolarisation' of the cells is highly probable as the actual cause of differential changes in growth, permeability, etc., on the upper and lower sides. A polarisation, in which surface layer potentials also take part, will alter the electrical impedance and the ohmic resistance of the tissue as well. Geo-polarisation may thus differentiate speeds of auxin transport, but the movement of all other ionised substances will be involved similarly, e.g. the diffusion of salt ions through the tissue. Geopolarisation would evoke a state reminiscent of morphological polarity, but considerably more easily reversible.

Assuming a geopolarisation also provides a possibility of explaining the geotonic phenomena. The fact that the tip of a root or stem grows at different rates in the two vertical positions, $+90°$ and $-90°$, may be due to the diametrically opposed geo-polarisation of the transverse walls of the cell reticulum. The geoelectric effect must work in such a way that ions, e.g. of auxin, diffusing or translocated in other ways, migrate in one direction more quickly than in the opposite.

Geopolarisation could also explain the peculiar fact that the longitudinal force occurring in side roots among other places does not inhibit or favour geotropic perception, but only the reaction. Orthogeotropic induction, as we learned above, evokes a strong geoelectric effect in the primary meristem, which contributes to an increased auxin supply to the lower side. The geoelectric effect also causes a transverse polarisation of the whole organ, which may cause local biochemical differences between the lower and upper sides. The transverse cell walls are, of course, not polar-ised in the horizontal position, the position of maximal geotropic stimulus of the organ. The more the organ departs from the horizontal position, the more the trans-verse walls are subjected to a geopolarisation, at the same time that the polarisation of the longitudinal walls decreases. The geopolarisation of the transverse walls reaches its maximum value in the vertical position of the organ; and from this follows the acceleration of retardation of auxin translocation discussed above.

In the above discussion of the stimulations due to gravity, hard and fast conclusions on particular questions have been avoided. As long as such fundamental matters as the relations between auxins, auxin synergists, antiauxins and inhibitors remain uncertain, one cannot proceed far with the analysis of the facts described. The import-ance of the observations on the adjustments to auxin concentration, i.e. the shifts in the position of the optimum, is also uncertain.

The physiological analysis of geotropism reveals three effects occurring simultaneously or successively: (1) the geotropic primary reaction, (2) the geotropic secondary or counter-reaction, and (3) the geotonic effect. Both presentation times and reaction times are very variable in the two geotropic reactions. The dying away of the reaction is also very variable and, in the counter-reaction, may be so long drawn out that it persists as a fixed epi- or hypo-nasty. The geotonic longitudinal force dies out very quickly.

Of special interest for the study of the geotropic primary reactions is the periodic course of the die-away curve. Figures 189 and 190 reproduce two series of experiments with main and side roots of *Pisum*. It is seen that, when the first reaction dies out, it is followed by second, third, etc., reaction periods with diminishing amplitude. One can scarcely imagine that the geotropic primary reaction still persists after the first period; autotropic inductions and over-curvatures, which only gradually end in an equilibrium position, are certainly involved. The strikingly constant length of the periods is thus an expression of the reaction and die-away times of the autotropic movement.

That an autoperiodic oscillation arises after the initial externally stimulated reaction is, of course, due to the stimulus and reaction occupying different times and to the stimulus dying away earlier than the reaction. In autotropism the presence of a curvature acts as stimulus to a counter-curvature, while the original stimulus dies away. The over-curvature gives a new autotropic stimulus in the opposite direction, and so on. This type of reaction is general in stimulus-physiology and can also be illustrated by intermittent external stimulations, e.g. in the fluctuating movements of a growing point before attaining the geotropic equilibrium position. The oscillations here are more regular. In autotropism the reaction itself provides the next stimulus, and the oscillations are less regular.

A requirement for the formation of fluctuating movements is thus a definite difference of phase between two antagonistically operating stimuli. If the effects of two opposed stimuli are simultaneous, damping occurs without oscillations. Such dampings are observed e.g. in the interaction of the primary reaction and the counter-reaction (Fig. 179). The requirements for the formation of fluctuations are, however, always

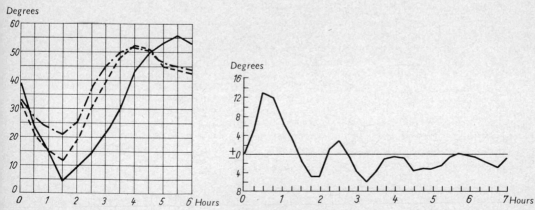

Fig. 189. Periodic oscillations of three main roots of *Pisum* which were first geotropically stimulated for five minutes and then automatically recorded on the klinostat. The primary geopositive reaction occupies $1\frac{1}{2}$ hours and the first counter-reaction about 3 hours (after LUNDEGÅRDH 1926).

Fig. 190. Periodic oscillations after geotropic stimulation of a side root of *Pisum* for 30 minutes. The root was then observed at 90° (after LUNDEGÅRDH 1926).

afforded by the interaction of reactions with very different presentation and reaction times. In phototropism there are interesting damped oscillations, caused by the interplay of antagonistic photoreactions.

C. Phototropism

The movements caused by light, together with the effects of gravity, provide the plant with a suitable orientation of its parts in the surroundings. The unalterable force of gravity determines the main structural lines—the upward thrust of the stem, the downward penetration of the roots and the spread of the side branches and lateral roots. Light, on the other hand, is variable in its direction and intensity, and the phototropic movements appear as deviations from the strict geotropic scheme, but deviations which provide a better utilisation of the light. For the scientific study of movements in response to a stimulus, phototropism offers the advantages that the plant can easily be kept in a stimulus-free initial state and that both direction and intensity of the stimulus can be varied without difficulty.

1 THE PHOTOTROPIC STIMULUS—REACTION CHAIN

The mechanism of phototropic reaction is in principle the same as in geotropism. Usually a single organ reacts both geo- and phototropically, e.g. grass coleoptiles and shoot tips, and according to FITTING a reaction may result from the summation of sub-threshold light and gravity impulses. Some roots, e.g. those of *Sinapis arvensis* (Fig. 191; GUTTENBERG 1941) also show both geo- and phototropic sensitivity.

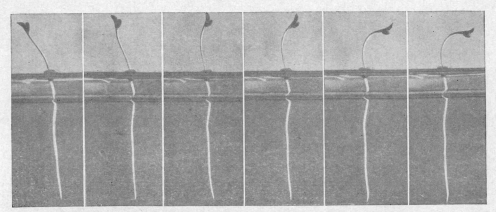

Fig. 191. Phototropic reactions of a seedling of *Sinapis arvensis* which was illuminated from the right. There is a positive reaction of the hypocotyl, and a negative reaction of the root.

Where perception is localised in a special part or zone of the organ, the perception zone is usually the same for both kinds of stimulus. As the primary stimuli are very different and certainly influence the protoplasm in quite different ways, one must assume that only the stages following the perception, that is transmission and reaction, follow identical courses.

In terms of auxin research it is thought that the light arriving from one side either directly influences the production or activation of growth substance in the zone of movement, or alternatively that the free auxin in the perception organ is caused to flow in greater amount to the shaded side than to the illuminated. One can also imagine, of course, that the speed of migration of the auxin is differentiated on the way.

The assumption of a redistribution of the free auxin caused by unilateral illumination was put forward first by CHOLODNY and later by WENT and is accepted by many later workers (e.g. GUTTENBERG 1941; cf. AUDUS 1953). The fundamental fact that an unequal distribution of the auxin evokes a curvature, was shown by pioneer researches in which e.g. an excised coleoptile tip was placed asymmetrically on the stump. The decapitated coleoptile then curves away from the side on which the tip is placed.

The assumption of a redistribution of freely migrating auxin in the reaction zone is less probable. By analogy with geopolarisation there might be a polarisation of auxin in light perception, such that the mobile auxin is shifted towards the shaded side. Ideas about a photopolarity recognisable by potential differences have been developed by SCHRANK (1946, 1950, 1953), BACKUS and SCHRANK (1952) and others.

According to a theory propounded by BLAAUW, the phototropic reaction can be conceived of as a differentiated light growth-reaction (cf. p. 399), i.e. the light may influence the production or activation of the auxin directly. BLAAUW believed that the phototropic induction depends, not on the direction of the light, but only on the amount of light perceived. According to him the reaction arises exclusively because of the difference of illumination between the front and rear sides of an organ, and does not depend on the direction. The phototropic curvature would thus be the result of the separate light growth-reactions of the two sides.

DE CANDOLLE (1832) had already put forward the idea that the positive phototropic curvature was caused by the increased extension of the more weakly illuminated side, that is from a kind of partial etiolation. OPPENOORTH (1941), however, showed that the general lowering of the auxin content of the growing point which determines a negative light growth-reaction follows directly on illumination and to the same extent on both the light and shaded sides. The photo-inactivation of auxin (cf. p. 376), which occurs with unilateral illumination, is distributed evenly over the perception zone. The inactivation may possibly have some connection with the formation of a lumi-auxin lactone or the like. GUTTENBERG and ZETSCHE (1956) found no direct effects of light on the formation of auxin, but an indirect effect through photosynthetic products. On the other hand, they found an influence of light on auxin translocation.

The unequal distribution of auxin on the light and shaded sides becomes noticeable only some time after illumination, and according to OPPENOORTH, in *Avena* coleoptiles it reaches its maximum only after 1-2 hours, when the speed of curvature is at its greatest. It seems, therefore, that one must separate the light growth-reaction from the phototropic reaction. The former signifies a general photo-activation or inactivation of the auxin. The latter seems to be due to a transverse *photopolarisation*, which causes a lateral displacement of the growth-substance towards the shaded side (cf. e.g. BRAUNER 1955; BÜNNING *et al.* 1956 on the other hand found no support for assuming a lateral displacement of the auxin).

It is not yet clear whether inactivation of auxin plays a part in positive phototropism. The investigations of OPPENOORTH (1941) and others showed that the so-called second phototropic reaction (see below) operates with an anomalous mechanism. Some experiments showing that the light growth-reaction has a different light optimum from that of phototropism support the duality of the light effect (LUNDEGÅRDH 1922;

Fig. 192). It would not be far wrong to assume provisionally that the light growth-reaction participates to a certain extent in phototropism, but that displacement due to polarisation of the perception organ constitutes the essential factor.

Although auxin research has been more concerned with phototropism than with geotropism, even in phototropism the quantitative relations between the auxin concentrations of the two sides and the simultaneous intensity of reaction are not entirely clear. It must be borne in mind that methods of determination are still inadequate. OPPENOORTH (1941), who followed the whole course of the reaction with determinations of auxin, found however positive proofs of the existence of such a relation.

It is surprising that the sum of the amounts of auxin on the shaded and light sides is usually smaller than that in straight-growing controls (BURKHOLDER and JOHNSTON 1937). In assessing these data one must consider that, as mentioned above, a general light-growth reaction occurs even with unilateral illumination (Fig. 192). This may be referred to the observed changes of the total amount of active auxin (Fig. 193). In the *Avena* coleoptile the average growth decreases after unilateral light stimulation. A minimum occurs at about 190 lux-seconds, and the curve then rises again (SIERP 1921, LUNDEGÅRDH 1921, 1922). The positive phototrophic reaction, on the other hand, reaches its maximum at 50 lux-seconds and changes over much sooner than the light growth-reaction into a negative reaction. These results thus early led to the important conclusion that the general light growth-reaction and phototropism were partly due to separate light perceptions.

The chemico-physical nature of light perception has so far not been investigated at all. One may suppose that, at least in the light growth-reaction (cf. p. 339), photo-chemical processes are involved. In Chapter 9 we referred to the light-sensitive

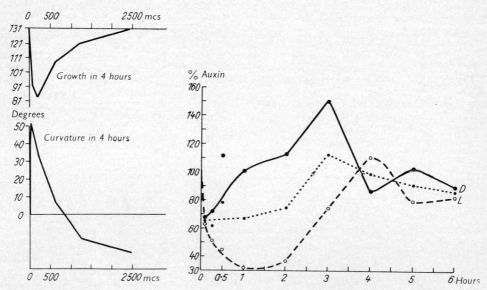

Fig. 192. Light growth-reaction (above) and phototropic reaction (below) of *Avena* coleoptiles after stimulation with amounts of light between 3 and 2500 lux-seconds (after LUNDEGÅRDH 1922).

Fig. 193. Changes in the auxin content of the illuminated (*L*) and the unilluminated (*D*) side of a coleoptile after exposure to 500 lux-seconds from a mercury lamp. The dotted curve shows the average auxin content (after OPPENOORTH 1941).

reaction between active and inactive auxin, that is auxin-a-lactone→lumiauxin-a-lactone in combination with the reversible equilibrium auxin-a⇌auxin-a-lactone. These data refer to the auxin of KÖGL, about whose distribution in plants little is known. Later GALSTON (1950) found a strong sensitising effect of riboflavin on the photolysis of β-indolylacetic acid (IAA). REINERT (1953) also assumes that the light growth-reaction is responsible for the phototropic curvature in BLAAUW's sense and that riboflavin, not carotene, acts as a sensitiser. It should not be overlooked, however, that there are also data which indicate a light polarisation at the growing point. This could arise e.g. by photodissociation of asymmetrically constructed molecules, which then arrange themselves in the direction of illumination. Photoelectric effects could also arise by accumulation of photosensitive ions at the boundary layer membranes. Effects of light on membranes have been found by potential measurements (SCHRANK) and by measurements of permeability (TRÖNDLE, BRAUNER, DILLEWIJN et al.). The changes of potential at cell surfaces due to light remind one strongly of the geo-electric phenomenon. As with geotropism, one must be cautious in applying the hypothesis of electrophoretic redistribution of the auxin flowing down from the growing point. A photopolarisation could also act by local changes of rate of auxin formation or activation, in the same way as was discussed in relation to the mechanism of gravity perception.

The question of the nature of the photosensitisers has also not been finally settled. The hypothesis put forward by BÜNNING (1937, 1939), that carotene might be the sensitiser, seems to have to give way more and more to the view that riboflavin fulfils this function, though carotene may have some protective effect (REINERT 1953). It is in any case certain that the spectral sensitivity of the phototropic objects suggests the collaboration of yellow pigments (Fig. 195). An interesting case is the sporangiophore of *Pilobolus kleinii*, in which the pigments lie at a point on which the rays of light are focussed (Fig. 194). This example illustrates the importance of form (the lens effect) and transparency for the direction of the light rays inside an organ. Even in the absence of sensitisers the protoplasm may possess some light sensitivity, which e.g. could suffice for the weak phototropic perception at the base of the *Avena* coleoptile (HAIG 1935) although pigments are not entirely lacking there. BAUERJI et al. (1946) state that in *Chlamydomonas* both motility and sex determination are governed by the carotinoid protocrocin. Chlorophyll has been stated to be the sensitiser in leaves (cf. BÜNNING 1939).

The mechanism of phototropic movement in the light-sensitive fungi, e.g. *Pilobolus* and *Phycomyces*, consists of an unequal stretching of the wall as a result of changes in elasticity. With a positive reaction the membrane is more strongly stretched on the shaded side. The curvature decreases on plasmolysis.

Changes in the elasticity of the wall may have an effect in higher plants also. The first indication of a reaction in *Avena* coleoptiles is in fact an asymmetry of the tip. Later the reaction spreads to the final stages of cell extension. As in geotropism, biochemical differences between the upper and lower sides of a curvature are observed,

Fig. 194. The course of light rays in the sporangiophore of *Pilobolus kleinii* on illumination obliquely from above. The pigments at the base, due to the lens effect, are illuminated more strongly on the shaded side (after VAN DER WEY).

in the intensity of respiration, sugar content, pH, surface potential (Fig. 196), etc. These effects show that the stimulus directly or indirectly affects the whole biochemical working of the cell.

Phototropism offers excellent opportunities for determining the distribution of sensitivity to the stimulus in the organ, and the *Avena* coleoptile has been investigated in special detail. Some results of an investigation by LANGE (1929) are given below (the values are in relation to the sensitivity 1 mm from the tip):

Table 30

Distance from the coleoptile tip (in mm)	Relative phototropic sensitivity
0—0·1	81·5
0·1—0·2	71·7
0·2—0·3	52·0
0·3—0·4	43·3
0·4—0·5	22·1
0·5—0·6	9·3
0·6—0·7	4·8
0·7—0·8	2·3
0·8—0·9	2·5
0·9—1·0	1·0

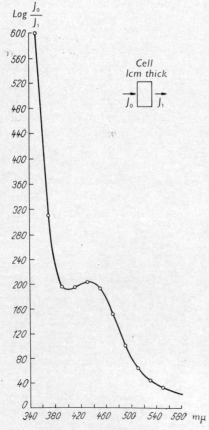

The maximal sensitivity may lie, according to these results, in a few epidermal cells of the coleoptile tip, a fact which undoubtedly supports the idea of a light-polarisation as the primary induction of phototropic stimulus. The correlative ('symplastic') nature of auxin production in the tip region follows from the interesting observation that, if the tip is cut off, the cells lying under the wound gradually take over auxin production and a 'physiological coleoptile tip' is regenerated. There is, however, no morphological regeneration of the tip.

We have discussed above the views developed by various workers on the mechanism of the phototropic stimulus-reaction chain, but we found that at present it is scarcely possible to set up a general scheme that will cover all the observations. This is, however, likely to be lacking when some workers are so keen to defend only one of the possible theories. Thus BLAAUW's theory, according to which all phototropic curvatures are only modified light growth-reactions, is opposed to the theory of WENT and CHOLODNY of a photopolarisation in the zone of perception. It may well be

Fig. 195. Absorption spectrum of the acetone extract of the tip (3 mm) of *Avena* coleoptiles (after OPPENOORTH 1941).

that both types of reaction act together. Such an interpretation could help to explain the optimum curve of the primary reaction and the onset of a phototropic counter-reaction. For example, with weak light, and especially in the region of the positive primary reaction, a photopolarisation might be involved, whereas with stronger stimulation, and in the region of the counter-reaction, a secondary auxin inactivation might be conceivable. From our knowledge of growth substances, we must stress the importance of separating pure auxin effects from the effect of inhibitors, etc.; but this cannot be done at present.

Several workers have attempted to illuminate a coleoptile tip unilaterally with a narrow beam of light in such a way that the light direction can be varied. One can, for example, illuminate the tip from above tangentially. In this case the light gradient is at right angles to the light direction (one side illuminated and the opposite one dark). Such experiments have been varied in different ways, but the results obtained are not always unequivocal, on account of the difficulty of determining the direction of the light rays in a multicellular organ, in which the scattering of the light has to be taken into account. Numerous experiments of DARWIN, VON GUTTENBERG, BUDER *et al.* seem to support BLAAUW's theory.

LUNDEGÅRDH (1922) investigated the effect of the following variations of illumination. Coleoptile tips were illuminated:

(1) tangentially and at right angles to the longitudinal axis;
(2) tangentially from two sides, with such an angle between the beams of light that the side away from the light source was illuminated; and
(3) one half of the coleoptile illuminated obliquely from above, in which the angle of incidence of the light ray was calculated in such a way that the light rays illuminated only one side of the coleoptile.

In all these experiments the coleoptiles reacted on the average in such a way that some importance must be ascribed to the direction of the light rays in the zone of induction.

If together with these results one remembers that the light growth-reaction and light curvature-reaction do not coincide (Fig. 192), and also remembers the results of auxin research, one is reminded anew how complex the apparently simple tropistic stimulus processes are. To the above discussion of the possible nature of stimulus perception,

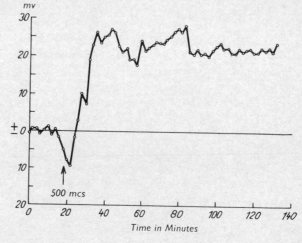

Fig. 196. The potential difference between the illuminated and un-illuminated sides of an *Avena* coleoptile after exposure to 500 lux-seconds (after OPPENOORTH 1941).

it should also be added that the results of experiments with unicellular (coenocytic) organs, e.g. fungal hyphae, should not be transferred uncritically to those of higher plants. The transmission of stimuli is wholly or mainly missing in the former. BLAAUW, BUDER, CASTLE et al. have shown convincingly how in *Phycomyces* the phototropic curvature is determined only by differences in illumination within the lens-shaped cell. The lens effect may be altered, as BUDER (1918, 1919) showed, without changing the direction of illumination by substituting paraffin for water as medium. The altered refraction then brings about an inversion of the phototropic reaction (see also the discussion in BRAUNER 1954). Similar experiments have been carried out with the rhizoids of certain liverworts which are normally negatively phototropic (DASSEK 1939).

Epidermal cells are also usually constructed like convex lenses. and for this reason HABERLANDT (1924) ascribed to them a function as light-perception organs. According to him the light was focussed on the rear wall and there perceived. It was, however, found that coating the leaf with gelatine or dipping it in paraffin oil (KNIEP, NORD-HAUSEN) in spite of the alteration in the path of the light, did not change the intensity of the phototropic perception.

The transverse polarisation of the perception organ brought about in these or other ways causes, in *Avena* coleoptiles for example, a redistribution of the mobile auxin at the growing point, so that after transmission the illuminated side receives less auxin than the shaded. The rate of translocation may amount to 8 mm per hour, a speed which can scarcely be explained as a mere diffusion of the molecules. An acceleration of translocation might be conceivable e.g. by gliding along adsorption surfaces, by electrophoresis, anion respiration, etc. The idea of electrophoretic transport originated with WENT (1932). The criticism usually directed against it is often due to misunderstanding, but on the other hand, as we have repeatedly emphasised, one should not rely too much on electrophoresis, as decisive facts are still lacking. One can at least say that the auxin transport through parencyhmatous organs is connected with vital processes. This appears both from the temperature constants and from the inhibitory effect of narcotics. It may be noted in passing that electrophoretic transport also presupposes the collaboration of biochemical processes. The necessary potentials can certainly be directed or reversed by geo- or photo-polarisation, but a continuous production of current requires a steady production of orientable ions in metabolism. Unfortunately only specialised organs, such as coleoptiles, have been subjected to detailed analyses of stimuli. It may be supposed that a closer study of more massive organs, e.g. shoot tips, would reveal more about the possible re-orientation of the auxin already existing in the zone of curvature. OVERBEEK (1938) reported some experiments with the hypocotyl of *Raphanus* pointing in this direction. Difficulties are, however, always encountered in distinguishing between an accumulation of auxin due to transport towards the shaded side, and one due to new formation taking place there.

2 THE RELATIONS BETWEEN AMOUNT OF STIMULUS AND REACTION

The product law applies to phototropism as much as to geotropism, so long as the stimuli only just exceed the threshold value. BLAAUW, who discovered this law in 1909 at the same time as FRÖSCHEL, obtained the following figures for 'just visible reaction' with *Avena* coleoptiles.

Table 31

Light intensity (lux)	Duration of stimulus (seconds)	Amount of light (lux-sec)
0·00017	154800	26·3
0·00085	21600	18·6
0·00477	3600	17·2
0·0898	240	21·6
5·456	4	21·8
1902·0	0·01	19·0
26520·0	0·001	26·5

As follows from the last column, the amount of stimulus necessary for the threshold value, with the exception of the two extreme values (first and last), is about constant. OEHLKERS (1927) obtained quite considerable deviations from the product law with *Phycomyces*, and the law is now considered an approximation. It is clear that at the extreme values of the time of illumination the time factor must cause deviations.

The course of the reaction agrees in principle with that of geotropic curvature. If the angle of deflection of the coleoptile tip is measured, one can distinguish a starting phase in which the rate is low, a eumotor phase with high and almost constant speed, and a dying-away end phase. The course of the curve is sigmoid with a pronounced straight part in the middle (Fig. 197).

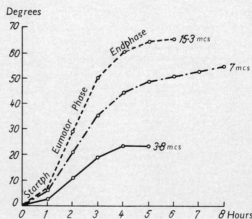

Fig. 197. The course of the positively phototropic reaction of *Avena* coleoptiles after increasing amounts of stimulation (3·8-15·3 lux-seconds). The reaction was recorded by ciné in red light and the curvature measured as the angle of deflection of the tip. The curves are derived from average values from a large number of observations (after LUNDEGÅRDH 1922).

There is little sign of an autotropic counter-reaction in *Avena* coleoptiles. Starting with low amounts of light and proceeding to higher, there is a corresponding increase both in the speed and in the final amount of curvature. Even at 3·2 lux-seconds coleoptiles raised in the dark give a reaction of 33° at room temperature. The sensitivity, of course, varies with variety, temperature, etc.

The relation between amount of stimulus and reaction is shown in the following example (LUNDEGÅRDH 1922, p. 14):

Table 32

Amount of stimulus (lux-sec)	Speed of reaction (degrees per hour)
3·84	8·33
7·02	15·10
15·29	23·52

2G

With small amounts of stimulus, up to about 10 lux-seconds, the speed keeps approximately level with the amount of stimulus, but with further increase it rises more slowly. The exact measurements of angle used in these experiments with cinematograph exposures (in yellow light) is a more exact method than merely noting 'just visible reaction'.

With continually increased stimulation one finally reaches an optimum above which both the speed of reaction and the final angle decrease, as shown in the following table:

Table 33

Amount of stimulus (lux-sec)	Maximal curvature (degrees)
3·2	15·1°
6·3	35·4°
12·6	52·3°
25·3	38·6°
50·6	36·6°

With amounts of stimulus of about 1,000 lux-seconds visible reaction completely disappears, and the coleoptile is then apparently aphototropic. With still further increase in the amount of stimulus the reaction changes over to *negative*, and in its turn shows a maximum at 4,000-10,000 lux-seconds. The curve reaches a second stage of insensitivity at several hundred thousand lux-seconds, and then finally turns upwards at about 2 million lux-seconds to a *second (positive) reaction optimum*, which at still greater amounts of stimulus again decreases (Fig. 198).

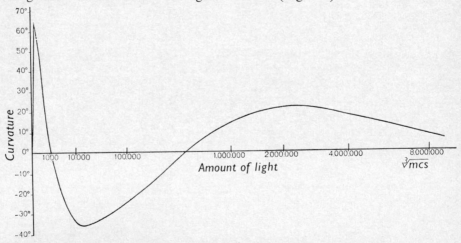

Fig. 198. The relations between illumination (in lux-seconds, mcs) and direction and intensity of the phototropic reaction of *Avena* coleoptiles (after LUNDEGÅRDH 1922).

The relation between the amount of stimulus and reaction is thus represented by a waved curve passing through positions of insensitivity. The length of the phases increases, while the amplitude of reaction decreases.

The interplay between two visible reactions can be explained, as in geotropism, as the interaction of two opposite impulses, one positive and one negative. Between them there is the difference that the (negative) counter-reaction needs much greater amounts of stimulus than the primary reaction.

Increases in the intensity of light can be carried without technical difficulty to far greater lengths than the acceleration of gravity. The interaction between the phototropic reactions therefore emerges with the greater clarity.

It becomes clear that an interplay of two opposite reactions actually occurs in the first phase of the phototropic stimulus-reaction curve (Fig. 198), if a time recording is made of the movements of the coleoptile tips in the region of the curve around its first point of insensitivity. One then sees (Fig. 199) how the more quickly induced positive reaction soon has to give way to a negative reaction setting in later. One also finds, as in autotropism, etc., periodic, gradually diminishing oscillations which reveal competing impulses during the dying down of the reaction and extend the reaction time.

The experiments just described date from a time before the beginning of real research on auxins, and an interpretation of them in the light of our limited present knowledge of auxins is difficult. It seems, however, to follow clearly from them that the first positive reaction is governed by a simple perception process, e.g. a photo-polarisation of the auxin-producing growing point. The counter-reaction induced by greater amounts of stimulus could on the other hand very well arise from a quite different kind of perception, e.g. formation of a second growth substance in the reaction zone. This counter-reaction would have nothing in common with the positive light-growth reaction in BLAAUW's sense. In the second phase of the stimulus-reaction curve, yet other photo-induced processes or growth substances certainly take part, while the primary auxin is destroyed by light. It is in fact difficult to imagine that the primary reaction still persists in the higher phases of the curve. The destruction of the auxin by light, which has already been shown experimentally, may suffice to prepare the ground for new growth substances.

The assumption of at least two different light perceptions is supported to some extent by a number of data available in the literature about the independent reaction of tip and base in the *Avena* coleoptile. If only the tip (0·5 mm) is illuminated, one gets strong positive curvatures even at amounts of light which otherwise would evoke negative reaction, e.g. a positive curvature of 48° after stimulation with 3,840 lux-seconds (LUNDEGÅRDH 1922). A fifth to a quarter of the total sensitivity lies in the tip, and an illumination with the amount of light mentioned would thus correspond to about 800 lux-seconds for the whole coleoptile; which would lead to insensitivity or to negative curvature. These observations support the interpretation proposed above, that the first negative counter-reaction is due to the formation of a second growth substance on the illuminated side of the reaction zone.

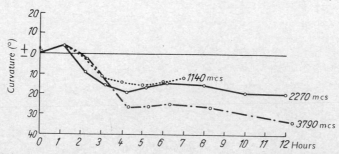

Fig. 199. The phototropic reaction of *Avena* coleoptiles after stimulation with amounts of light (1140-3790 lux-seconds) which lie near the first point of insensitivity (cf. Fig. 198). The interplay between the positive and negative reactions can be observed (after LUNDEGÅRDH 1922).

WILDEN (1939) has investigated in *Avena* coleoptiles the distribution of the auxin between the light and the shaded sides. In the phase of the first positive reaction he obtained the distribution 83 : 17 in favour of the shaded side. In the first negative curvature phase the distribution was reversed: it was 62 : 38 in favour of the light side. The second positive reaction again showed 64 : 36 in favour of the shaded side. The direction of curvature, and to a certain extent the curvature maximum, thus reflect the distribution of the auxin, which in itself is certainly not surprising. It nevertheless remains unknown whether the same auxin is concerned in the different phases. This *a priori* would seem unlikely because of the indications of a photodestruction of auxin. The assumption of a photodestruction of auxin as the cause of the second positive reaction, which was put forward by KONINGSBERGER and VERKAAIK, still appears probable, and for the first negative counter-reaction one must probably fall back on assuming a synthesis of a second growth substance. There is also the possibility of course that at medium light intensities auxin formation is stimulated in the basal parts of the coleoptile (cf. above), an idea which was expressed also by OPPENOORTH (1941).

The above measurements of the distribution of auxin between the convex and concave sides of a curved organ give little insight into the growth-substance or inhibitor mechanism in the fluctuation between positive and negative reactions. ZIMMERMAN and HITCHCOCK (1942) showed e.g. that tomato plants after being kept for several days in the dark become ageotropic because of lack of auxin—a result which agrees with the later findings of GUTTENBERG and ZETSCHE (1956). The former workers, however, think that a still unknown sensitising factor has an effect here. HUBER and FUNKE, SEGELITZ, NAUNDORF *et al.* speculate in a fairly systematic way about the collaboration of auxin in phototropic movements of roots. GEIGER-HUBER (1945) showed that repeated decapitation of a root finally makes it negatively geotropic because of the reduction of the auxin content. Conversely, supply of β-indolylacetic acid (IAA) to negatively geotropic shoots causes a reversal to a positive reaction.

The optimum curve of the effect of auxin has by no means been adequately analysed. Experience in other regions of physiology shows that optimum curves as a rule result from two opposed processes, one positive and one negative. One therefore asks here also, how the counter-reaction of the auxin effect arises. Since in experiments where auxin is supplied artificially the counter-reaction develops independently of external stimuli, it must originate from the auxin itself. Here one thinks first of the auxin destruction which is always going on in an organ, catalysed by peroxidases, etc. (Chap. 4); and an obvious supposition would be that an inhibitor (antiauxin) arises as an intermediate product of this destruction. If this secondary inhibitor has a weaker effect than the auxin, the counter-reaction can only arise with high initial quantities of auxin, as actually applies both for geotropic and phototropic counter-reactions. In phototropism, apart from this hypothetical antiauxin formation, there is also the breakdown of auxin by light already mentioned.

The quantitative relations between the amount of stimulus and the intensity of reaction are thus rather complicated, especially with large amounts of stimulation, when decomposition products of the primary auxin come into play. As long as one remains in the phase of weak light stimuli, which e.g. in *Avena* coleoptiles evoke a purely positive reaction, the quantitative relations remain simpler and more comprehensible. The difference between the simple reaction curve, as it appears in Fig. 197, and that of a mono- or multimolecular reaction, is the fact that the latter sets in with a maximal and almost uniform speed, and then gradually after bending convexly ends in an asymptotically straight line. The speed of such a reaction is determined at every moment by the concentration of the reacting components still present. The corresponding course of the tropistic reaction begins only with the onset of the eumotor phase. It may be imagined that this phase starts at the moment when the auxin stream, modified by the stimulated tip, has permeated the whole reaction zone. The kinetic similarity between simple chemical reactions and the main period of curvature after the initial stage can be explained by the fact that auxin is consumed in its stimulation of growth. It cannot be maintained without further proof that this auxin consumption in parallel with the growth is identical with the effects of an 'auxin oxidase' observed *in vitro*. It seems much more likely to be of quite a different nature. In this process, moreover, as follows from the lack of relation between tropism and autotropism (p. 429), no inhibitors (antiauxins etc.) are formed. For the formation of inhibitors (antiauxins) only excess auxin, i.e. what is accumulated with a supra-optimal supply, can be drawn on. This interpretation is in good agreement with the facts described above and with the assumption that the secondary inhibitors arise by breakdown of auxin at the relevant point, that is in the reaction zone.

The initial phase deviating from the simple reaction kinetics reflects a quite different process, the transmission of auxin. It is clear that the auxin flowing from the tip first influences only a small part of the reaction zone and only gradually extends its influence over the whole, according to the rate of transport. At this point the eumotor phase commences. The course of the initial stage thus reflects the speed of the basipetal auxin flow.

The validity of the WEBER-FECHNER law has been established for phototropism also. Applied to the behaviour of the *Avena* coleoptile this means that the coleoptile can, for example, distinguish between 10 and 12 lux-seconds, if the two stimuli come from diametrically opposite directions; the absolute difference here is only 2 lux-seconds. With a stimulation of 100 lux-seconds the counter-stimulation must amount to 120 lux-seconds to be perceived, an arithmetical difference of 20 lux-seconds. It is usual to explain the difference of sensitivity as due to a change of tonus (e.g. PRINGSHEIM 1926). But, as was explained in the previous chapter, it is more satisfactory to attribute the gradation of sensitivity to a consumption of 'perception substance' increasing with the amount of stimulus.

A gradation of sensitivity also occurs with successive stimuli from opposite sides, as shown in the following series of experiments (LUNDEGÅRDH 1922):

Table 34

Amount of stimulus in lux-seconds (difference of 14 lux-sec)		Reaction in degrees after		
One side	Opposite side	2 hrs	4 hrs	6 hrs
14	0	37	62	61
28	14	33	44	45
42	28	8	30	32
56	42	3	23	23

The damping effect that follows the negatively phototropic primary reaction soon diminishes and the original sensitivity is reached again after about an hour (cf. ARISZ 1915). In this time therefore the 'perception substance' is regenerated.

3 DIAPHOTOTROPISM (TRANSVERSE PHOTOTROPISM)

Of the plant members which orientate themselves at right angles to the incident light, leaves may be mentioned first. Whilst only a small number of leaves react geotropically, phototropic sensitivity is fairly widespread; but the leaves of grasses, Liliaceae and Cactaceae, for example, are aphototropic. A good example of diaphototropic leaves is afforded by the shade leaves of *Acer platanoides* (FRANK 1870, LUNDEGÅRDH 1916).

Maple leaves move by means of curvatures and twistings of the upper and lower pulvini of the petiole, which itself remains straight. The basal pulvinus of the petiole acts first in the movements. Only after the extent of its reach has been exhausted does the upper joint contribute (Fig. 199). The leaf laminae serve as the phototropic receptor organs and are orientated exclusively by the light stimulus. The petioles on the other hand also show geotropic sensitivity (Fig. 200).

With higher intensity of illumination (direct sunlight) the diaphototropic sensitivity changes over into a *plagiophototropic*, so that the leaves at the periphery of the tree crown take up an inclined position. Ecologically this provides a partial protection against the heat of direct sunlight. The leaves of *Tropaeolum* appear to react similarly to those of the maple (BRAUNER and VARDAR 1950).

Some diaphototropic leaves react so quickly that they follow the movement of the sun, e.g. *Malva neglecta* (YIN 1938). Diaphototropism occurs also in lower plants, e.g. in the thallus of the liverwort *Marchantia*. A special position is taken up by the *compass plants*; their leaves are negatively diaphototropic towards the strong mid-day sun and so place themselves in the north-south direction. Examples of such plants are

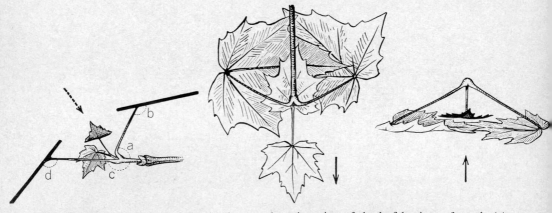

Fig. 200. Effect of unilateral illumination on the orientation of the leaf laminae of maple (*Acer platanoides*). The basal joints *a* and *c* first participate in the movement (after LUNDEGÅRDH 1916).

Fig. 201. Effect of gravity and light on the orientation of maple leaves. The plant is placed upside down and the illumination comes from behind. The petioles are geotropically curved upwards, but the laminae orientate themselves at 90° to the direction of light incidence. In the drawing on the left the arrow shows the direction of gravity; the plant is viewed from the side. In the drawing on the right the arrow shows the direction of the light and the plant is viewed from above; the phototropic reaction is very obvious (after LUNDEGÅRDH 1916).

Lactuca scariola (DOLK 1931) and *Iris pseudacorus*. If an *Iris* plant is placed in such a way that the leaves are moved from their natural position they turn again back into the compass direction. The leaves of some trees from warm habitats also assume a profile position. *Aster linosyris* behaves in a different way and belongs to the 'sundial' or gnomon plants (HÜBER 1934).

Certain leaves move, as described for the maple, by means of joints, which retain their ability to move for a period after the growth of the lamina is finished. Especially well known are the leaves of *Mimosa*, Oxalideae, etc., which are provided with specially formed pulvini that retain their ability to move after they are mature. It has been found that their movements, which belong to the category of movements of variation, are due to changes of the osmotic value or of the permeability. Water is either given up or taken up, resulting in unilateral changes of turgor, which lower or raise the leaf.

Turgor movements induced by light can be observed in the leaves of *Mimosa*, *Phaseolus* and other leguminous plants, leaflets of *Robinia pseudacacia* (BRAUNER 1947), etc. If the pulvinus of a leaflet of *Phaseolus* is illuminated from above, the leaf raises itself; if it is illuminated from below it sinks downwards. Illumination from the side induces a torsion movement, and with simultaneous illumination both from above and from below the leaf takes an intermediate position.

As SNOW (1945) has shown, torsion movements in the pulvini of beans can also be evoked by treatment with IAA. The participation of osmotic forces is seen from the fact that the pulvini react differently in air and in water. This is because the water exuded during a fall in osmotic pressure in air is quickly evaporated or conducted away and a subsequent increase of the osmotic value does not result in an immediate turgor extension, which, on the other hand, does happen if the pulvinus is surrounded by water. In spite of numerous experiments on variation movements (PFEFFER, LEPESCHKIN, BRAUNER *et al.*) their mechanism is still obscure.

The phototropic reactions of pulvini are accompanied, like those of growth movements, by a counter-reaction which develops if the illumination continues for a long time. The counter-reaction may be succeeded by another, and so on, so that periodic leaf-movements arise, which are released either by a single short-duration stimulation or during long-period illumination, e.g. in *Averrhoa bilimbi* or *Desmodium gyrans*. If the reactions die away quickly, oscillations arise of the same type as in the tropisms, i.e. with gradually decreasing amplitude. The endogenous variation movements which are mentioned in Section F are of a somewhat special type.

The production of auxin in phototropically sensitive leaves seems to be a function of the lamina (BRAUNER 1954). Movements of the petiole, which cease after abscission of the lamina, can thus be caused to show renewed activity by an artificial supply of auxin. The formation of auxin in chlorophyll-containing organs seems to be dependent on the photosynthetically formed carbohydrates, whereas in root tips and in tissue cultures auxin is formed in the dark (SKOOG 1947). As light also inactivates auxin, there is probably a balance in illuminated leaves between its photosynthesis and photolysis.

LAIBACH and FISCHNISCH (1938) assume that a photodynamic effect collaborates in perception. According to their ideas, if half of a leaf is darkened, more active auxin flows from that side to the petiole and causes a movement towards the light. Similar experiments were made with *Fatsia japonica* (YAMANE 1940); but there are also cases in which no movement resulted. In these the direction of the light seems to determine perception rather than mere differences in illumination.

The occurrence of filaments of positively phototropic cells at the base of the respiratory cavities of *Marchantia* has been quoted in support of the theory of photopolarisation. It is assumed that the palisade cells of the leaves of higher plants could play a similar role. There is a difference, however; for in *Marchantia* the filaments of green cells also execute the movement, whereas in higher plants it is the lamina that is the organ of perception. It must also be remembered that in shade leaves which are diaphototropic the palisade parenchyma is very weakly developed, whereas sun leaves which are usually plagiophototropic show well developed palisades. It is easier to suppose that the phototactic chloroplast movements have something to do with light perception.

It will be seen from the examples just given that the mechanism of leaf movement is extraordinarily complicated. Both curvatures and torsions are involved and there are also correlations between, for example, laminae and petioles and between tops and bottoms of the latter.

The peculiar successive reactions of the lower and upper pulvini of maple petioles afford special support for the idea developed above that auxin is used up during the course of a reaction. If there is to be a continued functioning of auxin in the second, later activated, pulvinus the amount of auxin flowing in must be great enough for some to remain over for this second reaction. This train of thought was outlined by LUNDEGÅRDH (1916-18). An alternative explanation is a different threshold value for auxin in the basal and apical pulvini, in which the former has the higher sensitivity. The threshold value of the apical joint would thus be exceeded only with strong stimuli; with weaker stimuli the auxin would flow through without causing a reaction and be effective only in the basal joint.

Reversals of sensitivity are commonly found in phototropism as in geotropism. In *Linaria cymbalaria* the pedicels are at first positively phototropic, and then during fruit formation negatively phototropic. Similar changes in reaction have been observed in *Tropaeolum majus* and many other plants.

The phototropism of roots was studied by PILET (1952) and BRUMFIELD (1955). The former worked with lentil roots, the latter with Timothy grass roots. BRUMFIELD found a positive primary reaction, which was succeeded by a negative counter-reaction. Both reactions were inhibited by 2,4,6-trichlorophenoxyacetic acid (2,4,6-T), which had little influence on growth. Here, therefore, one meets again the hormonal difference between simple growth-reactions and tropistic reactions.

Phototropic reversals are often combined with geotropic, a fact that suggests an influence on the processes in the reaction zone. In repeated experiments roots were treated with dyestuffs, e.g. erythrosin (see e.g. GUTTENBERG 1941), with the object of inducing phototropic sensitivity. The sensitivity actually observed seems to be explained by unilateral photodestruction of auxin already present. The normal phototropic perception obviously requires the presence of a link between the primary light absorption and the mechanism for redistribution of the auxin, etc.

4 THE DEPENDENCE OF TROPISTIC REACTIONS ON OTHER EXTERNAL FACTORS

As tropisms, with few exceptions such as those of the turgor-actuated leaf pulvini, are growth-movements, they are naturally subject to the same environmental factor as general growth. The influence of nutrients can be left out of account here. As usual, the temperature effect follows an optimum curve, both for the threshold value and for the latent time (RUTGERS 1912 et al.). The necessity of free oxygen for the photo-tropic reactions of the Avena coleoptile was early shown by WIESNER (1878) and later by CORRENS, WORTMANN, VAN AMEIJDEN (1917), and others. The last-named also showed that even perception was inhibited by oxygen deficiency. Tropistic movements are also inhibited by narcotics. Phototropic sensitivity is inhibited by mere traces of coal gas or tobacco smoke in the atmosphere; and ethylene and carbon monoxide are particularly toxic. Carbon dioxide in higher concentrations also acts as a narcotic (cf. Chap. 4). With 40%-45% of CO_2 in the air, growth and tropisms of Helianthus annuus were inhibited (CHAPMAN et al. 1924), and stomata react also with CO_2. BORGSTRÖM (1939) states that auxin transport is inhibited by narcotics.

It has already been mentioned that the geotropic reaction of roots is strongly dependent on the humidity and salt content of the medium. Ca^{++} occupies a special position among the cations. CHOLODNY (1923) and WARNER (1928) found that alkali cations (K and Na) have a retarding effect on geotropic reaction, which may be connected at least partly with the displacement of calcium ions. Supply of Ca and Mg had some accelerating effect. According to CHOLODNY distilled water retards the reaction. Besides the special effect of calcium, which is indispensable for the proper condition of the wall-producing cell surface, there are also, of course, the general effects of the ionic balance. What is true of calcium may apply to some extent to magnesium, i.e. it may give to some organic components of the cell surface, such as the nucleotides, a correct condition and charge for their function.

D. Chemo-, Hydro- and Thermotropisms

Chemotropism expresses itself as the curvature of roots, fungal hyphae, pollen tubes, etc., in the direction to, or away from, a diffusion gradient. Examples of positive chemotropism are cells with growing tips, e.g. root hairs, etc., which are brought to places of higher nutrient concentration simply by means of an inhibition of growth on one side of the tip. Pollen tubes are 'attracted' by secreted sugars or by proteins from the embryo sac. Hypothetically one can conceive that the chemotropically effective substances regulate the hydration and elasticity of the growing cell wall as well as the biochemical processes in the protoplasmic membrane inside it. In multi-cellular organs relations may be more complicated, since a complete reaction sequence may be traversed, although naturally movements may also occur as a result of simple membrane effects.

A chemotropic perception can be thought of as a unilateral change of speed of an enzymically catalysed reaction acting differentially on the auxin distribution and transmitted in the usual way to the zone of movement. FITTING (1936-7) in his studies of protoplasmic streaming showed that the protoplasm can exhibit an extraordinarily high irritability towards amino acids. Less than 10^{-8} M L-histidine and L-methyl-histidine evoked protoplasmic streaming in the leaf cells of Vallisneria spiralis. The specificity of the effect was illustrated by the different effects of the D- and L-forms of histidine, aspartic acid and alanine.

Such hints about the possible mechanism of chemotropism cannot conceal the fact that surprisingly little study has been given to these ecologically very important move-ments, in contrast with the zealous study of geo- and phototropisms. Thus little is known about the effect of auxins, though the curvature obtained by the unilateral application of auxin from outside is itself a kind of chemotropism. Only in the chemotropic reactions evoked by neutral salts is it possible to find analogies with geo- and phototropic reaction mechanisms.

Knowledge of chemotropism was extended at an early stage by MIYOSHI (1894), who studied the hyphae of a number of fungi, e.g. *Saprolegnia*, *Mucor*, *Penicillium* and *Aspergillus*, and was the first to recognise the chemotropism of pollen tubes (see also LIDFORSS 1909). The chemotropism of roots was investigated by PORODKO (1925).

Fungal hyphae are chemotropically attracted by ammonium salts, phosphates, glucose and sucrose. Roots also can show a specific sensitivity. The roots of *Lupinus albus*, used by PORODKO, react readily with electrolytes, while a number of non-electrolytes, e.g. sucrose and urea, remain without effect. PORODKO states that, in general, anions give positive reactions and cations negative. He also attempted to analyse the process in greater detail and was able to show that there is a transmission of the stimulation and that perception is located chiefly in the root tip. He also brought forward arguments for an approximate validity of the product law.

The investigations of PORODKO on chemotropism date from before the breakthrough in auxin research. The characteristic surface potentials of roots and their presumptive importance for the electrophoretic transport of dissociated growth substances and inhibitors from the tip to the extension zone (see above) were also unknown at that time. We want to draw special attention here to the influence of the surface potential on the auxin dissociation in the outside wall of the epidermis. It was emphasised earlier that the rate of elongation of the epidermal walls largely determines rapid changes in growth, which affect even the tropisms. Starting from the reasonable assumption that the auxin anions are more active than the neutral molecules, we drew the inference that every change of pH in the root surface, which lies in the range of the pK value of auxin (about 4·75-5·00), will involve a rapid change in growth (or elongation). Such changes in pH are readily induced by electrolytes. In distilled water and 'de-salted' roots the specific charge of the root surface determines the negative potential with values from 100 to 200 millivolt and pH values of 4·2. The dissociation of auxin in the external wall of the epidermis is strongly depressed by such values and, theoretically, should cause an increased elongation, which has actually been observed under these conditions.

In an electrolyte solution the root potential sinks as metallic cations are exchanged for H-ions of the root surface. The increased dissocation of auxin which results may then reduce growth; and this also has been observed. The changes in growth may, however, be very different according to the powers of exchange of the cations and anions, and on account of special effects, such as those of Ca^{++}.

It is a general rule that the cations of the electrolyte lower the surface negative potential of roots (that is, increase the pH), while the anions conversely lower the positive potential (that is, lower the pH). The change of potential which actually occurs is thus a resultant between the effects of cations and anions. The cation effect almost always predominates, although e.g. in a comparison between KCl and KNO_3 in equal concentrations a higher negative potential (that is, lower pH) stood out clearly in the nitrate. In general, however, it is true that the negative surface potential decreases with increasing concentration of an electrolyte. Parallel with this go a rising pH value and increasing dissociation of auxin and other acids in the epidermal surface. One may thus expect a decreased elongation to develop parallel with the rising concentration of the electrolyte. The special power of exchange or the special growth-effect of individual cations and anions may cause complications.

Applied to chemotropism, the facts recalled above mean that a concentration gradient of an electrolyte must act in such a way that the dissociation of auxins, etc., becomes relatively greater on the side towards the diffusion gradient. The resulting local inhibition of root elongation causes a chemotropic curvature in accordance with PORODKO's results.

Apart from the direct effect of salts on the dissociation of auxin in the surface of a root, the internal micro-currents caused by the potentials (cf. p. 381) are naturally influenced also. Both changes operate in the same direction. The general weakening of the potential difference between root tip and extension zone (cf. Figs. 160 and 159), which occurs in salt concentrations over about $0·001$ M, lowers the electrophoretic transport capacity. The reduction in the supply of auxin to the extension zone so produced causes an increase in growth, and with a unilateral salt effect a negatively chemotropic movement. A re-examination of PORODKO's experiments in the author's laboratory gave especially clear negative curvatures with roots stimulated by $CaCl_2$ solutions. Here the special stimulus to growth of the Ca ions probably adds to the general chemotropic effect.

PORODKO's conclusion that the root tip perceives the chemotropic stimulus agrees with the above, though the explanation is probably rather different from PORODKO's. A basipetal electrophoretic transport of auxin presupposes of course that the auxin is produced in the root tip. If the centre of auxin production is removed, that is if the root tip is cut off, auxin translocation gradually ceases, but the salt effect on the auxin already in the extension zone persists. A chemotropic reaction can thus still occur, but it is weaker than with an intact root tip. One can thus suppose that the chemotropic perception extends over the whole root surface, but that the reaction can be developed in its full strength only in intact roots. The chemotropic perception, according to the interpretation put forward here, thus differs from the geo- and photo-tropic in that there are as yet no arguments for a specific tip perception.

A special kind of chemotropism is *galvanotropism* (BAYLISS 1907), i.e. a curvature induced by an electric current. An electric current which flows along one side of a root naturally causes potential changes that will affect ion exchange. Changes in the dissociation of the auxins in the surfaces of the epidermal cells of the elongating zone are thus to be expected. It is therefore not necessary to regard, as AMLONG, BÜNNING and others did, a transverse displacement of auxin in the tissue as the cause of the reaction. Nevertheless, such an effect might, of course, play some part. Galvano-tropism has also been observed in pollen tubes (WOLFF 1935). In this case high potential differences (up to 200 millivolts) have often been noted between the stigma and the ovule.

Rheotropism is the curvature of roots to or against the direction of flow of water. The phenomenon was first described by JÖNSSON (1883) and later studied by NEW-COMBE, BERG, JUEL *et al.* Roots of Gramineae and Crucifereae are rheotropically sensitive, and also hyphae of *Botrytis cinerea* which react positively. NEWCOMBE found an optimal sensitivity in radishes with a rate of flow of 100-500 cm per minute. It is difficult to give an explanation of the curvatures, since they include the whole lower part of the root, not only the extension zone. Pressure vibrations may possibly be involved, as they are always present when water flows round solid bodies. According to SEN-GUPTA (1929) rheotropism may be simply a kind of chemotropism; he obtained no curvatures in distilled water.

Some effects of water on plant form may be mentioned here, e.g. a reduced rhizoid formation in *Marchantia* and *Riccia*. Root-hair formation in higher plants, as is well-known, is also affected differently by water and moist air. Root formation is certainly favoured by inceased transpiration. In these cases complicated reactions are obviously involved, such as changes in the turgidity of the walls and protoplasm of growing cells. Ionic influences and gas exchange (O_2 and CO_2) may also be important.

The term *aerotropism* was introduced by MOLISCH. By it he understood the curvature of roots, etc., towards or away from oxygen, but aerotropic curvatures occur also with other gases, e.g. CO_2 and ammonia (SAMMET 1905). These movements are probably due to a direct effect on the elongating zone; decapitated roots still react. The gases mentioned also influence respiration, of course, and a simple side effect of a change in respiration on the speed of cell extension may be concerned.

Hydrotropism refers to movements induced by moisture gradients in air, soil, etc. SACHS early demonstrated in a well-known experiment the positive hydrotropism of roots in the ground. The seedlings grew in a shallow basket filled with damp earth; the roots coming out of the soil of the basket curved sideways, so that they clung to the moist substrate. Nevertheless, the supposedly great ecological importance of hydrotropism has been doubted (LOOMIS and EWAN 1936). The rhizoids of liverworts are positively hydrotropic, while the sporangiophores of many fungi, e.g. *Phycomyces* and *Coprinus*, react negatively. The thallus of *Marchantia* is said to be transversely hydrotropic.

HOOKER (1915) studied the reaction of *Lupinus* roots to different moisture gradients. Positively hydrotropic reaction did not occur below 80%-100% relative humidity and a gradient of 0·2% per cm; the optimal gradient was 0·4% per cm.

If one starts with the assumption of a bioelectrophoresis of auxin, one must also take into account the resistance to the current in the external circuit (cf. Fig. 160). This circuit flows through the epidermis and/or the medium. A lower moisture content of the external epidermal walls, i.e. a high ohmic resistance in the external circuit, will, other things being equal, inhibit auxin transport, i.e. will increase the elongation rate and so introduce a curvature of the root away from the drier surroundings. A medium that is a good conductor thus increases the auxin-transporting currents inside. The ideas of SCHRANK (1950, 1953) that a 'short circuit' would have the opposite effect are misleading. One must imagine the root tip as an electric battery with the positive pole at the tip and the negative pole in the middle of the extension zone. The medium or the external wall of the epidermis represents the external circuit linking the poles. A 'short circuit' thus strengthens the internal circuit to a maximum.

In hydrotropism also the data on the function of the root tip as the organ of perception must be judged with care. The experimental facts can be just as well explained by assuming that the tip is the centre of auxin production and that the hydrotropic 'perception' is due to a change in the ohmic resistance in the external circuit of the auxin-transporting 'root battery'. In the hydrotropism of fungal hyphae local changes in the hydration of the cell-wall may influence growth directly. Here we have, as in most of the thermotropic responses, processes which deviate physiologically from geo- and phototropism and are in general simpler.

The same general characteristic may apply also to *thermotropism*. As temperature variations induce heat growth-reactions, which in many respects resemble light growth-reactions, and as the rate of growth is generally a function of temperature, one can think of thermotropic movements simply as local heat growth-reactions. Conduction of heat in the organ must, of course, be slow enough to allow a unilateral increase in temperature to induce a local change in growth. As in light inductions, it may often be difficult to separate conduction of heat and effects of radiation such as infra-red light. There are also experimental difficulties in the proper control of air humidity. Many alleged causes of thermotropism may in reality be hydrotropisms (HOOKER et al.). A thermal radiation may be able to cause a polarisation of the auxin production centre in the same way as visible light does, but nothing about this is yet known. In addition local temperature effects may naturally evoke changes in auxin transmission, the water balance, the rate of metabolism, etc., i.e. in processes which can be separated from each other only with difficulty.

E. Hapto- and traumatotropism

In describing the organisation of the cell the importance of the surface layer in regulating enzymatic processes was emphasised. The orientation of the molecules in such a film can be destroyed mechanically. By such means chemical processes may be influenced, and this can be thought of as perception of a stimulus. It forms the cell-physiological background for the *hapto-* or *thigmotropic movements* induced by mechanical stimulation.

Haptotropic movements were early studied e.g. by DARWIN and PFEFFER in tendrils, but they also occur in other growing organs.

According to STARK (1916) seedlings are particularly sensitive and react even to a weak contact. Growing shoots, petioles and inflorescence stalks are also sensitive to contact. STARK stimulated the organs by stroking them with a small rod of cork. He found that haptotropism follows the same laws as other stimulus perceptions, e.g. the summation of sub-threshold stimuli, the quantitative relationships between stimulation and reaction, and the WEBER-FECHNER law.

The phenomena of fatigue and damping can also be demonstrated by applying electrical stimuli (BÜNNING 1939, p. 147). The haptotropic reaction time is in general shorter than that of geo- or phototropism. A further characteristic of haptotropism is the limitation of the reaction to a small region round the point of stimulus; conduction is very restricted and slow. There is usually a specific delimitation of the sensitive zone. The tip of the *Avena* coleoptile (3-4 mm) is quite insensitive, whereas the base reacts. One can conclude from this that haptotropism operates on quite a different plan from geo- and phototropism and also that auxin transmission is not involved, as in chemotropism.

Tendrils are threadlike organs, which can be regarded morphologically as reduced leaves, parts of leaves, petioles or shoots. They react on contact with solid bodies and serve ecologically as climbing organs. Tendrils are common in the families Cucurbitaceae, Bignoniaceae and Leguminosae. Tendrils may be simple, as in the bryony, or branched, as in peas.

The reaction of a tendril is a positive curvature towards the surface of contact. If the support is cylindrical, the tendril gradually wraps itself round it. The response is not limited to an inhibition of growth at the surface of contact; an acceleration of growth usually takes place on the opposite side, which according to FITTING (1903) may be very considerable, e.g. in *Passiflora* and *Sicyos* (Fig. 203). In this way there arises a mean acceleration of growth of the stimulated tendril. As in the other tropisms, the primary reaction is followed by a counter-reaction, and periodic oscillations have also been observed.

The holding ability of the tendrils is usually reinforced by circumnutations, as in twining plants. Some tendrils are isotropic and others sensitive only on one side. In the latter, stimulation tends to cause an inhibition on the non-sensitive side. Characteristic of most dorsiventrally constructed tendrils is the spiral constriction which follows the haptotropic reaction and which is due to the upper side growing more strongly than the under side. If the tip of the tendril has already anchored itself the tightening of the spiral brings the plant into closer contact with the support. During the rolling up points of reversal (Fig. 204) are developed for mechanical reasons.

The relatively unspecific nature of mechanical stimulations is due to the fact that vibration can affect the whole submicroscopic structure of protoplasm. It may be noted that electric shock also causes reaction. As was mentioned above, haptotropic stimulation can generally be referred to disturbances in the relative positions of orientated molecules. The usually observed 'action currents' which occur after mechanical stimulation are readily comprehensible as the result of a re-orientation of molecules and ions arranged in layers or films. One may surmise that in haptotropically sensitive cells, there are structural combinations which are easily distorted mechanically.

Perception of the stimulus is facilitated anatomically by the thinness and arching of the epidermal walls and by 'tactile pits' (HABERLANDT) (Fig. 205). The extraordinary sensitivity of tendrils was shown in investigations by DARWIN and PFEFFER (1885). In *Passiflora gracilis* haptotropic stimulation was evoked by a 1·23 mg platinum loop, and in *Sicyos angulatus* contact with a cotton thread weighing 0·00025 mg was sufficient. Usually, however, tendrils are less sensitive than this.

PFEFFER distinguished sharply between contact stimulation by touching or rubbing against a solid object, and stronger mechanical shaking (shock effect), e.g. by wind or water. Many tendrils in fact react only on contact with solid bodies, and not e.g. with a moist gelatine layer. This is probably a matter of degree, depending on the

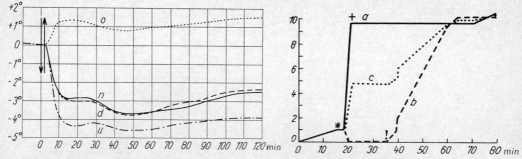

Fig. 202. The turgor reaction of the pulvini of *Phaseolus multiflorus* induced by light. Stimulation is indicated by the arrows. *o*—reaction after illumination from above, *u*—from below and *n*—from both sides. *d* is the calculated difference between *o* and *u*, and coincides with the curve for bilateral illumination. The abscissa gives the time in minutes (after BRAUNER).

Fig. 203. The growth in length of a tendril of *Sicyos* after mechanical stimulation. *a*—upper side, *b*—under side, *c*—the middle line of the tendril. The stimulation begins at the asterisk and ends at the plus sign. The abscissa gives the time in minutes (after FITTING).

disturbance of the molecular arrangement in the protoplasmic surfaces. It is easy to understand that even a slight difference of pressure may suffice if the points affected lie so close together that the molecular film is structurally distorted. A larger difference of pressure between two points lying farther apart would cause only a harmless bending of the film. The frequency of the shocks may also be important. Investigations with short (ultrasonic) vibrations might be fruitful. It is well known that ultrasonic vibrations attack the protoplasmic organisation strongly.

Fig. 204. Attachment movements of the tendrils of *Cucurbita*. The picture shows the different stages of the movement and the position of reversal in the final tightening of the spiral (after LUNDEGÅRDH 1915).

The structural distortions caused by mechanical stimulations naturally evoke secondary processes. The frequency of cell division is influenced as well as the average rate of growth. They may increase in tendrils, but are partially inhibited in the fruit stalk of *Coprinus*. Anatomically the formation of mechanical tissues is favoured by mechanical stimulus; but the connection between cause and effect is often obscure. The formation of mechanical tissues can often be stimulated by an unfavourable water balance or nitrogen deficiency.

Very strong mechanical stimulation damages cells, and movements arising in this way are *traumatotropic*. After mechanical injuries coagulations and vacuoles appear in the protoplasm, i.e. profound changes which are mostly fatal. An increase in viscosity can be measured by the speed of sedimentation of starch grains, etc., on centrifuging. There are also changes of permeability. Due to increases of permeability or sudden reductions of the osmotic value water may pass out into the intercellular spaces (NICOLAI 1929). The resulting decrease of turgor may explain the rapid curvature towards the wound. Changes in the protoplasmic consistency, e.g. by the formation of coacervates (Chap. 1), may also be studied in plasmolysed cells. Such profound changes naturally affect neighbouring cells, which show increases of respiration rate and changes in growth.

The correlative inhibitions which exist between the cells of a normal tissue and by which the size of the cells is held within certain limits fail at wound surfaces. This allows increased growth and cell division i.e. callus formation. The observed increases in respiration may be due partly to stimulation of the cytochrome system, as can be observed e.g. with slices of storage tissue. A formation of so-called *necrohormones* (wound hormones), which transfer the wound stimulus to neighbouring cells has also been assumed. HABERLANDT especially went to much trouble to find such hormones. The active substance was named 'traumatic acid' and, according to HAAGEN-SMIT (1948), it contains 2-dodecendioic acid $HOOC \cdot CH : (CH_2)_8 \cdot COOH$. HABERLANDT also assumes the occurrence of other more species-specific wound hormones; others may be unspecific e.g., tyrosine and auxin.

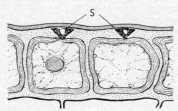

Fig. 205. Epidermal cells from the lower side of a tendril of *Cucurbita pepo* with tactile pits. *S*—Calcium oxalate crystals (after HABERLANDT).

Small traumatic stimulations cause only incidental disturbances. e.g. increases of permeability and decreases of turgor. Water is exuded, but is again absorbed after healing. Such changes in turgor cause movements, ordinarily towards the point of contact. When a root is wounded a positive traumatic curvature thus arises. After the onset of healing or regeneration a secondary stimulation of growth follows on the wounded side leading to a negative reaction. Usually only this secondary reaction is termed traumatic. As in haptotropism, conduction of the stimulus is very restricted, but the impulse may be transmitted to the other side of the organ as a weak stimulation of growth, which weakens the negatively traumatotropic curvature.

Traumatic reactions can be observed not only in roots, where the ecological importance is apparent, but also in dicotyledonous seedlings from which one cotyledon has been removed (STARK). An injury to the lamina evokes a positively traumatotropic reaction in the petiole. The removal of flowers can also cause curvatures of the stalks. Auxins may collaborate in such long-distance transfers of the stimulation since they are formed in the lamina and after the injury the supply to the corresponding side of the stalk decreases. The transmission of the stimulus to distances of 10 cm or more, which was observed by STARK in certain cases, in which several stem internodes were passed, probably also involved auxins. Regeneration could cause a stimulation of auxin synthesis, even though the direct wound stimulus temporarily reduces the auxin content. An interpretation of STARK's results in the light of auxin research thus encounters no difficulties.

F. Nastic Movements

The tropisms are orientation movements which assist the nutritional physiology of the plant. They bring the organs that take up and produce nutrients into suitable positions for their functions. The nasties are also mostly stimulated from without, and are governed by light, gravity, temperature, chemical and mechanical stimuli, and the sequence perception—transmission—reaction is passed through more or less completely. As the direction of the nastic movements is determined from inside, their ecological importance is much more restricted than those of tropisms. The utility of many nastic phenomena, e.g. the sleep movements of flowers and leaves, is doubtful, but others undoubtedly have an ecological function. There are naturally transitions between tropisms and nasties. The long-duration gravity inductions in side shoots show how short the step between the two may be.

1 PHOTO- AND THERMONASTY

The *sleep movements* (nyctinasty) of flowers and leaves were known quite early. They are regulated partly by light and partly by temperature. The flower clusters of many Compositae, which close in the evening (*Calendula, Bellis, Hieracium*, etc.), the flowers of *Oxalis* and others are *photonastic*. Exceptionally, as in *Tragopogon brevirostris*, the flowers close not only in the evening but also in strong midday light. The 'point of change' can be very different, e.g. some flowers, such as *Ipomaea*, close in the early afternoon. LINNÉ early remarked the differences in light sensitivity and composed a 'floral clock'. In the night-flowering plants, e.g. *Nicotiana*, certain Cactaceae (*Cereus grandiflorus* and *C. nycticalus*, the 'queen of the night'), *Oenothera, Silene noctiflora*, etc., the usual plan of movement is inverted, and these flowers open as the intensity of light decreases. In all cases growth movements are concerned, which depend on a physiological dorsiventrality.

Thermonastic movements are encountered particularly in spring plants where the ecological adaptation is fairly obvious; the closing of the flowers as the temperature falls, e.g. in *Tulipa, Crocus* and *Anemone nemorosa*, protects the sexual organs. Usually the flower stalks take a part in the nyctinastic movements, and as the flowers close the stalk also bends, and the flower thus nods. In certain water-lilies the flowers sink to the water level, whilst during the day they are lifted up out of the water.

The nyctinastic movements of deciduous leaves have been studied in greater detail, especially in leaves with pulvini. The movements are ordinarily photonastic, though in certain cases, e.g. in *Phaseolus*, they should rather be called transversely phototropic. There is among leaves a great multiplicity of adopted positions and types of movement. Some lower the leaves, e.g. *Oxalis*, other raise them up, e.g. *Cassia* and *Robinia*, and in some pinnate leaves the pinnules move differentially, e.g. in *Trifolium*. Often the petiole raises itself and the lamina drops, e.g. in *Phaseolus multiflorus*. In certain plants the leaves are horizontal during the day and lower or raise themselves by night; in others the opposite occurs, making an analogy with day and night flowers. The fact that many leaves are horizontal in diffuse daylight and inclined in direct sunlight may, however, be due to adjustments of dia- or plagiophototropisms. In leaves active movements can also be simulated by turgor oscillations.

The nyctinastic leaf movements which have been described in numerous works by PFEFFER (1915), STOPPEL, KLEINHOONTE (1932), BÜNNING (1944) and others are due, like those of flowers, to a physiological dorsiventrality of the parts of the growing laminae or stalks responsible for the movements. The dorsiventrality is expressed in differential movements of the dorsal and ventral sides. It has been found that in *Crocus* and *Tulipa*, for example, the upper side of the petals responds to increase in

2H

temperature more quickly than the under side. This physiological dorsiventrality often has a morphological basis that can be demonstrated anatomically. Pulvini in particular, show morphological dorsiventrality.

The dorsiventrality may, as in the case of beech shoots, be initially induced by gravity, and then transferred to all organs budded off from the tip of the shoot. Other examples of gravity-induced dorsiventrality are only weakly fixed and may be inverted even at a fairly advanced stage. In *Acacia* and *Biophytum* the sleep movements occur in the same relation to the stem, whether the plant is placed vertically or upside-down, but *geonyctinastic* plants afford examples of an inversion of dorsiventrality, in which the leaves of plants turned upside-down orientate themselves in relation to gravity and not to the morphology of the stem.

The real nature of the difference in ability to react between the upper and lower sides is not properly known. Speculations have been made concerning changes in pH, and differences in the cell-sap concentration have also been noted.

The nyctinastic rhythm, which normally follows a 12:12 hour plan, can be induced in many plants in shorter periods, e.g. in the leaves of *Albizzia* in 3:3 hours and in *Calendula* in 4:4 hours of alternate light and dark. In other plants, however, the endogenous diurnal rhythm is so strong that it overrides induction by shorter periods, such as a 6:6 hour rhythm in *Canavalia ensiformis* (KLEINHOONTE 1932). Even in those plants in which the diurnal rhythm is less strongly fixed there is a resistance to change, which is expressed as a distortion of the imposed rhythm, sometimes tending to accelerate it and sometimes to retard it.

In the plant world there is obviously a tendency to *endogenous rhythm* or daily periodicity. A short period of illumination often suffices to induce diurnal rhythmical fluctuations in plants which have been kept for a considerable time in the dark. At times some have attempted to interpret this endogenous rhythm as a characteristic impressed on the protoplasm from the start. Other workers have industriously sought external causes running parallel with the natural change between day and night, such as daily changes in the degree of ionisation of the air; but there seems to be no evidence for discussion. It should be remarked that even in plants with a strongly fixed 24-hour rhythm individual variations are large; the length of the periods is only approximately 24 hours. The endogenous diurnal rhythm of the nyctinastic movements is a special case of secondary periodic oscillations such as those we met in the tropisms, whose variation movements are restricted to the stimulated shoot or root tips. The nyctinastic movements are connected with the nutritional rhythm of the whole plant, especially with the assimilatory variations in the carbohydrate balance, and the pH values, etc.

Geonastic inductions are also tenaciously retained, e.g. in the geotropic secondary (counter-) reaction of side shoots. If these are moved from their normal geotropic position of rest, curvatures result. The phenomenon is usually termed *epinasty*, although in reality a secondary effect of a very long-lasting geotropic induction is involved. Auxin differences can be shown to be the cause of these epinastic movements (BOTTELIER 1954). On the other hand it is justifiable to speak of the *photo-epinasty* or *-hyponasty*, of many leaves that assume their flat form only after illumination. The light in this case fulfils a morphogenic function. The same result is sometimes attained in the dark, when the necessary biochemical factors are present without light.

According to YIN (1941), the nyctinastic movements of the leaves of *Carica papaya* are due to rhythmic daily variations of auxin production.

2 CHEMO- AND HAPTONASTY

Nastic movements evoked by chemical stimuli are more or less restricted to insectivorous plants. Special attention has been devoted to the *chemonastic* movements of
Drosera tentacles (cf. p. 55). DARWIN and CORRENS found that they react only weakly,
or not at all, with distilled water, whereas a solution of nitrogenous compounds, both
organic substances and ammonium salts, causes a response. Other salts are also
effective. As little as 0.4 μg of ammonium phosphate suffices, but the reaction time
becomes considerably shorter at higher concentrations. The curvature of *Drosera*
tentacles towards the centre of the lamina is due to unequal growth of the upper and
lower sides, and fully grown tentacles do not react (HOOKER 1916, 1917). An autotropic straightening follows the chemonastic curvature after a considerable time lag.
There is a definite conduction of the stimulus. Induction probably occurs in the tips
of the gland, and a transmission of stimulus can follow from one tentacle to
another. According to DARWIN conduction of the stimulus is not interrupted if one
cuts through the conducting tissues. So it must also be able to go through the living
parenchyma cells. It is said that the vascular bundle makes faster transmission
possible. Here one is reminded of the transport of auxin.

The conduction of stimulus in *Drosera* tentacles seems to be connected with aggregation of the protoplasm (p. 55), which however, is obviously more directly connected
with the secretory function of the tentacles. The movements of the tentacles are not
exclusively nastic, but also direct themselves according to the transmission of the
stimulus. By this combination of nasty and tropism an insect caught even at the edge
of the leaf is enfolded by the tentacles. The epidermal cells of the tentacles are provided
with tactile pits. They are also stimulated mechanically to a certain extent, but the
chemonasty is much stronger than the haptonasty.

The leaves of *Dionaea* also show chemonastic movements, when the short-stalked
glandular papillae are stimulated by nitrogenous materials. In this case, however, the
chemonastic reaction is much weaker than the rapid closing up of the leaves after
mechanical stimulation. The leaves of *Pinguicula vulgaris* also show chemonastic
movements.

3 SEISMONASTY

A well-known example of nastic movements, elicited by mechanical stimuli, is given
by the leaves of *Mimosa pudica*. The speed of the movements is surprising, and this
applies probably even more to *Dionaea* leaves and the pistils of *Centaurea*, *Berberis* and
Helianthemum. The speed of the reaction is connected with the fact that seismonastic
movements, unlike the tropisms, are pronouncedly all-or-none reactions. One can
imagine that the reaction suddenly releases a force pent up behind a barrier.

In the seismonastic movements of *Mimosa pudica* the leaf pinnules close together
and the petioles sink. The latent time after the first stimulation varies, according to
temperature, from only 0.1 to 1.0 second. The reaction, however, occupies several
seconds. After about half an hour the leaves have regained their original position.
The movements depend on the pulvini and the changes of turgor taking place in
them.

The nature of the turgor changes is still not completely known. Changes in permeability both for water and salts are often spoken of. The water permeability can only affect the timing of the turgor effect and therefore attracts only a secondary interest. An increase in permeability for osmotically effective substances naturally leads to an exudation of water from an elastically extended cell. BLACKMAN and PAINE, however, found that the amount exuded was not sufficient to explain the observed drop in turgor. From this it seems to follow that the change in permeability is not a full explanation. There remains the possibility of a sudden diminution of the osmotic value inside the cells.

The overall osmotic value of the cell includes the imbibitional pressure of the protoplasm. This is influenced by factors which change its hydration (cf. BALL 1944). A sudden diminution of the osmotic value, including hydration, can happen in various ways; e.g. by changes of the dissociation constants of a labile molecule, by a sudden combination of two or more low-molecular substances, or by adsorption of an osmotic material on a high-molecular substance. One can only assume that the protoplasmic structure is the site of such changes. If the cell vacuole is large in comparison with the protoplasmic lining, one must suppose a rapid exchange between the phases, which is not easy. If, on the other hand, the protoplast constitutes a considerable fraction of the cell volume, its intrinsic pressure can contribute considerably to the turgor. In this case rapid changes, e.g. in the ionic properties of the protoplasm, could cause sudden contractions.

An obvious indication of the *contractility of protoplasm* is given by the sudden movements and contractions which were early observed after mechanical or electrical stimulation of the protoplasts of *Tradescantia* hairs which line the walls and form bridles across the vacuoles. Here probably very rapid changes of potential difference between the bridles and the vacuole surrounding them are involved; i.e. processes reminiscent of nerve conduction or muscle contraction in the animal organism. It seems rather improbable that the osmotic changes observed in seismonastic reactions should be regulated by ordinary biochemical enzyme equilibria, e.g. of the type starch⇌sugar.

What has fixed attention and caused a multitude of investigations on *Mimosa* is the *conduction* of stimulus which it reveals. When the tip of a leaf is stimulated the pinnate leaflets shut together one pair after another; then the petiole sinks down, and finally the stimulation is passed to neighbouring compound leaves. According to RICCA (1916), SNOW (1925) and others the stimulus seems to be conducted partly in the xylem but partly also in the phloem, thus indicating some degree of communication between the two systems in the leaf. The presence of a hormone, which can be transmitted through a non-living zone like auxin, has been considered. Most workers on *Mimosa*, however, distinguish two or three types of stimulus conduction, which are evoked by stimuli of different strengths and which take place at different rates. Apart from conduction of a hormone there is also the possibility of the rapid transmission of a hydrostatic pressure wave, which might be due to turgor changes occurring in the primary stimulation. It is not excluded that the pulvini may act as a kind of relay, i.e. they may be stimulated by a pressure wave to hormone production, which then passes the impulse on.

The presence of a stimulus-conducting system anatomically differentiated and analogous to that of animals, which HABERLANDT among others sought to identify with the tubular tannin-containing cells in the phloem, has not been confirmed. It might on the other hand be conceivable that the cambiform cells provide some kind of stimulus conduction. As the primary reaction consists of a considerable fall in turgor (2-3 atm) on the lower side of the pulvinus so that water is exuded into the intercellular spaces, electrical currents must presumably arise, and it is probable that they also collaborate in transmitting the stimulus. The perception itself can of course also produce currents (cf. AUGER 1936). Transmission of electric currents through living protoplasm has been demonstrated e.g. in *Nitella* cells (Fig. 206). For such an electrical

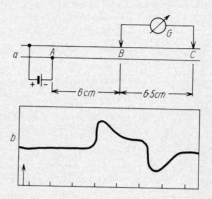

Fig. 206. Electric currents in *Nitella translucens*. *a*—experimental arrangement for measurements. The cell is electrically stimulated at *A* and the current measured between *B* and *C* with the galvanometer *G*. *b* shows the variation in the potential difference between *B* and *C* in the course of a minute (abscissa divided into 10-second periods). After about 30 seconds the stimulus is transmitted from *A* to *B*. After about another 30 seconds *C* is reached. The impulse is negative at *B* and positive at *C* (after AUGER).

transmission the plasmodesmata may be of service. As the rising sap-stream in the xylem always contains salts and ionised compounds are conducted also in the phloem, the requirements for electrical conduction are always present. To what extent such electrical transmission of stimuli actually occurs is however at present unknown.

Finally, in the long-distance transport of stimuli the conduction of ions along a surface film may be considered. The speed of such transport agrees very well with that of an electric current. Electrical effects are involved, of course, in all kinds of ion transport. Investigations by UMRATH and SOLTY (1936) and FITTING (1936) point to the formation of an 'exciting substance' (allegedly a hydroxy acid with a molecular weight of about 500), which can then be transmitted like a hormone. Even a concentration of 10^{-8} may elicit reaction in *Mimosa pudica*.

Seismonastic movements illustrate with great precision the complexity of stimulation processes, which show the following phases: (1) *perception*, which in this case can be referred to the distortion of the protoplasmic structure, (2) the immediate *stimulation*, which consists either of the formation of a stimulus substance or of electrical currents, or both, (3) *transmission*, which consists of the diffusion, surface layer transport or electrophoresis of an exciting substance or of direct electrical transmission, (4) finally the *reaction* elicited at the end point of the transmission.

Plants do not usually require for their functions any faster conduction or reaction than those provided, for example, by auxin translocation or growth movements. The variation movements in specially constructed pulvini show that even the apparently sluggish reactions of plants can be considerably accelerated. The sudden contraction of the stamen filaments of *Centaurea* is almost as fast as the muscular movement of an animal. It may possibly depend on a contractility of the protoplasm similar to that in muscle fibres, though there are great differences in the speed of conduction. The movements of *Mimosa* leaves show a conduction speed of only 2-14 mm per second, whereas in nerves speeds up to 30,000 mm per second have been measured.

The ecological importance of the movements of *Mimosa* leaves is very obscure; on the other hand the movements of the stamen filaments of *Cynara, Centaurea, Helianthemum, Berberis, Sparmannia africana* and others appear to be more significant, since they obviously facilitate pollination by insects. The movements of the stigmas of *Mimulus luteus* also belong to the same category. In *Centaurea* the filaments of the stamens contract by 20%-30% and in *Sparmannia* and *Mimulus* the exudation of water from the cells can be observed microscopically. The latent period in these seismonastic movements is usually less than a second, and the reaction is completed in a few seconds. Restoration of sensitivity takes only one or, at most, a few minutes.

The leaves of *Dionaea muscipula*, which shut together, react hapto- or seismonastically, with perception of the stimulus taking place in the long brush-like hairs on the upper (inner) side of the leaf. Here the latent period is only about a second at room temperature and the shutting up takes about 5-6 seconds. With intermittent stimulation with sub-threshold impulses the transmission and reaction times increase considerably, especially with long intervals. It seems that compressing the thin-walled cells at the base of the hair initiates induction. HABERLANDT was able to find definite arrangements for easier reception of mechanical stimuli in *Centaurea* stamens. Organs that perceive mechanical stimuli are generally found to be provided with arrangements that facilitate a deformation of the protoplasm, such as crystalline inclusions in the cells. The sensitive hairs of *Dionaea*, etc., tend to be called *stimulators*. The response mechanism of *Dionaea* differs from most seismonastic reactions by involving a growth-movement. For this reason the restoration of its sensitivity requires an extended period, and often fails.

4 THE PHONONASTY OF THE STOMATA

The stomata are regulated by turgor movements, and their light-sensitivity can be thought of as a photonastic variation movement. The ecologically more important response to changes in the water balance could be thought of as a complex hydronasty. The movements involved were discussed earlier. The respiration openings of the liverworts also show movements which are in some way similar to those of the stomata (ZIEGENSPECK 1941).

According to investigations by HARMS (1936), the photonastic reaction of the stomata shows a definite latent period, usually lasting 10-20 minutes. The intensity of the opening reaction depends to a certain extent on the intensity of illumination. The data on the spectral sensitivity of the stomata are in some ways contradictory. In general, blue-green rays appear to have a greater effect than red. Here, as in phototropism, a sensitising effect of carotene has been considered, but the riboflavins also absorb mainly in the blue-violet. Furthermore one may suspect a sensitising effect of chlorophyll, an effect which need not necessarily coincide with photosynthesis. These questions have not been finally settled.

The collaboration of photosynthesis in the movements of the stomata has, of course long been suspected, since their opening is usually associated with an increase of the osmotic value of the guard cells. It can scarcely, however, be a simple question of the balance between sugar$\rightleftharpoons$starch, as this is shifted towards the right by illumination (see e.g. HEATH 1947). A secondary formation of osmotically effective hexoses might result from activities of the amylases and phosphorylases stimulated by light. Osmotic regulation, however, could also go via respiration and the tricarboxylic acid cycle, that is e.g. by formation or respiration of malic acid. How complicated the phenomenon is appears from the fact that in *Rumex acetosa* the pH value of the cell sap is increased on illumination. Even external pH changes influence the closing movements; the stomata close with an increase of pH and open again with a decrease. The only conclusion that can at present be drawn from these facts is that there is an interaction of enzyme processes which, as is well-known, are extraordinarily sensitive to pH. Alterations of the pH value occur even with alterations of the partial pressure of CO_2 in the cell. A reduction of this, e.g. when photosynthesis begins, leads to an increase of pH.

Changes in the hydration and turgescence of the protoplasm might also influence the turgor distension of the guard cells. From this point of view it is of interest to find that WEBER observed changes in the configuration of the protoplasm of the guard cells which suggested changes in hydration. He showed that the guard cells from an open stoma give 'concave plasmolysis', but from a closed stoma 'convex plasmolysis'. The form of the nucleus also shows differences, and after a decrease in turgor coacervate formations can be observed in the cell sap. It is known that the hydration of the protoplasm is influenced by pH changes and this may help to explain the pH effects mentioned.

Stomatal movements have aroused special interest in connection with photoperiodism. Investigations by GREGORY, PEARCE and PORTSMOUTH show that the rhythm of the stomata is changed by altering the lighting sequence. If the rhythm of illumination deviates too far from the normal the stomata may even develop a tendency to close during the day and to remain open at night. As this affects photosynthesis unfavourably, it may be supposed that the photoperiodic effect is to some extent associated with the nastic rhythm of the stomata themselves and with the balance between carbohydrate and nitrogen nutritions which it controls. As the photonastic movements of the stomata ordinarily take place quickly and can easily be repeated, the causation is perhaps the other way round, the photosynthetic reactions being the primary ones and the alteration in the stomatal rhythm secondary.

G. Taxes

The mobile unicellular organisms e.g. Flagellates and Volvocaceae, as well as the swarm spores and spermatozoids equipped with cilia, also show orientation movements induced by light, chemical stimuli, etc., which are termed *taxes*.

In a taxis the stages of the stimulus-reaction chain are the same as in the tropisms of fairly anchored plants. For easily understandable reasons, however, the transmission of stimulus falls more into the background. Perception and reaction take place within the individual cell, although they are usually spatially separated. The small dimensions make a more precise study of the transmission of stimulus difficult. The mechanism of movement of the cilia has been touched on already, but is dealt with in greater detail below.

Phototactic perception appears to be often induced by yellow pigments, especially carotenes as in phototropism. The eye spot of the Volvocaceae, the *stigma*, contains orange-yellow carotenoids which have not yet been analysed further. In *Chlamydomonas eugametos* the carotenoid crocin occurs (MOEWUS 1938). The illumination of the eye spot is sometimes increased by lens-shaped thickenings of the protoplasm (Mast 1936; see also Fig. 207).

The meaning of the light absorption spectrum has not been fully explained, and not all phototactically sensitive cells react to the same extent. The action spectrum of *Rhodospirillum rubrum* is, according to Milatz and Manten (1953), identical with the absorption spectrum of the pigments. Thomas and Goedheer (1953) found that the carotenoids are less effective in phototaxis than in photosynthesis. Haxo and Clendenning (1953) also found that the positive phototaxis of *Ulva*-gametes depended on blue-violet light. Bünning and Schneiderhöhn (1956) investigated *Euglena gracilis* and found positive phototactic reaction with a main peak at 490-500 mμ and a subsidiary peak at 415-430 mμ. Light of wavelengths over 550 mμ is ineffective. They believe that the stigma is necessary only for the positive phototaxis, and not for the negative reaction which is purely phobic (see below). In *Eudorina elegans* and *Volvox minor*, according to data in the literature, the sensitivity maximum lies at about 490 mμ and in *Pandorina* and *Spondylomorum* at 435 mμ. That a sensitising pigment is not an indispensable necessity for phototactic perception follows from the observation that both the colourless and coloured types of *Chilomonas* react with ultraviolet light (366 mμ). Sensitising pigments other than carotene also occur, e.g. haemochromes in *Euglena heliorubescens*.

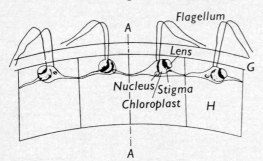

Fig. 207. Longitudinal section through the edge of a *Volvox* colony. *G*—mucous layer, *H*—the hyaline part of the cells, *A*—*A* the longitudinal axis of the colony (after Mast 1936).

The presence of a coloured eye-spot is probably not an essential for phototactic perception, and there are moreover types with stigmas which show no reaction, such as the purple bacteria. These react only weakly with green and blue light, but show a maximum in the infra-red. The movements of the chloroplasts of higher plants are considerably more sensitive towards the blue rays absorbed by carotene than towards the red which are absorbed by chlorophyll (Voerkel 1934). Chlorophyll is not essential for the phototaxis of chloroplasts, since the plastids react phototactically in etiolated tissues.

The phototactic movements are divided into *phobic* and *topic*. In the former the organisms react with differences in illumination without respect to the direction; and in the latter case they swim directly towards or away from a light-source. One can compare the phobic reaction type with the nasties and the topic with the tropisms. The phobic type of reaction thus depends on the protoplasmic organisation. In the purely phobic movements the cilia beat either frontwards or backwards, according to the difference between light and darkness. In the topic movements the direction of the vibrations of the cilia is determined by the direction of the light. Characteristically the capacity for tactic orientation never gets beyond a kind of pseudotopic method of reaction. Completely anisotropic reactivity never seems to be achieved.

The *movement mechanisms of the cilia* has been studied with dark-field illumination and the polarisation microscope. Stroboscopic methods have also been used. In these the object is illuminated through a rotating sectorised diaphragm, so that the flashes of light come in the same rhythm as the strokes of the cilia. The cilia thus appear to stand still and can be studied in different stages of movement. The frequency of the strokes of the cilia can also be easily determined in this way. The backward movement of the water can be studied by means of particles of indian ink mixed with it. Papers on the movement of cilia are available from ÚLEHLA, BUDER, METZNER, PETERS, KRIJGSMAN and others.

In *Chromatium* a broom of cilia at the back of the cell acts like a propeller. The speed of rotation is 40-60 revolutions per second (Fig. 208). The spirillae (Fig. 209) have a

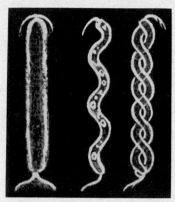

Fig. 208. The flagellate *Chromatium okenii* in dark-field illumination. The large arrow shows the direction of movement, and the small arrows the recoiling water currents (after METZNER).

Fig. 209. *Spirillum volutans* in dark-field illumination (after METZNER).

tuft of cilia at each end. The body moves itself by rotation, and the direction of movement is determined by co-ordination of the two tufts of cilia, of which only one needs to be stimulated in order to determine the pattern of beating of the other. In *Clostridium* the direction of movement is reversed if the cilia are curved sideways. The Peridinieae have at one end two cilia of which the one working in the longitudinal direction steers the body through the water whilst the one placed transversely causes rotation.

In all these species the cilia operate in a sort of snakelike oscillation. If there are many cilia in the broom or tuft, the individual cilia are put into operation in rapid succession one after the other. There are, however, examples of an oar-like movement of cilia, e.g. in the spermatozoids of *Adiantum cuneatum* (Fig. 210). Here the cilia remain straight during the stroke, but are curved in the return so that the resistance of the water is diminished.

The cilia show optical anisotropy, and in certain cases a fine structure can be distinguished. In order to explain the movements reference has been made to the bellows-like construction of large molecules, which fold together or unfold according to the charges on the side groups. Changes of charge can be brought about e.g. by cation exchange (cf. Chap. 1). If the cilium is constructed of spirally plaited fibrillar molecules, a change of charge proceeding from the base to the tip must cause a snake-like movement. With a bilateral construction of the cilium, oar-like movements could arise. Repetition of the impulse of course presupposes a source of energy. Reserves of glucose are accordingly found in spermatozoa, whereas autotropic flagellates themselves prepare the necessary respiratory material by photosynthesis.

The rhythmic repetition of ciliary contraction is connected with the construction of the cilium and with an energy transfer taking place in it, as is shown by the fact that detached cilia continue the movements for a short time. The mechanism resembles in principle the rhythmic nastic movements in which a supply of energy builds up a movement potential behind a barrier, which at a certain height of potential breaks through or 'explodes'. The function of the cilia has accordingly been found to depend on the redox potential (NOMURA 1933). It may be imagined that the oxidation processes taking place in the substance of the cilia provide the charges on the side chains of the fibrillar molecules, e.g. by means of high-energy phosphates. The adenosine phosphates may themselves also form spiral molecules. The mere transport of a phosphoric acid group along such a molecule should in itself suffice to evoke a wave of contraction.

An example of an organism that reacts phobically is *Thiospirillum jenense* (BUDER 1919). Here the direction of movement of the cilia is reversed when the organism comes out of the light into darkness, and it then swims in the opposite direction as long as the illumination remains unchanged. The organism thus rebounds into the field of light.

The photosensitivity of the motile organisms is usually quite considerable. For the gametes of *Ulva lactuca* the light maximum for the positive reaction is about 30 lux (HAXO and CLENDENNING 1953). The differentiating sensitivity can also be acute, e.g. 10% (as a difference between 18 and 20 lux). The relative sensitivity diminishes, however, with the intensity of the light. The summation of stimuli in phototactic organisms shows similarities with the phototropism of higher plants. Phobic organisms give reversed reactions at high light intensities, so that too bright surroundings are avoided. Phobic types of reaction are shown also by Nostocaceae and *Oscillatoria*.

Examples of topic movements are given by Flagellates and Volvocaceae. They swim in the direction of the light, usually with rotation about their own axis. The reaction can, however, often appear as a modified phobic movement (MAST 1936). *Volvox* colonies react to uniform reductions of light intensity by the cilia reversing their direction of stroke, while the rotation also ceases. If the illumination is increased the cilia strike more outwards, so that forward movement decreases and rotation increases. With lateral illumination these reactions are combined, so that the cilia on the shaded side brake the rotation, while the cilia on the illuminated side turn the colony into the direction of the light (Fig. 211).

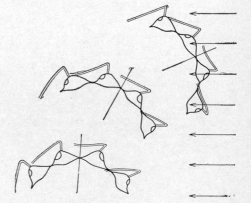

Fig. 210. Oar movements of the cilia of a spermatozoid of *Adiantum cuneatum*. 1-4 forward stroke, 5-10 return movement (after METZNER).

FIG. 211. Adjustment of a positively chemotactic *Volvox* colony in the direction of the light (after MAST).

In the Peridinieae also the orientation takes place stepwise. In oblique light the sensitive spot at the base of each cilium is shaded once during each rotation of the body. At the same time the movement of the cilium is temporarily altered and this automatically causes an adjustment into the direction of the light (METZNER 1930, cf. also BÜNNING and SCHNEIDERHÖHN 1956 on *Euglena*).

The taxes are, of course, influenced like the tropisms by general factors such as temperature, pH, CO_2, salts, etc.

The photo- and chemotactic *movements of the chloroplasts* and the movements of the nucleus on growing root hairs are rather like the movements of *Amoeba*, though no pseudopodia are formed. Alterations of form are, however, observable with both chloroplasts and nuclei.

It has long been thought that in the movement of whole protoplasts or of individual organelles surface tension comes into play. The relationships of course are by no means simple, since the boundary layers of the living substance are probably composed of mono- or multi-molecular layers of orientated molecules. There are also the electrical potential differences which, naturally, are altered non-uniformly if, for example, a stream of neutral salts impinges on one side. The cohesion of the surface layer, its hydration, etc., can also easily be altered unilaterally. Any of these may cause movements of a free-floating organelle. In the chloroplasts the surface may be influenced by the direction of diffusion of the carbon dioxide, etc. There are thus many points of departure for speculations on the mechanism of the movements of chloroplasts, nuclei, mitochondria, etc., but it must be admitted that few definite facts are yet known.

There are also passive movements of the organelles. They are carried along with the protoplasmic streaming, e.g. in *Nitella* and *Elodea*. In other cases, as e.g. in root hairs, the nucleus is moved to a large extent independently of the protoplasmic streaming.

The chloroplasts are usually dispersed, which by analogy with ultramicrosuspensions may suggest a boundary charge against the surrounding protoplasm. If colloidal particles are discharged they form aggregates, i.e. they are precipitated. Chloroplasts are seen to aggregate if the illumination is too intense, or in plasmolysis. In the latter a partial discharge of the chloroplast surface by an increased effect of neutral salts is readily supposed.

In diffuse light the chloroplasts collect mainly on the well-illuminated external and internal walls of the leaf. During the night there is a tendency to collect on the walls at right angles to the leaf surface. Very strong light can also produce this reaction (Fig. 212). One gets the impression that the chloroplasts are not directly phototactic,

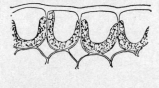

Fig. 212. Epidermal cells with chloroplasts from a cross-section of a leaf of *Selaginella serpens*; above—the position in the morning, below—in the evening (after BÜNNING).

but that their movements are regulated by a combined effect of light and chemical stimuli with the latter coming particularly from the transverse walls. One could not go far wrong in characterising the movements of the chloroplasts as a chemotaxis modified by light.

Under natural conditions phototaxis and *chemotactic movements* are of the greatest importance for free-moving organisms and cells, since in this way they are enabled to seek out appropriate concentrations of nutrients, carbon dioxide, oxygen, etc.

Like the streaming of protoplasm enclosed within walls, the movements of cells provided with cilia, especially the heterotrophic bacteria, are also very sensitive to amino acids, peptides, peptones and the proteins built from them. The steric configuration of the amino acids is very important for chemotactic movements. In addition a general sensitivity towards H- and OH-ions is evident; in Myxomycetes H-ions evoke positively and OH-ions negatively chemotactic movements.

In investigations on the chemotactic activity of various substances one utilises either the phenomenon of fatigue or the principle of summation of sub-threshold stimuli. A chemotactically inactive substance does not diminish the sensitivity for a subsequent dose of an effective substance, i.e. the effects of the two substances are not additive. As in phototaxis, the mechanism of movement of chemotactic effects is ordinarily of a phobic type.

PFEFFER early hinted at the function of malic acid as a chemotactic attraction for the spermatozoids of the Archegoniates and showed the validity of the WEBER-FECHNER law. In his experiments he put a capillary tube supplied with malic acid into a drop of a very dilute solution of the same substance containing fern spermatozoids. These were attracted to the capillary tube provided that the difference in concentration was great enough. Similar experiments were made with *B. coli* and meat extract. Malic acid also attracts spermatozoids of *Salvinia*, *Isoëtes*, *Selaginella* and *Equisetum*. Citric acid fulfils the same function for *Lycopodium*, and glucose for mosses and some liverworts.

H. Mechanical Movements

In this group are collected movements which are not released by the perception of a stimulus by the protoplasm. The 'stimulus' releases mechanical tensions. The mechanical movements are very varied. The state of tension may be built up by living cells even when the release and reaction are purely mechanical,

Cohesion movements are made possible by the negative pressure that arises when water evaporates from cells with walls that are rigid and not easily penetrated by air. As a result of the vacuum the walls are stretched into a curve. Cohesion of the water and a low vapour pressure are essential. The classic example of a cohesion movement is the annulus of the fern sporangium, an incomplete ring of cells with U-shaped thickenings which clasps the otherwise thin-walled sporangium (Fig. 213). The increasing tension in the annulus as it dries out leads eventually to the rupture of the sporangium, and when the tension in the ring suddenly breaks down the spores are slung out.

In the sporangia of *Equisetum* and in the stamens of angiosperms opening is also facilitated by tensions of a similar kind. Cohesion movements are also carried out by the fibrous elaters occurring in the sporangia of mosses, Myxomycetes and certain fungi.

Examples of cohesion movements in living tissues are afforded by the leaves of grasses, which in *Elymus*, *Psamma*, *Festuca rubra* and other species, roll or fold together lengthwise as they dry. Turgor pressures are involved, but growth processes can also assist (BURSTRÖM 1942). The bladder traps of *Utricularia* also have a mechanism in which tissue tensions take a part. The sudden springing open of the fruits of *Impatiens noli tangere* and *Eschscholtzia* when they are touched is likewise due to the release of tensions due to non-uniform growth.

Hygroscopic movements can be referred to the swelling and contracting of dead cell walls. Their secondary and tertiary thickening layers usually have a spiral structure, in which the submicroscopic fibrils may be orientated in different directions. As a result a change of water content may cause twists and spiral tensions. Hygroscopic movements are encountered in many fruit capsules which open in dry air and close in moist; in the carpels of the Papilionaceae and in the peristomes of the spore capsules of mosses. According to FREY-WYSSLING these hygroscopic movements are due to changes of hydration in the tightly packed (1 mμ) fibrillar micelles, which cause the fibrils to separate or close together. If there are two thickening layers with their fibrils running in different directions, movements are inevitably caused. A well-known example is given by the awn of *Erodium cicutarium* (Fig. 214), which as the moisture content varies, carries out spiral turns which drive the cone-shaped seed, which is provided with barbs, into the ground.

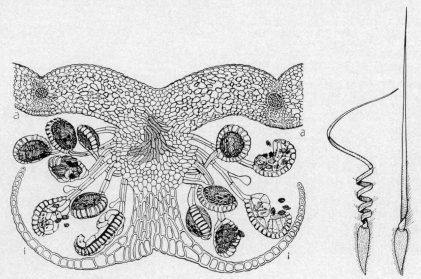

FIG. 213. Cross-section of a sorus of *Dryopteris filix mas. a*—the leaf mesophyll, *i*—indusium. The sporangia are at different stages of opening.

Fig. 214. Partial fruit of *Erodium cicutarium*. Left—in dry, right—in moist condition.

BIBLIOGRAPHY

AALTONEN, V. T., 1939, Comm. Inst. Forest. Fenn., **27**, 4.
AARNIO, B., 1934, Agrogeol. Julkais. Helsingfors. No. **35**.
ABDERHALDEN, R., 1947, Z. Vitamin-, Hormon- and Fermentforsch., **1**, 163.
ÅBERG, B., and RODHE, W., 1942, Symbol. Bot. Upsal., **5**, no. 3.
ÅBERG, B., 1943, Symbol. Bot. Upsal., **8**, no. 1.
— 1945, Lantbrukshögsk. Ann. (Uppsala), **13**, 239.
— 1947, Lantbrukshögsk. Ann., **15**, 37.
— 1956, The Chemistry and Mode of Action of Plant Growth Substances (London Symposium). 93.
— 1957, Ann. Rev. Plant Physiol., **8**, 153.
ABRAMS, R., 1951, J. Amer. Chem. Soc. **73**, 1888.
ABRAMSON, H. A., 1940, Trans. Faraday Soc., **36**, 5.
ABRAMSON, H. A., et al., 1942, *Electrophoresis of Proteins and the Chemistry of Cell Surfaces*. New York.
ADACHI, M., 1933, J. Soc. Trop. Agric. Taihoku Imp. Univers., **5**, 279.
ADAIR, G. S., and ADAIR, M. E., 1940, Trans. Faraday Soc., **36**, 23.
ADAM, N. K., 1941, *The Physics and Chemistry of Surfaces*. 3rd ed. London.
ADDICOTT, F. T., 1941, Bot. Gaz., **102**, 576.
ADLER, E., et al., 1938, Hoppe-Seylers Z., **255**, 14.
ÅKERMAN, A., 1917, Bot. Notiser, 145.
ALBAUM, H. G., and COMMONER, B., 1941. Biol. Bull., **80**, 314.
ALBAUM, H. G., and COHEN, P. P., 1943, J. Biol. Chem., **149**, 19.
ALBAUM, H. G., et al., 1946, J. Biol. Chem., **165**, 125.
ALBERTS-DIETERT, F., 1941, Planta, **32**, 88.
ALBRECHT, W. A., 1940, Amer. J. Bot., **28**, 394; Soil Sci. Soc. Amer. Proc., **5**, 8.
ALBRECHT, W. A., et al., 1942, Amer. J. Bot., **29**, 210.
ALEXANDER, J., 1944, *Colloid Chemistry Theoretical and Applied*. New York.
ALGERA, L., et al., 1947, Biochim. Biophys. Acta, **1**, 517.
ALLEN, R. C., 1943, Contrib. Boyce Thompson Inst., **13**, 221.
ALLEN, R. C., et al., 1947, Arch. Biochem., **14**, 335.
ALMEIDA, F. J. DE, 1941, Agron. Lusitana, **3**, 59.
ALSAC, N., 1942, Beih. Bot. Centralbl., **61**, Abt. A, 329.
ALSUP, F. W., 1942, Physiol. Zool., **15**, 168.
AMEIJDEN, U. P. VAN, 1947, Rec. Trav. Bot. Néerl., **44**, 149.
AMES, S. R., et al., 1946, J. Biol. Chem., **165**, 81.
AMLONG, H. U., 1939, Jahrb. wiss. Bot., **88**, 421.
AMOS, G. L. and WOOD, J. G., 1939, Austral. J. Exp. Biol. Med. Sci., **17**, 285.
ANDERSON, E., 1946, J. Biol. Chem., **165**, 233.
ANDERSON, E., and PIGMAN, W. W., 1947, Science, **105**, 601.
ANDERSON, F. G., 1929, Plant Physiol., **4**, 459.
ANDERSON, G., 1944, Dissertation. Lund.
ANDERSON, N. E., and HERTZ, C. H., 1955, Z. angew. Physik, **7**, 361.
ANGERER, C. A., 1942, Physiol. Zool., **15**, 436.
ANKER, L., 1955, Acta. Bot. Néerland., **5**, (**4**), 335.
APINIS, A., 1939, Latvijas Biol. Biedribas Raksti (Acta Biol. Latvica), **9**, 71.
APPLEMAN, C. O., and BROWN, R. G., 1946, Amer. J. Bot., **33**, 170.
ARCHBOLD, H. K., 1940, Biochem. J., **34**, 749.
ARENS, K., 1930, Planta, **10**, 814.
— 1933, Planta, **20**, 621.
— 1934, Jahrb. wiss. Bot., **80**, 769.
— 1936, Jahrb. wiss. Bot., **83**, 513.
ARENZ, B., 1941, Biochem. Z., **308**, 196.
ARISZ, W. H., 1915, Rec. Trav. Bot. Néerl., **12**, 1.
— 1943, Verh. Kon. Nederl. Akad. Wetensch., **45**, 794.
— 1946, Verh. Kon. Nederl. Akad. Wetensch., **48**, 420.
ARLAND, A., 1936, *Der experimentelle Nachweis der Beziehungen zwischen Wasserverbrauch und Ernährung bei Getreide*. Berlin.

ARMSTRONG, J. J., et al., 1958, Nature, **181**, 1692.
ARNDT, C. H., 1929, Amer. J. Bot., **16**, 179.
ARNOLD, A., 1931, Planta, **13**, 529.
ARNON, D. I., and HOAGLAND, D. R., 1940, Soil Sci., **50**, 463.
ARNON, D. I., et al., 1942, Plant Physiol., **17**, 515.
ARNON, D. I., and WESSEL, G., 1953, Nature, **172**, 1039.
ARNON, D. I., ICHIOKA, P. S., WESSEL, G., FUJIWARA, A., and WOOLLEY, J. T., 1955, Physiol. Plant-
    arum, **8**, 538, 552.
ARNON, D. I., WHATLEY, F. R., and ALLEN, M. B., 1957, Nature, **180**, 182.
ARONOFF, S., and MAKINNEY, G., 1943, J. Amer. Chem. Soc., **65**, 956.
ARONOFF, S., 1946, Plant Physiol., **21**, 393.
ARTHUR, M., et al., 1930, Amer. J. Bot., **17**, 416.
ARTHUR, J. M., and HARVILL, E. K., 1941, Contrib. Boyce Thompson Inst., **12**, 111.
ASAI, T., 1937, Japan. J. Bot., **8**, 343.
ASHBY, E., 1931, Plant Physiol., **6**, 715.
ASHIDA, J., 1934, Mem. Coll. Sci. Kyoto Univ., Ser. B, **9**, 141.
— 1935, Mem. Coll. Sci. Kyoto Univ., Ser B., **11**, 55.
ÅSLANDER, A., 1948, *Den svenska åkerjordens kalkbehov*. Stockholm.
ASTBURY, W. T., and BELL, F. O., 1938, Cold Spring Harbor Symp. Quant. Biol., **6**.
ATKINSON, H. J., et al., 1944, Sci. Agron. (Ottawa), **24**, 437.
ATLAS, SH. M., and FARBER, E., 1956, J. Biol. Chem., **219**, 31.
AUDUS, L. J., 1935, New Phytologist, **34**, 386.
— 1939, New Phytologist, **38**, 284.
AUDUS, L. J., and QUASTEL, J. H., 1947, Nature, **160**, 222.
AUDUS, L. J., 1949, Biol. Rev. **24**, 51.
— 1953, *Plant Growth Substances*. London.
AUDUS, L. J., and BROWBRIDGE, M. E., 1957, J. Exp. Bot., **8**, 105.
AUFDEMGARTEN, H., 1939, Planta, **29**, 643.
AUGER, D., 1936, *Comparaison entre la rythmicité des courants d'action cellulaires chez les végétaux
    et chez les animaux*. Paris.
AVERY, G. S., 1933, Amer. J. Bot., **20**, 565.
— 1942, Symp. Quant. Biol., **10**, 2.
AVERY, G. T., et al., 1937, Amer. J. Bot., **24**, 666.
— 1944, J. Exp. Med., **79**, 137.

BAATZ, I., 1939, Arch. Mikrobiol., **10**, 508.
BAER, H., et al., 1946, J. Biol. Chem., **162**, 65.
BAILEY, I. W., and TUPPER, W. W., 1918, Proc. Amer. Acad., **54**, 150.
BAILEY, I. W., 1923, Amer. J. Bot., **10**, 499.
— 1930, Z. Zellforsch. Mikr. Anat., **10**, 651.
BAIRATI, A., and LEHMANN, F. E., 1952, Experientia, **8**, 60.
BAKER, H., and JAMES, W. O., 1933, New Phytologist, **32**, 245.
BALL, E., 1946, Amer. J. Bot., **33**, 301.
BALL, E. G., 1944, Amer. Acad. Sci. N. Y., **45**, 363.
BALLARD, L. A. T., 1941, New Phytologist, **40**, 276.
BALLENTINE, R., and PARPART, A. K., 1940, J. Cell. Comp. Physiol., **16**, 49.
BALY, E. C. C., 1940, *Photosynthesis*. London.
BANDURSKI, R. S., 1955, J. Biol. Chem., **217**, 137.
BANGA, I., and PHILIPPOT, E., 1939, Hoppe-Seylers Z., **258**, 147.
BANGA, I., and SZENT-GYÖRGYI, A., 1940, Science, **92**, 514.
BANGA, I., et al., 1947, Nature, **159**, 194.
BANNAU, M. W., 1951, Canad. J. Bot. **29**, 421. 1953, **31**, 63. 1955, **33**, 113. 1956, **34**, 175.
BARA, M., 1957, Istanbul Univ. fen Fakült. Mecm. Ser. B. **22**, 209.
BARANETZKY, J., 1901, Flora, **89**.
BARBER, H. N., and CALLEN, H. G., 1944, Nature, **153**, 109.
BARBIER, G., 1936, Ann. Agron., **1**, 568.
— 1945, Ann. Agron., **15**, 217.
BARKER, H. A., and KAMEN, M. D., 1945, Proc. Nat. Acad. Sci., **31**, 219.
BARKER, H. A., et al., 1945, Proc. Nat. Acad. Sci., **31**, 355.
BARKER, H. A., 1947, Antonie van Leeuwenhoek, **12**, 167.
BARNES, T. C., and BEUTNER, R., 1942, J. Cell. Comp. Physiol., **20**, 317.
BARRON, E. S. G., 1943, Biol. Symp., **10**, 27.
BARRON, E. S. G., and SINGER, T. P., 1945, J. Biol. Chem., **157**, 241.
BARROWS, F. L., 1939, Contrib. Boyce Thompson Inst., **11**, 61.

BARTHOLOMEW, J. W., and UMBREIT, W. W., 1944, J. Bacteriol., **48**, 567.
BARTLETT, G., 1942, (Dissertation). Univ. of Chicago.
BARTLEY, J., 1937, Proc. Nat. Acad. Sci., **23**, 385.
BARTON-WRIGHT, E. C., 1937, *General Plant Physiology*. London.
BASSHAM, J. A., BENSON, A. A., KAY, L. D., HARRIS, A. Z., WILSON, A. T., and CALVIN, M., 1953, Radiation Lab., Univ. California. Oct. 1953.
BAUER, PH., 1935, Planta, **24**, 446.
BAUERJI, B., et al., 1946, Science and Culture, **11**, 386.
BAULE, B., 1930, Planta, **10**, 84.
BAUMGARTNER, A., 1934, Z. Bot., **28**, 81.
BAWDEN, F. C., and PIRIE, N. W., 1945, Brit. J. Exp. Pathol., **26**, 277.
BAYLISS, J. S., 1907, Ann. Bot., **21**, 387.
BAZIN, S., 1945, Compt. Rend. Paris. **220**, 183.
BEAR, F. E., and TOTH, S. J., 1942, Ind. Eng. Chem., **34**, 49.
BEAUCHAMP, C. E., 1942, Plant Physiol., **17**, 165.
BECK, W. A., 1941, Stud. Inst. Divi Thomae, **3**, 113.
BECK, W. A., and ANDRUS, B., 1943, Bull. Torrey Bot. Club, **70**, 563.
BECKER, W. A., 1938, Bot. Rev., **4**, 446.
BEHR-NEGENDANK, C., 1939, Biol. Centralbl., **59**.
BEHRE, L., 1929, Planta, **7**, 208.
BEILER, A., 1938, Jahrb. wiss. Bot., **87**, 356.
BEINERT, H., 1956, Biochim. Biophys. Acta, **20**, 588.
— 1957, J. Biol. Chem., **225**, 465.
BĚLAŘ, K., 1939, Z. Zellforsch. Mikro. Anat., **10**, 73.
BĚLEHRÁDEK, J., 1929, Protoplasma, **7**, 232.
BĚLEHRÁDEK, J., and BĚLEHRADKOVA, M., 1929, New Phytologist, **28**, 313.
BĚLEHRÁDEK, J., 1935, *Temperature and Living Matter*. Berlin.
BELJAKOV, E., 1929, Planta, **8**, 269.
— 1930, Planta, **11**, 727.
BELVAL, H., 1930, Chinese J. Physiol., **4**, 365.
BENDRAT, M., 1929, Planta, **7**, 508.
BENNET, J. P., 1945, Soil Sci., **60**, 91.
BENNET-CLARK, T. A., 1932, Sci. Proc. Roy. Dublin Soc., **20**, 293.
— 1933, New Phytologist, **37**, 128, 197.
BENNET-CLARK, T. A., and BEXON, D., 1943, New Phytologist, **42**, 65.
BENNET-CLARK, T. A., and KEFFORD, N. P., 1951, J. Exp. Bot. **2**, 169.
BENSLEY, R. R., 1942, Science, **96**, 389.
BENSON, A., and CALVIN, M., 1947, Science, **105**, 648.
BERGER, J., and AVERY, G. S., 1944, Amer. J. Bot., **31**, 199.
BERGER, J., et al., 1946, J. Gen. Physiol., **29**, 379.
BERGMANN, M., 1942, Adv. Enzymol., **2**, 49.
BERNHEIM, K., 1930, Beih. Bot. Centralbl., **46**, 347.
BERNSTEIN, L., 1945, Plant Physiol., **20**, 540.
BERRY, L. J., and BROCK, M. J., 1946, Plant Physiol., **21**, 542.
BERTHOLD, G., 1886, *Protoplasmamechanik*. Leipzig.
BERTRAND, G., 1948, Rec. Trav. Chim. Pays-Bas, **57**, 569.
BERTRAND, G., and BERTRAND, D., 1946, Compt. Rend. Paris, **222**, 572.
BEST, R. J., 1945, Austral. J. Exp. Biol. Med. Sci., **23**, 221.
BEZSONOV, N., and LEROUX, H., 1945, Nature, **156**, 474.
BICKENBACH, K., 1932, Beitr. Biol. Pflanz., **19**, 334.
BIEBL, R., 1937, 1939, Beih. Bot. Centralbl., **57**, 381. Protoplasma, **28**, 562.
BIERBERG, W., 1909, Flora, **98**, 57.
BIRAUD, H., 1938, Jahrb. wiss. Bot., **87**, 93.
BIRCH-HIRSCHFELD, L., 1919, Jahrb. wiss. Bot., **59**, 171.
BJÖRKMAN, E., 1942, Symbol. Bot. Upsala, **6**, no. 2.
— 1943, Norrlands Skogsvårdsförbunds Tidskr., **1**.
BLAAUW, A. H., 1915, 1916, Z. Bot., **6**, 641, **7**, 465.
— 1918, Meded. Landbouwhoogesch. Wageningen, **15**, 89.
BLAAUW, A. H., et al., 1930, Verh. Kon. Nederl. Akad. Wetensch., **26**, no. 7.
BLACKMAN, F. F., 1905, Ann. Bot., **19**, 281.
BLACKMAN, F. F., and PAINE, M., 1918, Ann. Bot., **32**, 69.
BLACKMAN, F. F., 1928, Proc. Roy. Soc., B, **103**, 412, 491.
BLACKMAN, G. E., 1945, Nature, **155**, 500.
BLAGOVESTJENSKIJ, A. V., 1935, Planta, **24**, 276.

BLAGOVESTJENSKIJ, A. V., 1937, Bull. Biol. Med. Exp. USSR, **3**, 235.
BLANCHARD, K. C., 1940, Cold Spring Harbor Symp., Quant. Biol., **8**, 1.
BLANK, F., and FREY-WYSSLING, A., 1941, Ann. Bot., **8**, 71.
BLANK, F., and DEUEL, H., 1943, Vierteljahrsschr. Naturforsch. Ges. Zürich, **88**, 161.
BLANK, F., 1947, Bot. Rev. **13**, 241.
BLISS, M., 1939, Amer. J. Bot., **26**, 620.
BLOCH, R., 1943, Bot. Rev., **9**, 261.
BOBKO, E. V., and SCHENNRENKOVA, N. P., 1945, Compt. Rend. Acad. USSR, **46**, 115.
BODENBERG, E. T., 1929, Amer. J. Bot., **16**, 229.
BOERI, E., and TOSI, L., 1954, Arch. Biochim. Biophys., **52**, 83.
— — 1956, Arch. Biochim. Biophys., **60**, 463.
BOGEN, H. J., 1938, Planta, **28**, 535.
— 1940, Z. Bot., **36**, 65.
— 1953, Fortschr. Bot., **14**, 256.
BOLLARD, E. G., 1956, Nature, **178**, 1189.
BÖMEKE, H., 1939, Arch. Mikrobiol., **10**, 385.
BONNER, J., 1936, Bot. Rev., **2**, 475.
BONNER, J., and ENGLISH, J., 1937, Science, **86**, 2233.
BONNER, J., and DERVIRIAN, PH. S., 1939, Amer. J. Bot., **26**, 661.
BONNER, J., and GREENE, J., 1939, Bot. Gaz., **101**, 491.
BONNER, J., 1942, Bot. Gaz., **103**, 581.
BONNER, J., and GALSTON, A. W., 1944, Bot. Gaz., **106**, 185.
BONNER, J., and WILDMAN, S. G., 1946, Arch. Biochem., **10**, 497.
BONNER, J., 1946, Bot. Rev., **12**, 535.
— 1948, Arch. Biochem., **17**, 311.
— 1957., Austral. J. Sci., **19**, 127.
BONNER, J., and FOSTER, R. J., 1955, J. Exp. Bot., **6**, 293.
— — 1955, The Chemistry and Mode of Action of Plant Growth Substances Symposium, London, 295.
BONNER, W. D., 1957, Ann. Rev. Plant Physiol., **8**, 427.
BOOIJ, H. L., 1940, Rec. Trav. Bot. Néerl., **37**, 1.
BOON-LONG, T. S., 1941, Amer. J. Bot., **28**, 333.
BOONSTRA, A. E. H. R., 1930, Planta, **10**, 108.
— 1937. Z. Pflanzenzücht., A, **21**, 115.
BORESCH, K., 1928, Biol. Z., **202**, 190.
BORGSTRÖM, G., 1939, Kungl. Fysiogr. Sällsk. Förh. (Lund), **9**, no. 12.
BORRISS, H., 1934, Planta, **22**, 644.
— 1936, Ber. deutsch. Bot. Ges., **54**, 472.
BORRISS, H., and BUSSMAN, T., 1939, Jahrb. wiss. Bot., **88**, 351.
BOSE, S. R., 1943, Science and Culture, **8**, 389.
BOSIAN, G., 1933, Z. Bot., **26**, 209.
BOSWELL, J. G., and WHITTING, G. C., 1938, Ann. Bot., **2**, 847.
— — 1940, New Phytologist, **39**, 241.
BOTTELIER, H. P., 1934, Rec. Trav. Bot. Néerl., **31**, 474.
— 1939, Rec. Trav. Bot. Néerl., **36**, 658.
— 1954, Ann. Bogoriensis, **1**, 185.
BÖTTICHER, R., and BEHLING, L., 1939, Flora, **34**, 1.
BOUILLENNE, R., 1926, Ann. Physiol. Physicochim. Biol., 426.
BOUILLENNE, R., and BOUILLENNE-WALRAUD, M., Lejeunia, **11**, 17.
BOURNE, G., et al., 1942, *Cytology and Cell Physiology*. London.
BOURNE, G. H., 1951, *Cytology and Cell Physiology*. Oxford.
BOUSSINGAULT, T. B., 1864, Ann. Sci. Nat. Bot., **1**, 314.
BOUYOUCOS, G. J., and MICK, A. H., 1940, Soil Sci. Soc. Amer. Proc., **5**, 77.
BOUYOUCOS, G. J., 1947, Soil Sci., **64**, 71.
BOYER, P. D., et al., 1943, J. Biol. Chem., **149**, 529.
BOYNTON, B. W. R., et al., 1941, Proc. Amer. Soc. Hortic. Sci., **38**, 17.
BOYNTON, D., and COMPTON, O. C., 1944, Soil Sci., **57**, 107.
BOYSEN-JENSEN, P., 1932, *Die Stoffproduktion der Pflanzen*. Jena.
— 1938, *Growth Hormones in Plants*. 2nd Edit. New York.
BRACHET, J., and MIRSKY, A. E., 1959, *The Cell, Biochemistry, Physiology, Morphology*. New York.
BRADBURY, F. R., and JORDAN, D. O., 1942, Biochem. J., **36**, 287.
BRADFIELD, J. K. G., 1947, Nature, **159**, 467.
BRAND, G., et al., 1946, Nature, **158**, 323.
BRANDENBURG, E., 1939, Phytopathol. Z., **12**, 1.

BRAUN-BLANQUET, J., and WALTER, H., 1931, Jahrb. wiss. Bot., **74**, 697.
BRAUNER, L., and KÖCKEMANN, A., 1931, Jahrb. wiss. Bot., **75**, 304.
BRAUNER, L., et al., 1940, Rev. Fac. Sci. Univ. Istanbul, Ser. B, **5**, 266.
BRAUNER, L., 1942, Rev. Fac. Sci. Univ. Istanbul, **7**, 46.
BRAUNER, L., and BRAUNER, M., Rev. Fac. Sci. Univ. Istanbul, Ser. B, **8**, 264.
BRAUNER, L., 1947 Rev. Fac. Sci. Univ. Istanbul, Ser. B, **12**, 35.
— 1953, Z. Bot., **41**, 291.
— 1954, Ann. Rev. Plant Physiol., **5**, 163.
— 1955, Z. Bot., **43**, 467.
BRAUNER, L., and VARDAR, Y., 1950, Rev. Fac. Sci. Univ. Istanbul, (B) **15**, 269.
BRENCHLEY, W., and WARINGTON, K., 1927, Ann. Bot., **41**, 167.
BRENCHLEY, W. E., 1932, J. Agric. Sci., **22**, 704.
— 1947, Bot. Rev., **13**, 169.
BRENNER, W., 1920, Ber. deutsch. Bot. Ges., **38**, 277.
— 1930, Acta Bot. Fenn., **7**.
— 1931, Svensk Bot. Tidskr., **25**, 147.
— 1931, Acta Bot. Fenn., **9**.
BREWIG, A., 1933, Planta, **20**, 734.
— 1937, Z. Bot., **31**, 481.
BRIAN, P. W., 1958, Nature, **181**, 1122—1123.
BRIGGS, G. E., and ROBERTSON, R. N., 1957, Ann. Rev. Plant Physiol., **8**, 11.
BROADFOOT, W. M., and TYNER, E. H., 1939, Soil. Sci. Soc. Amer. Proc., **4**, 156.
BROOKS, S. C., 1939, J. Cell. Comp. Physiol., **14**, 383.
BROUWER, R., 1954, Acta Bot. Néerland., **3**, 162.
BROWN, A. H., and GODDARD, D. H., 1941, Amer. J. Bot., **28**, 319.
BROWN, A. J., and WORLEY, F. P., 1912, Proc. Roy. Soc., B, **85**, 546.
BROWN, H. T., and ESCOMBE, F., 1900, Phil. Trans. Roy. Soc., B, **193**, 223.
BROYER, T. C., 1939, Bot. Rev., **5**, 531.
BROYER, T. C., and HOAGLAND, D. R., 1943, Amer. J. Bot., **30**, 261.
BROYER, T. C., 1947, Bot. Rev., **13**, 125.
BRÜCKE, E., 1861, *Die Elementarorganismen*. Sitz. ber. Akad. Wiss. Wien, **44**.
BRUMFIELD, R. T., 1955, Amer. J. Bot., **42**, 958.
BRUNS, A., 1925, Bot. Arch, **11**, 40.
BUDER, J., 1919, Jahrb. wiss. Bot., **58**, 105.
BUKATSCH, F., 1940, Planta, **31**, 209.
— 1942, Jahrb. wiss. Bot., **90**, 293.
BULL, H. B., 1940, Cold Spring Harbor Symp. Quant. Biol., **8**, 63.
— 1944, J. Amer. Chem. Soc., **66**, 1499.
BUNGENBERG DE JONG, H. G., and BONNER, J., 1935, Protoplasma, **24**, 198.
BÜNNING, E., et al., 1930, Planta, **11**, 67.
BÜNNING, E., 1937, Planta, **27**, 148, 583.
— 1939, *Die Physiologie des Wachstums und der Bewegungen der Pflanzen*. Berlin. (new Edit. 1948, 1953).
— 1944, Biol. Centralbl., **64**, 161; Flora, **38**, 93.
BÜNNING, E., and HERDTLE, H., 1946, Z. Naturforsch., **1**, 93.
BÜNNING, E., and GLATZLE, D., 1948, Planta, **36**, 199.
BÜNNING, E., and KANTT, R., 1956, Biol. Centralbl., **75**, 356.
BÜNNING, E., and SCHNEIDERHÖHN, G., 1956, Arch. Mikrobiol., **24**, 80.
BÜNNING, E., REISENER, H. J., WEYGAND, F., SIMON, H., and KLEBE, J. F., Z. Naturforsch., **11**b, 363.
BURK, D., 1939, Symp. Quantit. Biol., **7**, 420.
BURKHOLDER, P. R., and JOHNSTON, 1937, Smithsonian Misc. Coll., **95**, no. 20.
BÜRKLE, B., 1929, Bot. Arch., **26**, 385.
BURNET, F. M., and STANLEY, W. M., *Plant and Bacterial Viruses*. New York.
BURNS, G. R., 1942, Amer. J. Bot., **29**, 381.
BURR, G. O., 1936, Proc. Roy. Soc., B, **120**, 42.
BURRIS, R. H., 1941, Science, **94**, 238.
BURRIS, R. H., and HAAS, E., 1944, J. Biol. Chem., **155**, 227.
BURRIS, R. H., and WILSON, P. W., 1946, J. Biol. Chem., **165**, 595.
BURSTRÖM, H., 1929, Medd. Centralanstalten, no. 356.
— 1934, Svensk bot. tidskr., **28**, 157.
BURSTRÖM, H., and BORATYNSKI, K., 1936, Lantbrukshögsk. Ann. (Upsala), **3**, 147.
BURSTRÖM, H., 1937, Medd. Centralanstalten, no. 475.
— 1939, Planta, **30**, 129; Lantbrukshögsk. Ann. (Upsala), **7**, 247.
— 1941, Lantbrukshögsk. Ann., **9**, 264. Bot. Notiser, 310.

BURSTRÖM, H., 1942, Lantbrukshögsk. Ann., **10**, 1. Lantbruksakad. Tidsr., **81**, 257. Bot. Notiser, 351.
— 1943, Lantbrukshögsk. Ann., **11**, 1. Arkiv Bot., **32** A, no. 7, Vetenskapsakademien (Stockholm).
— 1945, Lantbrukshögsk. Ann., **13**, 1.
— 1955, Bot. Notiser (Lund), **108**, 400.
— 1956, Physiol. Plantarum, **9**, 682.
BURSTRÖM, H., and HANSEN, B. A. M., 1955, The Chemistry and Mode of Action of Plant Growth Substances Symposium, London, 134.
BURSTRÖM, H., SJÖBERG, B., and HANSEN, B., 1956, Acta Agric. Scand., **6**, 155.
BUSSE, M., and KANDLER, O., 1956, Planta, **46**, 619.
BUSWELL, A. M., 1942, J. Physiol. Chem., **46**, 575.
BUTENANDT, A., 1953, Naturwiss., **40**, 91.
BUTLER, J. A. V., 1946, Nature, **158**, 153.

CAMP, A. F., 1945, Soil Sci., **60**, 157.
CANNON, R. K., 1926, Biochem. J., **20**, 927.
CANNON, W. A., 1925, Carnegie Inst. Washington. Publ. 368.
CAPPALETTI, C., 1939, Nuov. Giorn. Bot. Ital., **46**, 334.
CARDON, B. P., and BARKER, H. A., 1947, Arch. Biochem., **12**, 165.
CARLIER, A., and BUFFEL, K., 1955, Acta Bot. Néerl., **4**, 551.
CARR, C. W., and SOLLNER, K., 1944, J. Gen. Physiol., **28**, 119.
CARRICK, D. B., 1930, Cornell Univ. Agr. Exp. Sta. Mem., 131.
CARROL, G. H., 1943, Bot. Rev., **9**, 41.
CARTELLIERI, E., 1935, Jahrb. wiss. Bot., **82**, 460.
— 1940, Sitzungsber. Akad. Wiss. Wien. Math.-Nat. Kl., Abt. I, **149**, 95.
CASPERSSON, T., and SCHULTZ, J., 1940, Proc. Nat. Acad. Sci., **26**, 507.
CASTLE, E. S., and HONEYMAN, 1935, J. Gen. Physiol., **18**, 385.
CASTLE, E. S., 1940, J. Cell. Comp. Physiol., **15**, 285.
CERNESCU, N. C., 1931, Anuaral Inst. Geol. Român., **16**.
CHAMBERS, R., 1942, Proc. Eighth Amer. Sci. Congr., **3**, 25.
CHAPMAN, G. W., 1931, New Phytologist, **30**, 119.
CHAPMAN, H. D., and CURTIS, D. S., 1940, Soil Sci. Soc. Amer. Proc., **5**, 191.
CHAPMAN, H. D., and LIEBIG, G. F., 1940, Hilgardia, **13**, 141.
CHAPMAN, H. D., and BROWN, S. M., 1943, Soil Sci., **55**, 87.
CHAPMAN, R. E., et al., 1924, New Phytologist, **23**, 50.
CHAUDHRI, I. I., 1956, Beitr. Biol. Pflanzen, **32**, 451.
— 1956, Z. Bot., **44**, 319.
CHIBNALL, A. C., 1923, J. Biol. Chem., **55**, 333.
— 1939, *Protein Metabolism in the Plant*. London.
CHIN, C. H., 1950, Nature, **165**, 926.
CHODAT, F., and ANAUD, P., 1936, Bull. Soc. Bot. Suisse, **46**, 266.
CHODAT, F., 1940, Compt. Rend. Soc. Phys. Hist. Natur. Genève, **57**, 247.
CHOLODNY, N., 1923, Ber. deutsch. Bot. Ges., **41**, 300.
CHONDHURY, J. K., 1939, Proc. Roy. Soc., B, **127**, 238.
CHRISTENSEN, H. N., and HASTINGS, A. B., 1940, J. Biol. Chem., **136**, 387.
CLAPHAM, A. R., 1945, New Phytologist, **44**, 105.
CLARK, W. G., 1937, Plant Physiol., **12**, 409, 737.
CLARK, W. M., KIRBY, W., and TODD, A., 1958, Nature, **181**, 1650.
CLAYSON, D. H. F., 1942, 1943, Chem. Ind., **61**, 516, **62**, 49.
CLELAND, R., and BONNER, J., 1956, Plant Physiol., **31**, 350.
CLEMENTS, H. F., 1937, Research Stud. State Coll. Washington, **5**, 1.
CLENDENNING, K. A., 1956, Chemistry in Canada. Aug. 1956.
CLENDENNING, K. A., and GORHAM, P. R., 1952, Arch. Biochim. Biophys., **37**, 56.
CLENDENNING, K. A., and HAXO, F. T., 1956, Canad. J. Bot., **34**, 214.
COBB, M. J., 1932, Soil Sci., **33**, 325.
COHEN, S. S., 1954, *Chemical Pathways of Metabolism*. 1. Chapter V.
COHN, E. J., 1941, Ann. Acad. Sci. New York, **41**, 79.
COHN, E. J., and EDSALL, J. T., 1943, *Proteins, Amino Acids and Peptides as Ions and Dipolar Ions*.
COLE, K. S., 1940, Cold Spring Harbor Symp. Quant. Biol., **8**, 110.
COLEMAN, R., 1942, Soil Sci., **54**, 237.
COLLANDER, R., and BÄRLUND, H., 1933, Acta Bot. Fenn., no. **11**.
COLLANDER, R., 1941, Plant Physiol., **16**, 691.
COLLANDER, R., et al., 1943, Protoplasma, **37**, 327.
COLWELL, W. E., 1943, Soil Sci., **56**, 71.
COMAR, C. L., 1942, Bot. Gaz., **104**, 122.

COMAR, C. L., and NELLER, J. R., 1947, Plant Physiol., **22**, 174.
COMMONER, B., 1940, Biol. Rev., **15**, 168.
COMMONER, B., and THIMANN, K. V., 1941, J. Gen. Physiol., **24**, 279.
COMMONER, B., 1942, Plant Physiol., **17**, 682.
CONWAY, E. J., 1945, Biol. Rev. Cambridge Phil. Soc., **20**, 56.
— 1958, Biochem. J., **69**, 265.
COOK, R. L., and MILLAR, C. E., 1940, Soil Sci. Soc. Amer. Proc., **5**, 227.
CORI, C. F., and CORI, G. T., 1946, Ann. Rev. Biochem., **15**, 187.
CORMACK, R. G. H., 1935, New Phytologist, **34**, 30.
— 1945, Amer. J. Bot., **32**, 490.
— 1948, Canad. J. Res. **26**, Sect. C, 263.
CORSON, S. A., 1943, Proc. Oklahoma Acad. Sci. **23**, 31.
COSTER, C., 1927, Rec. Trav. Bot. Néerl., **24**, 257.
— 1931, Planta, **15**, 540.
— 1932, Landbouw, **8**, No. 6.
— 1933, Landbouw, **9**, No. 1.
CRAFTS, A. S., 1931—1933, Plant Physiol., **6**, 1, **7**, 183, **8**, 81.
— 1939, Bot. Rev., **5**, 471.
— 1943, Chron. Bot., **7**, 386.
— 1946, Plant Physiol., **21**, 345.
— 1948, Discussions Faraday Soc., No. 3, 153.
CRANE, E. E., et al., 1948, Biol. J., **43**, 321.
CRANE, F., HAUGE, J. G., and BEINERT, H., 1955, Biochim. Biophys. Acta, **17**, 293.
CRIST, J. W., and DYE, M., 1931, J. Biol. Chem., **91**, 127.
CROCKER, W., 1916, Amer. J. Bot., **3**, 99.
— 1938, Bot. Rev., **4**, 235.
CROOKS, D. M., 1933, Bot. Gaz., **95**, 209.
CROSS, B. E., 1954, J. Chem. Soc. 4670.
CUNNINGS, R. W., and CHANDLER, R. F., 1940, Soil Sci. Soc. Amer. Proc. **5**, 80.
CURRAN, H. R., and MYERS, A. T., 1943, J. Bacteriol., **45**, 485.
CURTIS, O. F., and SCOFIELD, H. T., 1933, Amer. J. Bot., **20**, 502.
CURTIS, O. F., 1935, *The Translocation of Solutes in Plants*. New York, London.
— 1936, Plant Physiol., **11**, 595.
CURTIS, O. F., and HERTY, D., 1936, Amer. J. Bot., **23**, 528.
CURTIS, O. F., 1938, Amer. J. Bot., **25**, 761.
CZAPEK. F., 1897, Ber. deutsch. bot. Ges., **15**, 124.
— 1922, *Biochemie der Pflanzen*. 2nd. Edit. Jena.

DAINTY, M., et al., 1944, J. Gen. Physiol., **27**, 355.
DALY, J. M., 1954, Arch. Biochim. Biophys., **51**, 24.
DAM, H., GLAVIND, J., and GABRIELSEN, E. K., 1947, Acta Physiol. Scand., **13**, 9.
DAMM, O., 1901, Beih. Bot. Centralbl., **11**, 219.
DAMODARAN, M., and VENKATESAN, T. R., 1941, Proc. Indian Acad. Sci., Sect B, **13**, 345.
DAMODARAN, M., et al., 1946, Proc. Indian Acad. Sci., Sect. B, **23**, 86.
DANIELLI, J. F., 1941, Biochem. J., **35**, 470.
— 1946, Nature, **157**, 755.
DANNENBERG, H., and KIESE, M., 1952, Biochem. Z., **322**, 395.
DARLINGTON, C. D., 1937, *Recent Advances in Cytology*. 2nd Edit..
DARLINGTON, C. D., and AMMAL, E. K., 1946, *Chromosome Atlas of Cultivated Plants*.
DAS, N. K., PATAN, K., and SKOOG, F., 1956, Physiol. Plantarum, **9**, 640.
DASSEK, M., 1939, Beitr. Biol. Pflanz., **26**, 125.
DASTUR, R. H., 1925, Ann. Bot., **39**, 769.
DASTUR, R. H., and MALKANI, T. J., 1933, Indian J. Agric. Sci., **3**, 157.
DAVIDSON, J. N., and WAYMOUTH, C., 1944, Biochem. J., **38**, 39.
DAWSON, C. R., and TARPLEY, W. B., 1951, in *The Enzymes* (Sumner and Myrbäck) Vol. 2, 454.
DAWSON, H., and REINER, J. M., 1942, J. Cell. Comp. Physiol., **20**, 325.
DAWSON, H., and DANIELLI, J. F., 1943, *The Permeability of Natural Membranes*. Cambridge.
DAWSON, R. F., 1946, Plant Physiol., **21**, 115.
DAXER, H., 1934, Jahrb. wiss. Bot., **80**, 363.
DEAN, L. A., and RUBINS, E. J., 1945, Soil Sci., **59**, 437.
DEAN, R. B., 1942, Proc. Soc. Exp. Biol. Med., **50**, 162.
DEGEN, A., 1905, Bot. Z., **63**, 163.
DELAPORTE, B., 1939, Rev. Gén. Bot., **51**, 449.
DELEANO, N. T., 1911, Jahrb. wiss. Bot., **49**, 129.

DELLINGSHAUSEN, M. VON, 1933, Planta, **21**, 51.
DENFFER, D. VON, 1941, Jahrb. wiss. Bot., **89**, 543.
DENNES, A. R. T., 1951, Science, **133**, 203.
DENNY, F. E., 1930, Contrib. Boyce Thompson Inst., **2**, 592.
— 1946, Contrib. Boyce Thompson Inst., **14**, 257.
DERVICHIAN, D. G., 1943, J. Chem. Physics, **11**, 236.
DESAI, M. C., 1937, Plant Physiol., **12**, 253.
DETMER, W., 1880, *Vergleichung der Physiologie des Keimungsprozesses*. Jena.
DETTWEILER, CHR., 1942, Planta, **33**, 258.
DEUEL, H., 1943, Trav. chim. aliment. Hygiène, **34**, 41.
DE WIT, J. L., 1957, Acta Bot. Néerl., **6**, (1), 1.
D'HOORE, J., and FRIPIAT, J., 1948, Soil Sci., **66**, 91.
DIEHL, J. M., et al., 1939, Rec. Trav. Bot. Néerl., **36**, 711.
DIJKSTRA, S. J., 1937, Rec. Trav. Bot. Néerl., **34**, 334.
DILLON-WESTON, W. A. R., 1931, Nature, **127**, 483; **128**, 67.
DINGLE, H., and PRYCE, A. W., 1940, Proc. Roy. Soc. Ser. B., Biol. Sci., **129**, 468.
DITTMER, H. J., 1937, Amer. J. Bot., **24**, 417.
DIXON, H. H., and ATKINS, W. R. G., 1915—1916, Sci. Proc. Roy. Dublin Soc., **14**, 374, **15**, 51.
DIXON, H. H., 1924, *The Transpiration Stream*. London.
DOERFEL, F., 1930, Bot. Arch., **30**, 1.
DOLK, H. E., 1930 (Dissertation). Utrecht.
— 1931, Amer. J. Bot., **18**, 195.
DOPOSCHEG-UHLAR, J., 1911, Flora, **102**, 24.
DÖRING, H., 1932, Planta, **18**, 405.
DÖRR, M., 1941, Bot. Centralbl. Abt. A, **60**, 679.
DORYLAND, C. G. T., 1916, Dakota Agric. Exp. Sta. Bull., 116.
DOUNCE, A. L., 1943, J. Biol. Chem., **147**, 685.
DOYER, L. C., 1915, Rec. Trav. Bot. Néerl., **12**, 369.
DRAKE, M., et al., 1941, J. Amer. Soc. Agron., **33**, 454.
DU BUY, H. G., 1940, Proc. Univ. Med. Biol. Soc. Bull. Sci. Med., **24**.
DU BUY, H. G., and OLSON, R. A., 1940, Amer. J. Bot., **27**, 401.
DUFRENOY, J., and REED, H. S., 1946, Plant Physiology, **21**, 416.
DUGGAR, B. M., 1936, *Biological Effects of Radiation*. New York, London.
DUNN, M. S., 1949, Physiol. Rev., **29**, 219.
DUNNE, T. C., 1932, Hilgardia, **7**, 207.
DU RIETZ, E., 1932, Beih. Bot. Centralbl., **59**, 61.
DUTTON, H. J., and MANNING, W. M., 1941, Amer. J. Bot., **28**, 516.
DUYSENS, L. N. M., 1952. *Transfer of Excitation Energy in Photosynthesis*. Utrecht 1952.
— 1956, Biochim. Biophys. Acta, **19**, 1.
DYAR, M. T., and ORDAL, E. J., 1946, J. Bacteriol. **51**, 149.

EAMES, A. J., and MACDANIELS, L. H., 1947, *An Introduction to Plant Anatomy*. 2nd Edit. New York, London.
EATON, F. M., 1942, J. Agric. Res., **64**, 357.
— 1943, Amer. J. Bot., **30**, 663.
— 1944, J. Agric. Res., **69**, 237.
EATON, F. M., and JOHAM, H. E., 1944, Plant Physiol., **19**, 507.
EDLBACHER, S., and BAUR, H., 1938, Hoppe-Seylers Z., **254**, 275.
EDSALL, T., 1942, Adv. Coll. Sci., **1**, 270.
EGAMI, F., 1957, Svensk kem. Tidskr., **69**, 562.
EGLE, K., and SCHENK, W., 1952, Beitr. Z. Biol. Pflanz., **29**, 75.
EHRKE, G., 1929, Planta, **9**, 631.
— 1931, Planta, **13**, 221.
— 1934, Int. Rev. ges. Hydrobiol. Hydrogr., **31**, 373.
EHRMANTRAUT, H. C., and RABINOWITCH, E., 1952, Arch. Biochem. Biophys., **38**, 67.
EIDMANN, F. E., 1943, Schriftenreihe Hermann-Göring-Akad. deutsch. Forstwiss., **5**.
EIJK, M. VAN, 1939, Rec. Trav. Bot. Néerl., **36**, 559.
EISELSBERG, C. VON, 1937, Biologia Generalis, **13**, 529.
EKDAHL, I., 1944, Arkiv f. Bot. Vetenskapsakademien (Stockholm), **31** A, no. 5.
— 1953, (Dissertation). Upsala.
ELLÉE, O., 1939, Beitr. Biol. Pflanz., **26**, 250.
ELO, J. E., 1937, Ann. Bot. Soc. Zool.-Bot. Fenn. Vanamo, **8**, No. 6.
ELVEHJEM, C. A., and WILSON, P. W., 1939, *Respiratory Enzymes*.
ELVERS, I., 1943, Svensk Bot. Tidskr., **37**, 331.

EMERSON, R., 1929, J. Gen. Physiol., **12**, 609.
EMERSON, R., and ARNOLD, W., 1932, J. Gen. Physiol., **15**, 391.
EMERSON, R., and LEWIS, C. M., 1939, Amer. J. Bot., **26**, 808.
EMERSON, R., and LEWIS, C. M., 1943, Amer. J. Bot., **30**, 165.
EMERSON, R. L., et al., 1944, Amer. J. Bot., **31**, 107.
EMERSON, R., and CHALMERS, R., 1955, Plant Physiol., **30**, 504.
EMMETT, H. E. G., and ASHBY, E., 1934, Ann. Bot., **48**, 869.
ENDRES, G., 1934, Liebigs Annalen., **512**, 54.
ENDRES, G., et al., 1939, Liebigs Annalen, **537**, 205.
ENGARD, CH. J., and NAKATA, A. H., 1947, Science, **105**, 577.
ENGEL, H., 1930, Planta, **12**, 60.
— 1931, Z. Pflanzen-Ernähr. Düng. Bodenkunde, A, **21**, 32.
— 1939, Jahrb. wiss. Bot., **88**, 816.
ENGELMANN, T. W., 1883, Pflügers Arch. Ges. Physiol., **30**, 90.
ENGLISH, J., et al., 1939, J. Amer. Chem. Soc., **61**, 3434.
EPERJESSY, G., 1941, Math. Naturwiss. Anz. ungar. Akad. Wiss., **59**, 882.
EPSTEIN, E., 1955, Plant Physiol., **30**, 529.
ERDTMAN, H., 1944, Svensk Kem. Tidskr., **56**, 2.
ERICKSON, R. O., 1947, Nature, **159**, 275.
ERIKSSON and QUENSEL, 1938, Biochem. J., **32**, 585.
ERKAMA, J., 1947, Ann. Acad. Sci. Fenn. Ser. A, II, 25.
ERMAN, C., 1926, Ber. deutsch. Bot. Ges., **44**, 432.
ERNEST, E. C. M., 1935, Plant Physiol., **10**, 553.
ESAU, K., 1939, Bot. Rev., **5**, 373.
— 1953, *Plant Anatomy*, New York, London.
ETTLINGER, L., 1946, Schweiz. Z. Pathol. Bakteriol., **9**, 352.
EVANS, E. A., 1942, Science. **96**, 25.
EVANS, G. C., 1939, J. Ecol., **27**, 436.
EVANS, M., 1932, Biol. Rev., **7**, 181.
EYSTER, H. C., 1942, Plant Physiol., **17**, 686.
— 1946, Plant Physiol., **21**, 366.

FÅHRAEUS, G., and LINDEBERG, G., 1953, Physiol. Plantarum, **6**, 150—158.
FARR, W. K., 1940, Nature, **146**, 153.
— 1941, Contrib. Boyce Thompson Inst., **12**, 181.
FELDBACH, I., 1938, Beih. Bot. Centralbl., Abt. A, **58**, 223.
FERNANDES, D. S., 1923, Rec. Trav. Bot. Néerl., **20**, 107.
FERRI, M. G., 1945, Contrib. Boyce Thompson Inst., **14**, 51.
FILZER, P., 1933, Jahrb. wiss. Bot., **79**, 9.
— 1939, Ber. deutsch. Bot. Ges., **57**, 155.
FINCH, L. R., and CARR, D. J., 1956, Austral. J. Biol. Sci., **9**, 355.
FIRBAS, F., 1931, Jahrb. wiss. Bot., **74**, 459.
FIEQ, A., and PAVAN, C., 1957, Nature, **180**, 983.
FISCHER, H., 1936, Z. Bot., **30**, 449.
FITTING, H., 1912, Z. Bot., **4**, 81.
— 1903, Jahrb. wiss. Bot., **38**, 545.
— 1936. Jahrb. wiss. Bot., **82**, 696.
— 1937, Jahrb. wiss. Bot., **83**, 270.
— 1942, Jahrb. wiss. Bot., **90**, 417.
FLEURY, P., and COURTOIS, J., 1946, Helv. Chim. Acta, **29**, 1297.
FLINT, L. H., and MCALISTER, E. D., 1935, Smithsonian Miscell. Coll., **94**, no. 5.
— — 1937, Smithsonian Miscell. Coll., **96**, no. 2.
FLORELL, C., 1956, Physiol. Plantarum, **9**, 236.
FÖCKLER, H., 1938, Jahrb. wiss. Bot., **87**, 45.
FOREMAN, F. W., 1938, J. Agric. Sci., **28**, 135.
FOSTER, A. S., 1936, Bot. Rev., **2**, 349.
FOSTER, J. W., and WAKSMAN, S. A., 1939, J. Bacteriol., **37**, 6.
FRANCK, J., and FRENCH, C. S., 1941, J. Gen. Physiol., **25**, 309.
FRANCK, J., and GAFFRON, H., 1941, Adv. Enzymol., **1**, 199.
FRANCK, J., 1945, Rev. Modern Physics, **17**, 112.
FRANCK, J., and LOOMIS, W. E., 1949, *Photosynthesis in Plants*.
FRANCK, J., 1953, Arch. Biochem. Biophys., **45**, 190.
FRANK, A. B., 1870, *Die natürliche wagerechte Richtung von Pflanzenteilen*.
FRANK, H., 1958, Naturwiss., **45**, 200.

FREELAND, R. O., 1944, Plant Physiol., **19**, 179.

FREI, H., 1942, Centralbl. Bakteriol., II, **104**, 326.

FRENKEL, A. W., 1956, J. Biol. Chem., **222**, 823.

FREUDENBERG, K., and BOPPEL, H., 1940, Ber. deutsch. Chem. Ges., **73**, 609.

FREUNDLICH, H., 1942, Symposion on the Structure of Protoplasm (W. SEIFRITZ).

FREY-WYSSLING, A., 1938, *Submikroskopische Morphologie des Protoplasmas und seine Derivate* (Engl. Edit. *Submicroscopic Morphology of Protoplasm*, 1953).

— 1940, Ber. deutsch. bot. Ges., **58**, 166.

— 1941, Ber. schweiz. bot. Ges., **51**, 321.

— 1944, Ann. Bot., **8**, 71.

— 1945, Arch. Julius Klaus-Stift., Ergbd., **20**, 381.

— 1958, *Die pflanzliche Zellwand*. Berlin.

FREY-WYSSLING, A., and MÜHLETHALER, K., 1946, Prisma, Pt. 5.

FRIEDRICHSEN, I., 1944, Planta, **34**, 67.

FRIES, N., 1938, Symbol. Bot. Upsala, **3**, 2.

— 1946, Ark. f. Bot., **33** A, no. 7. Vetenskapsakademien (Stockholm).

FRITSCHE, G., 1933, Beih. Bot. Centralbl., Abt. I., **50**, 251.

FRÖSCHEL, P., and FUNKE, G. L., 1939, Natuurwet. Tijdschr., **21**, 348.

FRÖSCHEL, P., 1956, Acta Bot. Neerl., **5**, (3), 264.

FUJITA, 1931, Rep. Bult. Sci. Fak. Terk. Kyushu Imp. Univ., **4**, no. 4.

FUKSIDA, Y., 1935, Pflanzenforsch. (Kolkwitz), **19**.

FUNKE, H., and SÖDING, H., 1947—1948, Forsch. Fortschr., 21/23, Planta, **36**, 341.

FURCHGOTT, F. R., and PONDER, E., 1941, J. Gen. Physiol., **24**, 447.

FÜSSER, K., 1933, Planta, **19**, 485.

GAARDER, T., and ALVSAKER, E., Medd. Vestlandets Forstl. Forsöksstation. Bergen. 1938.

GABOR, D., 1947, Nature, **159**, 591.

GABRIELSEN, E. K., 1935, Planta, **23**, 474.

GABRIELSEN, E. K., and LARSEN, P., 1935, Kgl. Danske Vidensk. Selsk. Biol. Medd., **11**, no. 8.

GABRIELSEN, E. K., 1940, Dansk Bot. Arkiv, **10**, 1.

— 1942, Kgl. Veter. og Landbohøiskole, Aarsskr. (Copenhagen), **20**, 28.

— 1947, Experientia, **3**, 1.

— 1948, Nature, **161**, 139.

GAEBLER, O., 1956, *Enzymes: Units of biological Structure and Function*. New York.

GAERTNER, TH., and BRAUNROTH, E., 1935, Beih. Bot. Centralbl. A., **53**, 554.

GAFFRON, H., 1939, Biol. Centralbl., **59**, 228.

— 1940, Amer. J. Bot., **28**, 204.

— 1942, J. Gen. Physiol., **26**, 195, 241.

GAFFRON, H., and RUBIN, J., 1942, J. Gen. Physiol., **26**, 219.

GAFFRON, H., 1946, in *Currents of Biochemical of Research*, 25 (GREEN).

GAFFRON, H., BROWN, A. H., FRENCH, C. S., LIVINGSTON, R., RABINOWITCH, E. J., STREHLER, B. L., and TOLBERT, N. E., 1957, *Research in Photosynthesis*. Nat. Res. Council. Acad. Sci. N. Y.

GAGETTI, A., 1947, Lavori Bot., 413.

GALSTON, A. W., 1943, Amer. J. Bot., **30**, 331.

— 1947, J. Biol. Chem., **169**, 465.

— 1950, Bot. Rev., **16**, 361.

GARDNER, R., and WHITNEY, R. S., 1943, Soil Sci., **56**, 63.

GARNER, W. W., and ALLARD, H. A., 1920, J. Agric. Res., **18**, 553.

GARNER, W. W., 1929, Proc. Intern. Congr. Plant Sci., **2**, 1050.

GASSNER, G., 1915, Z. Bot., **9**, 609.

— 1925, Ber. deutsch. bot. Ges., **43**, 132.

— 1930, Z. Bot., **23**, 767.

GASSNER, G., and GOEZE, G., 1934, Ber. deutsch. bot. Ges., **52**, 321.

GASSNER, G., and FRANKE, W., 1934, Phytopathol. Z., **7**, 315.

GASSNER, G., and GOEZE, G., 1935, Ergebn. Agrikulturchem., **4**, 106.

GAST, P. R., 1937, Medd. Statens Skogsförsöksanst. (Stockholm), **29**, 587.

GATES, F. L., 1930, J. Gen. Physiol., **14**, 31.

GATES, R. R., 1942, Bot. Rev., **8**, 337.

GAUGER, W., 1929, (Dissertation). Königsberg.

GAUGER, W., and ZIEGENSPECK, H., 1929, Bot. Arch., **27**, 327.

— — 1930, Bot. Arch., **30**, 109.

GÄUMANN, E., and JAAG, O., 1936, Ber. schweiz. bot. Ges., **45**, 412.

GÄUMANN, E., 1938, Ber. deutsch. bot. Ges., **56**, 396.

GÄUMANN, E., and JAAG, O., 1939, Ber. schweiz. bot. Ges., **49**, 178.

en490 BIBLIOGRAPHY

GÄUMANN, E., and BÖHM, E., 1947, Helv. Chim. Acta, **30**, 24.
GÄUMANN, E., and JAAG, O., 1947, Ber. schweiz. bot. Ges., **57**, 3.
GÄUMANN, E., et al., 1947, Experientia, **3**, 1.
GAUTHERET, R. J., 1947, Sixth Growth Symposium, 21.
GEIGER, R., 1942, *Das Klima der bodennahen Luftschicht*. 2nd Edit.
GEIGER-HUBER, M., and HUBER, E., 1945, Experientia, **1**, 26.
GEITLER, L., 1941, Ergebn. Biol., **18**, 1.
GELTZER, F., 1930, Exp. Invest. Inst. Water Econ. Middle Asia. Ser. G, **10**.
GERASSIMOFF, J. J., 1902, Z. allgem. Physiol., **1**, 220.
— 1904, Bull. Soc. Imp. Naturalist., **1**.
GERICKE, S., 1940, Pflanzenbau, **18**, 69.
GERICKE, S., and RENNENKAMPF, F., 1940, Bodenkunde Pflanzenernähr., **18**, 305.
GERRETSEN, F. C., 1937, Ann. Bot., **1**, 207.
GESSNER, F., 1930, Mitt. Naturw. Ver. Neuvorpommern und Rügen. Greifswald, **57**, 1.
GESSNER, F., and WEINFURTER, F., 1952, Ber. deutsch. bot. Ges., **65**, 47.
GEST, H., KAMEN, M. D., and BREGOFF, H. M., 1950, J. Biol. Chem., **192**, 153.
GEYLER, TH., 1866, Jahrb. wiss. Bot., **4**, 479.
GIBBS, R. D., 1939, Canad. J. Res., **17**, 460.
GIESSLER, A., 1928, Flora, **123**, 133.
GILBERT, F. A., 1951, Bot. Rev., **17**, 671.
GILBERT, S. G., 1940, Bot. Gaz., **102**, 105.
GILBERT, S. G., and SHIVE, J. W., 1945, Soil Sci., **59**, 453.
GILBERT, S. G., et al., 1946, Plant Physiol., **21**, 290.
GILE, P. L., and FENSTAL, I. C., 1943, J. Agric. Res., **66**, 49.
GILMAN, H., 1944, *Organic Chemistry*. Vol. 2.
GLASSTONE, V. F., 1942, Amer. J. Bot., **29**, 156.
GLICK, D., et al., 1945, Science, **102**, 429.
GLOCK, W. S., 1941, Bot. Rev., **7**, 649.
GLÖMME, H., 1928, Medd. Norske Skogforsöksväsen. **10**.
GLOVER, J., 1941, Ann. Bot., **5**, 25.
GODDARD, D. R., 1935, J. Gen. Physiol., **19**, 45.
GODDARD, D. R., and SMITH, P. E., 1938, Plant Physiol., **13**, 241.
— 1944, Amer. J. Bot., **31**, 220, 270.
GODDARD, D. R., and STAFFORD, H. A., 1954, Ann. Rev. Plant Physiol., **5**, 115.
GOEBEL, K., 1928, *Organographie der Pflanzen*. Vol. 1. 3rd Edit.
GOEDHEER, J. C., 1955, Biochem. Biophys. Acta, **16**, 471.
GOLA, G., 1946, Mem. R. Accad. Naz. Linc. Cl. Sci. Fis., Math. Nat. Ser., **8**, 1, 262.
GOLDACRE, R. J., 1952, Int. Rev. Cytol., **1**, 135.
GOODALL, D. W., 1946, Ann. Bot., **40**, 305.
GOODALL, D. W., and GREGORY, F. G., 1947, Imp. Bot. Hort. Plant Crops. Techn. Comm. No. 17.
GOODALL, D. W., GRANT LIPP, A. E., and SLATER, W. G., 1955, Austral. J. Biol. Sci., **8**, 301.
GOODWIN, H., et al., 1932, J. Ecol., **20**, 157.
GOODWIN, R. H., and GODDARD, D. R., 1940, Amer. J. Bot., **27**, 234.
GOODWIN, R. H., and OWENS, O. H., 1947, Plant Physiol., **22**, 197.
GORDON, H. K., and CHAMBERS, R., 1941, J. Cell. Comp. Physiol., **17**, 97.
GORDON, S. A., 1946, Amer. J. Bot., **33**, 160.
GORHAM, P. R., and CLENDENNING, K. A., 1951, Arch. Biochem. Biophys., **37**, 199.
GORSKI, F., 1929, Acta Soc. Bot. Polon., **6**, 1.
— 1930, Bull. Acad. Polon. Sci. Lettr. Sér. B.
GORTER, C. J., and FUNKE, G. L., 1937, Planta, **26**, 532.
GORTNER, R. A., 1938, *Outlines of Biochemistry*. 2nd Edit.
GOUWENTAK, C. A., 1941, Verh. Kon. Nederl. Akad. Wetensch., **44**, 3.
GOUY, G. L., 1910, J. Phys., **9**, 457.
GRAČANIN, M., 1935, Fac. Agr. Forest. Univ. Zagreb. Lab. Nutr. Plant, **1**, Ser. 1.
GRADMANN, H., 1923, Jahrb. wiss. Bot., **62**, 449.
— 1932, Jahrb. wiss. Bot., **76**, 558.
— 1934, Jahrb. wiss. Bot., **80**, 92.
GRALÉN, N., 1946, J. Colloid Sci., **1**, 453.
GRANICK, S., 1950, Harvey Lectures, Ser. 44, 220.
GRANLUND, E., and WENNERHOLM, S., 1934, Sveriges Geol. Undersökn. Årsbok, **28**, no. 4.
GREEN, D. E., 1941, *Mechanisms of Biological Oxidations*.
— 1946, *Currents of Biochemical Research*.
— 1955, Proc. Second Internat. Conf. on Biochem. Problems of Lipids. Ghent. 233.
GREENBERG, D. H., and WINNICK, T., 1940, J. Biol. Chem., **135**, 781.

GREENWOOD, M., and POSUETTE, A. F., 1947, Nature, **159**, 542.
GRÉGOIRE, V., 1935, Compt. Rend., Paris., **200**, 1127, 1349.
GREGORY, F. G., 1926, Ann. Bot., **40**, 1.
GREGORY, F. G., and ARMSTRONG, J. I., 1936, Proc. Roy. Soc. Ser. B, **121**, 27.
GREGORY, F. G., and PEARSE, H. L., 1937, Ann. Bot., **1**, 3.
GREGORY, F. G., and SEN, P. K., 1937, Ann. Bot., **1**, 521.
GRIM, R. E., 1942, J. Geol., **50**, 225.
GRONER, M. G., 1936, Amer. J. Bot., **23**, 381.
GUILLIERMOND, A., 1919, Compt. Rend., Paris, **164**, 644.
— 1941, *The Cytoplasm of the Plant Cell.*
GUILLIERMOND, A., and GAUTHERET, R., 1946, Rev. gén. Bot., **53**, 25.
GULICK, A., 1941, Bot. Rev., **7**, 433.
GULLAND, J. M., et al., 1945, Ann. Rev. Biochem., **14**, 175.
GÜNTHER-MASSIAS, M., 1928, Z. Bot., **21**, 129.
GUSTAFSON, F. G., 1932, Amer. J. Bot., **19**, 823.
— 1939, Science, **90**, 306.
— 1941, Amer. J. Bot., **28**, 947.
— 1944, Plant. Physiol., **19**, 551.
— 1946, Plant Physiol., **21**, 49.
— 1955, Plant Physiol. **30**, 444.
GUT, R. CH., 1929, *Le gaz carbonique dans l'atmosphère forestière.* Berne.
GUTHRIE, J. D., 1939, Contrib. Boyce Thompson Inst., **11**, 29.
GUTTENBERG, H. VON, 1931, Ann. Jardin Bot. Buitenzorg, **41**, 1.
GUTTENBERG, H. VON, and BUHR, H., 1935, Planta, **24**, 163.
GUTTENBERG, H. VON, 1941, Fortschr. Bot., **10**, 260.
— 1943, Biol. Centralbl., **63**, 256.
— 1944, Planta, **34**, 49.
— 1947, Planta, **35**, 360.
GUTTENBERG, H. VON, and ZETSCHE, K., 1956, Planta, **48**, 99.

HAAGEN-SMIT, A. J., 1939, Ergebn. Hormonforsch,, **2**, 347.
HAAGEN-SMIT, A. J., et al., 1942, Amer. J. Bot., **29**, 500.
HAAN, I. DE, 1935, Protoplasma, **24**, 186.
HAAS, A. R. C., 1941, Plant Physiol., **16**, 405.
— 1941, Soil Sci. **51**, 17.
HAAS, E., 1943, J. Biol. Chem., **148**, 481.
HAAS, H. F., and BUSHNELL, L. D., 1944, J. Bacteriol., **48**, 219.
HAAS, J. 1955, *Physiologie der Zelle*, Berlin.
HABER, W., 1958, Flora, **146**, 109.
HABERLANDT, G., 1900, Ber. deutsch. bot. Ges., **18**, 261.
— 1902, Sitz. ber. Akad. Wien, Math.-Nat. Kl. **111**, I, 69.
— 1913, Sitz. ber. Akad., Berlin, **16**, 318.
— 1919, Sitz. ber. Akad., Berlin, **19**, 721.
— 1924, *Physiologische Pflanzenanatomie.* 6. Edit. (Eng. trans. *Physiological Plant Anatomy* trans.
    M. Drummond, 1914).
HAGENE, P., 1931, Rev. gén. Bot., **43**, 1.
— 1932, Bull. Sci. Bourgogne, **2**, 1.
HAGIHARA, B., et al., 1956, Nature, **178**, 629.
HAIG, C., 1935, Biol. Bull. mar. biol. Lab., Woods Hole, **69**, 305.
HALLDAL, P., 1958, Physiol. Plantarum. **11**, 118.
HAMNER, K. C., and BONNER, J., 1938, Bot. Gaz., **100**, 388.
HAMNER, K. C., et al., 1942, Bot. Gaz., **103**, 586.
HAMNER, K. C., 1944, Ann. Rev. Biochem., **13**, 575.
HANDLEY, W. R. C., 1936, New Phytologist, **35**, 456.
HANES, C. S., 1940, Nature, **145**, 348.
HANNIG, E., 1911, Flora, **102**, 209.
HANSEN, E., 1942, Bot. Gaz., **103**, 543.
HANSON, E. A., 1939, Rec. Trav. Bot. Néerl., **36**, 180.
— 1941, Austral. J. Exp. Biol. Med. Sci., **19**, 157.
HANSTEIN, J. VON, 1880, Bot. Abh. 3, 4.
HARDEN, A., and YOUNG, W. J., 1906, Proc. Roy. Soc. B, **77**, 405.
— — 1908, Proc. Roy. Soc. B, **80**, 299.
HARDER, R., 1924, Jahrb. wiss. Bot., **64**, 169.
HARDER, R., et al., 1931, Jahrb. wiss. Bot., **75**, 45.

HARDER, R., 1935, Nachr. Ges. Wiss. Göttingen, 1, 181.
HARDER, R., et al., 1936, 1938, Nachr. Ges. Wiss. Göttingen, 2, 1136, 3, 135.
HARDER, R., and STÖRMER, I., 1936, Jahrb. wiss. Bot., 83, 401.
HARDER, R., and WITSCH, H., 1942, Planta, 32, 547.
HARDER, R., and GÜMMER, G., 1944, Jahrb. wiss. Bot., 91, 359.
— — 1947, Planta, 35, 88.
HARDER, R., 1948, Symp. Soc. Exp. Biol., 2, 117.
HARDER, R., and BÜNSOW, R., 1958, Planta, 51, 201.
HÄRDTL, H., 1930, Bot. Archiv, 29, 1.
HARINGTON, C. R., 1947, Nature, 159, 319.
HARKINS, W. D., and ANDERSON, T. F., 1937, J. Amer. Chem. Soc., 59, 2189.
HARMS, H., 1936, Planta, 25, 155.
HARRINGTON, J. F., 1944, Proc. Amer. Soc. Hort. Sci., 45, 313.
HARRIS, J. O., 1946, J. Biol. Chem., 162, 11.
HARRIS, M., et al., 1942, Ind. Eng. Chem., 34, 833.
HÄRTEL, O., 1937, Ber. deutsch. bot. Ges., 55, 310.
HARTSUIJKER, K., 1935, Rec. Trav. Bot. Néerl., 32, 516.
HARVEY, E. B., 1938, Biol. Bull., 71, 101.
— 1939, Trans. Faraday Soc., 33, 943.
HASSID, W. Z., 1943, Quart. Rev. Biol., 18, 311.
HAUSER, G. F., 1941, Die nichtaustauschbare Festlegung des Kalis im Boden. (Dissertation.) Wagen-
    ingen.
HAXO, F. T., and CLENDENNING, K. A., 1953, Biol. Bull., 105, 103.
HAYWARD, H. E., 1938, The Structure of Economic Plants.
HAYWARD, H. E., and LONG, E. M., 1941, Bot. Gaz., 102, 437.
HAYWARD, H. E., 1942, U. S. Dept. Agric. Tech. Bull., 186.
— 1942, Bot. Gaz., 104, 152.
HEATH, O. V. S., 1938, New Phytologist, 37, 385.
HEATH, O. V. S., and GREGORY, F. G., 1938, Ann. Bot., 2, 811.
HEATH, O. V. S., 1947, Nature, 159, 647.
HEILBRONN, I. M., and PHIPERS, R. F., 1935, Biochem. J. 29, 1369.
HEILBRUNN, L. V., 1914, Jahrb. wiss. Bot., 54, 357.
— 1929, Protoplasma, 8, 58.
HEINECKE, A. J., and CHILDERS, N. F., 1937, Cornell Univ. Agr. Exp. Sta., Mem., 201.
HEITZ, E., 1936, Planta, 26, 134.
HELLERMAN, L., and PARKINS, H. E., 1934, J. Biol. Chem., 107, 241.
HEMBERG, T., 1947, Acta Horti Bergiani, 14, no. 5.
— 1949, Physiol. Plantarum, 1, 24.
HENRICI, M., 1921, Verh. Naturforsch. Ges. Basel, 32, 107, 125.
HENRY, H., and STACEY, M., 1943, Nature, 151, 671.
HEPBURN, J. S., and JOHN, E. Q., 1920, J. Franklin Inst., 189, 147.
HÉRISSEY, A., 1946, Compt. Rend., Paris, 223, 47.
HERSCHLER, A., 1933, Arbeit. Biol. Reichsanst. Land- und Forstwirtsch., 20, 633.
HERTEL, W., 1939, Flora, 133, 143.
HERZOG, F., 1938, Jahrb. wiss. Bot., 87, 211.
HESS, K., et al., 1939, Naturwiss., 27, 622.
HESSELMAN, H., 1904, Beih. Bot. Centralbl., 17, 311.
— 1937, Medd. Statens Skogsförsöksanstalt (Stockholm), 30, 529.
HESTRIN, S., et al., 1947, Nature, 159, 64.
HEVESY, G., and HAHN, L., 1940, Kgl. Danske Vidensk. Selsk. Biol. Medd., 15, 7.
HEYN, A. N. J., 1940, Bot. Rev., 6, 515.
HIBBARD, P. L., 1943, Soil Sci., 56, 433.
HICKS, P. A., 1928, New Phytologist, 27, 1.
HIGHKIN, H. R., 1956, Plant Physiol. 31, 399.
HILL, A. W., 1908, Ann. Bot., 22, 245.
HILL, H., and ROACH, W. A., 1940, Ann. Bot., 4, 515.
HILL, R., 1939, Nature, 103, 881.
HILL, R., and HARTREE, E. F., 1953, Ann. Rev. Plant Physiol. 4, 115.
HILL, R., and WITTINGHAM, C. P., 1953, New Phytologist, 52, 133.
HIRST, E., and JONES, J., 1942, J. Chem. Soc., 70
HOAGLAND, D. R., and DAVIS, A. R., 1923, J. Gen. Physiol., 5, 629.
HOAGLAND, D. R., 1930, Contrib. Marine Biol. Stanford.
— 1939, Amer. J. Bot., 26, 675.
HOAGLAND, D. R., and BROYER, T. C., 1942, J. Gen. Physiol., 25, 865.
HOAGLAND, D. R., 1944, Lectures on the Inorganic Nutrition of Plants, New York.

HOAGLAND, D. R., 1945, Soil Sci., **60**, 119.
HOFE, F. VON, 1933, Planta, **20**, 354.
HOFER, B., 1889, Jen. Z. Naturwiss., **17**, 105.
HOFFMANN, C., 1929, Jahrb. wiss. Bot., **71**, 214.
— 1932, Planta, **16**, 413.
HOFFMAN, W., 1939, Bodenkunde und Pflanzenernähr., **13**, 139.
HOFFMANN-BERLING, H., and KANSCHE, G. A., 1951, Z. Naturforsch., **6b**, 63.
HOFFMAN-OSTENHOF, O., 1947, Science, **105**, 549.
HÖFLER, K., 1918, Ber. deutsch. Bot. Ges., **36**, 414.
— 1930, Jahrb. wiss. Bot., **73**, 300.
— 1940, Ber. deutsch. bot. Ges., **58**, 292.
— 1942, Ber. deutsch. bot. Ges., **60**, 179.
— 1942, Phytopathol. Z., **14**, 192.
HÖFLER, and WEIXL-HOFMANN, H., 1939, Protoplasma, **32**, 416.
HOFMEISTER, L., 1939, Protoplasma, **33**, 399.
HOGEBOOM, G. H., et al, 1946, J. Biol. Chem., **165**, 615.
HOLDHEIDE, W., et al., 1936, Ber. deutsch. bot. Ges., **54**, 168.
HOLM-JENSEN, I., et al., 1944, Acta Bot. Fenn., **36**.
HÖLZL, J., 1955, Sitz.ber. Osterr. Akad. Wiss. Math.-Nat. Kl. Abt. 1., **164**, 659.
HONERT, T. H., VAN DEN, 1930, Rec. Trav. Bot. Néerl., **27**, 149.
— 1932, Verh. Kon. Nederl. Akad. Wetensch., **35**, 1104.
— 1935, 7: Ned.-Ind. Naturwetensch. Congres, 482.
— 1937, Natuurkund. Tijdschr., **97**, 150.
HOOGEHEIDE, F. J. C., 1944, Bot. Rev., **10**, 599.
HOOKER, H. D., 1915, Ann. Bot., **29**, 265.
— 1916, 1917, Bull. Torrey Bot. Club, **43**, 1, **44**, 389.
HOOVER, S. R., and ALLISON, F. E., 1940, J. Biol. Chem., **134**, 181.
HOOVER, W. H., 1937, Smithsonian Miscell. Coll., **95**, no. 21.
HOPE, A. B., 1953, Austral. J. Biol. Sci., **6**, 594.
HOPE, A. B., and ROBERTSON, R. N., 1953, Austral. J. Sci., **15**, 197.
HORECKER, B. L., and KORNBERG, A., 1946, J. Biol. Chem., **165**, 11.
HORECKER, B. L., and SMYRNIOTIS, P. Z., 1953, J. Amer. Chem. Soc., **75**, 1009, 2021.
HORN, I. T., 1940, *Über Darstellung und Eigenschaften der Pektinsäure*.
HOROWITZ, N. H., and HEEGARD, E., 1941, J. Biol. Chem., **137**, 475.
HOUGHTALING, H. B., 1940, Bull. Torrey Bot. Club, **67**.
HOWLETT, F. S., 1936, Ann. bot., **50**, 767.
HUBER, B., and HÖFLER, K., 1930, Jahrb. wiss. Bot., **73**, 351.
HUBER, B., 1930, Z. Bot., **23**, 839.
— 1932, Ber. deutsch. bot. Ges., **50**, 89.
— 1934, Flora, **129**, 113.
— 1935, Ber. deutsch. bot. Ges., **53**, 711.
HUBER, B., and SCHMIDT, E., 1936, Tharandt. Forstl. Jahrb., **87**, 369.
HUBER, B., et al., 1937, Tharandt. Forstl. Jahrb., **88**, 1017.
HUBER, B., 1937, Jahrb. wiss. Bot., **84**, 671.
HUBER, B., and SCHMIDT, E., 1937, Ber. deutsch. bot. Ges., **55**, 514.
HUBER, B., 1939, Fortschr. Bot., **8**, 193/194.
HUMPHREYS, TH. E., and CONN, E. E., 1956, Arch. Biochem. Biophys., **60**, 226.
HUNTER, F. E., and FORD, L., 1955, J. Biol. Chem., **216**, 357.
HURD-KARRER, A. M., 1930, J. Maryland Acad. Sci. **1**, 115.
— 1938, Amer. J. Bot., **25**, 666.
— 1939, Amer. J. Bot., **26**, 834.
HUSZAK, S., 1937, Z. Physiol. Chem, **247**, 239.
HUTCHINSON, G. E., 1945, Soil Sci., **60**, 29.
HYLMÖ, B., 1953, Physiol. Plantarum, **6**, 333.

ILJIN, W. S., 1928, Protoplasma, **3**, 558.
— 1929, Planta, **7**, 45.
— 1932, Jahrb. wiss. Bot., **77**, 220.
— 1933, Protoplasma, **19**, 414.
— 1934, Protoplasma, **22**, 299.
— 1936, Beih. Bot. Centralbl., **54**, 569.
— 1938, Bull. Ass. Russe rech. Sci., **7**, (12), 45.
IRMAK, L. R., 1943, Rev. Fac. Sci. Univ. Istanbul, Ser. B, **8**, 201.
ITALLIE, T. B., VAN, 1937, Bodenkunde Pflanzenernähr., **50**, 303.

ITERSEN, G. VAN, and MEEUSE, A. D. J., 1941, Verh. Kon. Nederl. Akad. Wetensch., **44**, 770, 897.
IVANOV, L. A., and ORLOWA, J. M., 1931, J. Soc. Bot. Russie, **16**, 139.
IZARD, C., 1956, Compt. Rend. Paris, **242**, 2027.

JACCARD, P., 1933, Planta, **19**, 713.
JACOB, A., and ALTEN, F., 1942, Arb. über Kalidüngung, 3. Series.
JACOBI, W., 1926, Österr. Bot. Z., **75**, 29.
JACOBS, W. P., and MORROW, I. B., 1957, Amer. J. Bot., **44**, 823.
JACOBSON, L., and OVERSTREET, R., 1947, Amer. J. Bot., **34**, 415.
JAMES, G. M., and JAMES, W. O., 1940, New Phytologist, **39**, 266.
JAMES, W. O., 1928, Proc. Roy. Soc., B, **103**, 1.
— 1930, Ann. Bot., **44**, 173.
JAMES, W. O., and BAKER, H., 1933, New Phytologist, **32**, 315.
JAMES, W. O., and HORA, F. B., 1940, Ann. Bot., **4**, 107.
JAMES, W. O., et al., 1941, Biochem. J., **35**, 588.
JAMES, W. O., and CRAGG, J. M., 1943, New Phytologist, **42**, 28.
JAMES, W. O., et al., 1944, New Phytologist, **43**, 62.
JAMES, W. O., 1946, Ann. Rev. Biochem., **15**, 417.
— 1953, *Plant Respiration*. Oxford.
JANKE, A., and WOZAK, M., 1934, Arch. Mikrobiol., **5**, 108.
JAQUES, A. G., 1938, J. Gen. Physiol. **21**, 775.
JEFFREY, E. C., 1917, *The Anatomy of Woody Plants*. Chicago.
JENNY, H., and OVERSTREET, R., 1938, Proc. Nat. Acad. Sci. **24**, 384.
JENNY, H., 1946, J. Colloid. Sci., **1**, 33.
JENSEN, H. L., 1932, J. Agric. Sci., **22**, 1.
JIMBO, T., 1931, Sci. Rep. Tohoku Imp. Univ., Biol., **6**, 285.
JOFFE, J. S., and LEVINE, A. K., 1939, Soil Sci. Soc. Amer. Proc., **4**, 157.
JOHANNSEN, W., 1900, *Das Atherverfahren beim Frühtreiben etc*.
JOHANSSON, N., 1926, Svensk Bot. Tidskr., **20**, 107.
— 1929, Jahrb. wiss. Bot., **71**, 154.
— 1929, Svensk Bot. Tidskr., **23**. 241.
— 1934, Svenska Skogsvårdsfören. Tidskr., **51**.
JOHNSON, F. H., 1955, *The Luminescence of Biological Systems*, Washington.
JOHNSON, J. M., and BUTLER, G. W., 1957, Physiol. Plantarum, **10**, 100.
JOHNSON, M. P., and BONNER, J., 1956, Physiol. Plantarum, **9**, 102.
JOHNSTON, E. S., 1934, Smithsonian Misc. Coll., **92**, 1.
JOLIOT, P., 1957, Compt. Rend. Paris, **244**, 2736.
JONES, J., and GORTNER, R. A., 1932, J. Phys. Chem., **387**.
JÖNSSON, B., 1893, Fysiogr. Sällsk. Handl. (Lund), **4**.
JORDAN, P., 1938, Physik. Z. **39**, 345.
JOST, L., 1922, Bot. Abhandl., **1**.
— 1932, Z. Bot., **25**, 481.
— 1942, Z. Bot., **35**, 161.
JUEL, I., 1946, Dansk Bot. Arkiv, **12**, 1.
JUNGERS, V., and DONTRELIGUE, J., 1943, La Cellule, **49**, 409.
JUNGES, W., 1957, Planta, **49**, 11.
JUNKER, E., 1941, Koll.-Z., **95**, 213.
JUTISZ, M., and LEDERER, E., 1947, Nature, **159**, 445.

KAHHO, H., 1937, Cytologia (Fujita-Jubilee Vol.), 129.
KAKESITA, K., 1930, Japan. J. Bot., **5**, 219.
— 1942, Biol. Rev., **17**, 28.
KALCKAR, H. M., 1947, Nature, **160**, 143.
KAMEN, M. D., 1946, Bull. Amer. Museum Nat. Hist., **87**, 101.
KAMEN, M. D., and TAKEDA, Y., 1956, Biochim. Biophys. Acta, **21**, 518.
KAMIYA, W., 1959, *Protoplasmic Streaming*. Protoplasmatologia. Wien.
KAMP, H., 1930, Jahrb. wiss. Bot., **72**, 403.
KAPLAN, R., 1940, Naturwiss., **28**, 79.
KARRER, P., 1939, *Lehrbuch der organischen Chemie*. 6. Aufl. (4th Engl. Edit. 1950).
— 1948, Endeavour, **7**, 3.
KATO, J., 1951, Mem. Coll. Sci. Univ. Kyoto. Ser. B., **20**, 32.
— 1953, Mem. Coll. Sci. Univ. Kyoto Ser. B., **20**, 189
KEFFORD, N. P., and KELSO, J., M., 1957, Austral. J. Biol. Sci., **10**, 60.
KEILIN, D., 1925, Proc. Roy, Soc. B., **98**, 312.

KEILIN, D., and HARTREE, E. F., 1939, Proc. Roy. Soc. B., **127**, 167.
KEILIN, D., and MANN, T., 1944, Nature, **153**, 107.
KEILIN, D., and HARTREE, E. F., 1946, Nature, **157**, 801.
KEILIN, D., and HARTREE, E. F., 1947, Antonie van Leeuwenhoek, **12**, 115.
KEILIN, D., and SMITH, J. D., 1947, Nature, **159**, 692.
KEILIN, D., and HARTREE, E. F., 1949, Biochem. J., **44**, 205.
— — 1949, Nature, **164**, 254.
— — 1951, Biochem. J., **49**, 88.
KELLER, B., 1925, J. Ecol., **13**, 224.
KELLEY, J. B., and MIDGLEY, A. R., 1943, Soil Sci., **55**, 167.
KELLEY, W. P., et al., 1931, Soil Sci., **31**, 25.
KELLNER, K., 1955, Biol. Zentralbl., **74**, 662.
KENNAWAY, COOK, et al., 1937—1940, Amer. J. Cancer, **29**, 33, 39.
KENTEN, R. H., and MANN, P. J. G., 1953, Biochem. J. **53**, 498.
— 1957, Biochem., J. **65**, 179.
KERL, H. W., 1929, Planta, **9**, 407.
KERSTING-MUNSTER, 1938, Forschungsdienst, **5**, 48.
KESSLER, E., 1955, Arch. Biochem. Biophys., **59**, 527.
— 1957, Arch. Mikrobiol., **27**, 166.
— 1957, Planta, **49**, 505.
KESSLER, O. W., 1932, Die Feldberegnung. 2. Folge, **111**.
KESSLER, W., and RUHLAND, W., 1938, Planta, **28**, 159.
KIDD, F., 1914, Proc. Roy. Soc., B., **87**, 408.
— 1917, New Phytologist, **17**, 44.
KIDD, F., et al., 1921, Proc. Roy. Soc. B, **92**, 368.
KIDD, F., et al., 1940, Ann. Bot., **4**, 1.
KIESEL, A., 1925, Z. physiol. Chem., **150**, 149.
KIM, CH. M., 1955, Ecol. Rev, **14**, 109.
KINOSHITA, S., 1939, Bot. Mag., **53**, 83.
KINZEL, W., 1913, *Frost und Licht als beeinflussende Kräfte bei der Samenkeimung.*
KISSER, J., and POSSNIG, W., 1932, Beitr. Biol. Pflanze, **20**, 77.
KISSER, J., and LINDENBERG, L., 1940, Jahrb. wiss. Bot., **89**, 89.
KIVINEN, E., 1931, J. Sci. Agric. Soc. Finl., **10**.
— 1932, Bull. Agrogeol. Inst. Finl., no. 33.
— 1933, Soil Res. **3**, 196.
— 1938, J. Sci. Agric. Soc. Finl., **10**, 147.
KLEBS, G., 1883, Untersuch. Bot. Inst. Tübingen, **1** ,233.
— 1886, Tagebl. Vers. Naturforsch. und Ärzte, Berlin.
— 1888, Untersuch. Bot. Inst. Tübingen, **2**, 489.
— 1896, *Die Bedingungen der Fortpflanzung bei einzelligen Algen und Pilzen.*
— 1903, *Wilkürliche Entwicklungsänderungen.*
KLEIN, G., and TAUBÖCK, K., 1930, Jahrb. wiss. Bot., **73**, 193.
KLEINHOONTE, A., 1932, Jahrb. wiss. Bot., **75**, 679.
KLEMM, P., 1895, Jahrb. wiss. Bot., **38**, 627.
KLING, H., 1958, Protoplasma, **49**, 364.
KLOTZ, I. M., 1946, Arch. Biochem., **9**, 109.
KLUYVER, A. J., and HOOGERHEIDE, J. C., 1933, Verh. Kon. Nederl. Akad. Wetensch., **36**, 596.
KLUYVER, A. J., 1934, Chem. Weekly, **31**, 18.
KLUYVER, A. J., and MANTEN, A., 1942, Antonie van Leeuwenhoek, **8**, 71.
KLUYVER, A. J., and SCHNELLEN, C. G. T. P., 1947, Arch. Biochem., **14**, 57.
KNAPP, R., and FURTHMANN, S., 1954, Ber. deutsch. bot. Ges., **67**, 252.
KNAPP, R., 1958, Die Naturwiss., **45**, 408.
KNAYSI, G., 1938, Bot. Rev., **4**, 83.
— 1944, *Elements of Bacterial Cytology.*
— 1946, J. Bacteriol., **51**, 113.
KNEEN, E., and SANDSTEDT, R. M., 1943, J. Amer. Chem. Soc., **65**, 1247.
KNIEP, H., 1905, Flora, **94**, 129.
KNODEL, H., 1938, Planta, **28**, 704.
— 1939, Jahrb. wiss. Bot., **87**, 557.
KNOTT, J. E., 1939, Cornell Univ. Agric. Exp. Sta. Mem., **218**.
KNUDSEN, L., 1913, J. Biol. Chem., **14**, 159.
KÖCKEMANN, A., 1932, Planta, **17**, 669.
KÖCKEMANN, 1936, Beih. Bot. Centralbl., **55** A, 191.
KOEPFLI, J. B., et al., 1938, J. Biol. Chem. **122**, 763.

KOFFLER, H., and KOBAYASHI, T., 1957, Arch. Biochem. Biophys., 67, 246.

KÖGL, F., and VERKAAIK, B., 1944, Hoppe-Seylers Z., 280, 162.

KÖGL, F., and SCHURINGA, G. J., 1944, Hoppe-Seylers Z., 280, 148.

KÖGL, F., et al., 1944, Hoppe-Seylers Z., 280, 135.

KÖHLER, E., 1942, Biol. Zentralbl., 62, 203.

KÖIE, M., 1938, Kgl. Danske Videnskab. Selsk. Skr., 7, 2.

KOIZUMI, T., and KAKUKAWA, T., 1940, Sci. Rep. Tôhoku Univ. Biol., 15, 105.

KOK, A. C. A., 1931, Verh. Kon. Nederl. Acad. Wetensch., 34, 918.

— 1933, Rec. Trav. Bot. Néerl., 30, 23.

KOK, B., 1947, Enzymologia, 13, 1.

— 1957, Nature, 179, 583.

KOKETSU, R., 1930, Bull. Sci. Fak. Terk. Kyushu Imp. Univ., 4, no. 2.

— 1932, J. Dept. Agric. Kyushu Imp. Univ., 3, 149.

KOKIN, S., 1930, Arb. Ukrain. Inst. Angew. Bot., 1, 154.

KOLTERMANN, O., 1927, Angew. Bot., 9, 289.

KOMEN, J. G., 1956, Biochim. Biophys. Acta, 22, 9.

KONDO, M., et al., 1932, Ber. Ohara Inst. landwirtsch. Unters., 5, 243.

KONING, H. C., 1933, *Het Winden van Schlingerplanten*. Dissertation. Utrecht.

KOPP, C., 1942, Biochem. Z., 310, 191.

KOPP, M., 1948, Ber. schweiz. bot. Ges., 58, 283.

KORIBA, K., 1937, Bot. Mag., 51, 461.

KOSAKA, H., 1931, 1933, J. Dept. Agric. Kyushu Imp. Univ., 3, 29, 251, 4, 95.

KOSTYTJEV, S., et al., 1930, Planta, 11, 117.

KOZLOVSKA, A., 1933, Polska Akad. Prace Roln.-Lesne, no. 8.

— 1936, Protoplasma, 27, 9.

KRABBE, G., 1886, *Das gleitende Wachstum bei der Gewebebildung der Gefässpflanzen.*

KRAMER, P. J., 1933, Amer. J. Bot., 20, 481.

— 1939, J. Elisha Mitchell Sci. Soc., 55, 243.

— 1939, Amer. J. Bot., 26, 784.

— 1941, Amer. J. Bot., 28, 446.

— 1944—1945, Bot. Rev., 10, 525, 11, 310.

KRAMER, P. J., and CLARK, W. S., 1947, Plant Physiol., 22, 51.

KRASSINSKY, N., 1930, Protoplasma, 9, 621.

KRAUS, G., 1880, Abh. Naturforsch. Ges. Halle, 15, II.

— 1911, *Boden und Klima auf kleinstem Raum*. Jena.

KREBBER, O., 1932, Arch. Mikrobiol., 3, 588.

KREBS, H. A., 1937, Lancet, 233, 736.

— 1941, Nature, 147, 560.

KRETOVIC, V. L., et al., 1954, Biochimica, 19, 208—215.

KRETSCHMER, L., 1930, Verh. Zool.-Bot. Ges. Wien, 80, 163.

KRIJGSMAN, B. J., 1925, Arch. Protistenkunde, 52, 478.

KROGH, A., 1946, Proc. Roy. Soc., B, 133, 140.

KROTKOV, G., 1941, Plant Physiol., 16, 799.

KROTKOV, G., and HELSON, V., 1946, Canad. Journ. Res., C, 24, 126.

KUBLI, H., 1947, Helv. Chim. Acta. 30, 453.

KUBO, H., 1939, Acta Phytochim. (Japan), 11, 195.

KUBOWITZ, F., 1937—1939, Biochem. Z., 292, 221; 299, 32.

KUHN, R., et al., 1942, Naturwiss., 30, 407.

KUHN, R., 1944, Ber. deutsch. Chem. Ges., 77, 219.

KÜHNE, W., 1864, *Untersuchungen über das Protoplasma und die Kontraktilität.*

KUIJPER, J., 1910, Rec. Trav. Bot. Néerl., 7, 131.

KUIKEN, K. A., et al., 1943, J. Biol. Chem., 151, 615.

KUILMAN, L. W., 1930, Rec. Trav. Bot. Néerl., 27, 287.

KÜMMER, H., 1932, Ber. deutsch. bot. Ges., 50, 300.

KUNITZ, M., 1947, J. Gen. Physiol., 30, 291.

KURAISHI, S., and OKUMURA, F. S., 1956, Bot. Mag. Tokyo, 69, 817.

KURSSANOV, A. L., 1934, Planta, 22, 240.

KÜSTER, E., 1910, Z. Bot., 2, 716.

— 1913, *Ueber Zonenbildung in Kolloiden Medien.*

— 1916, *Pathologische Pflanzenanatomie*. 2nd Edit.

— 1923, Biol. Zentralbl., 43, 301.

KYLIN, H., 1938, Svensk Bot. Tidskr., 32, 238.

— 1939, Kungl. Fysiogr. Sällsk. Förh. Lund, 9, no. 18.

— 1946, Kungl. Fysiogr. Sällsk. Hand. Lund, 16, no. 12.

KYLIN, A., and HYLMÖ, B., 1957, Physiol. Plantarum, 10, 467.

LABAW, L. W., and WYCKOFF, R. W. G., 1957, Arch. Biochem. Biophys., **67**, 225.
LAIBACH, F., and FISCHNISCH, O., 1938, Jahrb. wiss. Bot., **86**, 33.
LAING, H. E., 1940, Amer. J. Bot., **27**, 574, 861.
LAL, B, N., 1945, Ann. Bot., **9**, 283.
LAMPEN, J. O., et al., 1947, Arch. Biochem., **13**, 33.
LAMPRECHT, H., 1944, Agr. Hort. Genet., **2**, 3.
LANDAU, N., 1956, Nature, **178**, 1128.
LANG, A., and MELCHERS, G., 1943, Planta, **33**, 653.
LANG, K., 1952, *Der intermediäre Stoffwechsel*. Berlin, Göttingen, Heidelberg.
LANGE, S., 1929, Jahrb. wiss. Bot., **71**, 1.
LANGMUIR, I., 1939, Proc. Roy. Soc., Ser. A, **170**, 1.
LARDY, H. A., and ELVEHJEM, C. A., 1945, Ann. Rev. Biochem., **14**, 1.
LARDY, H. A., and ZIEGLER, J. A., 1945, J. Biol. Chem., **159**, 343.
LARSEN, P., 1936, Det forstl. Forsöksvaes. i Danmark, **14**, 13.
— 1943, K. Danske Videnskab. Selsk. Biol. Medd., **18**, 1.
— 1944, Dansk Bot. Ark., **11**, 1.
— 1946, Naturens Verden, 7.
— 1947, Amer. J. Bot., **34**, 349.
— 1947, Nature, **159**, 842.
LARSEN, P., 1955, Symposium on The Chemistry and Mode of Action of Plant Growth Substances. London, 76.
LARSEN, P., and BONDE, E., 1953, Nature, **171**, 180.
LAUSBERG, TH., 1935, Jahrb. wiss. Bot., **81**, 769.
LEA, D. E., 1946, *Actions of Radiation on Living Cells*.
LEAMER, R. W., 1942, Ohio State Univ. Abs. Doct. Diss. No. 40, 183.
LEBEDINCEV, E., 1930, Protoplasma, **10**, 52.
LEE, B., and PRIESTLEY, J. H., 1924, Ann. Bot., **38**, 525.
LEE, E., 1911, Ann. Bot., **25**, 52.
LEHMANN, E., 1919, Z. Bot., **11**, 161.
LEHMANN, W., 1906, *Flüssige Kristalle und die Theorie des Lebens*.
LEHNINGER, A. L., et al., 1958, Science, **128**, 450.
LEICK, E., and PROPP, G., 1930, Mitt. Naturw. Ver. Neuvorpommern und Rügen, **57**, 79.
LEICK, E., 1932, Beih. Bot. Centralbl., **49**, Ergbd., 160.
— 1934, Ber. deutsch. bot. Ges., **51**, 409.
LEININGEN-WESTERBURG, W., GRAF ZU, 1931, Handbuch der Bodenlehre (Blanck), **9**, 348.
LEINWEBER, F. J., 1956, Z. Bot., **44**, 337.
LEMBERG, R., 1953, Nature, **172**, 619.
LEMBERG, R., and LEGGE, J. W., 1949, *Hematin Compounds and Bile Pigments*. New York 1949.
LENHOFF, H. W., and KAPLAN, N. O., 1953, Nature, **172**, 730.
LEONARD, M. J. K., and BURRIS, R. H., 1947, J. Biol. Chem., **170**, 701.
LEOPOLD, A. C., and PRICE, C. A., 1956, *The Chemistry and Mode of Action of Plant Growth Substances*, 271.
LEPESCHKIN, W. W., 1930, Amer. Bot., **17**, 950.
— 1939—1940, Protoplasma, **34**, 355, **35**, 95.
LERNER, A. B., and BARNUM, C. P., 1946, Arch. Biochem., **10**, 417.
LEVAN, A., and ÖSTERGREN, G., 1943, Hereditas, **39**, 381.
LEVITT, J., and SCARTH, G. W., 1936, Canad. J. Res. Sec. Bot. Sci., **14**, 267.
LEVITT, J., 1946, Plant Physiol., **21** ,562.
LEVY, H., and SCHADE, A. L., 1948, Arch. Biochem., **19**, 273.
LEWIS, F. T., 1935, J. Bot., **22**, 741.
LIBBRECHT, W., and MASSART, L., 1935, Compt. Rend. Soc. Biol. Paris, **119**, 1193.
LICHSTEIN, H. C., and UMBREIT, W. W., 1947, J. Biol. Chem., **170**, 329.
LIDFORSS, B., 1909, Z. Bot., **1**, 443.
LIEBICH, H., 1941, Z. Bot., **37**, 129.
LIEBIG, G. F., and VANSELOW, A. P., 1942, Soil Sci., **53**, 341.
LIMBACH, S., 1929, Centralbl. Bakteriol., 2. Abt., **79**, 1.
LINDAHL, P. E., et al., 1946, Nature, **158**, 746.
LINDEBERG, G., 1944, Symbol. Bot. Upsal., **8**, no. 2.
LINDNER, R. C., and HARLEY, C. P., 1942, Science, **96**, 565.
LIPMANN, F., 1941, Adv. Enzymol., **1** 99.
— 1945, J. Biol. Chem., **158**, 515.
LITYNSKI, T., 1935, Trav. Inst. Chim. Agr. Univ. Cracovie, **3**, 3.
LIVERMAN, J. L., and LANG, A., 1956, Plant Physiol., **31**, 147.
LIVINGSTON, L. G., 1933, Amer. J. Bot., **32**, 75.

LJUBIMENKO, W., et al., 1930, Arbeit. Ukrain. Inst. angew. Bot., **1**, 111.

LLOYD, F. E., 1933, Trans. Roy. Soc. Canada, 3rd Ser. Appendix A, **27**, 1.

LOCKHEAD, A. G., 1940, Canad. J. Res., **18**, 42, 129.

LOEB, J., 1915, Bot. Gaz., **60**, 249.

LOEHWING, W. F., 1930, Plant Physiol., **3**, 293.

— 1937, Bot. Rev., **4**, 195.

LOHMANN, K., and KOSSEL, A. J., 1939, Naturwiss., **27**, 595.

LÖHNIS, M., 1937, Meded. Landbouwhoogesch. Wageningen, **41**, 1.

LÖHR, E., 1953, Physiol. Plantarum **6**, 529.

LONGLEY, A. E., 1941, Bot. Rev., **7**, 263.

LOO, S. W., 1936, Chinese J. Exp. Biol., **1**, 1.

— 1945—1946, Amer. J. Bot., **32**, 13, **33**, 156, 295.

LOO, T. L., 1931, J. Fak. Agric. Hokkaido Imp. Univ., **30**, 1.

LOO, T. L., and LOO, S. W., 1935, Sci. Rep. Nat. Centr. Univ., Ser. B, Biol., **2**, 51.

LOOFBOURROW, J. R., 1940, Rev. Modern. Phys., **12**, 267.

— 1941, Nature, **148**, 113.

LOOKEREN CAMPAGNE, R. N. VAN, 1955, Kon. Nederl. Akad. Wetensch. C, **58**, 548.

LOOMIS, W. E., and EWAN, L. M., 1936, Bot. Gaz., **97**, 728.

LORING, H. S., and CARPENTER, F. H., 1943, J. Biol. Chem., **150**, 381.

LORING, H. S., and PIERCE, J. G., 1944, J. Biol. Chem., **153**, 61.

LOUIS, J., 1935, La Cellule, **44**, 87.

LÖWENECK, M., 1930, Planta, **10**, 185.

LUCK, J. M., et al., 1946, Chem. Eng. News, **24**, 1235.

LUCKETT, S., and SMITH, F., 1940, J. Chem. Soc., 1114.

LUETSCHER, J. A., 1947, Physiol. Rev., **27**, 621.

LUGG, J. W. H., 1946, J. Proc. Austral. Chem. Inst., **13**, 88.

LUGG, J. W. H., and BEST, R. J., 1945, Austral. J. Exper. Biol. Med. Sci., **23**, 235.

LUMRY, R., SPIKES, J. D., and EYRING, H., 1954, Ann. Rev. Plant Physiol, **5**, 271.

LUNDBLAD, K., 1945, Kungl. Lantbruksakad. Tidskr. (Stockholm), **84**, 435.

LUNDEGÅRDH, H., 1910, Jahrb. wiss. Bot., **48**, 285.

— 1911, Kungl. Svenska Vetenskapsakad. Handl., **47** (Stockholm), no. 3.

— 1913, Arch. Entwicklungsmech., **37**, 509.

— 1914, Ber. deutsch. bot. Ges., **32**, 77.

— 1914, Jahrb. wiss. Bot., **53**, 421.

— 1916, Svensk Bot. Tidskr., **10**, 438.

— 1916, Kungl. Svenska Vetenskapsakad. Handl., **56**, no. 3.

— 1917, Kungl. Fysiogr. Sällsk. Handl. N. F., **28**, no. 6, **30**, no. 1.

— 1918, Kungl. Fysiogr. Sällsk. Handl. N. F. (Lund), **29**, no. 27.

— 1918, Botaniska Notiser (Lund), 65.

— 1919, Botaniska Notiser (Lund) 1.

— 1921, Ber. deutsch. bot. Ges., **39**, 195, 223.

— 1921, Svensk Bot. Tidskr., **15**, 46.

— 1922, *Zelle und Zytoplasma* (Linsbauers Handb. Pflanzenanat. Vol. 1). Berlin.

— 1922, Ark. Bot. Vetenskapsakademien (Stockholm), **18**, no. 3.

— 1924, Biochem. Z., **146**, 564; **149**, 207; **151**, 296; **154**, 195.

— 1924, *Der Kreislauf der Kohlensäure in der Natur*. Jena.

— 1926, Planta, **2**, 152.

— 1927, Flora, **21**, 273.

— 1928, Medd. Centralanstalten, no. **331**.

— 1929 and 1934, *Die quantitative Spektralanalyse der Elemente*. Jena.

— 1932, *Die Nährstoffaufnahme der Pflanze*. Jena.

LUNDEGÅRDH, H., et al., 1932, Svensk Bot. Tidskr., **26**, 271.

LUNDEGÅRDH, H., and BURSTRÖM, H., 1933, Planta, **18**, 683.

— — 1933, Biochem. Z., **261**, 235.

— — 1935, Biochem. Z., **277**, 223.

LUNDEGÅRDH, H., 1935, Naturwiss., **23**, 313.

— 1936, Lantbrukshögsk. Ann. (Upsala), **3**, 49.

— 1937, Biochem. Z., **290**, 104.

— 1938, Biochem. Z., **298**, 51.

— 1939, Planta, **29**, 419.

— 1940, Lantbrukshögsk. Ann. (Upsala), **8**, 233.

— 1941, Protoplasma, **35**, 548.

— 1941, Lantbrukshögsk. Ann. (Upsala), **9**, 127.

— 1942, Lantbrukshögsk. Ann. (Upsala), **10**, 31.

LUNDEGÅRDH, H., 1942, Naturwiss., **30**, 144.
— 1942, Soil Sci., **54**, 177.
— 1943, Lantbruksakademiens Tidskr. (Stockholm), **82**, 99.
— 1943, Ark. Bot. Vetenskapsakademien, (Stockholm) **31** A, no. 2.
LUNDEGÅRDH, H., and STENLID, G., 1944, Ark. Bot., Vetenskapsakademien, **31** A, no. 10.
LUNDEGÅRDH, H., and BURSTRÖM, H., 1944, Lantbrukshögsk. Ann. (Uppsala), **12**, 51.
LUNDEGÅRDH, H., 1945, Ark. Bot. Vetenskapsakademien (Stockholm), **32** A, no. 12.
— 1945, *Die Blattanalyse*. Jena.
— 1946, Nature, **157**, 575.
— 1946, Ark. Bot., Vetenskapsakademien, **33**A no. 5.
— 1947, Ann. Rev. Biochem., **16**, 503.
— 1948, Discuss. Faraday Soc., no. **3**, 139.
— 1949, Lantbrukshögsk. Ann. (Uppsala), **16**, 339, 372.
— 1949, Ark. Bot. Vetenskapsakademien, **1**, 289, 295.
— 1949, Physiol. Plantarum, **2**, 388—401.
— 1950, *Lärobok i växtfysiologi med växtanatomi*. Stockholm.
— 1950, Physiol. Plantarum, **3**, 103—151.
— 1950, Nature, **165**, 513—514.
— 1951, Nature, **167**, 71.
— 1951, Ark. Kemi (Stockholm), **3**, 69—79; 469—494.
— 1951, *Leaf analysis*. Trans. R. L. Mitchell. Hilger & Watts, London.
— 1952, Nature, **169**, 1088.
— 1952, Ark. Kemi (Stockholm, **5**, 97—146.
— 1953, Nature, **171**, 477; 521;) **172**, 303.
— 1953, Proc. 7th Int. Bot. Congress, Stockholm 1950, 765.
— 1954, Nature, **173**, 939—941.
— 1954, Ark. Kemi (Stockholm), **7**, 451—478.
— 1954, Analyse des plantes et problèmes des engrais minéraux: 1—6. Paris.
— 1954, Ark. Bot. (Stockholm), **3**, 89—119.
— 1954, Physiol. Plantarum, **7**, 375—384.
— 1954, Symp. Soc. Exp. Biol., **8**, 262—296.
— 1955, Physiol. Plantarum, **8**, 84—105, 142—163.
— 1955, Ann. Rev. Plant Physiol., **6**, 1—24.
— 1956, Acta Chem. Scand., **10**, 1083—1096.
— 1956, Biochim. Biophys. Acta, **20**, 469—487.
— 1957, *Klima und Boden in ihrer Wirkung auf das Pflanzenleben*. 5th Edit. Jena. (Earlier Eng. trans. *Environment and Plant Development* trans. E. Ashby, 1931).
— 1957, Biochim. Biophys. Acta, **25**, 1—12.
— 1958, Biochim. Biophys. Acta, **27**, 355—365.
— 1958, Nature, **181**, 28—30.
— 1958, Biochim. Biophys, Acta, **27**, 653—654.
— 1958, Physiol. Plantarum, **11**, 332—346, 564—571, 585—598.
LUNDEGÅRDH, P. H., 1947, Lantbrukshögsk. Ann. (Uppsala), **15**, 1.
LUNDSGAARD, E., 1932, Biochem. Z., **249**, 250.
LÜSCHER, E., 1936 (Dissertation). Bern.
LUTTKUS, K., and BÖTTICHER, R., 1939, Planta, **29**, 325.
LUTZ, H. J., et al., 1937, Yale Univ. School Forestry Bull. **44**.
LYON, T. L., and BUCKMAN, H. O., 1943, *The Nature and Properties of Soils*. New York.
LYR, H., 1957, Naturwiss., **44**, 235.

MAASS, W., 1935 (Dissertation), Greifswald.
MACDOUGAL, D. T., 1926, Carnegie Inst. Publ. 365, 373.
MACHLIS, L., 1944, Amer. J. Bot., **31**, 183, 281.
MACHT, D. I., 1945, Proc. Soc. Exp. Biol. Med., **60**, 217.
MACKINNEY, G., 1935, J. Biol. Chem., **111**, 75.
MADDEN, S. C., and WHIPPLE, G. H., 1940, Physiol. Rev., **20**, 194.
MÄGDEFRAU, K., 1931, Z. Bot., **24**, 417.
MAGNESS, J. R., 1934, Proc. Amer. Soc. Hort. Sci., **32**, 651.
MAGNUS, W., 1913, Ber. deutsch. bot. Ges., **31**, 290.
MALLERY, T. D., 1935, Ecol. Monogr., **5**.
MANGHAM, S., 1917, Ann. Bot., **31**, 293.
MANN, P. J. G., and QUASTEL, J. H., 1946, Nature, **158**, 154.
MANN, T., and LUTWAK-MANN, C., 1944, Ann. Rev. Biochem., **13**, 25.
MANNING, D. T., and GALSTON, A. W., 1955, Plant Physiol., **30**, 225.

2 K

MANTEN, A., 1948, *Phototaxis, Phototropism and Photosynthesis in purple Bacteria and blue-green Algae*. Dissertation. Utrecht.
MANTON, J., 1945, J., 1945, Ann. Bot., **9**, 155.
MAPSON, L. W., and GODDARD, D. R., 1951, Biochem. J., **49**, 592.
MARGOLIASH, E., 1952, Nature, **170**, 1014.
MARINETTI, G. V., SCARAMUZZINO, D. J., and STOTZ, E., 1957, J. Biol. Chem., **224**, 819.
MARSH, F. L., 1941, Bot. Gaz., **102**, 812.
MARSH, P. B., and GODDARD, D. R., 1939, Amer. J. Bot., **26**, 724, 767.
MARSH, R. P., and SHIVE, J. W., 1941, Soil Sci., **51**, 141.
MARSHAK, A., 1944, J. Gen. Physiol., **28**, 95.
MARTENS, P., 1934, La Cellule, **43**, 289.
MARTHALER, H., 1937, Jahrb. wiss. Bot., **85**, 76.
— 1939, Jahrb. wiss. Bot., **88**, 723.
MARTIN, E., 1943, Carnegie Inst. Public., **550**.
MARTIN, E. V., and CLEMENTS, F. E., 1935, Plant Physiol., **10**, 613.
MARTIN, E. V., 1940, Plant Physiol., **15**, 449.
MARTIUS, C., 1943, Hoppe-Seylers Z., **279**, 96.
MASKELL, E. J., and MASON, T. G., 1929, Ann. Bot., **43**, 205.
— — 1930, Ann. Bot., **44**, 1. 233, 657.
MASON, H. S., 1955, Adv. Enzymol., **16**, 105.
MASON, H. S., ONOPRYENKO, I., and BUHLER, D., 1957, Biochim. Biophys. Acta, **24**, 225.
MASON, T. G., and LEWIN, C. J., 1926, Roy. Dublin Soc. Sci. Proc., **18**, 203.
MASON, T. G., and MASKELL, E. J., 1931, Ann. Bot., **45**, 125.
— — 1934, Ann. Bot., **48**, 119.
MASON, T. G., and PHILLIS, E., 1941, Plant Physiol., **16**, 399.
— — 1945, Ann. Bot., **9**, 345.
MASSART, L., et al., 1947, Experientia, **3**, 289.
MAST, S. O., 1936, *Biological Effects of Radiation* (Duggar), **1**, 573.
MATSKOV, E. F., and FARFEL, R. L., 1940, Bull. Acad. Sci. USSR, Ser. Biol., 347.
MATTSON, S., 1931, Soil Sci., **30**, 459, **31**, 57, **32**, 343.
— 1932, Soil Sci. **34**, 209.
— 1933, Soil Sci. **36**, 149.
MATTSON, S., and GUSTAVSSON, Y., 1934, Lantbrukshögsk. Ann. (Upsala), **1**, 33.
MATTSON, S., and NILSSON, I., 1935, Lantbrukshögsk. Ann., **2**, 115.
MATTSON, S., and GUSTAVSSON, Y., 1937, Soil Sci., **43**, 421, 433.
MATTSON, S., and WIKLANDER, L., 1940, Lantbrukshögsk. Ann., **8**, 1.
— — 1940, Trans. Faraday Soc., **36**, 306.
MATTSON, S., 1946, Acta Agr. Suec., **2**, 185.
MAVRODINEAU, R., 1956, Applied Spectroscopy, **10**, 51, 137.
MAYER, D. T., and GULICK, A., 1942, J. Biol. Chem., **146**, 433.
MAXIMOV, N. A., 1926, *The Physiological Basis of Drought Resistance of Plants*.
— 1929, Protoplasma, **7**, 259.
— 1929, Biol. Zentralbl., **49**, 513.
— 1934, Herb. Plant Ser. Bull. 16.
MAXIMOV, N. A., and SOIKINA, G.S., 1940, Univ. N. G. Chernyshevsk., **15**, No. 1.
MAZIA, D., 1940, Cold Spring Harbor Symp. Quant. Biol., **8**, 195.
— 1941, Cold Spring Harbor Symp. Quant. Biol., **9**, 40.
— 1952, in *Modern Trends in Physiology and Biochemistry*. E. S. G. Barrow Ed. New York.
McALISTER, E. D., 1935, Smithsonian Misc. Coll., **93**, No. 7.
— 1937. Smithsonian Misc. Coll., **95**, No. 24.
McALISTER, E. D., and MYERS, J. E., 1940, Smithsonian Inst. Publ. Misc. Coll., **99**, 6.
McCALLA, A. G., and WOODFORD, E. K., 1938, Plant Physiol., **13**, 695.
McCALLA, T. M., 1940, J. Bacteriol., **40**, 23.
— 1941, J. Bacteriol., **41**, 775.
McCOLLOCH, R. J., and KERTESZ, Z. I., 1947. Arch. Biochem., **13**, 217.
McCREADY, R. M., and HASSID, W. Z., 1941, Plant Physiol., **16**, 599.
McHARGUE, J. S., 1945, Soil. Sci., **60**, 115.
McILWAIN, H., 1946, Nature, **158**, 898.
McKAY, E., 1935, Plant Physiol., **10**, 425.
McKEE, H. S., 1949, New Phytologist, **48**, 1.
MEEUSE, A. D. J., 1941, Rec. Trav. Bot. Néerl., **35**, 288.
— 1941, Bot. Rev., **7**, 249.
MEHL, J. W., 1938, Cold Spring Harbor Symp. Quant. Biol., **6**, 218.
MEIER, F. E., 1936, Smithsonian Misc. Coll., **95**, No. 2.

MEISCHKE, D., 1936, Jahrb. wiss. Bot., **83**, 359.
MELIN, E., 1925, *Untersuchungen über die Bedeutung der Baummykorrhiza*. Jena.
— 1936, Handb. Biol. Arbeitsmethoden. Abt. II T. **4**., 1015.
MENKE, W., 1939, Hoppe-Seylers Z., **263**, 104.
MENKE, W., and JACOB, E., 1942, Hoppe-Seylers Z., **272**, 229.
MER, C. L., 1940, Ann. Bot., **4**, 397.
MES, M. G., and AYMER-AINSLIE, K. M., 1935, South Afric. J. Sci., **32**, 280.
METSÄVAINIO, K., 1931, Ann. Bot. Soc. Zool.-Bot. Fenn., No. **1**.
METZNER, P., 1920, Jahrb. wiss. Bot., **59**, 325.
— 1929, Z. Bot., **22**, 225.
— 1930, Planta, **10**, 281.
— 1937, Ber. deutsch. bot. Ges., **55**, 16.
MEVIUS, W., and ENGEL, H., 1929, Planta, **9**, 1.
MEVIUS, W., 1930, Z. Bot., **23**, 481.
MEVIUS, W., and DIKUSSAR, I., 1930, Jahrb. wiss. Bot., **73**, 633.
MEVIUS, W., 1935, Jahrb. wiss. Bot., **81**, 327.
MEYER, A., 1887, Landwirtsch. Versuchsstat., **34**, 127.
— 1896, Bot. Ztg., **54**, 187.
— 1920, *Die morphologische und physiologische Analyse der Zelle*. Jena.
MEYER, B. S., 1938, Bot. Rev., **4**, 531.
MEYER, B. S., and ANDERSON, D. B., 1939, *Plant Physiology*. New York.
MEYER, K. H., and MARK, H., 1930, *Der Aufbau der hochpolymeren organischen Naturstoffe*. Leipzig.
MEYER, K. H., 1935, Ass. Chimistes Genève.
MEYER, K. H., and SIEVERS, J. F., 1936, Helv. Chim. Acta., **19**, 987.
MEYER, K. H., 1939, Helv. Phys. Acta. **12**, 349.
— 1942, *Natural and Synthetetie High Polymers*. New York.
MEYER, K. H., and BERNFELD, P., 1946, Helv. Chim. Acta, **29**, 52.
MEYER, S. L., and FORD, C. H., 1943, Plant Physiol., **18**, 530.
MEYERHOF, O., 1930, *Die chemische Vorgänge im Muskel*. Berlin.
MEYERHOF, O., et al., 1942, *A Symposium on Respiratory Enzymes*. Madison.
MICHAELIS, G., and MICHAELIS, P., 1934, Beih. Bot. Centralbl., Abt. B, **52**, 333.
MICHAELIS, L., 1940, Ann. New York Acad. Sci., **40**, 39.
MICHAELIS, P., 1934, Jahrb. wiss. Bot., **80**, 169, 337.
MICHEL-DURAND, E., 1939, Monogr. Sci. Natur., **22**, 94.
MICHENER, H. D., 1939, Amer. J. Bot., **26**, 109.
— 1942, Amer. J. Bot., **29**, 558.
MILATZ, J. M. W., and MANTEN, A., 1953, Biochim. Biophys. Acta, **11**, 17.
MILLAR, C. E., and TURK, L. M., 1943, *Fundamentals of Soil Science*. New York and London.
MILLER, C. O., SKOOGH, F., OKUMURA, F. G., SALZA, F. G. VON, and STRONG, F. M., 1955/56, J. Amer. Chem. Soc., **77**, 2662, **78**, 1375.
MILLER, E. C., 1938, *Plant Physiology*. New York and London.
MILLER, G. L., and PRICE, W. C., 1946, Arch. Biochem., **10**, 467,
MILOVIDOV, P., 1936, *La constitution chimique et physico-chimique du noyau cellulaire*. Prague (Chap. 1 C).
MILTHORPE, J., and ROBERTSON, R. N., 1948, Austral. J. Exp. Biol. Med. Sci., **26**, 189.
MIRSKY, A. E., and POLLISTER, A. W., 1943, Biol. Symp., **10**, 247.
MITCHELL, H. K., and ELROY, W. O., 1946, Arch. Biochem., **10**, 343.
MITCHELL, H. L., and ROSENDAHL, R. O., 1937, Black Rock Forest Papers, **1**, No. 10.
MITCHELL, R. L., 1945, Soil Sci., **60**, 63.
MITSCHERLICH, E. A., 1928, Schrift. Königsberg Gelehrt. Ges., Nat. Kl., **5**, 17.
MITSCHERLICH, E. A., et al., 1935, Schrift. Königsberg Gelehrt. Ges., Nat. Kl., **12**, 31.
MITTENZWEI, H., 1942, Hoppe-Seylers Z., **275**, 93.
MIYOSHI, M., 1894, Bot. Ztg., Abt. 1, **52**, 1.
MOEWUS, F., 1938, Jahrb. wiss. Bot., **86**, 753.
MOGK, W., 1914, Arch. Entwicklungsmech., **38**, 584.
MOHL, H. VON, 1944, Bot. Ztg. **2**, 273.
— 1851, *Grundzüge der Anatomie und Physiologie der vegetativen Zelle*
MOHR, H., 1956, Planta, **46**, 534.
MOLDTMANN, H. G., 1939, Planta, **30**, 298.
MOLISCH, H., 1909, *Das Warmbad als Mittel zur Treiben der Pflanzen*. Jena.
— 1913, *Mikrochemie der Pflanzen*. Jena.
MÖLLER, C. M., 1947, Det forstl. Forsögsvaes. i. Danmark, **19**, 105.
MOMMAERTS, W. F. H. M., 1940, Verh. Kon. Nederl. Akad. Wetensch., **43**, 3.
MÖNCH, I., 1937, Jahrb. wiss. Bot., **85**, 506.
MONTERMOSO, J. C., and DAVIS, A. R., 1942, Plant Physiol., **17**, 473.
MONTFORT, C., 1927, Jahrb. wiss. Bot., **66**, 105.

MONTFORT, C.,1934, Jahrb. wiss. Bot., **79**, 493.
— 1941, Naturwiss., **29**, 238.
MONTFORT, C., and ZÖLLNER, G., 1942, Bot. Arch., **43**, 393.
MORINAGA, T., 1926, Amer. J. Bot., **13**, 126.
MORTON, R. A., 1958, Nature, **182**, 1764.
MOSER, F., 1940, Soil Sci. Soc. Amer. Proc., **5**, 147.
MOTHES, K., 1935, Fortschr. Bot., **5**, 207.
MOTHES, K., et al., 1939—1940, Planta, **30**, 289.
MOTHES, K., 1940, Planta, **30**, 726.
— 1956, Angew. Bot., **30**, 125—128.
MULDER, E. G., 1938, (Dissertation), Wageningen.
— 1940, Antonie van Leeuwenhoek, **6**, 99.
MULLINS, L. J., 1941, J. Cell. Compar. Physiol., **18**, 161.
MURAKAMI, R., 1939, J. Agr. Chem. Soc. Japan., **15**, 291.
MURAKAMI, S., 1940, Acta Phytochim., **11**, 213.
MURNEEK, A. E., 1937, Univ. Missouri Coll. Agr. Res., Bull., **268**.
MYERS, J., and BURR, G. O., 1940, J. Gen. Physiol., **24**, 45.
MÜLLER, D., 1928, Planta, **6**, 23.
— 1935, Jahrb. wiss. Bot., **81**, 497.
— 1944, Friesia, **3**, 52.
MÜNCH, E., 1930, *Die Stoffbewegungen in der Pflanze*.
— 1938, Jahrb. wiss. Bot., **86**, 581.
— 1939, Flora, **34**.
MYRBÄCK, K., and AHLBORG, K., 1940, Biochem. Z., **307**, 69.
MYRBÄCK, K., and VASSEUR, E., 1943, Hoppe-Seylers Z., **277**, 171.
MYRBÄCK, K., 1945, Suomen Kemistilehti, No. 11—12.
— 1947, Congr. Intern. Ind. Ferment., Ghent.
— 1948, Ergebn. Enzymforsch., **10**.
MYRBÄCK, K., and NEUMÜLLER G., 1950, *The Enzymes*, Vol I, Part 1, 653.

NADEL, M., 1938, *Thèses*, Sér. A, No. 380, Paris.
NÄGELI, K. VON, 1879. *Theorie der Gärung*.
NAKAMURA, H., 1937, Acta Phytochim., **9**, 189, 231.
NATANSOHN, A., 1904, Jahrb. wiss. Bot., **39**, 638.
NAUMANN, E., 1930, Int. Rev. ges. Hydrobiol. and Hydrograph., **24**, 81.
NAVEZ, A. E., 1931, Protoplasma, **12**, 86.
NEBEL, B. R., 1939, Bot. Rev., **5**, 563.
NEEFF, F., 1914, Z. Bot., **6**, 465.
NEGER, F. W., 1913, *Biologie der Pflanzen*. Stuttgart.
NEILANDS, J. B., 1953, J. Biol. Chem., **197**, 701.
NEISCH, A. C., 1939, Biochem. J. **33**, 300.
NELSON, C. D., and GORHAM, P. R., 1957, Canad. J. Bot., **35**, 703.
NĚMEC, B., 1900—1902, Ber. deutsch. bot. Ges., **18**, 241, **20**, 339.
— 1905, *Studien über die Regeneration*. Berlin.
— 1910, *Das Problem der Befruchtungsvorgänge und andere zytologische Fragen*. Berlin.
NEUWOHNER, W., 1938, Planta, **28**, 644.
NEWCOMER, E. H., 1940, Bot. Rev., **6**, 85.
NEYDEL, K., 1930, Biochem. Z., **228**, 451.
NICHOLAS, D. J. D., and NASON, A., 1954, J. Biol. Chem., **211**, 183.
NICHOLS, G. E., 1934, Ecology, **15**, 364.
NICKERSON, W. J., and THIMANN, K. V., 1943, Amer. J. Bot., **30**, 94.
NICOLAI, E., 1929, *Over verandering van de permeabilitaet in wortelcellen*. (Dissertation).
NIEL, C. B. VAN, 1931, Arch. Mikrobiol., **3**, 1.
NIEL, C. B. VAN, and MULLER, F. M., 1931, Rec. Trav. Bot. Néerl., **28**, 245.
NIEL, C. B. VAN, 1937, Ann. Rev. Biochem., **6**, 595.
— 1941, Adv. Enzymol., **1**, 263.
— 1943, Physiol. Rev., **23**, 338.
— 1953, J. Cell Comp. Physiol., **41**, 11.
NILLSEN, N., 1928, Planta, **6**, 376.
NIELSEN, N., and HARTELIUS, V., 1945, Compt. Rend. Labor. Carlsberg. Sér. Physiol., **24**, 117.
NIEMANN, W., 1932, Angew. Bot., **14**, 1.
NIETHAMMER, A., 1928, Biochem. Z., **197**, 273.
— 1937, *Die mikroskopische Bodenpilze*. Berlin.
NIGHTINGALE, G. T., et al., 1931, Plant Physiol., **6**, 605.

NIGHTINGALE, G. T., et al., 1932, Plant Physiol., **7**, 565.
NIGHTINGALE, G. T., 1933, Bot. Gaz., **95**, 35.
NIGHTINGALE, G. T., and MITCHELL, J. W., 1934, Plant Physiol., **9**, 217.
NIKLEWSKI, B., et al., 1937, Bodenkunde und Pflanzenernähr., **49**, 294.
NILSSON, R., 1941, Arch. Mikrobiol., **12**, 63.
NITSCH, J. P., 1956, Plant Physiol., **31**, 94.
NITSCHE, H., 1937, Österr. Bot. Z., **86**, 161.
NIUS, E., 1931, Jahrb. wiss. Bot., **74**, 34.
NOACK, K., 1922, Z. Bot., **14**, 1.
NOACK, K., and PIRSON, H., 1939, Ber. deutsch. bot. Ges., **57**, 442.
NOACK, K., et al., 1940, Naturwiss., **28**, 172.
NOACK, K., and TIMM, E., 1942, Naturwiss., **30**, 453.
NOACK, K., 1943, Biochem. Z., **316**, 166.
NOBBE, 1876, *Handbuch der Samenkunde.*
NODDACK, W., 1939, Z. phys. Chem., A, **185**, 207, 241.
NOGGLE, G. R., 1946, Lloydia, **9**, 153.
NOGUCHI, Y., 1931, Japan. J. Bot., **4**, 238, **5**, 351.
NOMURA, S., 1933, Protoplasma, **20**, 85.
NORDAL, A., 1940, Arch. Pharmaz., **278**, 289.
NORKRANS, B., and RÅNBY, B. G., 1956, Physiol. Plantarum, **9**, 198.
NORRIS, A. D., 1946, Nature, **157**, 408.
NORTHRUP, J. H., 1930, J. Gen. Physiol., **13**, 739.
NOVAK, F. A., 1937, Mohelno. Sv. 1 a, Brno. 115.
NUERNBERGK, E., and DU BUY, H. G., 1932—1935, Ergebn. Biol., **9**, 358, **10**, 207, **13**, 325.

OGSTON, A. G., 1947, Physiol. Rev., **27**, 228.
OHGA, I., 1926, Amer. J. Bot., **13**, 754.
OHLE, W., 1935, Naturwiss., **23**, 480.
ÖHOLM, L. W., 1944, Soc. Sci. Fenn. Comm. Phys.—Math., **12**, 9.
OKADA, Y., 1930, Sci. Rep. Tôhoku Univ., Ser. 4, **5**, 41.
OKUNUKI, K., MATSUBARA, H., NISHIMURA, SH., and HAGIHARA, B., 1956, J. Biochem., **43**, 857.
OLSEN, C., 1935, Compt. Rend. Labor. Carlsberg, Sér. Chim., **21**, 15.
— 1936, Compt. Rend. Labor. Carlsberg, Sér. Chim., **21**, 129.
— 1937, Compt. Rend. Labor. Carlsberg, Sér, Chim., **22**, 405.
— 1941, Compt. Rend. Labor. Carlsberg, Sér. Chim., **23**, 101.
— 1942, Compt. Rend. Labor. Carlsberg, Sér. Chim., **24**, 69.
OLSON, O. E., et al., 1942, Soil Sci., **53**, 365, **54**, 47.
OLSON, R. A., and DU BUY, H. G., 1940, Amer. J. Bot., **27**, 392.
OLTMANNS, F., 1922, *Morphologie und Biologie der Algen.* Jena.
ONCLEY, J. L., 1959, Biophysical Science. Reviews of Modern Physics, **31**, 1—568.
OPPENHEIMER, C., 1933, *Chemische Grundlagen der Lebensvorgänge.* Leipzig.
OPPENHEIMER, C., and STERN, K. G., 1939, *Biological Oxidations.* The Hague.
OPPENHEIMER, H. R., 1945, Palest. J. Bot., Rehovoth Ser., **5**, 112.
OPPENOORTH, W. F. F., 1939, Verh. Kon. Nederl. Akad. Wetensch., **42**, 902.
— 1941, Rec. Trav. Bot. Néerl., **38**, 289.
ORDIN, L., and KRAMER, P. J., 1956, Plant Physiol., **31**, 468.
ORDIN, L., CLELAND, R., and BONNER, J., 1957, Plant Physiol., **32**, 216.
ORNSTEIN, L. S., et al., 1938, Enzymologia, **5**, 110.
ÖRSKOV, S. L., 1946, Acta Path. Microbiol. Scand., **22**, 523.
ORTH, R., 1937, Jahrb. wiss. Bot., **84**, 358.
OSBORNE, D. J., BLACKMAN, G. E., et al., 1955, J. Exp. Bot., **6**, 392.
OSTER, G., and STANLEY, W. M., 1946, Brit. Journ. Exp. Pathol., **27**, 261.
OSTERHOUT, W. J. V., 1943, J. Gen. Physiol., **26**, 293.
— 1945, J. Gen. Physiol., **28**, 347.
— 1947, J. Gen. Physiol., **30**, 439.
— 1947, Bot. Rev., **13**, 194.
OUDMAN, J., 1936, Rec. Trav. Bot. Néerl., **33**, 352.
OVERBECK, F., 1934, Z. Bot., **27**, 129.
OVERBEEK, J. VAN, 1938, Plant Physiol., **13**, 587.
— 1939, Bot. Rev., **5**, 655.
— 1939, Bot Gaz., **101**, 450.
1941, Amer. J. Bot., **28**, 1.
— 1942, Cold Spring Harbor Symp. Quant. Biol., **10**, 126.
— 1942, Amer. J. Bot., **29**, 677.

OVERBEEK, J. VAN., 1944, Ann. Rev. Biochem., **13**, 631.
— 1947, Amer. J. Bot., **34**, 266.
OVERBEEK, J. VAN, et al., 1946, Amer. J. Bot., **33**, 100.
OVERKOTT, O., 1939, Bot. Arch., **39**, 389.
OVERSTREET, R., and JENNY, H., 1939, Soil Sci. Soc. Amer. Proc., **4**, 125.
OVERSTREET, R., et al., 1940, Proc. Nat. Acad. Sci. U.S.A., **26**, 688.
OVERSTREET, R., et al., 1942, Amer. J. Bot., **29**, 227.
OVERSTREET, R., and JACOBSON, L., 1946, Amer. J. Bot., **33**, 107.
OVERTON, J. B., 1902, Pflügers Arch. ges. Physiol., **92**, 115.

PAAUW, F. VAN DER, 1932, Rec. Trav. Bot. Néerl., **29**, 497.
PAECH, N., 1935, Planta, **24**, 78.
PALADE, E. G., 1952, Anat. Rec., **114**, 427.
PALLADIN, W., 1909, Biochem. Z., **18**, 151.
PALLMANN, H., 1930, Kolloidchem. Beih., **30**, 334.
PALLMANN, H., and HAFFTER, P., 1933, Ber. schweiz. bot. Ges., **42**, 357.
PALLMANN, H., et al., 1938, Bodenkunde and Pflanzenernähr., **54/55**, 94.
PALLMANN, H., et al., 1940, Ann. Fac. Agron. Bucharest, **1**.
PALMER, K. J., and LOTSKAR, H., 1945, J. Amer. Chem. Soc., **67**, 883.
PANKAKOSKI, A., 1935, Ann. Bot. Soc. Vanamo, **6**, No. 7.
PARKER, M. W., et al., 1946, Bot. Gaz., **108**, 1.
PARKS, R. Q., and SHAW, B. T., 1941, Soil Sci. Soc. Amer. Proc., **6**, 219.
PARKS, R. Q., et al., 1944, Plant Physiol., **19**, 414.
PASTEUR, L., 1876, *Études sur la bière*.
PATSCHOVSKY, N., 1920, Beih. Bot. Centralbl., **37**, 259.
PAULING, L., 1945, J. Amer. Chem. Soc., **67**, 555.
— 1950, *The Nature of the Chemical Bond and the Structures of Molecules and Crystals*.
PAULING, L., COREY, R. B., and BRANSON, H. R., 1951, Proc. Nat. Acad. Sci. USA, **37**, 205.
PAVLYCHENKO, T. K., 1937, Ecology, **18**, 62.
PEARSALL, W. H., 1922, Amer. Naturalist, 269.
PEARSALL, W. H., and BILLIMORIA, M. C., 1937, Biochem. J. **31**, 174.
PEARSON, R. W., and PIERRE, W. H., 1940, Soil Sci. Soc. Amer. Proc., **5**, 285.
PEECH, M., and BRADFIELD, R., 1940, Soil Sci., **55**, 37.
PEKAREK, J., 1930, Protoplasma, **10**, 510.
PENMAN, H. L., 1942, Proc. Roy. Soc. B, Biol. Sci., **130**, 416.
PENZES, A., 1938, Bot. Közlemények, Budapest, **35**, 22.
PEPKOWITZ, L. P., and SHIVE, J. W., 1944, Soil Sci., **57**, 143.
PERNER, E. S., and PFEFFERKORN, G., 1953, Flora, **140**, 98.
PERRENOUD, H., 1943, Trav. chim. alim. et d'hygiène, **34**, 327.
— 1944, Kolloid-Z., **107**, 16.
PETERING, H. G., et al., 1939, J. Amer. Chem. Soc., **61**, 3525.
PETERS, N., 1929, Arch. Protistenkunde, **67**, 291.
PETERSBURGSKIJ, A., 1944, Bull. Acad. Sci. USSR, Cl. Sci. Math. Nat. Ser. Biol., **205**.
PETERSON, R. W., and WALTON, J. H., 1943, J. Amer. Chem. Soc., **65**, 1212.
PETRIE, A. H. K., 1937, Austral. J. Exp. Biol. Med. Sci., **15**, 385.
PETRIE, A. H. K., and WOOD, J. G., 1938, Ann. Bot., **2**, 887.
PETRIE, A. H. K., and WILLIAMS, R. F., 1938, Austral. J. Exp. Biol. Med. Sci., **16**, 347.
PETRIE, A. H. K., 1943, Biol. Rev., **18**, 105.
PFEFFER, W., 1877, *Osmotische Untersuchungen*. Leipzig.
— 1885—1886, Untersuch. Bot. Inst. Tübingen, **1**, 483, **2**, 182.
— 1890, Abh. Sächs. Akad. Wiss. Math.-Nat. Kl., **16**, 185.
— 1897—1904, *Pflanzenphysiologie*, 2. Edit. Leipzig. (Eng. Trans. *The Physiology of Plants*. vols. I, II, III, trans. A. J. Ewart, Oxford, 1900—1903).
— 1915, Abh. Sächs. Akad. Wiss. Math.-Nat. Kl., **34**, 3.
PFEIFFER, H., 1912, Bot. Gaz., **53**, 436.
— 1925, New Phytologist, **24**, 65.
— 1940, *Experimentelle Cytologie*
— 1942, Protoplasma, **36**, 616.
PFLEIDERER, H., 1933, Z. Bot., **26**, 305.
PHAFF, H. J., 1947, Arch. Biochem., **13**, 67.
PHILLIS, E., and MASON, T. G., 1937, Nature, **140**, 370.
— — 1939, Ann. Bot., **3**, 889.
— — 1940, Ann. Bot., **4**, 635.
— — 1941, Ann. Bot., **5**, 15.

PHINNEY, B. O., 1956, Nat. Acad. Sci. (New York), **42**, 185.
PHINNEY, B. O., WEST, C. A., RITZEL, M., and NEELY, P. M., 1957, Proc. Nat. Acad. Sci., U.S.A., **43**, 398.
PICCARD, A., 1904, Jahrb. wiss. Bot., **40**, 94.
PICKEN, L. E. R., 1940, Biol. Rev., **15**, 133.
PIEKARSKI, G., 1940, Arch. Mikrobiol., **11**.
PIERCE, E. C., and APPLEMAN, C. O., 1943, Plant Physiol., **18**, 224.
PIGMAN, W. W., and GOEPP, R. M., 1948, *Chemistry of the Carbohydrates*. New York.
PILET, P. E., 1952, Bull. soc. randoise sci. nat., **65**, 197.
PIPER, C. S., 1942, J. Agric. Sci, **32**, 143.
PIRSCHLE, K., 1929, Planta, **9**, 84.
— 1930, Jahrb. wiss. Bot., **72**, 335.
— 1931, Planta, **14**, 583.
— 1932, Jahrb. wiss. Bot., **74**, 297.
— 1934, 1935, Planta, **23**, 177, **24**, 649.
— 1937, Ergebn. Biol., **15**, 67.
— 1939, Ergebn. Biol., **17**, 255.
— 1941, Naturwiss., **29**, 165.
— 1941, Biol. Zentralbl., **61**, 452.
PIRSON, A., 1937, Z. Bot., **31**, 193.
— 1939, Planta, **29**, 231.
— 1955, Ann. Rev. Plant Physiol., **6**, 71.
PIRSON, A., and BERGMANN, L., 1955, Nature, **176**, 309.
PISEK, A., and CARTELLIERI, E., 1931, Jahrb. wiss. Bot., **75**, 195.
— — 1932, Jahrb. wiss. Bot., **75**, 643.
— — 1933, Jahrb. wiss. Bot., **79**, 131.
PISEK, A., and BERGER, E., 1938, Planta, **28**, 124.
PISEK, A., and CARTELLIERI, E., 1939, Jahrb. wiss. Bot., **88**, 20.
PLICE, M. J., 1934, Cornell Univ. Agric. Exp. Sta., Mem., **166**.
— 1944, Soil Sci. Soc. Amer. Proc., **8**, 408.
PLOTHO, O., 1940, Arch. Mikrobiol., **11**, 285.
POLIS, B. O., and MEYERHOF, O., 1947, J. Biol. Chem., **169**, 389.
POLLAK, H., 1928, J. Gen. Physiol., **11**, 539.
POMA, G., 1922, Bull. Acad. Roy. Belg. Sci., **8**, 81.
PONTECORVO, G., 1952, Adv. Enzymol., **13**, 121.
POPESCO, S., 1926, Bul. Agric. Bucarest. **4**, No. 96.
POPP, H., and BROWN, FL., 1933, Bull. Torrey Bot. Club, **60**, 161.
PORODKO, T. M., 1925, Jahrb. wiss. Bot., **64**, 450.
PORTER, J. R., 1946, *Bacterial Chemistry and Physiology*.
POTTER, V. R., and DUBOIS, K. D., 1943, J. Gen. Physiol., **24**, 391.
POTTER, V. R., 1946, J. Biol. Chem., **165**, 311.
PRAT, H., 1948, Bot. Rev., **14**, 603.
PRÁT, S., 1929, Arch. Protistenkunde, **68**, 415
— 1936, Verh. Intern. Kongr. Lichtforsch., 181.
— 1936, Protoplasma, **26**, 113.
PRATT, R., and FONG, J., 1940, Amer. J. Bot., **27**, 431.
PREISING, F. A., 1930, Bot. Arch., **30**, 241.
PRESTON, R. D., 1939, Biol. Rev., **14**, 281.
PRESTON, R. D., and CLARK, C. S., 1944, Proc. Leeds Phil. Soc., **4**, 201.
PRESTON, R. D., and DUCKWORTH, R. B., 1946, Proc. Leeds Phil. Soc., **4**, 343.
PRESTON, R. D., 1947, Proc. Roy. Soc. B, **134**, 202.
PRIANISJNIKOV, D., 1923, Ber. deutsch. bot. Ges., **41**, 138.
— 1933, Z. Pflanzenernähr. Düng., A, **30**, 38, 134.
— 1934, Die Phosphorsäure, **1**, 1.
PRICE, C. C., 1946, *Mechanism of Reactions at Carbon-Carbon Double Bonds*.
PRICE, W. C., et al., 1946, Arch. Biochem., **9**, 175.
PRICKETT, P. S., 1928, New York State Agric. Exp. Sta. Tech. Bull., No. 147.
PRIESTLEY, J. H., 1924, New Phytologist, **23**, 1.
PRIESTLEY, J. H., and RADCLIFFE, F. M., 1924, New Phytologist, **23**, 161.
PRIESTLEY, J. H., 1925, New Phytologist, **24**, 271.
— 1926, New Phytologist, **25**, 145.
PRIESTLEY, J. H., and TONG, D., 1927, Proc. Leeds Phil. Soc., **1**, 199.
PRIESTLEY, J. H., 1929, New Phytologist, **28**, 54.
— 1930, New Phytologist, **29**, 96, 316.

PRIESTLEY, J. H., and SCOTT, L. I., 1935, Ann. Bot., **49**, 161.
PRIESTLEY, J. H., et al., 1935, Proc. Leeds Phil. Soc., **3**, 42.
PRIESTLEY, J. H., 1943, Bot. Rev., **9**, 593.
PRINGSHEIM, E. G., 1926, Z. Bot., **18**, 209.
— 1930, Planta, **11**, 528.
— 1931, Jahrb. wiss. Bot., **74**, 249.
— 1936, Beih. Bot. Centralbl., A, **55**, 100.
PRUD'HOMME VAN REINE, W. J., 1935, Rec. Trav. Bot. Néerl., **22**, 468.
PUCHER, G. W., et al., 1947, Plant Physiol., **22**, 1.
PULVER, R., and VERZAR, F., 1940, Nature, **145**, 823.
PURVIS, O. N., 1934, Ann. Bot., **48**, 919.
PYRKOSCH, G., 1936, Protoplasma, **26**, 418, 520.

QUASTEL, J. H., STEPHENSON, M., and WHETHAM, M. D., 1925, Biochem. J., **19**, 304.
QUEDNOW, K. G., 1930, Bot. Arch., **30**, 51.
QUISPEL, A., 1938, Verh. Kon. Nederl. Acad. Wetensch., **41**, No. 4.

RAADH, E., and SÖDING, H., 1957, Planta, **49**, 47.
RAALTE, M. H., VON, 1940, Ann. Jard. Bot. Buitenzorg, **50**, 99.
RABIDEAU, G. S., and BURR, G. O., 1945, Amer. J. Bot., **32**, 349.
RABINOWITCH, E., 1945, *Photosynthesis and Related Processes*. New York.
RACKER, F., 1954, *Mechanism of Enzyme Action*. Baltimore.
RAISTRICK, H., et al., 1931, Phil. Trans. Roy. Soc., B, **220**, 1.
RALEIGH, G. J., 1946, Plant Physiol., **21**, 194.
RAMSHORN, K., 1934, Planta, **22**, 737.
RANDLES, C. I., and BIRKELAND, J. M., 1944, J. Bacteriol., **47**, 454.
RANSON, S. L., and PARIJA, B., 1955, J. Exp. Bot., **6**, 80.
RAVEL, J. M., and SHIVE, W., 1946, J. Biol. Chem., **166**, 407.
RAY, P. M., and THIMANN, K. V., 1955, Science, **122**, 187.
— — 1956, Arch. Biochem. Biophys., **64**, 193.
RAYNER, M. C., 1926, New Phytologist, **25**, 1, 65, 171, 248, 338.
— 1927, New Phytologist, **26**, 22, 85.
REED, H. S., 1944, Amer. J. Bot., **31**, 193.
REHM, S., 1937, Jahrb. wiss. Bot., **85**, 788.
REID, M. E., 1929, Amer. J. Bot., **16**, 747
REINERT, J., 1953, Z. Bot., **41**, 103.
— 1955, Naturwiss., **42**, 18.
— 1957, Fortschr. Bot., **19**, 343.
REINOLD, L., 1954, New Phytologist, **53**, 218.
RENNER, O., 1915, Handwörterbuch Naturwiss., **10**, 538.
— 1932, Planta, **18**, 215.
REPP, G., 1939, Jahrb. wiss. Bot., **88**, 554.
RESÜHR, 1935, Protoplasma, **24**, 531.
— 1939, Planta, **30**, 471.
REUTER, L, 1942, Protoplasma, **36**, 321.
RIBBERT, A., 1931, Planta, **12**, 603.
RICCA, U., 1916, Nuovo Giorn. Bot. Ital., **23**, 51.
RICHARDS, F., J., 1927, New Phytologist, **26**, 187.
— 1938, Ann. Bot., **2**, 491.
RICHARDS, F. J., and SHENG-HAN, SH., 1940, Ann. Bot., **4**, 403.
RICHARDS, F. J., 1944, Ann. Bot., **8**, 323.
RICHARDS, F. J., and BERNER, E., 1954, Ann. Bot., **18**, 15.
RICHTER, G., 1959, Biochim. Biophys. Acta, **34**, 407.
RIPPEL, A., 1926, Jahrb. wiss. Bot., **65**, 819.
— 1936, Phytopathol. Z., **9**, 507.
RIPPEL, A., and LOHRMANN, W., 1940, Ges. Wiss. Göttingen. Nachr. Biol., **3**, 239.
RIS, H., and MIRSKY, A. E., 1951, Exp. Cell. Res., **2**, 263.
RISS, M. M., 1913, Jahrb. wiss. Bot., **53**.
ROBBINS, W. J., 1937, Amer. J. Bot., **24**, 243.
— 1940, Bull. Torrey Bot. Club, **67**, 762.
— 1942, Proc. Eighth Amer. Congr. Sci., **3**, 277.
— 1946, J. Arnold Arboretum, **27**, 480.
ROBERG, M., 1931, Centralbl. Bakteriol., II, **84**, 196.
— 1934, Jahrb. wiss. Bot., **79**, 472.

ROBERG, M., 1935, Jahrb. wiss. Bot., **82**, 65.
ROBERTS, E. A. H., and SARMA, S. N., 1940, Biochem. J., **34**, 1517.
ROBERTSON, R. N., 1941, Austral. J. Exp. Biol. Med. Sci., **19**, 265.
— 1944, Austral. J. Exp. Biol. Med. Sci., **22**, 237.
ROBERTSON, R. N., and TURNER, J. S., 1945, Austral. J. Exp. Biol. Med. Sci., **23**, 63.
ROBERTSON, R. N., and THORN, M., 1945, Austral. J. Exp. Biol. Med. Sci., **23**, 305.
ROBERTSON, R. N., et al., 1947, Austral. J. Exp. Biol. Med. Sci., **25**, 1.
ROBERTSON, R. N., and WILKINS, M. J., 1948, Austral. J. Sci. Res., Ser. B., **1**, 17.
ROBERTSON, R. N., WILKINS, M. J., and HOPE, A. B., 1955, Nature, **175**, 640.
ROBINSON, G. M., and ROBINSON, R., 1935, J. Chem. Soc., **744**.
ROBINSON, W. O., and EDGINGTON, G., 1945, Soil Sci., **60**, 15.
— — 1946, Soil Sci., **61**, 341.
ROBORGH, J. R., and THOMAS, J. B., 1948, Verh. Kon. Nederl. Akad. Wetensch., **51**, 87.
RODHE, W., 1948, Symbol. Bot. Upsal., **10**, no. 1.
RODRIGO, F. A., 1955, (Dissertation). The Hague.
ROGERS, H. T., et al., 1942, Soil Sci., **54**, 353.
ROGERS, L. L., and SHIVE, W., 1947, J. Biol. Chem., **169**, 57.
ROMIJN, G., 1931, Verh. Kon. Nederl. Akad. Wetensch., **34**, 289.
ROODENBURG, J. W. M., 1937, Ber. deutsch. bot. Ges., **55**, 5.
— 1940, Rec. Trav. Bot. Néerl., **37**, 301.
ROPP, R. S., 1946, Ann. Bot., **10**, 353.
ROSENDAHL, R. O., 1942, Soil Sci. Soc. Amer. Proc., **7**, 477.
ROSENE, H. F., 1947, J. Cell. Comp. Physiol., **30**, 15.
ROSETTER, F. N., and JACOBS, W. P., 1953, Amer. J. Bot., **40**, 276.
ROSSI, G. DE, 1932, Bull. Soc. Ital. Soc. Int. Microbiol. (Fortschr. Bot., **2**, 226).
ROTHEN, A., 1946, J. Biol. Chem., **163**, 345.
— 1947, J. Biol. Chem., **167**, 299.
ROUBAIX, J. DE, 1941, Publ. Inst. Belge Amél. Betteraves No. **6**, 39.
ROUSCHAL, E., 1935, Akad. Wiss. Wien. Akad. Anzeiger, No. **16**.
— 1935, Sitz. ber. Akad. Wiss. Wien. Math.-Nat. Kl. I, **144**, 313.
— 1938, Österreich. bot. Z., **87**, 42.
— 1938, Flora, **132**, 305.
— 1938, Jahrb. wiss. Bot., **87**, 436.
— 1941, Planta, **32**, 66.
— 1941, Flora, **35**, 135.
ROUTIEN, J. B., and DAWSON, R. F., 1943, Amer. J. Bot., **30**, 440.
ROUX, W., 1912, *Terminologie der Entwicklungsmechanik*. Leipzig.
RUBEN, S., et al., 1939, Science, **90**, 570.
RUBEN, S., and KAMEN, M. D., 1940, J. Amer. Chem. Soc., **62**, 3443.
RUBEN, S., et al., 1941, J. Amer. Chem. Soc., **63**, 877.
RUBEN, S., 1943, J. Amer. Chem. Soc., **65**, 279.
RUCH, F., 1945, Vierteljahrsschr. Naturforsch. Ges. Zürich, **90**, 214.
RUDOLPH, H., 1933, Ber. Sächs. Akad. Wiss. Math.-Phys. Kl., **85**, 107.
RUFELT, H., 1956, Physiol. Plantarum, **9**, 154.
— 1957, Physiol. Plantarum, **10**, 231, 373, 485, 500.
RUGE, U., 1939, Z. Bot., **33**, 529.
RÜHL, A., 1936, Loodusuur. Seltsi Aruand. Dorpat, **42**, 186.
RUHLAND, W., 1908, Jahrb. wiss. Bot., **46**, 1.
— 1912, Jahrb. wiss. **51**, 376.
— 1924, Jahrb. wiss. Bot., **63**, 321.
RUHLAND, W., and WETZEL, K., 1926—1929, Planta, **1**, 558, **3**, 765, **7**, 503.
RUHLAND, W., 1934, Deutsche Forschung, **23**, 139, 173, 201.
— 1935, Ber. Sächs. Akad. Wiss. Math.-Phys. Kl., **87**, 37.
RUHLAND, W., and RAMSHORN, K., 1938, Planta, **28**, 471.
RUSKA, H., 1940, Kolloid-Z., **92**, 276.
RUSSELL, E., J., 1937, *Soil Conditions and Plant Growth*. 7th Edit. London.
RUSSELL, R. S., 1940, J. Ecol., **28**, 289.
RUSSOW, E., 1883, Sitz. ber. Dorpat. Naturforsch. Ges., **29**, 350, 562.
RUTGERS, A. A. L., 1912, Rec. Trav. Bot. Néerl., **9**, 1.
RUTTEN-PEKELHARING, C. J., Rec. Trav. Bot. Néerl., **7**, 241.
RYSSELBERGHE, F., 1902, Rec. Inst. bot. 'Leo Errera', Bruxelles, **5**, 220.
RYTZ, W., 1939, Ber. schweiz. bot. Ges., **49**, 339.

SABININ, D. A., 1925, Bull. inst. rech. biol. univ. Perm, **4**, Suppl. 2.

SACHS, J. VON, 1875, *Geschichte der Botanik*. München. (Eng. trans., GARNSEY and BALFOUR, 1906, Oxford).
— 1878, Arb. Bot. Inst. Würzburg, **2**, 46.
— 1887, *Vorlesungen über Pflanzenphysiologie*. 2nd Edit. Leipzig. (Eng. trans. H. M. WARD, 1887, Oxford)
— 1892, Flora, **75**, 1.
SAIZEVA, A. A., 1929, Bull. de l'inst. Lesshaft, **15**, 137.
SAKAMURA, T., and KANAMORI, H., 1935, J. Fac. Sci. Hokkaido Univ., Ser. 5, **4**, 65.
SALISBURY, F. B., and BONNER, J., 1956, Plant Physiol., **31**, 141.
SALMINEN, A., 1933, J. Sci. Agric. Soc. Finland, **5**, 1.
SAMMET, R., 1905, Jahrb. wiss. Bot., **41**, 611.
SANDE-BAKHUYZEN, H. L., VAN DE, 1937, *Studies on Wheat Grown under Constant Conditions*. Stanford Univ.
— 1947, Versl. Landbouwkund. Onderzoek., No. 53., **4**, B.
SANTEN, A. M. A. VAN, 1938, Verh. Kon. Nederl. Akad. Wetensch., Sect. 1, **41**, 513.
SATTLER, H., 1929, Planta, **9**, 315.
SAPOZHNIKOV, D. I., 1937, Microbiology, USSR, **6**, 643.
SCARSETH, G. D., 1943, Better Crops with Plant Food, **27**, 11.
— 1943, Soil Sci., **55**, 113.
SCARTH, G. W., 1927, Protoplasma, **2**, 498.
SCARTH, G. W., et al., 1940, Cold Spring Harbor Symp. Quant. Biol., **8**, 102.
SCARTH, G. W., 1944, New Phytologist, **43**, 1.
SCHAEDE, A. L., and THIMANN, K. V., 1940, Amer. J. Bot., **27**, 659.
SCHAEDE, R., 1930, Planta, **11**, 243.
SCHAFER, J., 1938, Plant Physiol., **13**, 141.
SCHAFFNIT, E., and VOLK, A., 1930, Phytopathol. Z., **1**, 535.
SCHAFFNIT, E., and WILHELM, A. F., 1933, Phytopathol. Z., **5**, 505.
SCHALES, O., et al., 1946, Arch. Biochem., **10**, 455.
SCHANDERL, H., and KAEMPFERT, W., 1931, Planta, **18**, 700.
SCHARRER, K., and SCHROPP, W., 1936, Z. Pflanzenernähr. Düng., **45**, 83.
SCHARRER, K., 1941, *Die Biochemie der Spurenelemente*.
SCHAUMANN, K., 1926, Jahrb. wiss. Bot., **65**, 851.
SCHIMPER, A. F. W., 1935, *Pflanzengeographie auf physiologische Grundlage*. 3rd Edit.
SCHLENK, F., 1951, in *The Enzymes* (Sumner, J. B., and Myrbäck, K.).
SCHLUMBERGER, O., 1926, Angew. Bot., **8**, 262.
SCHMALFUSS, K., 1936, Naturwiss. und Landwirtsch., **19**, 1.
SCHMIDT, A., 1917, *Bau und Funktion der Siebröhre der Angiospermen*. Jena.
— 1924, Bot. Arch., **8**, 345.
SCHMIDT, E., 1936, Tharandt. Forstl. Jahrb., **87**, 1.
SCHMIDT, H., 1930, Planta, **10**, 314.
SCHOPFER, W. H., 1943, *Plants and Vitamins*.
SCHÖNFELDER, S., 1930, Planta, **12**, 414.
SCHORN, M., 1930, Jahrb. wiss. Bot., **71**, 783.
SCHRANK, A. R., 1946, Plant Physiol., **21**, 362.
— 1950, Ann. Rev. Plant Physiol., **1**, 59.
— 1953, Plant Physiol., **28**, 99.
SCHRATZ, E., 1936, Jahrb. wiss. Bot., **83**, 133.
— 1937, Jahrb. wiss. Bot., **84**, 593.
SCHRÖDER, H., 1919, Naturwiss., **7**, 76.
SCHÜEPP, O., 1926, *Handbuch der Pflanzenanatomie* (Linsbauer), Vol. 4.
SCHULTZ, A. S., et al., 1940, J. Biol. Chem., **135**, 267.
SCHULZ, F, 1929, Gartenbauwissensch., **3**, 331.
SCHUMACBER, A.-L., 1948, Planta, **35**, 642.
— 1957, HER. deutsch. bot. Ges., **70**, 335.
SCHWABE, G., 1932, Protoplasma, **16**, 397.
SCOTT, B. I. H., MCAULEY, A. L., and JEYES, P., 1955, Austral. J. Biol. Sci., **8**, 36.
SCOTT, D. A., and MENDIVE, J. R., 1941, J. Biol. Chem., **140**, 445.
SCOTT, F. M., 1948, Science, **108**, 654.
SCOTT, G. T., 1944, J. Cell. Comp. Physiol., **23**, 47.
SCOTT, I. T., 1929, Amer. J. Bot., **16**, 631.
SCOTT, L. I., and PRIESTLEY, J. H., 1928, New Phytologist, **27**, 125.
SCOTT, L. T., 1928, New Phytologist, **27**, 141.
SCOTT, R., and ERICSSON, L. E., 1955, J. Exp. Bot., **6**, 348.
SCRIPTURE, P. N., and MCHARGUE, J. S., 1944, J. Amer. Agron. Soc., **36**, 865.

SEIBLE, D., 1939, Beitr. Biol. Pflanz., 26, 289.
SEIFRIZ, W., 1935, Bot. Rev. 1, 18.
SEIFRIZ, W., and URAGUCHI, M., 1941, Amer. J. Bot., 28, 191.
SEIFRIZ, W., 1942, Symposium on the Structure of Protoplasm. Iowa State Coll.
SEIFRIZ, W., and URBACH, E., 1944, Growth, 8, 221.
SEIFRIZ, W., 1945, Bot. Rev., 11, 231. Ann. Rev. Physiol., 7, 35.
SEN, B., 1934, Ann. Bot., 48, 143.
SEN-GUPTA, J., 1929, Z. Bot., 21, 353.
SENN, G., 1908, Gestalts- und Lageveränderungen der Pflanzenchromatophoren. Leipzig.
SEVAG, M. G., 1954, Erg. Hyg., 28, 424 — 448.
SEYBOLD, A., and VAN DER WEY, H. G., 1929, Rec. Trav. Bot. Néerl., 26, 97.
SEYBOLD, A., 1930, Ergebn. Biol., 5, 29, 6, 55.
— 1930, Naturwiss., 18, 323.
— 1931, Planta, 14, 386.
— 1932, Planta, 18, 479.
— 1933, Planta, 20, 577, 21, 251.
— 1936, Jahrb. wiss. Bot., 82, 741.
SEYBOLD, A., and EGLE, K., 1937, Planta, 26, 491.
SEYBOLD, A., and EGLE, K., 1938, Planta, 28, 87.
SEYBOLD, A., 1940, Sitzber. Heidelberg. Akad. Wiss., 8 Abh.
SEYBOLD, A., and EGLE, K., 1940, Bot. Arch., 40, 560.
SEYBOLD, A., et al., 1941, Bot. Arch., 42, 239.
SEYBOLD, A., and WEISSWEILER, A., 1943, Bot. Arch., 44, 102, 456, 551.
SHARP, L. W., 1934, Introduction to Cytology. 3rd Edit. New York and London.
— 1943, Fundamentals of Cytology. New York and London.
SHEMIN, D., and RUSSEL, C. S., 1953, J. Amer. Chem. Soc., 75, 4873.
SHERMANN, G. D., and MCHARGUE, J.S., 1942, Soil Sci., 54, 253.
SHIAN, Y. G., and FRANCK, J., 1947, Arch. Biochem., 14, 253.
SHIBATA, K., and TAMIYA, H., 1933, Acta Phytochim., 7, 191.
SHIBATA, M., 1929, Sci. Rep. Tôhoku Imp. Univ., 4 ser., Biol., 4, 431.
SHINKE, N., and SHIGENAGA, M., 1933, Cytologia, 4, 189.
SHIRLEY, H. L., 1929, J. Forestry, 27, 535.
— 1945, Bot. Rev. 11, 497.
SHIVE, J. W., 1945, Soil Sci, 60, 41.
SHIVE, J. W., and ROGERS, L. L., 1947, J. Biol. Chem., 169, 453.
SHOK, J., 1941, Plant Physiol., 16, 145.
SHREVE, F., 1934, Ann. Assoc. Amer. Geograph., 24, 131.
SHULL, O. A., 1920, Bot. Gaz., 69, 361.
SIDERIS, C. P., and YOUNG, H. Y., 1945, Plant Physiol., 20, 649.
SIDERIS, C. P., 1947, Plant Physiol., 22, 160.
SIDERIS, C. P., et al., 1947, Plant Physiol., 22, 127.
SIERP, H., 1921, Z. Bot., 13, 143.
— 1933, Flora, 128, 269.
SIERP, H., and BREWIG, A., 1935, Jahrb. wiss. Bot., 82, 99.
SIFTON, H. B., 1944, New Phytologist, 43, 87.
SIGURGEIRSSON, T., and STANLEY, W. M., 1947, Phytopathology, 37, 26.
SILBERSCHMIDT, K., 1925, Ber. deutsch. bot. Ges., 43, 475.
SILLINGER, P., and PETRU, E., 1937, Bot. Centralbl. A, 57 (Beih.), 173.
SIMON, S. W., 1908, Jahrb. wiss. Bot., 45, 351.
— 1912, Jahrb. wiss. Bot., 51.
SIMONIS, W., 1936, Jahrb. wiss. Bot., 83, 191.
— 1938, Planta, 29, 129.
— 1947, Planta, 35, 188.
SINGER, T. P., and KEARNEY, E., 1954, in The Proteins. New York.
SINGER, T. P., MASSEY, V., and KEARNEY, E., 1957, Arch. Biochem. Biophys., 69, 405.
SINNOTT, E. W., 1939, Amer. J. Bot., 25, 179.
SINNOTT, E. W., and BLOCH, R., 1939, Amer. J. Bot., 26, 625.
SINNOTT, E. W., 1942, Amer. Naturalist, 76, 253.
SISSON, W. A., 1941, Contrib. Boyce Thompson Inst., 12, 171.
SJÖSTRAND, F., 1953, Nature, 171, 30.
SKENE, M., 1943, Ann. Bot., 7, 261.
SKOOG, F., 1935, J. Cell. Comp. Physiol., 7, 227.
— 1940, Amer. J. Bot., 27, 939.
— 1942, Amer. J. Bot., 29, 568.

Skoog, F., 1947, Ann. Rev. Biochem., **16**, 529.
Skoog, F., and Tsui, C., 1948, Amer. J. Bot., **35**, 782.
Slade, R. E., et al., 1945, Nature, **155**, 497.
Slater, E. C., 1948, Nature, **161**, 405.
Small, J., and Maxwell, K. M., 1938, Protoplasma, **32**, 272.
Small, J., 1939, New Phytologist, **38**, 176.
— 1946, *Physiology and Plants.* New York.
Smit, J., and Mulder, E. G., 1942, Mede. Landbouwhoogesch. (Wageningen), **46**, No. 3, 1.
Smith, E. L., 1937, J. Gen. Physiol., **22**, 21.
— 1940, Science, **91**, 199.
— 1941, J. Gen. Physiol., **24**, 565.
Smith, E. L., and Coy, N. H., 1946, J. Biol. Chem., **164**, 367.
Smith, F. B., and Brown, P. E., 1932, J. Amer. Soc. Agron., **24**, 577.
Smith, J. H., 1940, Plant Physiol., **15**, 183.
Smith, M. E., 1944, Austral. J. Exp. Biol. Med. Sci., **22**, 257.
Snow, R., 1925, Proc. Roy. Soc., B, **98**, 188.
— 1931, 1932, Proc. Roy. Soc., B, **108**, 209, 305, **111**, 86.
— 1940, New Phytologist, **39**, 177.
— 1945, New Phytologist, **44**, 70, 110.
Söding, H., 1940, Z. Bot., **36**, 113.
— 1940, Ber. deutsch. bot. Ges., **57**, 465.
Söding, H., and Wagner, M., 1955, Planta, **45**, 557.
Söhngen, N. L., 1910, Rec. Trav. Chim., **29**, 238.
Solomon, M. E., 1945, Ann. Applied. Biol., **32**, 75.
Somers, I. I., and Shive, W., 1942, Plant Physiol., **17**, 582.
Sommer, A. L., 1945, Soil Sci., **60**, 71.
Sookne, A. M., and Harris, M., 1941, Textile Res. **11**, 307.
Sörensen, T., 1941, Medd. om Grönland, **125**, No. 9.
Spaning, M., 1941, Jahrb. wiss. Bot., **89**, 574.
Sparrow, A. H., and Rosenfeld, F. M., 1946, Science, **104**, 245.
Speidel, B., 1939, Planta, **30**, 67.
Spiegelmann, S., and Reiner, J. M., 1942, Growth, **6**, 367.
Spiegelmann, S., and Kamen, M. D., 1946, Science, **104**, 581.
Spruit, C. J. P., 1954, Proc. Int. Congr. Photobiol. Amsterdam, 1954.
Spurway, C. H., 1940, Science, **92**, 489.
— 1941, Michigan Exp. Sta. Spec. Bull., **306**, 1.
Staker, E. V., and Cunnings, R. W., 1941, Soil Sci. Soc. Amer. Proc., **6**, 207.
Stålfelt, M. G., 1922, Medd. Statens Skogsförsökanst., Stockholm, **18**, 5, 256.
Stålfelt, M. G., and Johansson, N., 1928, Skogshögskolans Festkr., Stockholm, **814**.
Stålfelt, M. G., 1928, Planta, **6**, 183.
— 1932, Svensk Bot. Tidskr., **26**, 45; Planta, **17**, 22.
— 1936, Svensk Bot. Tidskr., **30**, 343.
— 1937, Planta, **27**, 30; Svenska Skogsvårdsfören. Tidskr., 161.
— 1939, Svensk Bot. Tidskr., **33**, 383.
— 1939, Planta, **30**, 384.
— 1943, Ark. Bot. Vetenskapsakademien (Stockholm), **30** A, no. 12.
— 1945, Svensk Bot. Tidskr., **39**, 365.
— 1946, Ark. Bot. Vetenskapsakademien, **33** A, no. 4.
— 1954, Physiol. Plantarum, **7**, 354.
— 1955, Physiol. Plantarum, **8**, 572.
Stanley, W. M., 1940, J. Biol. Chem., **135**, 437.
Stanley, W. M., and Knight, C. A., 1941, Cold Spring Harbor Symp. Quant. Biol., **9**, 255.
Stanley, W. M., and Anderson, T. F., 1942, J. Biol. Chem., **146**, 25.
Stanley, W. M., 1946, *Currents in Biochemical Research* (Green), 13.
Stark, P., 1916, Jahrb. wiss. Bot., **57**, 189, 461.
— 1921, 1922, Jahrb. wiss. Bot., **60**, 67, **61**, 126.
Starkey, R. L., 1931, Soil Sci., **32**, 367.
— 1937, Soil Sci. **45**, 207.
Stedman, E., and Stedman, E., 1940, Nature, **152**, 556.
Steemann Nielsen, E., 1944. Dansk Bot. Ark., **11**, No. 2, 1–18.
— 1947, Dansk Bot. Ark., **12**, No. 8.
— 1947, Nature, **160**, 376.
— 1952, Physiol. Plantarum, **5**, 145.
— 1955, Physiol. Plantarum, **8**, 317, 945.

STEEMANN NIELSEN, E., 1957, Physiol. Plantarum, **8**, 317.
STEGMANN, G., 1940, Z. Bot., **35**, 385.
STEIN, W. H., et al., 1946, Ann. New York Acad. Sci., **47**, 59.
STEINBERG, R. A., 1936, Amer. J. Bot., **23**, 227; Bot. Gaz., **97**, 666.
— 1937, J. Agric. Res., **55**, 891.
STEINER, M., 1933, Jahrb. wiss. Bot., **78**, 564.
— 1934, Jahrb. wiss. Bot., **81**, 94.
— 1939, Ergebn. Biol., **17**, 152.
STENLID, G., 1947, Lantbrukshögsk. Ann. (Uppsala), **14**, 301.
— 1948, Physiol. Plantarum, **1**, 185.
STEPHENSEN, M., 1947, Antonie van Leeuwenhoek, **12**, 33.
STERN, K., 1933, *Pflanzenthermodynamik*. Berlin.
— 1943, Cold Spring Harbor Symp. Quant. Biol., **10**, 291.
STEWARD, F. C., and PRESTON, C., 1941, Plant Physiol., **16**, 85.
STEWART, W. D., and ARTHUR, J. M., 1934, Contrib. Boyce Thompson Inst., **6**, 225.
STICKLAND, L. H., 1935, Biochem. J., **29**, 889.
STILES, W., and LEACH, W., 1932, 1933, Proc. Roy. Soc., B, **111**, 338, **113**, 405.
STILES, W., 1935, Bot. Rev., **1**, 249.
— 1950, *An Introduction to the Principles of Plant Physiology*. 2nd Edit. London.
STILES, W., and SKELDING, A. D., 1940, Ann. Bot., **4**, 673.
STILES, W., 1945, Bot. Rev., **11**.
— 1946, Bot. Rev., **12**, 165.
— 1946, *Trace Elements in Plants and Animals*. Cambridge.
STILLE, B., 1938, Arch. Mikrobiol., **9**, 477.
STOCKER, O., 1924, Z., Bot., **16**, 1.
— 1928, *Wasserhaushalt der ägyptischen Wüsten- und Salzpflanzen*.
— 1930, Z. Bot., **23**, 27.
— 1931, Ber. deutsch. bot. Ges., **49**, 267.
— 1931, Jahrb. wiss. Bot., **75**, 494.
— 1933, Jahrb. wiss. Bot., **78**, 751.
— 1935, Planta, **24**, 40; Jahrb. wiss. Bot., **81**, 464.
STOCKER, O., et al., 1938, Jahrb. wiss. Bot., **86**, 556.
STOCKER, O., et al., 1944, Jahrb. wiss. Bot., **91**, 278.
STOLL, H., 1936, Naturwiss., **24**, 53.
STOWE, B. B., 1955, Biochem. J., **61**, ix.
STRAIN, H. H., 1935, J. Biol. Chem., **111**, 191.
— 1938, Carnegie Inst. Publ., No. 490.
STRASBURGER, E., 1891, *Über dem Bau und der Verrichtung der Leitungsbahnen in den Pflanzen*. Jena.
— 1901, Jahrb. wiss. Bot., **36**, 493.
STREBEYKO, P., 1938, Planta, **29**, 228.
STREET, H. E., 1949, New Phytologist, **48**, 84.
STREHLER, B. L., 1954, Phosphorus Metabolism, Baltimore, **2**, 491.
STRUGGER, S., 1938, Flora, **132**, 253.
— 1943, Naturwiss., **31**, 181.
— 1951, Ber. deutsch. Bot., Ges., **64**, 69.
— 1957, Protoplasma, **48**, 231.
STRUGGER, S., and BAUMEISTER, W., 1951, Ber. deutsch. bot. Ges., **64**, 5.
STROHMEYER, G., 1935, Planta, **24**, 470.
STUCKEY, J. H., and CURTIS, O. F., 1938, Plant Physiol., **13**, 815.
STUTZ, R. E., 1957, Plant Physiol., **32**, 31.
STUTZ, R. E., and BURRIS, R. H., 1951, Plant Physiol., **26**, 226.
SUCHTELEN, H. VAN, 1931, Arch. Pflanzenbau. A. **7**, 519.
SULLIVAN, J. T., and MYERS, W. M., 1939, J. Amer. Soc. Agron., **31**, 869.
SUMNER, J. B., 1926, J. Biol. Chem., **69**, 435.
SUTTER, E., 1944, Ber. schweiz. bot. Ges., **54**, 197.
SUTTON, W. B., and WERKMAN, C. H., 1954, Arch. Biochem. Biophys., **47**, 1—7.
SVEDBERG, T., and BROHULT, S., 1939, Nature, **143**, 938.
SWANBACK, T. R., 1939, Plant Physiol., **14**, 423.
SWEENEY, B. M., 1941, Amer. J. Bot., **28**, 700.
SWEENEY, B. M., and THIMANN, K. V., 1942, J. Gen. Physiol., **25**, 841.
SWEENEY, B. M., 1944, Amer. J. Bot., **31**, 78.
SZENT-GYÖRGYI, A., 1937, Acta Med. Szeged, **9**, 1.
— 1941, Science, **94**, 609.

Tadros, T. M., 1940, Bull. Fac. Sci. Cairo, No. 20.
    1945, Bull. inst. Egypte, 27, 265.
Tagawa, T., 1934, Japan. J. Bot., 7, 33.
    1937, J. Fac. Agric. Hokkaido Imp. Univ., 39, 271.
Tageeva, S., 1932, Planta, 17, 758.
Takenouchi, M., 1929, Bull. Sci. Fac. Terk. Kyushu Imp. Univ., 3, No. 3.
Talley, P. J., 1934, Plant Physiol., 9, 731.
Tamiya, H., 1932, Acta Phytochim., 6, 227
— 1933, Acta Phytochim., 7, 27.
— 1938, Cytologia, 8, 542.
Tamiya, H., and Usami, Sh., 1940, Acta Phytochim., 11, 261.
Tamiya, H., 1941, Acta Phytochim., 12, 173.
Tamiya, H., and Chiba, Y., 1949, Studies Tokugawa Inst., 6, (2), 1.
Tamiya, H., Iwanura, T., Shibata, K., Hace, E., and Nibei, T., 1953, Biochim. Biophys. Acta, 12, 23.
Tamm, O., 1931, Medd. Statens Skogsförsöksanstalt (Stockholm), 26, no. 2.
Tamm, C. O., 1954, A study of forest nutrition by means of foliar analysis. VIIIe Congr. Int. Bot. Paris 1954.
Tammes, P. M. L., 1933, Rec. Trav. Bot. Néerl., 30, 514.
Tang, Y. W., and Bonner, J., 1947, Arch. Biochem., 13, 24.
Tapping, L. E., 1937, Centralbl. Bakteriol., II, 97, 289.
Tauböck, K., 1942, Bot. Arch., 43, 291.
Taylor, C. V., 1940, Publ. Amer. Assoc. Ad. Sci., 14, 1.
— 1943, Ann. Rev. Biochem., 5, 17.
Taylor, D. L., 1942, Amer. J. Bot., 29, 721.
Taylor, H. S., et al., 1942, Molecular Films etc. New Brunswick.
Teale, F. W. J., and Weber, G., 1957, Biochem. J., 66, 8.
Tennent, H. G., and Vilbrandt, C. F., 1943, J. Amer. Chem. Soc., 65, 424.
Teodoresco, M. E. G., 1929, Ann. Sci. Nat. Bot., 11, 201.
Teorell, T., 1935, Proc. Soc. Exp. Biol. Med., 33, 282.
Teräsvuori, 1930, Über die Bodenacidität. Dissertation. Helsingfors.
Theorell, H., 1945, Nature, 156, 474.
— 1951, The Enzymes (Sumner and Myrbäck), Vol. 2, Part 1, 397.
Theorell, H., and Swedin, B., 1939, Naturwiss., 27, 95.
Thimann, K. V., and Skoog, F., 1934, Proc. Roy. Soc., B, 114, 317.
Thimann, K. V., 1937, Amer. J. Bot., 24, 407.
— 1939, Biol. Rev., 14, 314.
Thimann, K. V., and Skoog, F., 1940, Amer. J. Bot., 27, 951.
Thimann, K. V., et al., 1942, Amer. J. Bot., 29, 598.
Thimann, K. V., 1948, The Hormones. New York.
Thimann, K. V., Yoccum, C. S., and Hakett, D. P., 1954, Arch. Biochim. Biophys., 53, 239.
Thimann, K. V., and Samuel, E. W., 1955, Proc. Nat. Acad. Sci. U.S.A., 41, 1029.
Thoday, D., 1921, Ann. Bot., 35, 585.
— 1933, New Phytologist, 32, 274.
Thoday, D., and Jones, M. K., 1939, Ann. Bot., 3, 677.
Thoday, D., and Richards, K. M., 1944, Ann. Bot., 8, 189.
Thom, C., and Humfeld, H., 1932, Soil Sci., 34, 29.
Thomas, J. B., 1955, Conference on Solar Energy. Tuczon.
Thomas, J. B., and Goedheer, J. C., 1953, Biochim. Biophys. Acta, 10, 385.
Thomas, J. B., Goedheer, J. C., and Komen, J. G., 1956, Biochim. Biophys. Acta, 22, 1, 342.
Thomas, M., 1956, Plant Physiology, 4th Edit. London.
Thomas, W., and Mack, W. B., 1944, Proc. Amer. Soc. Hort. Sci., 44, 355.
Thomas, W., 1945, Soil Sci., 59, 353.
Thompson, W. R., and Hussey, R., 1932, J. Gen. Physiol., 15, 9.
Thornton, H. G., 1947, Antonie van Leeuwenhoek, 12, 85.
Thren, R., 1934, Z. Bot., 26, 449.
Thunberg, T., 1933, Handb. Biochem., Erg.-Werk, 1, 248.
Thurlow, J., and Bonner, J., 1948, Arch. Biochem., 19, 509.
Timofeeff-Ressowsky, N. W., 1940, Nova Acta Leopoldiana, 9, 209.
Tischler, G., 1934, Allgemeine Karyologie, 2nd Edit. Berlin.
Tischler, G., 1952, Allgemeine Pflanzenkaryologie. Suppl. Vol. Berlin.
Timonin, M. I., 1940, Canad. J. Res., 18, 307.
Tiselius, A., 1942, Adv. Coll. Sci., 1, 82.
Tissieres, A., 1954, Biochem. J., 58, 142.

TONZIG, S., and MARRÉ, E., 1955, Istit. Lombardo Sci. Lettere, 89, 243.
TOPCUOGLŮ, A., 1940, Tharandt. Forstl. Jahrb., 91, 485.
TOTTINGHAM, W. E., et al., 1934, Plant Physiol., 9, 127.
TOWNSEND, J., 1897, Jahrb. wiss. Bot., 30, 484.
TRAUB, H. P., 1946, Plant Physiol., 21, 425.
TREITEL, O., 1946, J. Colloid. Sci., 1, 327.
— 1947. J. Colloid Sci., 2, 453.
TRELEASE, S., et al., 1942, Science, 96, 234.
TRELEASE, S. F., and DI SOMMA, A. A., 1944, Amer. J. Bot., 31, 544.
TROMBETTA, V. V., 1942, Bot. Rev., 8, 317.
TUBA, J., et al., 1946, Canad. J. Res., 24, 182.
TUKEY, H. B., et al., 1945, Bot. Gaz., 107, 62.
TULASNE, R., and VENDRELY, R., 1947, Nature, 160, 225.
TUMANOV, I. I., 1930, Wiss. Arch. Landwirtsch., A, 3, 389.
— 1931, Phytopathol. Z., 3, 303.
TURESSON, G., 1922, Hereditas, 3, 211.
TURNER, J. S., 1938, New Phytologist, 37, 232, 289.
TURNER, J. S., and HANLY, V., 1947, Nature, 160, 296.
TWYMAN, E. S., 1946, New Phytologist, 45, 18.
TYNER, E. H., and WEBB, J. R., 1946, J. Amer. Soc. Agron., 38, 173.

ULICH, H., 1933, Hand- und Jahrb. chem. Physik, 6, 120.
ULRICH, A., 1942, Amer. J. Bot., 29, 220.
— 1943, Soil Sci., 55, 101.
UPHOF, J. C. T., 1941, Bot. Rev., 7, 58.
URSPRUNG, A., and BLUM, G., 1921, Ber. deutsch. bot. Ges., 39, 70.
URSPRUNG, A., and BLUM, G., 1928, Beibl. Vierteljahrsschr. Nat. Ges. Zürich, 73, 162.
URSPRUNG, A., 1935, Plant Physiol., 10, 115.
— 1938, Abderhaldens Handb. biol. Arbeitsmeth., 14, H. 7, Abt. XI.

VAN . . . (see the other part of the name).
VANHOEK, A., 1947, Biodynamica, 6, 81.
VARMA, S. C., 1938, Ann. Bot., 2, 203.
VASILJEV, I. M., 1930, Ber. deutsch. bot. Ges., 48, 27.
— 1931, Arch. Protistenkunde, 7, 126.
— 1931, Planta, 14, 225.
VEDSTRA, H., KRUYT, W., VAN DER STEEN, E. J., and ÅBERG, B., 1954, Rec. Trav. Chim. Pays-Bas, 73, 23.
VEGIS, A., 1932, Jahrb. wiss. Bot., 75, 726.
VELSEN, P. J., 1930, Verh. Kon. Nederl. Akad. Wetensch., 33, 405.
VERMEULEN, P., 1943, Nederl. Kruidk. Arch., 53, 125.
VERSCHAFFELT, E., 1912, Rec. Trav. Bot. Néerl., 9, 401.
VERWORN, M., 1915, Allgemeine Physiologie, 6th Edit. Jena.
VICKERY, H. R., and PALMER, J. K., 1956, J. Biol. Chem., 218, 225.
VICKERY, H. B., et al., 1933, Carnegie Inst. Wash. Publ. 445.
— 1941, Ann. New York Acad. Sci., 41, 87.
— 1945, Physiol. Rev., 25, 347.
VIETS, F., G., 1944, Plant Physiol., 19, 480.
VIGNEAUD, V. DU, 1942, Science, 96, 455.
VINOGRADSKIJ, S., 1887, 1890, Ann. Inst. Pasteur, 1, 548, 4, 213.
— 1947, Antonie van Leeuwenhoek, 12, 5.
VIRGIN, H. I., 1956, Physiol. Plantarum, 9, 280.
— 1956, Physiol. Plantarum, 9, 674.
VIRTANEN, A. I., 1945, Suomen Kemistilehti, 18 B, 48.
— 1947, Acta Chim. Scand., 1, 90.
— 1952, Ann. med. exp. biol., 30, 234—248.
— 1955, Proc. Third Intern. Congr. Biochem. Brussels 1955. 425.
VIRTANEN, A. I., HIETALA, P. K., and WAHLROS, Ö., 1957, Arch. Biochim. Biophys., 69, 486.
VISHNIAC, W., 1955, Ann. Rev. Plant Physiol., 8, 115.
VÖCHTING, H., 1892, Über Transplantationen am Pflanzenkörper. Tübingen.
— 1901, Jahrb. wiss. Bot., 34, 1.
— 1902, Bot. Ztg., 60, 87.
— 1908, Untersuchungen über experimentalen Anatomie und Pathologie der Pflanzenkörper, I. Tübingen.
VOERKEL, S. H., 1934, Planta, 21, 156.

VOGT, E., 1915, Z. Bot., **7**, 193.
VOLK, O. H., 1931, Z. Bot., **24**, 81.
— 1937, Z. Bot., **32**, 55.
VON . . . (see the other part of the name).
VOUK, V., and BENZINGER, F., 1929, Acta Bot. Univ. Zagreb, **4**, 1.
VREDE, H., 1930, Beitr. Biol. Pflanzen, **18**, 399.
VRIES, H. DE, 1885, Bot. Ztg., **43**, 1, 17; Jahrb. wiss. Bot., **16**, 465.
VRIES, M. A., DE, 1948 (Dissertation). Leiden.

WADA, B., 1940, Cytologia, **11**, 93.
WAGER, H. G., 1941, New Phytologist, **40**, 1.
WAGNER, F., 1940, Phytopathol. Z., **12**, 427.
WAKAYAMA, K., 1929, Cytologia, **1**, 68.
WAKSMAN, S. A., and JOFFE, J. S., 1922, J. Bacteriol., **7**, 239.
WAKSMAN, S. A., 1929, Trans. Second Comm. Intern. Soc. Soil Sci., A, Budapest.
— 1930, Amer. J. Sci., **19**, 32.
— 1931, Ecology, **12**, 32.
WAKSMAN, S. A., and GERRETSEN, F. C., 1931, Ecology, **12**, 32.
WAKSMAN, S. A., 1932, *Principles of Soil Microbiology*.
WAKEMAN, S. A., and HUTCHINGS, I. J., 1935, Soil Sci. **40**, 347.
WAKSMAN, S., 1936, *Humus*.
— 1938, Trans. Second Comm. Intern. Soc. Soil Sci., Helsingfors, 17.
WAKSMAN, S. A., et al., 1942, Soil Sci., **54**, 281.
WAKSMAN, S. A., 1947, *Microbial Antagonisms and Antibiotic Substances*. 2nd Edit. New York.
WALDVOGEL, M. J., and SCHLENK, F., 1947, Arch. Biochem., **14**, 484.
WALKLEY, J., 1940, New Phytologist, **39**, 362.
WALLACH, A., 1938, Z. Bot., **33**, 433.
WALTER, H., 1927, Z. Bot., **13**, 673.
— 1930, Z. Bot., **23**, 74.
— 1931, Z. Bot., **24**, 324.
— 1935, Fortschr. Bot., **5**, 251.
WALTER, H., and STEINER, M., 1936, Z. Bot., **30**, 65.
WALTER, H., 1939, Jahrb. wiss. Bot., **87**, 750.
— 1947, *Die Grundlagen des Pflanzenlebens*. 2nd Edit. Berlin.
WANDER, I. W., and BRODE, W. R., 1941, J. Optic. Soc. Amer., **31**, 402.
WANG, T.-K., and CHIA, C.-S., 1936, Dept. Agric. Chem. Coll. Agric. Univ. Peiping.
WANNER, H., 1944, Ark. Bot. Vetenskapsakademien (Stockholm), **31**, A, no. 9.
— 1945, Vierteljahrsschr. Naturforsch. Ges. Zürich, **90**, 98; Schweiz. Z. Pathol. Bakteriol, **8**, 64.
— 1948, Ber. schweiz. bot. Ges., **58**, 123.
WARBURG, O., and NEGELEIN, E., 1920, Biochem. Z., **110**, 66.
WARBURG, O., 1924, Naturwiss., **22**, 441.
— 1926, *Über den Stoffwechsel der Tumoren*. Berlin.
WARBURG, O., and CHRISTIAN, W., 1939, Biochem. Z., **301**, 221; **303**, 40.
WARBURG, O., and LÜTTGENS, W., 1944, Naturwiss., **32**, 161, 301.
WARBURG, O., 1946, *Schwermetalle als Wirkungsgruppen von Fermenten*. Berlin.
WARBURG, O., and LÜTTGENS, W., 1946, Biokhimiya, **11**, 303.
WARING, W. S., and WERKMAN, C. H., 1944, Arch. Biochem., **4**, 75.
WARINGTON, K., 1934, Ann. Bot., **48**, 744.
— 1946, Ann. Appl. Bot., **33**, 249.
WARMING, E., and GRAEBNER, P., 1933, *Lehrbuch der ökologischen Pflanzengeographie*. 4th Edit. Berlin.
WARNE, L. G. G., 1942, Ann. Bot., **29**, 875.
WARNER, T., 1928, Jahrb. wiss. Bot., **68**, 431.
WARTIOVAARA, V., 1942, Ann. Bot. Soc. Zool. Bot. Fenn., **16**, No. 1.
WASSERMANN, A., 1949, Ann. Bot., **13**, 79.
WASSINK, E. C., 1934, Rec. Trav. Bot. Néerl., **31**, 583.
WASSINK, E. C., and KERSTEN, J. A. H., 1944, Enzymologia, **11**, 282.
— — 1946, Enzymologia, **12**, 3.
WASSINK, E. C., 1946, Rec. Trav. Chim. Pay-Bas, **65**, 380.
WASSINK, E. C., and BOURMAN, M. A., 1947, Enzymologia, **12**, 178.
WASSINK, E. C., and WIERSMA, J. H., 1955, Acta Bot. Néerland., **4** (5), 657.
WATSON, D. J., 1947, Ann. Bot., **11**, 375.
WATSON, J. D., and CRICK, F. H. C., 1953, Nature, **171**, 737, 964.
WATSON, S. A., and NOGGLE, G. R., 1947, Plant Physiol., **22**, 228.
WEATHERBY, J. H., 1943, J. Cell. Comp. Physiol., **21**, 1.

WEAVER, J. E., and FLORY, E. L., 1934, Ecology, **15**, 333.
WEAVER, J. E., and CLEMENTS, F. E., 1938, *Plant Ecology*. 2nd. ed.
WEBER, F., 1916, Sitzber. Akad. Wiss. Wien, Abt. I, Math.-Nat. Kl., **125**, 189.
— 1925, Jahrb. wiss. Bot., **64**, 687.
— 1930, Protoplasma, **9**, 106, **10**, 598.
— 1932, Protoplasma, **15**, 522.
— 1934, Protoplasma, **22**, 4.
WEBSTER, G. C., 1954, Arch. Biochem. Biophys., **47**, 241—250.
WEEVERS, T., 1930, Verh. Kon. Nederl. Akad. Wetensch., **33**, No. 7.
— 1931, Rec. Trav. Bot. Néerl., **28**, 400.
WEINTRAUB, R. L., 1944, Bot. Rev., **10**, 383.
WEIS, F., 1932, Kgl. Danske Vid. Selsk., Biol. Medd., **10**, 3.
— 1933, Kgl. Veter. og Landbohöjskole. Aarsskr., **1**.
WEISSENBÖCK, K., 1940, Protoplasma, **34**, 585.
WEISSFLOG, J., and MENGDEHL, H., 1933, Planta, **19**, 182.
WEIXL-HOFMANN, H., 1930, Protoplasma, **11**, 210.
WENT, F. W., and THIMANN, K. V., 1937, *Phytohormones*. New York.
WENT, F. W., 1939, Verh. Kon. Nederl. Akad. Wetensch., **42**, 581.
— 1939, Amer. J. Bot., **26**, 109.
WENT, F. W., and WHITE, R., 1939, Bot. Gaz., **100**, 465.
WENT, F. W., 1941, Bot. Gaz., **103**, 386.
— 1941, Amer. J. Bot., **28**, 83.
— 1942, Plant Physiol., **17**, 236.
— 1943, Amer. Scientist, **31**, 189.
— 1943, Plant Physiol., **18**, 51.
— 1944, Amer. J. Bot., **31**, 597.
— 1945, Amer. J. Bot., **32**, 469.
WENT, F. W., and CARTER, M., 1945, Plant Physiol., **20**, 457.
WENT, F. W., 1945, Bot. Rev., **11**, 487.
WENT, F. W., and ENGELSBERG, R., 1946, Arch. Biochem., **9**, 187.
WENZEL, H., 1934, Bot. Centralbl. Abt. A, **52**, 73.
WERCKMEISTER, P., 1934, Gartenbauwiss., **8**, 607.
WEST, P. M., 1939, Nature, **144**, 1050.
WETMORE, R. H., and WARDLAW, 1951, Ann. Rev. Plant Physiol.
WETMORE, R. H., and JACOBS, W. P., 1953, Amer. J. Bot., **40**, 272.
WEY, H. G. VAN DER, 1932, Rec. Trav. Bot. Néerl., **19**, 187.
WHITAKER, D. M., 1942, J. Gen. Physiol., **25**, 391.
WHITE, J., 1907, Ann. Bot., **21**, 487.
WHITE, M. J. D., 1947, *The Chromosomes*, 3rd Edit.
WHITE, P. R., 1938, Amer. J. Bot., **25**, 223.
— 1941, Biol. Rev. **16**, 35.
WHITE, P. R., and BRAUN, A. C., 1941, Science, **94**, 239.
WHITE, P. R., 1942, Proc. Eighth Amer. Sci. Congr., **3**, 135.
— 1943, *A Handbook of Plant Tissue Culture*.
WHITNEY, R. S., and GARDNER, R., 1943, Soil Sci., **55**, 127.
WHYTE, R. O., 1939, Biol. Rev., **14**, 51.
— 1946, *Crop Production and Environment*.
WIEDOW-PÄTZOLD, H. L., and GUTTENBERG, H. VON, 1957, Planta, **49**, 588.
WIEGNER, G., and PALLMANN, H., 1930, Z. Pflanzenernähr. und Düngung, T. A, **16**, 1.
WIEGNER, G., 1931, Mitt. Gebiete Lebensmittelunters. und Hygiene, **22**, 327; J. Soc. Chem. Ind., **50**, 55, 65.
WIELER, A., 1883, Untersuch. Bot. Inst. Tübingen, **1**, 189.
WIENKE, L., 1940, Planta, **31**, 22.
WIERCINSKI, F. J., 1944, Biol. Bull., **86**, 98.
WIERSUM, L. K., 1946, Rec. Trav. Bot. Néerl., **41**, 1.
WIESNER, J., 1907, *Der Lichtgenuss der Pflanzen*. Wien.
WIKÉN, T., 1940, Arch. Mikrobiol., **11**, 312.
— 1948, Ark. Bot. Vetenskapsakadamien (Stockholm), **19**A, 201.
WIKLANDER, L., 1946, Lantbrukshögsk. Ann. (Uppsala), **14**, 1.
WILBRANDT, W., 1947, Ann. Rev. Physiol., **9**, 581.
WILDEN, M., 1939, Planta, **30**, 286.
WILDMAN, S. G., and GORDON, S. A., 1942, Proc. Nat. Acad. Sci. USA, **28**, 217.
WILDMAN, S. G., et al., 1947, Arch. Biochem., **13**, 131.
WILDMAN, S. G., and BONNER, J., 1947, Arch. Biochem., **14**, 381.

2 L

WILDMAN, S. G., and BONNER, J., 1948, Amer. J. Bot., **35**, 740.
WILHELM, A. F., 1930, Jahrb. wiss. Bot., **72**, 203.
WILLENBRINK, J., 1957, Planta, **48**, 269.
WILLIAMS, B. C., 1947, Amer. J. Bot., **34**, 455.
WILLIAMS, K. T., et al., 1940, U. S. Dept. Agric. Techn. Bull. 702.
WILLIAMS, R. F., 1946, Ann. Bot., **10**, 41.
WILLIAMSON, M. B., and GULICK, A., 1944, J. Cell. Comp. Physiol., **23**, 77.
WILLIAMSON, R. R., 1939, Bull. Math. Biophys., **1**, 151.
WILLSTÄTTER, R., and STOLL, A., 1913, *Untersuchungen über Chlorophyll*. Berlin.
—— 1918, *Untersuchungen über die Assimilation der Kohlensäure*. Berlin.
WILLSTÄTTER, R., 1928, *Untersuchungen über Enzyme*. Berlin.
WILSON, B. D., 1930, Soil Sci. **29**, 331.
WILSON, B. J., 1929, Soil Sci. **28**, 411.
WILSON, D. G., KING, K. W., and BURRIS, R. H., 1954, J. biol. Chem., **208**, 863—874.
WILSON, J. K., 1924, Cornell Univ. Agric. Exp. Sta., Mem., **18**, 1187.
WILSON, J. K., and WILSON, B. D., 1933, Cornell Univ. Agric. Exp. Sta., Mem., **148**.
WILSON, J. K., 1939, Cornell Univ. Agric. Exp. Sta., Mem. **221**.
WILSON, P. W., 1940, *The Biochemistry of Symbolic Nitrogen Fixation*. New York.
WINDISCH, F, et al, 1958, Naturwiss., **45**, 367.
WINFIELD, M. E., 1945, Austral. J. Exp. Biol. Med. Sci., **23**, 111, 267.
WINKLER, H., 1916, Z. Bot., **8**, 417.
WINTER, A. G., 1940, Z. Pflanzenkrankheiten, **50**, 444.
WINTERMANS, J. F. G. M., 1955, Meded., Landbouwhogesch. Wageningen, **55**, (2), 69.
WINTERS, E., 1940, Illinois Sta. Bull., **472**, 101.
WIRTH, P., 1946, Ber. schweiz. bot. Ges., **56**, 175.
WISSELINGH, C. VAN, 1910, Verh. Kon. Nederl. Akad. Wetensch., **12**, 685.
WITHROW, R. B., 1940, Plant Physiol., **15**, 609.
WITTINGHAM, C. P., 1956, J. Exp. Bot., **7**, 273.
WOHL, K., 1940, New Phytologist, **39**, 33.
WOLF, J., 1931, Planta, **15**, 572.
—— 1939, Planta, **28**, 60, **29**, 315, 450.
WOLFF, H., 1926, Jahrb. wiss. Bot., **66**, 1.
WOOD, H. G., 1946, Physiol. Rev., **26**, 198.
WOOD, J. G., 1932, Austral. J. Exp. Biol. Med. Sci., **10**, 89.
—— 1934, J. Ecol., **22**, 69.
—— 1938, Austral. J. Exp. Biol. Med. Sci. **11**, 237.
WOOD, J. G., and BARRIEN, B. S., 1939, New Phytologist, **38**, 125.
WOOD, J. G., 1941, Austral. J. Exp. Biol. Med. Sci., **19**, 313.
WOOD, J. G., and PETRIE, A. H. K., 1942, Austral. J. Exp. Biol. Med. Sci., **20**, 249.
WOOD, J. G., and WOMERSLEY, H. B. S., 1946, Austral. J. Exp. Biol. Med. Sci., **24**, 79.
WOOD, J. W., et al., 1947, Science, **105**, 337.
WOODFORD, E. K., and GREGORY, F. G., 1948, Ann. Bot., **12**, 335.
WRENGER, M., 1935, Z. Bot., **29**, 257.
WRENSHALL, C. L., and DYER, W. J., 1941, Soil Sci., **51**, 235.
WRIGHT, K. E., 1939, Plant Physiol., **14**, 171.
WRINCH, D., 1941, Collecting Nat., **16**, 177.
—— 1942, Nature, **150**, 380.
WUHRMANN, K., 1937, Protoplasma, **29**, 361.
WUHRMANN-MEYER, K., and M., 1939, Jahrb. wiss. Bot., **87**, 642.
WUHRMANN, K., and PILNIK, W., 1945, Experientia, **1**, 1.
WULFF, H. D., 1935, Planta, **24**, 602.
WÜRGLER, W., 1942, Ber. schweiz. bot. Ges., **52**, 239.
WURMSER, R., 1958, Compt. rend. (Paris), **246**, 3533.
WYCKOFF, R., 1932, J. Gen. Physiol., **15**, 351.
WYCKOFF, R. W. G., 1946, Nature, **158**, 263.

YABUTA, T., and HAYASHI, T., 1939, J. Agric. Chem. Soc. Japan., **15**, 403.
YAKUSHIJI, E., 1934, Acta Phytochim., **8**, 325.
YAMAGATA, S., 1934, Acta Phytochim., **8**, 117.
—— 1940, Acta Phytochim., **11**, 1.
YAMAGUCHI, S., 1937, J. Fac. Sci. Hokkaido Univ., V, **1**, 37.
YAMAHA, G., and ABE, S., 1934, Science Rep. Tokyo Bunrika Daigaku Sect. B, **1**, 221.
YAMANE, G., 1940, Bot. Mag. (Tokyo), **54**.
YAMAMOTO, A., 1933, Acta Phytochim., **7**, 65.

YAMASHITA, J., et al., 1957, Nature, **179**, 959.
YARWOOD, C. E., 1946, Bot. Rev., **12**, 1.
YASNI, K., 1938, Cytologia, **9**, 120.
YEMM, E. W., 1937, Proc. Roy. Soc., **123**, 243.
YIN, H. C., 1938, Amer. J. Bot., **25**, 1.
— 1941, Amer. J. Bot., **28**, 250.
— 1945, New Phytologist, **44**, 191.
YOCUM, L. E., 1935, Plant Physiol., **10**, 795.
YODA, Sh., 1958, Bot. Mag. (Tokyo), **71**, 207.
YOSHI, Y., and JIMBO, T., 1931, Science Rep. Tôhoku Univ., Ser. 4, Biol., **6**, 259.
— — 1932, Science Rep. Tôhoku Univ., Ser. 4, **7**, 65.

ZACHERL, H., 1956, Z. Bot., **44**, 409.
ZADMARD, H., 1939, Kolloid-Beihefte, **49**, 316.
ZALESKI, I., 1902, Ber. deutsch. bot. Ges., **20**, 433.
ZATTLER, F., 1932, Prakt. Blätt. Pflanzenbau Pflanzensch., **10**, 73.
ZEEUW, J. DE, 1938, (Dissertation), Leiden.
ZEUCH, L., 1934, Planta, **22**, 614.
ZEUTHEN, E., 1947, Nature, **160**, 577.
ZIEGENSPECK, H., 1941, Biol. Gen., **15**, 344.
ZIMMERMAN, M. H., 1958, Plant Physiol., **33**, 213.
ZIMMERMAN, P. W., and WILCOXON, F., 1935, Contrib. Boyce Thompson Inst., **7**, 209.
ZIMMERMAN, P. W., 1942, Cold Spring Harbor Symp. Quant. Biol., **10**, 152.
ZIMMERMAN, P. W., and HITCHCOCK, A. E., 1942, Contrib. Boyce Thompson Inst., **12**, 491.
ZIMMERMANN, P. W., 1943, Torreya, **43**, 98.
ZINZADZÉ, C. R., 1932, *Recherches sur la Nutrition artificielle des Plantes cultivées*. Paris.
ZIRKLE, C., 1937, Bot. Rev., **3**, 1.
ZITTLE, C. A., 1946, J. Biol. Chem., **163**, 111.
ZSCHEILE, F. P., 1941, Bot. Rev., **7**, 587.

GENERAL INDEX

(Biological and chemical names and chemical reactions are listed in separate indexes.) In the page-numbers, *italics* indicate main references to the Subject, and * (or **) indicate one (or more) Figure(s).

CHEMICAL INDEX

In the page-numbers, *italics* indicate main references to the Subject; * (or **) indicate one (or more) Figure(s), and † indicates a Graphic Formula.

2M*

BIOLOGICAL INDEX

(This consists mainly of botanical and microbiological names. Main *types* of plants and bacteria are given in the General Index.) In the page numbers, *italics* indicate main references to the Subject, and * (or **) indicate one (or more) Figure(s).

D